# HOW TO CHOOSE THE RIGHT PRINTING PROCESS

*when there are photographs or other halftones*

COPIES | 10 | 25 | 100 | 500 | 1,000 | 2,500 | 5,000 | 10,000 | 50,000 | 100,000 | 250,000

PHOTOSTAT

PHOTOGRAPHY (Contact prints)

WHITEPRINT

PHOTOGELATIN

OFFSET (Photo-offset lithography)

halftone

GRAVURE (Sheet-fed)

LETTERPRESS

ROTOGRA

Further information about each process will be found under the name of that process — use the book like a dictionary. In all of the above processes except letterpress either shiny or dull paper can be used. Good halftone reproduction in letterpress requires the use of shiny paper. The best letterpress halftone requires the use of the relatively expensive shiny paper.

# PRINTING AND
# PROMOTION HANDBOOK

# PRINTING AND
# PROMOTION HANDBOOK

## HOW TO PLAN, PRODUCE, AND USE PRINTING, ADVERTISING, AND DIRECT MAIL

*Daniel Melcher*
R. R. Bowker Co., Inc., Publishers

*Nancy Larrick*
Random House, Inc., Publishers

*SECOND EDITION*

McGRAW-HILL BOOK COMPANY, INC.
NEW YORK    TORONTO    LONDON    1956

## ACKNOWLEDGMENTS

The authors wish to acknowledge their great indebtedness to the many people who read and criticized sections of the manuscript of this book. Literally hundreds of individuals helped check it for accuracy.

# HOW TO USE THIS BOOK

The *Printing and Promotion Handbook* consists of an A-to-Z encyclopedia followed by four appendixes: Appendix 1, Type Faces; Appendix 2, Bibliography; Appendix 3, Graphic Arts Films; and Appendix 4, Postal Information.

In the A-to-Z arrangement of the main body of the book, you will find many rather detailed articles on such all-embracing subjects as PAMPHLETS; ADVERTISING; SHIPPING INFORMATION; and CAMPAIGN PLANNING. You will also find many brief, but highly specific, entries on procedures, techniques, services, and materials that are basic in various segments of the field of printing and promotion. Scattered throughout, in the appropriate alphabetical spot, there are definitions, references, and cross references.

This material has been arranged and cross-referenced to help the reader in many ways:

1. To look up answers to specific questions quickly and easily.
2. To ensure that no detail or possibility has been overlooked in a promotion or publicity campaign.
3. To explore the various facets of many related fields of information, just as you would use a primer or take a refresher course in a particular subject.

For example, if you have a general pamphlet problem, you can turn to the entry on PAMPHLETS and find a check list of factors that you should consider in planning a pamphlet as well as practical suggestions for efficient production and buying. This article will also refer you to other entries which will give specific details about such possibilities as the use of cold type, reverse plates, and even label printers. If you need to know more about paper for your pamphlet, you can refer to the entry on PAPER or that on PAPER SIZES AND WEIGHTS. And if you are concerned with the selection of type, you can turn to the entry on TYPE or to Appendix 1, Type Faces, which is a convenient type specimen book of text type and display faces.

When you look up POSTER, the authors assume you are saying, "Tell me all about posters." The handbook answers, "Well, how many of what kind? You say you need 1,000 posters in a few simple colors? Then consider silk screen."

v

You then look up SILK SCREEN which will tell you how silk-screen printing works, about how much it costs, when to use it, and where to buy it.

We believe it will be unnecessary to follow up more than three or four cross references at most to get the answer to a single problem. In many cases, the first reference will answer your question.

### For the Expert or the Beginner

The *Printing and Promotion Handbook* has been written for people—including beginners—who have to buy printing and direct mail services; for those who have to plan or prepare advertising, publicity, or information material of any kind, from covering letters to bound books; for anyone, in fact, who attempts to influence others by the printed or duplicated word. It also discusses films, recordings, radio, and television as intrinsic parts of a complete publicity or information program.

Unlike so many existing books, the *Printing and Promotion Handbook* is not primarily for the printer or the specialist. It assumes that most editors may also have to grapple with production and distribution problems. It further assumes that the reader who is considering a *printed* circular may also be interested in alternate ways and costs of achieving the same results—for example, by using a form letter or advertisement.

For these reasons, there are several entries which are particularly recommended as preliminary reading. They include CAMPAIGN PLANNING; ESTIMATING COSTS; SAVING MONEY; PRINTING; and DISTRIBUTION. In the Table of Contents, you will find many other basic entries grouped under general topics. A check of such entries will serve as a guide to the beginner who needs to build a good basic fund of information and as a form of insurance to the old hand who wants to be sure he has considered every possibility.

### What Information Will You Find?

We have assumed that the readers of this handbook are busy people in search of specific information and practical details. Therefore, we have given where-to-buy-it information for every type of service and product, typical current prices, suggestions on where to get additional information on specialized subjects, complete shipping information including postal information (Appendix 4) as well as rates and regulations of railway express, air express, rail freight, and trucking. Type specimens showing complete alphabets and character counts are given in Appendix 1, Type Faces. Books for further reading are listed and described in Appendix 2. They are referred to under appropriate entries throughout the handbook.

Firms listed in this handbook are not necessarily recommended in preference to firms not listed. Space does not permit a full listing. The authors have mentioned a few names as a service to readers without in any way vouching for the quality of their work or for the reasonableness of their prices. Some of the firms listed are those with whom the authors have dealt personally. Some have been recommended by friends. Some have been listed solely on the strength of information originating with those firms themselves.

No firm has paid to be listed in this handbook. The authors would appreciate hearing from any reader who has had bad luck with any listed firm, so that the name may be dropped in future editions.

The prices mentioned in these pages were included only after careful consideration. It would be easy to rely too heavily upon them unless they are used comparatively (see ESTIMATING COSTS). However, the authors felt that readers would want to know, for example, that rotogravure jobs are never priced under four figures, or that 1,000 8 x 11 leaflets *can* be bought for $8 or so in combination run offset, etc.

### Choosing the Right Printing Process and the Right Printer

Cross references are used very generously within the various entries, particularly under such far-reaching entries as PRINTING. This seemed especially desirable in view of the fact that "printing" is not one process, or three processes, but a whole host of specialized processes. There is one "best" process for practically any given job.

In fact, one of the first things that the beginner needs to know about printing is that *printing is a specialized business.* The first rule for getting professional and economical results is to go to the printer who specializes in the kind of work you want.

Any well-equipped printer *can* do practically anything; but he cannot necessarily do it economically. For instance, almost any printer can print a book. But a book printer is more likely to produce a professional-looking book. Almost any printer can print a poster or a label; but in certain circumstances a silk-screen printer can offer better posters for less money.

When a printer is offered a job that he is not very well equipped to handle, one of several things may happen:

1. He may suggest that the inquirer take the work where it can be done best.
2. He may accept the job, but subcontract it.
3. He may quote a price high enough to cover the cost of doing the job on his own not-quite-appropriate equipment, reasoning that it is the buyer's lookout if he does not know that he could get the work done more cheaply elsewhere.
4. He may not even know or admit that the work can be done better or less expensively elsewhere.

The best printers will follow the first or second course. When they subcontract work, they charge a commission for doing so but may nevertheless save the customer's time and money by knowing where to take the work and by being able to purchase it at "trade" rates.

Unfortunately, some job printers proceed along line 3 or 4. It is, therefore, well worth while for any buyer of printing or duplicating service to check with this handbook to make sure that he is asking for quotations from the right kind of printer.

## CHECK THIS LIST BEFORE GOING AHEAD WITH ANY PRINTING AND PROMOTION JOB

**Purposes:** What results are sought? Is the objective to change habits of thought, or secure action, create good will, or what?

**Audience:** Who must be reached with this information or message? Will the material get their interest, claim their confidence, answer their doubts, and be completely understandable to them?

**Means:** Might there be a better way to attain the desired result? (Pamphlet *versus* letter, advertising, radio, television, film, exhibit, etc.)

**Competition:** What competition for attention will this message be up against? Will the message be able to compete successfully for reader attention? Most messages compete against comics, picture magazines, and sports pages. There are millions of people who just do not read solid type.

**Time requirements:** Does the day-by-day schedule for this job assure time for editing, printing, addressing, and shipping? Or must the job and the specifications be altered to permit delivery on time?

**Mechanical requirements:** Do the specifications take account of

1. Space requirements at point of use? (Bulletin board, pocket, wallet, handbag, etc.)
2. Shipping method (envelopes, tubes, cartons, etc.)? Postal regulations?
3. Inserting or binding machine requirements?
4. Economic cutting of paper stock?
5. Size of printing presses?

**Delivery instructions:** Have accurate instructions been made up covering both shipping and receiving bulk lots? Have samples been ordered sent to all the proper people? Are labels or envelopes addressed for shipping single copies?

# CONTENTS

The *Printing and Promotion Handbook* consists of an encyclopedia (with articles arranged in alphabetical order) and four appendixes: Appendix 1, Type Faces; Appendix 2, Bibliography; Appendix 3, Graphic Arts Films; and Appendix 4, Postal Information.

Below, the important basic articles are grouped much as they might have been if the book had been divided into chapters. By referring to this listing, you may use the book for general study as easily as for spot reference. No page numbers are given since each entry will be found in its proper alphabetical place in the body of the book or in the proper appendix.

## HOW TO PLAN A COMPLETE CAMPAIGN

*See entries on* CAMPAIGN PLANNING; ESTIMATING COSTS; SAVING MONEY; SCHEDULING; DELIVERY; DISTRIBUTION; ADVERTISING; RADIO; TELEVISION; MOTION PICTURES; FILMSTRIPS; RECORDINGS; ADVERTISING AGENCIES; PUBLIC-RELATIONS CONSULTANTS

## HOW TO CHOOSE THE RIGHT PROCESS AND PRINTER

*See entries on* PRINTING; PRINTERS: HOW TO CHOOSE; and the charts inside the covers of this book

## HOW TO PLAN AND PRODUCE SPECIFIC PRINTED MATERIALS

*See entries on* PAMPHLETS; CIRCULARS; LETTERS; POSTERS; NEWSPAPERS; PERIODICALS; HOUSE ORGANS; DISPLAYS; SIGNS; OUTDOOR ADVERTISING; TRANSPORTATION ADVERTISING; LABELS; ENVELOPES; BOOKS; JACKETS; CATALOGUES; BUSINESS FORMS; BLOTTERS; CALENDARS

## THE MAJOR PRINTING PROCESSES

*See entries on* PRINTING; RELIEF PRINTING; PLANOGRAPHY; INTAGLIO; STENCIL; LETTERPRESS; OFFSET; LITHOGRAPHY; PHOTOGELATIN; OPTAK; GRAVURE; ROTOGRAVURE; ENGRAVING; SILK SCREEN; PRESSWORK; COLOR PRINTING; PHOTOGRAPHY: AS A PRINTING PROCESS

## OFFICE DUPLICATING PROCESSES

## USE OF CUTS AND PLATES

## SETTING TYPE, TYPING, HAND-LETTERING

## PHOTOGRAPHY

## EDITING AND PROOFREADING

## DESIGNING AND ILLUSTRATING

## SELECTING PAPER

## FOLDING, BINDING, AND FINISHING

*See entries on* MOUNTING AND FINISHING; FOLDING; SELF-COVER; BINDING; BOOK-BINDING; MECHANICAL BINDINGS; DIE CUTTING; STAPLING; PERFORATING; PEBBLING; VARNISHING

## HOW TO UTILIZE DIRECT MAIL ADVERTISING

*See entries on* DIRECT MAIL ADVERTISING; MAIL ORDER; LETTERSHOPS; MAILING LISTS; ADDRESSING; ADDRESSOGRAPH; ELLIOTT ADDRESSING; POLLARD ALLING ADDRESSING. *Also* in Appendix 4, Postal Information, *see entry on* MAILING-LIST CORRECTIONS

## POSTAL AND SHIPPING INFORMATION

*See entries on* RAILWAY EXPRESS; TRUCKING; RAIL FREIGHT; SHIPPING INFORMATION; WRAPPING AND PACKING. *Also* Appendix 4, Postal Information, in which entries are arranged alphabetically

## SPECIALIZED PRINTING

*See entries on* NOVELTY PRINTING; IMPRINTING; EMBOSSING; MARBLING; FOREIGN-LANGUAGE PRINTING; MUSIC PRINTERS; CONTAINER PRINTING; PACKAGES; CLOTH PRINTING; MAPS; TICKETS; NUMBERING; BADGES; GREETING CARDS; TAGS; BALLOONS; MATCHES; PENCILS; SEALS; DECALCOMANIAS; FLOCK PRINTING; LUMINESCENT PRINTING; THERMOGRAPHY

## ADDITIONAL INFORMATION

See Appendix 2, Bibliography; and Appendix 3, Graphic Arts Films

# A|a

**A.A.'s**  Abbreviation for author's alterations. (See AUTHOR'S ALTERATIONS.)

**abbreviations**  In this book abbreviations are listed alphabetically among the regular headings. (For the use of abbreviations in editorial work, see PROOFREADING and COPY PREPARATION.)

**A.B.C.**  Abbreviation for Audit Bureau of Circulations. (See ADVERTISING.)

**adcut**  See LOGOTYPE.

**Add-a-type**  This product is similar to Artype (see ARTYPE), except that it costs only 85 cents per sheet instead of $1. It comes in a wide range of type faces and sizes. For a catalogue of available faces, write to the manufacturer, Arthur Brown & Brother, 2 W. 46 St., New York 36.

**addressing**  See also ADDRESSOGRAPH; ELLIOTT ADDRESSING; HEYER ADDRESSER; LETTERSHOP; MAILING LISTS; MASTER ADDRESSER; POLLARD ALLING ADDRESSING; WEBER ADDRESSING MACHINE; DICK STRIP.

Envelopes can be hand-addressed by pen or typewriter at rates ranging from $10 to $15 per thousand, or can be machine-addressed from prepared plates at rates as low as $1.75 to $3.50 or $4 per thousand. Typing is generally no more expensive than pen addressing and tends to look neater. In fact, unless there is a substantial difference in the hourly wage, typing is noticeably cheaper. In almost every city there are lettershops equipped to handle addressing. In New York, one addressing firm which offers daily pick-up and delivery service is De Groodt Associates, 87–29 78 Street, Woodhaven 21, N.Y. For typing perforated gummed labels and supplying an original and two carbons of each address, their rate is about $2.50 per thousand above their ordinary base rate.

The leading methods of machine addressing are Elliott, Addressograph, and Pollard Alling. (See ADDRESSOGRAPH, ELLIOTT ADDRESSING, and POLLARD ALLING ADDRESSING.) Elliott address cards work on the stencil principle; Addressograph and Pollard Alling machines print with embossed metal plates through an inked ribbon. Some machines do every kind of addressing plus such specialized work as payrolls, inventories, post-card printing, automatic

1

selecting of keyed addresses, and billing. (See illustrations under ADDRESSOGRAPH and ELLIOTT ADDRESSING.)

Speedaumat is Addressograph's name for its lowest cost method of addressing. The Pollard Alling method is used chiefly on large-scale jobs upwards of 150,000 names.

For small users, there is also an addressing machine which sells for $31 with enough supplies to handle 500 names. This is called the Master Addresser and works on the spirit duplicator principle. (See MASTER ADDRESSER.) The addresses are typed, with special carbon paper, on a paper tape. The tape can be used for addressing envelopes up to 100 times before the work becomes too faint to be legible. The speed of addressing is about 15 to 20 envelopes per minute.

The Elliott method uses stencils which print much like a miniature mimeograph stencil and which can be cut on an office typewriter at envelope-addressing speed. A special attachment is used to hold the stencils. One address goes on each stencil, and the stencils are filed like index cards.

The other methods emboss each address on a thin metal plate by the use of a special graphotype embossing machine. The plates are printed through a wide ribbon to imitate actual typing.

Most lettershops and many magazine printers are equipped to do machine addressing work for their clients. Some have Elliott equipment, some Addressograph, some Pollard Alling. Any process will be satisfactory to most users. It is probably better to have all mailing work done under one roof than to invite delays by dealing with several firms.

However, large users of machine addressing will want to study the comparative claims of the different methods before making any installation or having it made for them by an outside service agency. It is expensive to make any change, even from one kind of

Addressograph plate to another, after work is once started.

Addressing costs are of four kinds: (1) the cost of installing and maintaining the equipment, (2) the cost of preparing the name plates, (3) the cost of mailing-list maintenance, such as making corrections, additions, and deletions (see MAILING LISTS), and (4) the cost of doing the actual addressing.

*Equipment costs.* Elliott equipment tends to require a smaller investment in machinery. Minimum equipment for handling a mailing list of about 500 names costs about $80. The lowest cost office machine is about $165, as against $115 for the Addressograph. Although Elliott address cards can be cut on an office typewriter, the Elliott stencil-cutting equipment is advisable for big runs and faster work. This special L. C. Smith typewriter costs about $250 (plus tax), in contrast to the price of $500 and up for much slower Addressograph embossing equipment. Elliott trays and cabinets cost less and take less space. The standard, heavy-duty Elliott addressing machine costs $500, against about $1,000 for the comparable Addressograph machine.

*Running costs.* When a large volume of work is to be handled, first costs may not be nearly so important as running costs. A comparison of the cost per thousand of preparing the name plates is given in the accompanying table. (Figures are based on estimates supplied by the companies.)

In general, more work goes into the Addressograph plates. Making a so-called CB Addressograph plate (in two parts) requires (1) embossing a metal strip, (2) inserting this strip in a frame, (3) taking a proof, and (4) trimming and inserting the proof in the frame. Whether or not a more useful address plate results is for the user to decide.

Comparative costs on list maintenance are hard to measure. Elliott address cards are lighter and more compact. A drawer containing 250 Elliott

|  | Elliott | Addresso-graph | Pollard Alling |
|---|---|---|---|
| Cost of address cards or plates (per thousand) | $20.00 | $ 6.00–30.00 | $ 4.50 |
| Cost for preparing these cards or plates with three-line address, plus index line or proof for identification | 24.00 | 35.00–50.00 | 20.50 |
| Cost of materials for making changes or substitutions on these cards or plates | 20.00 | 5.00 up | 4.50 |

addresses weighs 2¼ lb., as against a similar drawer holding 175 Addressograph plates weighing 14 lb. and a reel of 2,500 Pollard Alling plates weighing 9 lb. Running costs do not seem to show much variation one way or the other. Speeds of addressing are comparable on comparable models for Addressograph and Elliott, higher for Pollard Alling.

*Comparison of quality.* There are a few things that Addressograph machines will do particularly well, *e.g.*, make carbon copies, cut mimeograph stencils, print in two colors through a two-color ribbon, and print with special ink on paper offset (Multilith) plates and Ditto (spirit duplicating) masters.

A comparison between Elliott and Addressograph as to quality of work is a matter of opinion. Both processes are capable of producing both superior and inferior work.

Both processes can be used for striking in a name, address, and salutation at the head of a form letter. An Elliott fill-in of this sort is closer in appearance to a mimeographed form letter, since both are done by a stencil process; an Addressograph fill-in is closer to a multigraphed letter, since both are done through a ribbon. However, a perfectly matched fill-in is difficult if not impossible to get in either way. (See LETTERS and PROCESS LETTERS.)

Selective addressing is possible in all processes. The Pollard Alling equipment permits high-speed visual selection; the other addressing machines can be set either to accept or to reject any

stencil with a hole punched at any given position in its frame, or a plate with a notch or tab at any given position.

The "keying" or "tabbing" of address plates is a feature that needs to be used with care. There is little economy in running 10,000 plates through a machine in order to address 100 envelopes. Small lists should not be merged into one big keyed list if the small lists will be used more often separately than together. If, however, the usual practice is to use them all together, then it pays to merge the plates into one big, geographically arranged list, to simplify the problem of getting the mailings sorted and tied geographically in a form acceptable to the Post Office.

Magazines key their mailing lists, so that each month the machine will automatically drop from the list those whose subscriptions expire. One big book club punches the address card when a book is shipped to a subscriber, and again when it is paid for. This permits automatic billing.

In general, if a mailing list is likely to be used as many as eight to twelve times within two years, it may pay to put it on stencils or plates. This, however, depends on the rate of annual change in the list. A 20 per cent annual change is average.

*Addressing done by lettershop.* Lettershops are usually glad to maintain and run off lists of plates, but firms often prefer to do this themselves, both in the interests of greater accuracy and for greater speed in emergencies. Where magazines are concerned, the printer may maintain the mailing list

An Addressograph plate.

himself, or he may receive in advance of each issue addressed wrappers, envelopes, or labels.

In making arrangements for outside maintenance of a mailing list, one big user recommends getting both hourly rates and piecework rates. The same user gets new bids at intervals to keep prices right.

There are several methods of using IBM or Remington Rand punched cards as addressing masters. One puts an aniline-dye carbon image of the address right on the card, from which impressions can be taken directly by the spirit duplicating method. (See SCRIPTOMATIC.) Another method, under development by IBM and Haloid, copies the address on the card by xerography. (See XEROGRAPHY.) The Addressograph electronic addressing system uses an electronic eye to scan a typed address on the card and transfer it to tape—either to tape intended for direct pasting on magazines, envelopes, etc., or to a tape intermediary from which, with heat and pressure, the address image only can be transferred to envelopes or other surfaces. Finally, both IBM and Remington Rand card printers of the kind used in accounting work have been adapted for writing addresses from information punched into cards, at rates of 3,000 or so per hour. A limi-

tation here is that columns used for coding in the address (one column per character) are no longer available for coding-in other information—and there are only 90 columns.

**Addressograph** See also ADDRESSING. Addressograph machines, using several different sizes and styles of plates, are made in a number of models for addressing and for many other uses where information must be repetitively written. The name "Speedaumat" identifies the line of Addressograph machines that feature the low cost Speedaumat plate which has certain features particularly adaptable to the publishing business and certain types of large lists.

Metal plates are used. Characters are embossed on these plates in a special machine called a "Graphotype." The embossing produces raised letters which print through a wide, inked ribbon to give results closely duplicating handtyping.

The information on each Addressograph plate can be keyed through the use of special metal tabs affixed to the top of the plate. Thus the machine can be set either to print only plates having a tab in, say, position 2, or to print all plates except those having a tab in that position.

The card-index feature of the Addressograph plate, combined with the tabs, provides the user with a vertical filing system, often used as a master file for reference as well as for reproduction purposes.

Recent prices on Addressograph machines start at $115 for a hand-operated model with an automatic plate feed. The company has introduced many new developments in specialized single-plate imprinter models at prices ranging downward to under $50 per unit. Electrically operated machines range up to several thousand dollars, the price depending upon the production requirements of a given installation.

Graphotype machines are priced at

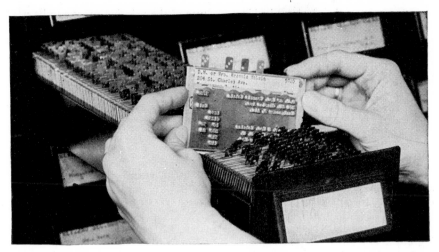

A tray of Addressograph plates. The embossed metal plate from which the printing is done slides into the lower portion of the frame. A proof of this embossed area slides into the upper portion of the frame. The plates shown carry metal tabs.

just under $500 and up—but it is not necessary to purchase one of these machines. Addressograph field offices and many lettershops maintain an embossing service.

Addressograph plate costs range from under $6 per thousand for Speedaumat plates in large quantities to $30 and more for multiple unit combinations of frame, printing plates, and index cards. The latter represent original requirements. The frames represent a capital investment because they can be used over and over again when changes occur. Blank replacement plates in many popular styles are priced from around $6 a thousand for complete inserts to less than $5 a thousand for many sectional inserts. There are more than 100 styles, and many variations within each style can be worked out to suit the individual requirements of a given problem.

The embossing of the metal plates is a process akin to typing but somewhat slower. An experienced Graphotype operator can produce from 30 to 100 three-line plates per hour. This rate is dependent largely upon whether the operator is using a hand-operated or the more expensive keyboard machine. In the last few years, two new Graphotype models have been introduced. The one features automatic plate feed and discharge, eliminating many hand operations. There is also a completely automatic Graphotype machine which operates from a punched tape. The tape is prepared as a byproduct of another typing operation on such machines as a Flexowriter or Teletype. All the operator has to do is to insert the tape and start the machine. As many as ten of these automatic Graphotype machines can be attended by one person.

There are two major contenders in the field of addressing machines: Addressograph and Elliott. (See ELLIOTT ADDRESSING.) Special advantages claimed for Addressograph are that embossed metal plates give more consistently uniform results (stencils can be cut well or badly); mistakes are easier to correct because the Graphotype operator simply back-spaces and either blanks out or embosses over; the plate can be identified with a printed proof of itself mounted right in the frame and an index card and so is easier to read, file, and handle; keys or tabs on plates can be changed at any time without making new plates; metal frames on multipart plates can be reused at a cost of less than a penny for newly embossed metal area; and the metal plate is fire-resistant and able to withstand water and fire-fighting chemicals.

In addition to addressing envelopes and labels, Addressograph machines can be used for making out monthly bills, time cards, payrolls, checks, etc., and for signing, numbering, and dating business records. In fact, for short messages, Addressograph plates and the same machine can be used for duplicating or imprinting.

Among the new models now on the market are accounting Addressograph units that not only perform all the traditional Addressograph functions, but also do certain types of accounting work. These machines operate from the familiar embossed Addressograph metal plates. The accounting information is carried in the form of punched holes in these plates. In certain of the larger accounting models, the holes from the plates are automatically interpreted and punched into tabulating cards as a by-product of the regular Addressograph imprinting run. Some Addressograph models start an operation with blank paper either in rolls or in flat sheets. The actual business form is duplicated automatically while the regular Addressograph run is being made.

**advertisements** See also ADVERTISING; ADVERTISING AGENCIES; MAT SERVICES.

The problems involved in writing, designing, and ordering a printed advertisement are very similar to those involved in producing pamphlets, letters, posters, etc. However, once the advertising medium has been chosen, this choice usually determines the nature of the printing process to be used and sets up some limitations on size, the nature of illustrations, and perhaps the use of color.

The easiest way to place an advertisement is through an advertising agency. The use of an agency need cost the advertiser no money since each agency receives a 15 per cent commission direct from the newspaper or magazine on all space purchased through that agency. Agencies do charge the client for special services beyond general advice on placement and on copy. (See ADVERTISING AGENCIES.)

Newspapers and magazines stand ready to set type and even to advise advertisers on layout without charge other than regular space rates. However, advertisers who place ads in a variety of media usually prefer to get them set up in one independent composition house so that they will have a uniformity of style. The advertisers supply plates, mats, or proofs to the periodical.

Periodicals that are printed by letterpress, including practically all newspapers and most magazines, print from cuts or type or plates. The advertiser must supply copy, or a duplicate plate made from his own type, and also supply, or at least pay for, any cuts required. Some periodicals, however, are printed by the offset or rotogravure process and, therefore, have no use for cuts or plates. They want reproduction proofs (or glassine proofs) and art work from which to make their own printing plates.

Before planning an ad, one should learn the following things about the periodical:

1. By what process is it printed? That is, are cuts needed or perhaps art work and reproduction proofs? Are mats acceptable? Should electros or other duplicate plates be blocked or unblocked?

2. Can halftones be used? Of what screen?

3. What is the exact size of the area being purchased?

4. What kind of competition for reader attention will the ad probably be up against, and what can be done to meet this competition successfully?

5. If the periodical is to set the ad in type, what type styles are available? In what sizes?

The answers to questions 1, 2, and 3 can be found quickly on the advertising rate card of the publication or from the guides published by Standard Rate and Data Service, Inc., 1740 Ridge Ave., Evanston, Ill. The answers to questions 4 and 5 can be found best by looking over a few numbers of the publication.

It cannot be assumed that any type style used in a publication is available to an advertiser; it may have been supplied by another advertiser in plate form. However, display type styles used editorially are generally available for advertising use. An easy way to specify type for a simple ad is to snip out lines of the type style desired and paste these to the layout. (See LAYOUT; DESIGN; COPY WRITING.)

**advertising**  See also ADVERTISEMENTS; ADVERTISING AGENCIES; OUTDOOR ADVERTISING; RADIO; TELEVISION; DIRECT MAIL ADVERTISING; MAIL ORDER; DISPLAYS; COPY WRITING; LAYOUT; CAMPAIGN PLANNING.

This whole book is about, or applies to, advertising in one form or another, but the emphasis is on the planning, writing, editing, and production of material that the purchaser will distribute himself.

However, in order to choose intelligently among the many ways of moving ideas and information from here to there, it is necessary to know something about all the channels of communication that are available. Hence this overly brief entry on the purchase of space in newspapers, general magazines, and business papers, and the purchase of time on radio and television.

For some excellent books on every aspect of advertising, consult the Bibliography.

The purchaser of newspaper or magazine advertising is buying more than just printing; he is buying distribution. He is paying for a chance to put his message before so many thousand or so many million people. To put a color page into 5,000,000 copies of a national magazine may cost close to $50,000 plus the cost of layout, art work, and plates. A half-hour network television show will cost around $54,000 for the time plus around $35,000 for the production.

Whether or not advertising will pay depends primarily upon the proportion of the audience who are really prospects for the advertiser's product or service. If only 10,000 *Life* readers are really prospects for an advertised product that is inexpensive, a page in *Life* may be a rather expensive way to reach them. If every *Life* reader is a potential buyer, then a page in *Life* may be an exceedingly good investment.

Advertising rates are, of course, obtainable on request to publications or radio stations. The advertising manager of each medium can usually supply not only rates, but also useful market-analysis material.

Circulation figures are usually quoted as "A.B.C." figures. This means that they have been audited and certified as correct by the Audit Bureau of Circulations. All large publications are members of the A.B.C. Smaller ones, which have not gone to the trouble and expense of joining it, usually issue their figures as "Publishers' Sworn Statements."

The A.B.C. audits only circulations that are at least 50 per cent paid. Magazines with a controlled free circulation may be audited by the B.P.A. (Business Publications Audit).

All newspapers and magazines will put the advertiser's message into type at no cost above the regular space charge, if they receive copy in time to permit this. Large advertisers, however, almost invariably make their own arrangements for typesetting, since this gives them a broader variety of types to choose from and greater control over appearance. They supply the publication with a complete plate ready for printing. (See also ADVERTISEMENTS.)

Data on circulation may be found in Ayer's "Directory of Newspapers & Periodicals" (N. W. Ayer & Son, Philadelphia 6, Pa., $30).

Monthly advertising rate guides are published by Standard Rate and Data Service, Inc., 1740 Ridge Ave., Evanston, Ill. These include: *Newspaper Rates and Data*, $27.50 a year; *Consumer Magazines and Farm Publications*, $30; *Business Publications*, $27.50; *Radio Rates and Data*, $35; and *Television Rates and Data*, $30.

*Magazine advertising.* Magazine rates run upward from about $2.50 per black-and-white page per thousand circulation. Circulation and page rates in a few media are shown in the table below.

Plates are, of course, required only by periodicals that are printed by the letterpress process. Magazines that are printed by offset or by rotogravure want art work, not plates. Weeklies usually want advertising plates three to ten days ahead of publication. Monthlies may need them three to six weeks ahead of publication, with color plates still further in advance.

*Newspaper advertising.* Newspaper rates run upward from about $2 per agate line per million of circulation. This is known as the "milline" rate. Another term, the "marline" rate, is the cost per agate line per billion dollars of retail sales in the market area covered. An agate line is an area one column wide by $\frac{1}{14}$ in. deep. The minimum milline rate quoted above converts (for comparison with magazine rates) to about $4.80 per large newspaper page per thousand circulation.

A full newspaper page is usually billed as about 2,400 agate lines. A common advertising rate in newspapers of small circulation is about 7 cents per agate line, or $1 per column inch.

Rates for national advertisers are usually higher than for local advertisers, a fact that has led many national advertisers to encourage their local outlets to advertise.

## Circulation and Page Rate of 14 National Magazines

| Magazine | Net paid circulation (6 month average) | Page size (nonbleed) | Page rate (black and white) | Rate per M circulation |
|---|---|---|---|---|
| Readers' Digest | Over 10 million | 4⅜ x 6½ | $26,500 | $ 2.65 |
| The American Weekly | 9,761,394 | 10 x 12⅛ | 24,250 | 2.48 |
| Life | 5,507,456 | 9⅜ x 12⅛ | 20,350 | 3.69 |
| The Ladies' Home Journal | 4,950,472 | 9⅜ x 12⅛ | 15,500 | 3.13 |
| Look | 3,877,651 | 9⅜ x 12⅛ | 14,080 | 3.63 |
| Collier's | 3,712,187 | 9⅜ x 12⅛ | 12,700 | 3.42 |
| The American Magazine | 2,660,502 | 7 x 10 | 7,840 | 2.94 |
| The New Yorker | 384,099 | 7 x 10³⁄₁₆ | 2,600 | 6.77 |
| Business Week | 258,443 | 7 x 10 | 2,315 | 8.97 |
| Fortune | 253,417 | 8⅞ x 11 | 3,495 | 13.80 |
| Harper's | 176,000 | 7 x 10 | 1,200 | 6.81 |
| Saturday Review | 136,434 | 7⅛ x 10 | 1,200 | 8.82 |
| The Reporter | 100,966 | 7¹⁄₁₆ x 10 | 665 | 6.58 |
| The Nation | 32,726 | 7 x 10 | 300 | 9.37 |

Newspaper rates may vary between different lines of merchandise or service, and also between preferred positions and run of paper (r.o.p.).

Daily newspapers will accept complete advertising plates up to a late hour the day preceding publication. Weeklies may require advertising plates one to three days ahead of publication date.

*Radio advertising.* Radio stations will sell an advertiser a ready-made or made-to-order show as well as the time to air it. Spot announcements may be purchased for from $5 to $200 a minute, depending on time of day, program, and station power. Local stations will frequently make a package deal for a series of spot advertisements at drastically reduced rates.

Radio stations cannot promise to deliver any given number of listeners, for obvious reasons. They do, however, have ways of estimating how many listeners did hear a given broadcast and will presumably listen to it again the next time it is on the air. They can thus provide very useful data on the potential number of listeners that an advertiser might hope to keep tuned to his program, provided the program is good enough.

Three different rating services give estimates of the number of radio sets that were tuned to a particular program.

Nielsen Radio Index ratings of network programs and regional coverage are made by attaching an automatic electronic recording instrument, known as a Nielsen Audimeter, to radios in homes constituting a chosen sample of the whole population.

Pulse Ratings are made by personal interview with radio users, usually only in metropolitan areas and the suburbs.

Hooperatings are calculated on the basis of local telephone calls made to a cross section of potential listeners while the program is on the air. A Hooperating is inaccurate to the extent that it covers only local telephone subscribers and cannot cover early morning and late evening programs except as listeners later recall what they heard at such hours. Hooperatings are estimates of local audiences only.

Radio advertising rates are given in *Radio Rates and Data* published by Standard Rate and Data Service, Inc. They range from about $25 an hour on very small stations to $720 per hour on large stations. The rates on a single station vary according to the length of the broadcast, the time of day or night, and the number of times for which the contract is drawn.

Typical rates for a one-minute spot announcement on a large station are:

$95 between the hours of 8 A.M. and 10:30 P.M., Monday through Saturday

$67 between the hours of 7 A.M. and 8 A.M. and 10:30 P.M. and 12:00 P.M., Monday through Saturday

**Circulation and Line Rates in Five Large Daily Newspapers**

| Newspaper | Daily circulation | Weekly line rate | Sunday circulation | Sunday line rate |
|---|---|---|---|---|
| The New York Times | 555,726 | $1.94 | 1,277,708 | $2.37 |
| Los Angeles Times | 431,989 | .90 | 826,929 | 1.51 |
| Chicago Tribune | 907,570 | 1.85 | 1,428,916 | 2.65 |
| Atlanta Journal (morning and evening) | 436,403 | 1.00 | 492,738 | 1.05 |
| Washington Post & Times Herald | 380,624 | .88 | 410,185 | .88 |

$340 for a package of five one-minute spot announcements per week

Typical rates for a one-minute spot announcement on a small station are:

$10 for one such spot between the hours of 6 P.M. and 10:30 P.M.
$9 each for a 13-time contract

For details on programming and program costs, see RADIO.

*Television advertising.* An advertiser can buy television advertising through three basic plans: (1) on a network basis, which means buying network time plus a program created by the network, by an outside program packager, or by the advertiser; (2) on a national spot basis, which means purchasing local station time and a program produced locally so as to place national advertising in a local region; and (3) by buying time on local stations and providing programs and spot announcements on film or with live talent.

On the local level, rates are usually quoted for five-minute announcements, 20-second to one-minute spot announcements within a program, or 10- to 20-second spots between programs. Spots of 10 to 20 seconds are usually on film; the others are sometimes on film, sometimes not. Local stations frequently buy film rights to syndicated films and sell time for spot announcements to local sponsors. The total time allocated to commercials within a program is limited to seven minutes per hour on daytime programs, six minutes per hour on night programs.

The advertiser who is interested in buying local television facilities will want to find out what time is available, what proof can be given as to the popularity of the station and its various programs, and the cost of buying time for commercial spots in existing programs.

The pulling power of network programs and certain metropolitan stations is estimated by various rating services which attempt to report how many television sets were turned to a particular program at a certain time.

Nielsen Television Index uses the Audimeter tape to record channels which are being viewed at various times by television sets in the selected sample. Reports are for network programs only, except in New York where there are enough Audimeters to make local market ratings significant.

Pulse Television Ratings are made by personal interviews and are used largely by local stations or national and local advertisers.

Hooper Teleratings are done by the telephone method plus a diary kept by the viewers.

ARB Ratings (American Research Bureau) are made through the diary technique. Like Pulse Ratings, but unlike the Nielsen Index, ARB Ratings report information on sustaining as well as commercial programs.

Trendex Ratings are made by telephone survey, sampling 600 homes in a quarter-hour period. This service operates exclusively in markets where at least three national networks have individual affiliates.

Television advertising rates are given in *Spot Television Rates and Data* published by Standard Rate and Data Service, Inc. They range from about $400 per hour on small stations to $6,000 per hour on large stations for Class A time, usually defined as 6:30 P.M. to 11:30 P.M. The rates on a single station vary with the time of day or night and the number of times for which the contract is drawn.

Typical rates for a one-minute announcement or a 20-second station break on a large city station are:

$1,500 between the hours of 8 P.M. and 10:30 P.M., Monday through Saturday
$500 between the hours of 9 A.M. and 6 P.M., Monday through Saturday

Typical rates for a one-minute announcement or a 20-second station break on a small station are:

$70 between the hours of 6:30 P.M. and 11:30 P.M., Monday through Saturday $28 between the hours of 7 A.M. and 2 P.M., Monday through Saturday

For details on programming and program costs, see TELEVISION.

**advertising agencies** See also ADVERTISING; CAMPAIGN PLANNING; PUBLIC-RELATIONS CONSULTANTS.

The privilege of working with a good advertising agency is a very real one. All large advertisers use agencies, and most small advertisers use them or wish they could.

A real agency-client relationship with continuity (as distinct from the kind of piecework relationship which may be satisfactory with an art agency or printer) can hardly begin until the account can yield for the agency at least one full-time salary. However, if your advertising budget is small, it may yet pay you to look into the possibilities of working with an agency. A good agency may well be able to show you how you can gain handsome returns by increasing your present budget.

The stock-in-trade of a good advertising agency is know-how in the techniques of sales promotion. Ad agencies may be, and often are, called upon to do all the following things: plan space advertising campaigns, plan radio and TV campaigns, plan direct mail advertising campaigns, edit house organs, plan posters and poster campaigns, plan fund-raising appeals, conduct market surveys, stage-manage conferences, and handle public relations.

Advertising agencies get a 15 per cent commission from magazines and newspapers on the space advertising that they place. They get a like discount from radio and TV stations in the larger cities. This is generally regarded as compensation only for their professional advice on media selection, copy, layout, etc. They bill the client for the cost of space and time, and for specific extra items like art work, typography, and program talent. When they pro-

cure for the client printed literature and other items on which they get no commission, they charge the client both for the money paid out and for the agency's own services.

A good agency can relieve you of jobs that aren't your meat, and thus free you for the important things you can't delegate. It can apply to your problems experience gained in other industries or organizations, and give you access to top skills in marketing, media selection, layout, copy writing, direct mail, public relations, etc., beyond what you could or should attempt to obtain from people on your own staff.

In choosing an agency it is well to remember that advertising agencies, like printers, do specialize. Often an advertiser will use one agency for space advertising, another for direct mail, and a third for public relations. One agency may specialize in book advertising, another in industrial advertising or in advertising for and to retailers.

For further information on the selection of an agency and ways to work with an agency, consult the books listed in Appendix 2, Bibliography.

**agate line** Newspaper advertising space is bought by the agate line. There are 14 agate lines to the column inch. Thus, an advertisement two columns wide by 2 in. deep would occupy 56 agate lines of space.

The following paragraph has been set in 5½-pt. (agate) type.

It is actually possible for an advertiser to get 14 lines of type into 1 in. of advertising space by using agate type (5 1/2 pt.). However, this is rarely done, except in legal notices and classified advertisements. The agate line is a measure of area, 1/14 in. high and one standard newspaper column wide, and has nothing to do with the size of type that may be printed in that space.

**airbrush** An airbrush is an implement for spraying liquids, especially a film of color, by means of a blast of air. It permits tone blending and soft effects almost impossible to achieve by any other method. Artists use the airbrush extensively for retouching photographs, as well as for producing original art work. Not all artists have airbrush equipment, which is relatively expensive. Although the airbrush is deceptively easy to use, it is hard to use well

Airbrush and holder.

and with restraint. A good book on the subject is "A Manual of Airbrush Techniques" by J. Carroll Tobias (New York, American Photographic Book Publishing Co., $3).

**air express**  See RAILWAY EXPRESS.

**airmail**  See Appendix 4, Postal Information.

**air parcel post**  See Appendix 4, Postal Information.

**All-Purpose Linotype**  See LUDLOW.

**alphabet length**  The alphabet length of any style and size of type is a measure of that type's compactness. It is the length (usually measured in points) of the alphabet as set in that style of type, abcdefghijklmnopqrstuvwxyz. Alphabet length can be converted easily into characters per pica (c.p.p.). (See TYPE.)

**ampersand**  The name of the symbol "&" used for the word "and."

**anchoring**  To anchor or "sweat" a printing plate or cut onto its block means to solder it on. Cuts can be soldered to wood blocks by inserting metal plugs in the wood. This used to be necessary wherever a cut had to be blocked close all around and had neither shoulders nor nonprinting areas through which nails could be driven. Anchoring is less common now that many engravers are blocking cuts with adhesives requiring neither shoulders nor nails.

**aniline printing**  See FLEXOGRAPHIC PRINTING.

**antique**  Books are commonly printed on an antique wove or antique laid paper, unless halftones are to be printed on the same paper as the text. Paper with an antique finish has no shine and bulks thicker than paper that has been calendered to a smooth finish. Eggshell paper is a smooth antique.

**APL**  Abbreviation for All-Purpose Linotype. (See LUDLOW.)

**Aquatone**  See OPTAK.

**art agencies**  See ART SERVICES.

**artists**  See also ART WORK; ART SERVICES; DESIGN; DESIGNERS; PHOTOGRAPHERS.

Many buyers of printing seem to find it much easier to procure ten thousand words than one good picture. They grant the effectiveness of pictures, but they do not know any artists, and besides they have the idea that artists cost a lot of money.

Artists exist in almost every town, and a good one is generally worth more than he is paid. A couple of attractive drawings or an excellent layout (see DESIGN and DESIGNERS) can easily double the effectiveness of any piece of printing.

Popular impressions to the contrary, most artists are just ordinary people trying to make a living. They are not eccentrics. The top men make big money, but many competent artists earn less than $150 a week and can turn out a lot of work in that time.

A free-lance artist has to charge more per hour than a salaried artist, of course, to tide him over between jobs, and because of the extra time he devotes to getting work.

$10 is a minimum price for a small spot drawing when a lot are ordered at once. For a single small drawing, prices of $15 and up are common minimums.

To keep his average income up to a reasonable level, a free-lance artist really needs to get at least $50 a day for the days he works. The result is that an artist frequently sets a minimum price for any job whether the assignment is one drawing or several. This is to reimburse him for the time spent in consultation.

Prices for art work are hard to pin down because they vary according to what the traffic will bear. If it is worth an advertiser's while to spend $50,000 to put a painting before the public, $1,000 for the artist does not seem so much. On the other hand, $100 for a book-jacket design is about all that a publisher can afford on a book with advertising appropriations that total less than $1,000. There may be as much work on a book jacket as on any poster or ad.

To find artists (1) inquire of local schools or colleges that teach art; (2) ask advertisers where they get the art that they use; (3) try the classified advertising columns; (4) go to an art agency or art service. (See ART SERVICES.)

Artists specialize. A man who can do the Disney type of caricatures may be quite unable to draw "straight," and vice versa. A good designer and mechanical draftsman may be poor on faces and figures. An illustrator showing complete ads as samples of his work may or may not be capable of doing the layout that frames the illustrations. He may not even have been responsible for the composition of his own illustrations—an art director may have roughed them out for him. To be safe, ask artists to use only those techniques in

which they are demonstrably skilled, regardless of their assurance that they can work in any technique.

Some art buyers maintain a file of artists under such headings as letterers; layout men who can make "roughs," "visuals," and "comprehensives"; designers (packages, etc.); illustrators (figures, heads); general, all-round artists; and cartoonists.

Artists who cannot show any samples of the type of work under consideration may reasonably be asked to submit rough sketches on speculation. Otherwise, it is customary and fair to pay something for preliminary sketches made to definite order even though no order for finished art work is placed.

An art buyer should have his ideas well thought out before he goes to an artist. Good artists are not necessarily also good gag men or promotion experts. If the buyer has been unable to decide just what he wants the drawings to say, the artist may have no better luck.

Artists may quote lower prices, if relieved of the task of research. For instance, suppose a drawing calls for a farm scene. Try to get photos showing the kind of cow, the kind of silo, the kind of barn roof, etc., that should go in the picture. Such research may take hours in the picture collection of a library or in searching old magazines. If the artist has to do the research, he charges for it.

Art buyers should read "Careers in Commercial Art" by J. I. Biegeleisen (Dutton, $4.00). It was written to give vocational guidance to would-be artists, but it offers the art buyer invaluable guidance on how artists specialize and what they charge.

**art services**  See also ARTISTS; ART WORK.

Art services are an important source of help for advertisers and editors. They fall into two classes: artists' representatives and art studios.

Artists' representatives are essentially salesmen who relieve their artist clients from the need of peddling their skills.

Art studios may also represent certain free-lance artists. In addition, they employ staff artists on a permanent basis and usually a competent art director, perhaps the head of the studio, whose own skill and advice are at the disposal of art buyers. Both kinds of art services can help an art buyer find the right artist or artists for a job.

Sometimes, however, a customer's problem plus an artist's skill are not enough to produce superior results. Something else must be added, namely, the ability of a good art director to visualize an answer to the problem and to prepare a layout ready for the artist to fill in. The best art services can solve such problems and, if an illustrator is weak at lettering, they can have the lettering done by another man.

The great advantage of working with an art service is its ability to relieve a client of such details as securing models, having photographs taken, retouching, having type set, ordering photostats and Velox prints, and pasting up.

Dealing with an art service costs more than dealing with the artist direct, because there is a commission to be paid. However, if the agency is able to suggest a competent but little-known artist in place of a big-name artist and get good results, the total cost may be less in the end.

Two splendid guides to firms and individuals specializing in art services are "Literary Market Place" and the "Buyers' Guide" of *Art Director and Studio News,* listed in Appendix 2, Bibliography.

**art techniques**   See DRAWING TECHNIQUES.

**art work**   See also ARTISTS; DRAWING TECHNIQUES; PHOTOGRAPHS; ILLUSTRATIONS.

Art work is an omnibus term used by layout men and printers to cover photographs, drawings, paintings, hand-lettering, etc. One assembles three things in preparation for ordering a printing job: manuscript, art work, and layout.

The destiny of most art work is to be photographed—to be tacked up in front of a copying camera and transferred to film as the first step in making printing plates. The exceptions are when it is to be traced, transferred, or copied as in mimeographing, hectograph work, etc.

Art work must, therefore, be kept scrupulously clean and flat (no folds). It is usually protected by a paper or transparent plastic flap and by mounting on heavy cardboard. Care in wrapping for mailing is particularly necessary.

Art work should never be prepared without foreknowledge of its intended use. The size to which it will be reduced, the method of reproduction, the paper to be used, and the likes and dislikes of the proposed audience—all these factors must be known to the artist if he is to do his work well. Whenever possible, artist and printer should discuss the work in advance. Otherwise, each may blame the other when results are disappointing.

Help in ordering, selecting, and evaluating art work may be obtained from excellent books on the subject listed in Appendix 2, Bibliography.

**Artype**   Artype, like Fototype (see FOTOTYPE), is a product that permits the setting of display type in the office or art department. A sheet of Artype, costing $1, consists of a 10- by 14-in. sheet of cellophane mounted temporarily on a paper backing. From three to eight impressions of each letter of the alphabet are printed on the underside of the cellophane. Under each is a horizontal line (later cut off), which helps to align the letters.

The letters to be used are cut out, one by one, with a knife or razor, peeled from the backing sheet, and arranged in the desired order. Tweezers help in positioning. When rubbed down, the letters stick firmly, since they carry their own adhesive. It is easy to align them by first ruling a faint blue guideline. Since the printing is underneath, they cannot be smudged. Since they are transparent they can be run across other art work, thus eliminating extra printers' or engravers' charges for doing this by stripping. Artype is available in black or white, and in more than 800 stock items of type faces, hand-lettered alphabets, arrows, numbers, symbols, and borders. The letters are sharp. Correct letter spacing and perfect joining of script letters are not difficult. Symbols, accents, adcuts, musical notes, etc., of your own choice will be made up to order. For free catalogue, write Artype, Inc., 127 S. Northwest Highway, Barrington, Illinois. Similar alphabets are made under the name "Craf-Type" by the Craftint Manufacturing Co., 1615 Collamer Ave., Cleveland 10, Ohio.

**ascender** The part of a small or lowercase (l.c.) letter that extends above the body of the letter, as in "b" and "d." A descender extends below the body of the letter, as in "p," "q," and "y." The size of a type face is measured from the top of the tallest character—whether a capital letter or a small letter with ascender—to the bottom of the lowest descender. (See illustrations under TYPE.)

**asterisk** A star-shaped symbol (*) used for reference to footnotes where the preferred superior numbers [1,2] might cause confusion, as in material containing figures. The dagger (†) and the double dagger (‡) may be used when a second and a third footnote occur on the same page. The full series is
* † ‡ § || ¶.

**ATF** Abbreviation for American Type Founders, leading makers of foundry or hand-set type. (See TYPE.)

**author's alterations** See also COPY PREPARATION; PROOFS; PROOFREADING.

Author's alterations, abbreviated A.A.'s, mean corrections in proofs which are not caused by any printer's error. On any bill for type composition there is likely to appear an item for author's alterations which is over and above the original estimate. When an incautious editor or author starts making proof changes that he should have made in manuscript, the charge for A.A.'s may easily exceed the cost of composition.

Printers are responsible for any failure to follow copy. They are not responsible for A.A.'s and will charge for them on a time basis. Making any change in any line usually involves resetting that line and perhaps the rest of the paragraph, getting out the galley of type in which the change occurs, pulling out the old lines, inserting the new, and then proofreading the change. The resetting alone may mean as much adjusting on the typesetting machine as was necessary in preparation for setting the whole job.

Some A.A.'s are almost inevitable. Book publishers usually allow their authors to make them without charge up to 10 per cent of the amount of the bill for typesetting. However, A.A.'s betray careless preparation of manuscript—a kind of carelessness for which there is a high monetary penalty.

**Auto-liner** A device for ruling evenly spaced parallel lines which is imported and sold at $10 by Eugene Dietzgen Co., Inc., 218 E. 23 St., New York. It is a sort of junior version of the Paraliner. (See PARALINER.)

**automatic electric typewriter** There are several automatic electric typewriters, including the Hooven, the Flexowriter,

## McGraw-Hill Book Company·Inc.

### McGraw-Hill Building
330 WEST 42ND STREET
NEW YORK 18, N.Y.

Mr. Fred Watts, Pres.
Santa Fe Citizens League
43 W. Lima Ave.
Santa Fe, New Mexico

Dear Fred,

The September NEWSLETTER will feature suggestions for the Fall Membership Drive and we
need news of the plans which proved successful last year.  Won't you send us a report
of the outstanding local club drives in
New Mexico?  Perhaps Jim Hays in Albuquerque
has something good to report.

We are particularly anxious to hav
suggestions which are both pr
can and novel, which can be
to the small as well as

HAND TYPED

Section of a Hooven letter showing hand-typed personalizing inserts.

the Auto-typist, and the Robotyper, which work on the player-piano principle. An operator first punches a master roll on a special typewriter. This roll controls the automatic machine.

A letterhead together with the desired number of carbons is inserted in the automatic typewriter in the regular way. The name and address of the recipient and the salutation are typed in manually by the operator. Then, at the flick of a switch, the machine begins to type the body of the letter by itself, while the operator is free to turn to another machine. (See illustration.)

If desired, the machine will stop at any point in the letter and ring a bell. The operator can then insert into the letter special information applicable only to the one recipient, after which the machine takes over again. A single operator can handle three or four machines at the same time.

The Auto-typist has two perforated rolls which may carry as many as 160 different paragraphs. With push-buttons the operator can select the paragraphs to be typed in each letter, thus speeding the answers to multi-question letters.

Automatically typed letters are completely indistinguishable from personally typed letters, because they are in fact individually typed and can be varied for each recipient.

Automatic electric typewriter work is expensive, however, and usually saves no time or money as against hand typing unless more than 50 similar letters are to be produced. (For comparative costs of duplicated letters, see LETTERS.)

Some find that the cheaper "process letters" can be just as effective as automatically typed letters. (See PROCESS LETTERS.)

**Autopositive**  See PHOTOCOPYING.

**Autoscreen film**  The Eastman Kodak Company offers lithographers a Kodalith Autoscreen Ortho Film with which it is possible to make high quality halftone negatives from photographic originals without either a ruled screen or a contact screen. The film itself is of such variable sensitivity that, if it is exposed to a pure white surface and developed, a dot pattern will be revealed varying in its density with the length of the exposure. Less time is required to make halftone negatives with this material than by conventional methods.

**Autostat**  See PHOTOCOPYING.

**Azograph**  See SPIRIT DUPLICATOR.

# B|b

**backbone** See SPINE.

**backing** A binder's term. In binding a 320-page book made up of ten 32-page units, for example, the units are gathered in the correct order (see GATH-ERING), sewed, and then backed (or perhaps rounded and backed).

The operation of backing consists of widening the back edge of the book (before the cover is applied) so that the width of the spine will be as wide as the thickness of the pages plus the thickness of the boards used in the case. Backing provides a sort of shoulder against which the cover of the book fits and is hinged. This shoulder is called the "joint." The backed book is then lined up with pieces of coarse crash and paper. The lined book is then "cased into" the cover by paste, pressure, and drying. (See illustration under BOOKBINDING.)

The term "backing" also refers to the heavy cardboard used to protect photographs and art work from damage in shipment.

**back up** To back up a sheet of paper that has already been printed on one side means to print on the other side of

it. Ink often has to dry before a sheet can be backed up. Perfector presses print a sheet and back it up in one operation, but normally a job is printed one day and is not backed up until the next.

**badges** Paper, ribbon, celluloid, plastic, enamel, and metal devices for the lapel are obtainable for campaign, convention, membership, and identification purposes at rates ranging from less than 1 cent to relatively high jewelry prices. The printing is part of the manufacturing process.

See the Classified Telephone Directory under Badges and Advertising Specialties for the names of local suppliers.

It is advisable to consult several firms, since prices vary widely. The 2-cent product of one firm may actually be more appropriate for the business in hand than the 12-cent item of some other firm.

Large manufacturers of badges, lapel buttons, and insignia have agents in the major cities and will have their local representative call on request. Two such firms are Bastian Brothers Co., 1600 Clinton Ave., N., Rochester 1,

18

N.Y.; and Whitehead and Hoag, 272 Sussex Ave., Newark 1, N.J.

**balloons** Toy balloons can be imprinted with advertising messages. For best results, the printing must be done when they are inflated. It can be done from type and stock cuts, or from specially made, deep-routed, zinc engravings.

Some suppliers of imprinted advertising balloons are the Van Dam Rubber Co., Inc., 1140 Broadway, New York; and Sterling Rubber Co., 4914 W. Wrightwood Ave., Chicago.

**basic weight, basis weight** See also PAPER SIZES AND WEIGHTS.

Many books are printed on paper of "basis weight" or "basic substance weight" 60 lb. This means that a ream (500 sheets) 25 by 38 in. in size weighs 60 lb. A 50-lb. paper is lighter; a 70-lb. paper is heavier.

To buy 60-lb. paper 35 by 45 in size, it is not necessary to figure out that 500 sheets of the larger size will weigh 99 lb. It is sufficient to order a ream of 35 by 45 paper in "substance 60." The bill will read "One ream, 35 × 45, substance 60, 99 lb. at — cents per pound."

Book-paper substance weights are based on the 25 by 38 size. Bond-paper substance weights are figured on a 17 by 22 basis. Cover-paper substance weights are figured on a 20 by 26 basis. Bristol-board substance weights are figured on a 22½ by 28½ or 22 by 28 basis. (See table under PAPER SIZES AND WEIGHTS.)

A 20-lb. bond is about the equivalent of a 50-lb. book paper.

**Baskerville** See Appendix 1, Type Faces.

**batter** Battered type is damaged type. A pressman reports a "press batter" when a cut, say, works loose from its mounting and gets crushed into adjoining matter.

**bearers** See also FOUNDRY PROOFS; PROOFS.

Type-high strips of metal or wood placed around the pages of type to protect them during the molding of electrotype or other duplicate plates. (See DUPLICATE PLATES.)

**bed** The surface of a printing press against which the type is clamped. When the type is in the press ready for printing, a publication is said to have been "put to bed."

**Ben Day** See SHADING TINTS.

**b.f.** Proofreader's abbreviation for boldface. (See BOLDFACE and PROOFREADING.)

**billboards** See OUTDOOR ADVERTISING.

**bimetal plates** Bimetal plates give the offset printer a printing surface from which he can run a million or more copies with the last copy being almost indistinguishable from the first.

One bimetal plate can outlast a whole series of conventional deep-etched plates and thus easily justify its extra cost on long runs.

Several different kinds of bimetal plates have been introduced, but the principle is much the same for all: The printing areas are surfaced with a grease-receptive metal, and the non-printing areas are surfaced with a water-receptive metal. (Conventional plates are made of the same metal throughout, treated to make it grease-receptive or water-receptive as desired.)

The International Printing Ink Corporation calls its version of these long-life offset plates the "Trimetal plate." The "Lithure plate" is a development of Time-Life-Fortune. A Danish version, now in use in the United States, is called the "Aller plate."

**binders' board** See also CARDBOARD. A stiff, high-grade composition board used in bookbinding, usually inside the cloth. (See illustration under BOOKBIND-ING.) Cheaper products used in the same way are chip board and pasted chip board.

**bindery** See also BINDING.

Many printers have no facilities of their own for the binding of books or pamphlets and send out their work to independent binderies.

Some binderies specialize in book or "edition" work. Others offer additional mounting and finishing services, including perforating, punching, round-cornering, eyeleting, tabbing, creasing, varnishing, easeling, gumming, etc. (See MOUNTING AND FINISHING.)

On small jobs it is often advisable to make the printer responsible for finished delivery, even though he has no binding facilities of his own and will add his own overhead charges to what the binder will charge.

On very large jobs, it may pay to deal separately with a binder. However, the printer must know who is going to bind the job, since he must print to suit the equipment of that bindery.

**binding** See also BOOK MANUFACTUR-ING; BOOKBINDING; MECHANICAL BIND-INGS; FOLDING; TRIM; DIE CUTTING; MOUNTING AND FINISHING; PADDING; VAR-NISHING.

Binding begins after a printer has laid the ink on the paper. It includes cutting, folding, trimming, gathering, stitching, pasting, insetting, casing-in, etc.

Since binding can easily cost more than all preceding operations, a knowledge of what each step costs is invaluable in planning printing to achieve the greatest effectiveness most economically.

The simplest and cheapest binding is none at all, e.g., the poster or one- or two-page leaflet that is finished the moment it comes off the press. Next is

the simple folded job, done either on a folding machine attached to the press or on a separate folding machine.

If a four-page, six-page, or French-fold (uncut eight-page) job can be accepted as it comes from the folding machine, the expense of an additional edge-trimming operation can be saved. (See FRENCH FOLD.)

However, pamphlets and books of eight pages and up, first must be folded, then stitched and trimmed. The trimming both opens the pages so they can be turned, and evens up the slightly uneven edges produced in the folding operation. Some folding machinery, such as that used for newspapers and newspaper supplements, will do rough trimming, producing serrated edges, as a part of the folding operation, thus eliminating the need for a separate trimming operation. Some folders also do slitting. (See SER-RATED EDGES.)

Note that the two sides of an unfolded sheet of paper make two pages. When folded, a sheet of paper gives the following results:

One fold—4 pages
Two folds—6 or 8 pages
Three folds—12 or 16 pages
Four folds—24 or 32 pages

Pamphlets and books should be designed around these units. Departure from them will necessitate the use of inserts or cancels. (See INSERTS and CANCEL.)

Before trimming folded sheets, the pages are usually fastened together by saddle-wire stitching, by side-wire stitching, or, for thicker booklets that must open flat, by thread stitching and/or gluing. Stitching is usually a separate operation. Some folding machines are equipped to insert wire staples as a part of the folding operation. Many apply a thin line of paste along the fold in 8-page or 12-page jobs, thus eliminating the need for stapling. (See STITCHING.)

## THESE LEAFLETS NEED NOT BE TRIMMED

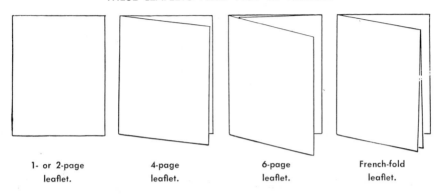

| 1- or 2-page leaflet. | 4-page leaflet. | 6-page leaflet. | French-fold leaflet. |

## THESE LEAFLETS MUST BE TRIMMED

| 8 pages after trim. | 8 pages before trim. | 12 pages before trim. | 16 pages before trim. |

## SPECIAL FOLDS

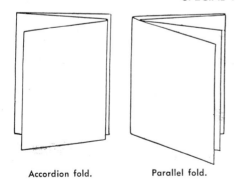

Accordion fold.     Parallel fold.

*Note:* The last fold should always be parallel to the grain of the paper (see *grain*). Otherwise booklets may handle badly during folding and may spring open. Paper must be ordered with grain the right way.

## STYLES OF BINDING

Self-cover,
saddle-wired.

Separate cover,
saddle-wired.

Perfect binding.

Side-wired.

Side-sewed
(Singer-sewed).

Side-wired with
pasted cover.

The Smyth-sewed binding (*left* and *above*) lets a thick book open flat. It consists of two or more separate signatures which are saddle-sewed and at the same time sewed to each other. "Perfect" bindings also open flat. Saddle wiring is most used for pamphlets under ¼ in. thick. Side-stitching is strong but will not open as flat as a Smyth-sewed binding. Steps in binding a book are shown in the illustrations under *bookbinding*.

A self-cover pamphlet is one with its cover on the same kind of paper as the text and printed along with the text. (See illustration.) This is always cheaper than a pamphlet having a cover of different paper and is often as satisfactory. Many small pamphlets can be run in two colors throughout for less than the cost of a one-color text and a separate cover. Larger booklets are often given stiff covers for both appearance and durability. The larger the booklet, the stronger the cover should be.

The steps in binding one 6- by 9-in. 64-page-plus-cover pamphlet follow: The text was run on 38- by 50-in. paper, printed both sides, and slit on the press into two 38- by 25-in. sections, each containing 32 pages. One section contained pages 1–16 and 49–64. The other contained pages 17–48. The four-page cover was run separately on a small press, on 9½- by 12½-in. cover paper.

The 25- by 38-in. flat sheets and the cover were folded to 6¼ by 9½ in. Then the first and second sections, or signatures, were gathered inside the cover and all were saddle-wired together. They were then stacked, smashed, and trimmed on three sides to 6 by 9 in. (See SIGNATURE; GATHERING; SMASHING; TRIM.)

The above job might have been bound as four 16's and a 4, instead of two 32's and a 4, but it would not have been handled as a 64 and a 4, since so large a signature folds awkwardly. It might also have been handled as a side-wired job, with the signatures laid beside each other instead of inside each other, stitched together about ⅛ in. from the fold, and then pasted inside the cover.

Books are generally printed in signatures of 16 or 32 pages, gathered, Smyth-sewed, smashed, furnished with end papers, trimmed on three sides, rounded and backed, and cased in. (See BOOK MANUFACTURING.) The cloth bind-

ing on a standard novel costs 25 to 50 cents.

The so-called perfect binding, used on telephone books (see illustration) is a glued binding, which can be much cheaper than other bookbinding methods on large jobs. The technique has been improved in recent years, thanks to developments in plastic adhesives. The low-cost binding of the 25-cent Pocket Books incorporates many interesting features, including stained edges and a laminated cover. (For information on spiral, plastic, and loose-leaf bindings, see MECHANICAL BINDINGS.)

Simple, standard binding operations are comparatively cheap. Putting one, two, or three folds into a piece of paper may cost no more than $2 per thousand. Putting two wire staples through an ordinary pamphlet may cost another $3 per thousand. Gathering (*e.g.,* putting one 16-page unit or signature inside another, and both inside a cover, preparatory to stitching) may cost another $3 per thousand. Trimming pamphlets of 8 to 64 pages may cost from $2 to $4 per thousand.

On the other hand, trick folds can run into more money. Some can be done only by hand; others have to be sent through the folding machine a separate time for each fold. Mechanical bindings are always more expensive than wire stitching. (See MECHANICAL BINDINGS.)

**black-and-white prints** See WHITE-PRINTS.

**blackface** See also BOLDFACE.
**This line is set in blackface type,** usually called "boldface," as distinct from lightface.

**black letter** See also Appendix 1, Type Faces.
𝔗𝔥𝔦𝔰 𝔰𝔢𝔫𝔱𝔢𝔫𝔠𝔢 𝔦𝔰 𝔰𝔢𝔱 𝔦𝔫 𝔞 𝔟𝔩𝔞𝔠𝔨-𝔩𝔢𝔱𝔱𝔢𝔯 𝔱𝔶𝔭𝔢, 𝔪𝔬𝔯𝔢 𝔠𝔬𝔪𝔪𝔬𝔫𝔩𝔶 𝔠𝔞𝔩𝔩𝔢𝔡 "𝔒𝔩𝔡 𝔈𝔫𝔤𝔩𝔦𝔰𝔥" 𝔬𝔯 "𝔱𝔢𝔵𝔱."
In Germany, this kind of type is still

widely used, especially in a lighter version called "Fraktur."

**bleed** See also CROP, CROPPING.

A photograph or piece of art work is said to bleed when it extends to the very edge of the printed page. To achieve this effect the page is trimmed

Layout for page containing photo to bleed top and right. Dotted lines show the edge of the paper before trim. Shaded part of the photo is lost in the trimming.

right through the picture. When a picture occupies the entire page of a magazine or pamphlet, with no margins at all, it is said to bleed on three sides and run flush to the gutter on the fourth side.

After being printed and folded, booklets of eight pages and over must be trimmed to open folds that would otherwise require the reader to use a paper knife. (See illustration under BINDING.) For example, a pamphlet that folds to 6¼ by 9½ in. must be trimmed to 6⅛ by 9¼ merely to open the pages. If there are bleed photos, it must usually be trimmed to 6 by 9 in. to make

sure that all photos actually will bleed.

If a photograph is to bleed, one must specify that it be reproduced ⅛ in. or 1 pica wider on the side or sides to bleed, and one must crop and scale it accordingly. (See illustration. *Warning:* see also GRIPPER EDGE.)

**blind stamping** Pressing a design into a book cover with tools or dies, not colored by ink or gold leaf. It is also called "blind tooling" and "blocking."

**block** See also CUT.

The word "block" is sometimes used synonymously with cut and engraving; *e.g.,* line block, halftone block, and (almost always) linoleum block.

To block a cut means to mount it on a wood or metal base. To block a cut type-high means to make its printing surface the same height as that of the printing type.

**block printing** Printing from hand-carved linoleum or wooden blocks. This is essentially a handicraft, not to be considered in the same category with the photomechanical, chemical, and power-driven processes used in commercial printing.

Its value is in its simplicity, its individuality, and its cheapness. A child can make a block print and use it quite effectively. On the other hand, the best block prints are the work of skilled artists of long experience.

A block print is made up of relatively heavy lines and solid areas as contrasted with the fine hairlines of an etching or engraving. The wood or linoleum will permit only the bolder, stronger lines.

A block is made for relief printing, carrying ink on the uncut surfaces and no ink in the depressions that have been carved out. (See RELIEF.)

To make a block print the design must first be drawn on tracing paper in the exact size and proportions desired in the final print. This design is transferred (by means of carbon paper) from the paper to the block in reverse so that the printed proof will be identical with the original.

Then with the tools appropriate for wood or linoleum block carving, the areas that are not to print are carved or routed out. The block is inked, proofs are taken, and with necessary improvements the block is ready to be run. The best effects are obtained when soft papers are used.

In comparison with metal plates the woodcut or linoleum block is very soft and hence impractical for long runs. For a short run, such as a program for a small club or the senior class play, it is both inexpensive and effective. Wood or linoleum blocks may be printed alongside type in a regular printing press.

To print in two colors, two blocks may be made and printed separately. Highly skilled artists sometimes make many blocks, each to reproduce a different color in a multicolor print. Interesting effects may also be obtained by painting-on the inks, several colors side by side, and thus getting several colors from a single impression.

**blotters** Advertising blotters, like calendars, have a chance of remaining within view of the prospective customer for a long time.

Photos cannot be printed on plain blotting paper. But almost anything can be printed on coated paper, which can be laminated to one side of blotting paper.

Practically any printer is equipped to produce advertising blotters economically. The letterpress process is perhaps used more often than offset.

Stock blotters are worth investigating. These come already printed with eye-catching illustrations in color and can be imprinted with any sales message and are obtainable from such firms as Brown & Bigelow, 1286 University Ave., St. Paul 4, Minn.; Lutz and

Sheinkman, 421 Hudson St., New York 14.

**blow-up** A blow-up of a photograph or an advertisement is an enlargement of it.

**blue-penciling** According to tradition, editors use a blue pencil when they cut, correct, or rewrite material. Many a reporter has complained that the rewrite man blue-penciled the best part of his story.

**blueprint** The blueprint method is used primarily for duplicating mechanical and architectural drawings. It does not permit enlarging or reducing.

For best results the original drawing is prepared in black ink on translucent paper. It is placed in contact with sensitized blueprint paper and exposed to strong light. The exposed paper is then washed. The result is that the paper turns blue wherever the light hit it and remains white where shielded by the black ink on the original drawing.

Blueprints can be made quickly and cheaply. They cost as little as 5 cents a square foot, with a minimum charge, and are usually procurable in any width up to 42 in., and in any length at all. They can be made from a relatively opaque master drawing, provided there is nothing on the back of it. Blueprints are always approximately the same size as the original—approximately, since the paper may stretch or shrink a little in the washing as in Photostating.

The so-called "whiteprints" made by the Ozalid and Bruning processes (see WHITEPRINT) are now displacing ordinary blueprints. They provide a more legible print showing black lines or colored lines on a white background like the original. They can be made about as cheaply as blueprints. Because they are developed dry, there is a minimum of difficulty about changes in dimensions during the developing.

The blueprint process is the oldest in the field, and for some time to come the word "blueprint" will probably be applied to any method of same-size photocopying from translucent originals.

Blueprints are made from the "flats" (the assembled films) used in making offset or other plates, to provide an advance check of how the plates will print. (See also VANDYKE.)

A same-size copy made in permanent printer's ink (as if lithographed) may be obtained at 20 cents per square foot from the Lithoprint Company, 145 Hudson St., New York 13. The process resembles both photogelatin and the hectograph.

**boards** See CARDBOARD.

**Bodoni** See Appendix 1, Type Faces.

**body** The body of a type character or slug is the piece of metal on which the letter or letters are cast. 10-pt. type can be cast on a 10-pt. body; it can also be cast on an 11-pt., 12-pt., or larger body to avoid the need for inserting one, two, or more points of leading between the lines as a separate operation.

The letter "W" must be cast on a wider body than the letter "i," but both are cast on bodies of equal height.

The term "body type" is sometimes used to mean small type, or text type, as opposed to headlines and display lettering.

**boiler plate** Stereotyped news and feature material prepared centrally by such agencies as Western Newspaper Union and supplied to small newspapers for use as filler.

**boldface** See also Appendix 1, Type Faces.

**This sentence is set in bold type or boldface, abbreviated b.f.**

When a manuscript is marked for the printer, a wavy line under certain words indicates that they should be set in boldface. Many kinds of type have boldface counterparts. Some boldface type has no corresponding lightface.

The well-known Bodoni series of types comes in four weights: Bodoni Book, Bodoni, **Bodoni Bold, Ultra Bodoni,** (also called Poster Bodoni).

Unfortunately for the designer, the same words sometimes mean different things. For instance, the Linotype Spartan series includes Spartan Light, Spartan Medium, **Spartan Heavy,** and **Spartan Black.** The identical faces, when put out by Intertype are called Futura Light, Futura Medium, Futura Demibold, and Futura Bold, respectively.

See charts entitled "The Futura Family" in Appendix 1.

A Linotype matrix will hold two faces, but not three. It is more common for printers to have roman and italic paired than roman and boldface.

**bond paper** See also PAPER.

Bond paper is made to present a good surface for pen and ink and is used for writing paper, typewriter paper, and miscellaneous leaflet work. It is suitable for offset printing.

Bond paper comes in basic substance weights (see BASIC WEIGHT) of 13, 16, 20, and 24 lb. to the ream of 500 17- by 22-in. sheets. Heavier papers of the same sort are called "ledger" papers. Sulphite bond is made of chemically treated wood pulp. Rag-content bonds contain 25, 50, 75, or 100 per cent of pulp made from rags, and offer somewhat greater permanence and strength if well made.

Bond papers come in colors as well as in white.

**book** See BOOK MANUFACTURING.

**bookbinding** See also BINDING; BOOK MANUFACTURING.

The basic steps in bookbinding are outlined in the accompanying illustration.

Folding each
32-page signature

End papers tipped(pasted)
to first and last signatures

1st 32 pages ← 2nd 32 pages ← 3rd 32 pages ← 4th 32 pages

Smyth sewing          Smashing

Trimming

Steps in binding a 128-page book, as shown above, include (1) folding (signatures could also have 8, 16, 24, 48, or 64 pages), (2) adding end papers and inserts, if any, (3) gathering in proper order (not shown), (4) sewing, (5) smashing, and (6) trimming. The next step, not shown, is to apply a thin coat of glue to the sewn edges, preliminary to the rounding and backing shown on the next page.

A remarkably clear and detailed demonstration of bookbinding is given in the 16mm. sound film *Bound to Last* which runs 18 min. and is available on loan from William J. Ganz Co., 40 E. 49 St., New York.

**book cloth**  See also BOOK MANUFACTUR-ING.

Cloth for binding books falls into three main categories: starch-filled cloth used for novels, etc.; pyroxylin-impregnated cloth; and pyroxylin-coated cloth or imitation leather much used for textbooks. (Impregnating does not change the appearance of the cloth; coating does.) New plastic impregnants and coatings are being developed.

Starch-filled cloth is least expensive but is vulnerable to water-spotting and soiling. It cannot be wiped clean as can impregnated or coated cloths. Impregnating gives a cloth water-resistance, but does not change its appearance. Coating conceals the original weave of the cloth, though a pattern may be pressed into it to simulate either cloth or leather.

Pyroxylin (another name for cellulose nitrate or celluloid) has for many

Crash   Paper   Glue

ROUNDING AND BACKING          ADDING BACKBONE REINFORCEMENT

Cloth   +   Board  Paper  Board   =   Cover

+ Ink or foil or blind stamping   =   TITLE

Binder's board   Binder's board   +   Paste   =   End paper   End paper

Case

The final steps in bookbinding, as shown above, are (1) rounding and backing (optional), (2) adding backbone reinforcement, called "lining-up," (3) making the covers or "cases," (4) stamping the cases, (5) casing-in.

years been the impregnant or coating most commonly used, but vinyl and other new plastic coatings are now coming into use.

The well-known buckram is a high grade of cloth available both starch-filled and -impregnated. Du Pont Fabrikoid is one of the better-known pyroxylin-coated cloths.

Book cloth comes in rolls 36, 38, 40, and 42 in. wide. Purchasers of bookbinding services do not ordinarily buy the cloth separately. They let the bookbinder do that.

**book jacket**  See JACKET.

**booklets**  See PAMPHLETS.

**book manufacturing**  See also BOOK-BINDING.

A bound book is really a collection of 16- or 32-page pamphlets put together with thread, glue, binders' board, and cloth. Any job printer could make a book, and any binder could bind one. However, printers who specialize in bookwork can almost invariably turn out a more professional-looking book, perhaps at considerably lower cost.

Three book manufacturers who offer both printing and binding services and who are staffed to assist in designing books are The Kingsport Press, Inc., Kingsport, Tenn. (sales offices at 1 E. 57 St., New York, and at 325 W. Huron St., Chicago); H. Wolff Book Manufacturing Co., 508 W. 26 St., New York; Quinn & Boden Co., Inc., Rahway, N.J. (sales office at 381 Fourth Ave., New York).

*Book publishers* are not book printers. Almost no book publisher maintains his own book-manufacturing plant. Publishers who ask authors to help pay for the publication of their books (except in the case of scholarly books of very limited appeal) are known in the trade as "vanity publishers." They promise "publication," but they actually deliver very little save "printing" and usually charge too much for that.

The cost of book manufacturing (not including author's royalty) is about one-fifth to one-quarter of retail book prices. Costs tend to go down as the number of copies printed goes up. Thus, it may be possible to make 5,000 copies of a $3 book for 60 cents each ($3,000), and also 25,000 copies of the same title for sale as a $1 reprint at 30 cents each ($7,500), typesetting having been taken care of. Editions in excess of 100,000 have to be run to get a cost of 10 cents a copy or so on paper-bound books to be sold on the newsstands at 25 cents retail.

Authoritative information on book manufacturing is given in concise, readable form in "A Primer in Book Production" by Frank B. Myrick (Bookbinding and Book Production Magazine, 1945. Out of print). See other books on the subject listed in the Bibliography.

Those who want to see the steps in book manufacturing should make arrangements for a showing of *Bound to Last*, a 16mm. sound film, which may be borrowed from William J. Ganz Co., 40 E. 49 St., New York.

**book paper** See PAPER.

**book postage rates** See Appendix 4, Postal Information.

**Bourges color system** Some sixty printers' ink colors or color tints may be obtained in the form of thin transparent sheets from Bourges, Inc., 80 Fifth Avenue, New York 11. The sheets are useful for laying in backgrounds (where color is not wanted, it will rub cleanly off the transparent base), for altering the color values of paintings and transparencies, for determining what effect will result when one color is printed over another, for making up dummies in color, etc.

Through the use of sheets, it is easy to "retouch" without touching the original art. A model's face can be made tanner, a blue automobile can be seen in green, duotone effects can be studied in advance of ordering the plates, backgrounds can be subdued to make desired subjects stand out.

The sheets can either be photographed as part of full-color art work or can be photographed separately to provide the engraver with ready-made color separations.

Copy may be prepared with Bourges sheets for flat-color line reproduction in two, three, four, and even five colors. Matched pencils and liquid colors also make it possible to build up the color for halftone reproduction. The reproduction of art prepared in this way saves about half the standard process cost as the colors are already separated for camera. Since Bourges sheets are matched to inks, and overlap in the same way inks do, Bourges copy acts as an accurate color proof of the final printed result.

There are 12 basic Bourges colors including black and white. Each is available in 10, 30, 50, 70, and 100 per cent values. The black and white sheets are particularly useful for correcting photographs.

Bourges sheets are also available with an adhesive backing that makes them helpful for presentations and displays and for the preparation of package designs and layouts in actual printing-ink colors.

Bourges also makes a transparent red-orange Transopaque sheet with the same removable coating. When it is used, separation copy may be prepared with an assurance of register accuracy impossible with black opaque.

The key to the Bourges system is a Color Guide composed of 3- by 5-in. sample swatches of all Bourges sheets. By laying these transparent swatches over your work, you can choose the exact printing color that is most appropriate.

Bourges sheets, either standard or adhesive, cost $4 for a full size sheet 18½ by 25 in. Half sheets cost $2 and quarter sheets $1. The handy Color Guide is $5; a complete manual with sample illustrations is $5. Free literature on the preparation and printing of Bourges materials is available at leading art dealers and from Bourges, Inc., 80 Fifth Avenue, New York 11.

**box, boxed**

---

This paragraph has been boxed, *i.e.*, put inside a box consisting of a plain ruled border. In this case a box made of 1-pt. rule was specified. (See RULES.) Boxes are often used to lend emphasis to certain material or to set it off from other text matter. Material to be boxed must, of course, be set narrower than lines in the same column that are not boxed.

---

**box printing** See also CONTAINER PRINTING.

Boxes are almost always printed by the manufacturer, although sometimes labels are printed separately and then affixed to them.

**break** When a printed job is to run in two or more colors, the printer must be given instructions as to the "break for color." This means indicating on the proofs or the layout, or both, which items are to be printed in black and which in what colors. A headline that is to be printed in red must be removed by the printer from the black form and put in the proper position in the red form.

**Bristol board** See also CARDBOARD.

Bristol boards, or Bristols, are papers of post-card weight or more, made to provide a certain stiffness or rigidity.

Index Bristols are made to take ink and erasing well. Wedding Bristols and mill Bristols are made to provide a good printing surface.

**broadsides** See CIRCULARS; PAMPHLETS.

**brochures** See PAMPHLETS.

**bronze proofs** In certain processes, notably rotogravure and deep-etch offset, bronze proofs of type matter are sometimes used. Bronze proofs, also called "glassines," are made with great care on transparent glassine paper and dusted with bronze powder while the ink is still wet.

The purpose of the bronzing is to make the letters even more opaque than black ink alone will make them. The proofs are then used as if they were photographic film, and it becomes unnecessary to make first a film negative from white paper proofs, and then a film positive from the film negative. (Only processes that work from film positives instead of film negatives can take advantage of this short cut.)

Some typographers use a special offset technique to print on both sides of glassine simultaneously, and the double layer of ink thus gives them the necessary opacity without bronzing.

**bronzing** See also BRONZE PROOFS.

Applying metallic powder to the

still-wet ink of a printed page to secure the effect of bronze, gold, silver, aluminum, etc.

**brush-coated paper** See COATED PAPER.

**brush drawing** See also WASH DRAWING; DRAWING TECHNIQUES.
A drawing made with a brush. Whether it is a line drawing or a wash drawing depends on the technique used. A brush dipped in India ink will usually make a solid line that can be reproduced as a line drawing. If the brush pulls the ink over the paper in a broken film, it may make a dry-brush drawing. A brush dipped in water color may make a wash drawing that must be reproduced by the halftone process. (See illustrations under DRAWING TECHNIQUES.)

**buckram** See BOOK CLOTH.

**bulk** See also PAPER.
"Bulk" refers to the thickness of paper. Antique paper bulks thicker than English-finish paper. A 60-lb. book paper may be ordered to bulk 400 pages to the inch or 600 pages to the inch, etc. The more calendering, the less bulk. (See CALENDERED PAPER.) Books are sometimes "bulked" (printed on bulked paper) to make them look like more for the money. However, bulked paper is inferior in strength and printing qualities to firmer paper. The fluff from bulked paper often "picks" and gets in the ink, causing troubles in the pressroom. Weight, bulk, and finish are characteristics that can be controlled during the manufacture of paper. Any two can be specified, but never all three.

**business forms** The simpler kinds of business forms can be produced by the methods reviewed under CIRCULARS and LETTERS. The economical printing of complicated forms requires specialized machinery. There are companies which make a specialty of designing and producing business forms to fit any need.

Some of the printing presses used in producing business forms are marvels of versatility. It becomes quite possible to print a six-part form on six kinds of paper, in six kinds of ink, and to insert five layers of one-time carbon paper (or to spot-carbonize the backs of the forms and thus dispense with the carbon paper), and to perforate any of the forms so that part serves as a shipping label, and to deliver completely assembled forms, as separate units, or in roll form, or in accordion-pleated form—and to do all of this as one operation on one machine.

Wherever information is being copied, the question may well be asked as to whether the copy could not have been created at the same time the original was created. For example, one typing of an order can yield, by means of carbon copies, the invoice, a duplicate invoice, a shipping label, a packing slip, an inventory control slip, a salesman's record, and a mailing list record. Information about discounts, etc., can appear on some copies and not on others if desired.

Where it proves impossible to get enough legible carbon copies to fill the need or where duplicate copies must be made on paper or card stock which is too heavy to transmit carbon impressions, the various duplicating-equipment manufacturers step into the picture with systems for putting the original information on a "master," all additional copies being made from this master by mimeograph, Multilith, Ditto, Addressograph, Elliott, or similar methods.

These firms (see DUPLICATING METHODS) are fond of pointing out that unprinted paper never becomes obsolete. They usually recommend that simple forms be duplicated right in the office, as needed.

Mimeograph, Multilith, and Ditto

also feature new techniques of duplicating business forms *in the same operation that fills in the blanks on those forms.* Mimeograph stencils, for example, are pre-impressed with the data and lines of the form. The blanks are filled in on the typewriter. Then both are duplicated together.

Some printers specializing in business forms of all types include Moore Business Forms, Inc., with offices in Niagara Falls, N.Y., Emeryville and Los Angeles, Calif., Denton, Texas, and Minneapolis; the Egry Register Co., and the Standard Register Co., both of Dayton, Ohio.

**business reply cards and envelopes**
See Appendix 4, Postal Information.

**butted**   See illustration under MITERED.

**buttons** See BADGES.

# C | c

**c.** Abbreviation for caps, used in c. & l.c. (caps and lower case), c. & s.c. (caps and small caps), etc.

**calendars** It is probably safe to suppose that calendars have been produced by every known printing and binding technique. (For information on how to order calendars printed, see, therefore, PAMPHLETS or POSTERS plus the intended BINDING or PRINTING process.)

Calendars are commonly ordered from stock, and merely imprinted (see IMPRINTING) with the advertiser's message. The biggest advertising calendar firm is Brown & Bigelow, 1286 University Ave., St. Paul 4, Minn. Another well-known firm offering many types and sizes of calendars and imprinting them to order is John Baumgarth Co., 3001 W. North Ave., Melrose Park, Ill.

**calendered paper** See also PAPER.

Paper is calendered to make it smooth; supercalendered to make it glossy. The process consists of passing the newly made paper between smooth cylinders under pressure. In supercalendering, one cylinder moves faster than the other, and a brushing action on the paper surface results. By means of calendering and supercalendering, an antique finish of high bulk becomes a smoother antique finish of lesser bulk, then a machine finish, then an English finish, then a supercalendered or "super" finish.

The more calendering a paper is subjected to, the better it will take halftones. Halftones of 110- and 120-line screen can be printed on English-finish or supercalendered stock. Coated paper is used for finer screens. (See COATED PAPER.)

**calligraphy** Beautiful writing or penmanship. Type faces resembling handwriting are referred to as "calligraphic" types.

**camera** Large copying cameras are used in every printing process for enlarging, reducing, same-size copying, and color separation. Most of them are built to enlarge as much as twice the size of the original, or reduce to one-half or one-quarter that size, although these limits can be exceeded either by making special adjustments or by copying and then recopying. (See PHOTOGRAPHY; PHOTOSTAT; and illustration under HALFTONE.)

**camera lucida** In making layouts it is often necessary to copy an illustration or an actual object in a size larger or smaller than the original. An optical device known as the "lucy," short for "camera lucida," is a great help at such times and is procurable at most art stores.

A very simple lucy employing a half-silvered mirror sells for about $2. Similar devices employing prisms cost some-

Camera lucida.

what more. To get an image bright enough to copy, put a very strong light on the original while keeping your copying paper under comparatively low illumination. The desired degree of enlargement or reduction can be obtained by adjusting the relative positions of the original and the viewing device.

Much more versatile lucy's can be obtained under such names as Lacey-Luci and Camera Lucikon. These are basically copying cameras designed to throw an enlarged or reduced image of any original onto a ground glass where it can be traced. In the Lacey-Luci, the ground glass is inclined like a drawing board. In the Camera Lucikon, the ground glass is horizontal like a table. These "visualizers" can also be used for photocopying, and are even pressed into duty as process

cameras and contact printing frames in small offset shops, silk-screen shops, etc. The Lacey-Luci is made by the Merritt Lacey Corporation, 31 Central Ave., Newark 2, N.J. The Camera Lucikon is made by the M. P. Goodkin Company, 889 Broad Street, Newark 2, N.J. Prices start at about $500.

**campaign planning** In most advertising or information campaigns, a number of different techniques are used simultaneously. They are coordinated to supplement each other and reach the desired groups with the greatest economy.

Every member of the audience must receive information in terms he can understand from sources that he trusts. All his doubts and reservations must be answered.

Information must be presented in a way that will capture his interest (including his self-interest); otherwise his mind will be closed. The average American may be apathetic about supplying milk to the tribes of Africa, but he is interested in getting more milk at a lower price for his own family.

He must receive the new information often enough to prevent his forgetting. Most people have to be exposed to a new idea at least three times before they can clear their minds of old conflicting information.

These requirements suggest the importance of a coordinated campaign to reach every prospect through

1. His reading (books, magazines, newspapers, direct mail)

2. His listening (radio, television, lectures)

3. His seeing (theater, films, slide films, television, and displays)

4. If possible, word of mouth via his friends, club, union, church, or children

The specialized approach often succeeds when the general approach does not. A man not reached by information through general channels may be wide open to an approach through his special interest, be he physician, parent, farmer, or union member. For example, manufacturers of union-made cigarettes have found it advantageous to emphasize that feature in advertisements published in labor papers.

Format and design must tie in with both audience and method of distribution. Those who enjoy reading *Time* will subconsciously be favorably disposed toward something of similar format. Those who do not like *Time* may be adversely prejudiced by anything that reminds them of it.

Campaigns have been criticized both as "too slick and professional" and as "too amateurish." The amateurish approach is disarming to some, but it may also evoke the reaction "those bunglers are probably as inept in their thinking as in their publicity work. . . ."

Campaign material that looks expensive should be carefully avoided by organizations that are appealing for contributions or trying to establish a record for efficient and economical administration. A Home for Indigent Ladies of Considerable Years should not, for example, use expensive book stock for a pamphlet soliciting $60,000 to build a new wing. Instead, paper and other campaign materials must reflect economical planning to appeal to the reader.

One universal rule is to be factual, specific, and honest in any campaign. Millions of dollars are wasted annually on material that is designed to reach the emotions but fails to appeal to common sense. Americans have become increasingly skeptical of promoters who promise everything.

Many campaigns are duds because, despite a great output of words, the essential facts are not told. Before going ahead, it is a good idea to test materials on outsiders who have no knowledge of the subject matter.

A rounded campaign may include all the following activities:

1. Paid publicity: advertising via newspaper, magazine, radio, television, or outdoor display; direct mail, using letters, pamphlets, blotters, etc.

2. Free publicity: news and feature coverage in newspapers, magazines, newsreels, and on the air through releases, press conferences, press agents, etc.

The Table of Contents of this book offers a good check list of the various kinds of promotional possibilities, each described under its own heading elsewhere in this book.

The chart on page viii lists the essential steps in launching any campaign.

Excellent material on this subject is given in the publications listed in the Bibliography.

**cancel**  A 28-page pamphlet is often printed as a 32-page pamphlet, and then four blank pages are canceled, *i.e.,* cut out and destroyed during the binding operation. These pages are called "cancels."

A book is said to have a "cancel title" if the original title page has been cut out, and a new one pasted in.

**c. & l.c.**  Abbreviation for caps and lower case. (See PROOFREADING.)

**c. & s.c.**  Abbreviation for caps and small caps. (See PROOFREADING.)

**caps, capitals**  See also PROOFREADING. "Caps," abbreviation for "capitals," is frequently used to indicate uppercase letters as distinct from small or lower-case letters. THIS SENTENCE IS SET IN CAPS. *THIS SENTENCE IS SET IN ITALIC CAPS.* This Sentence Is Set in Caps and Lower Case. THIS SENTENCE IS SET IN CAPS AND SMALL CAPS.

**caps and small caps**  See also PROOFREADING.

THIS SENTENCE IS SET IN CAPS AND SMALL CAPS (C. & S.C.). THIS SENTENCE IS SET IN EVEN SMALL CAPS. Most fonts of type include small caps in sizes up to, but not above, 14 pt. Although italic small caps have been cut for one or two faces, almost no printer can supply them.

**captions** A caption (legend) belongs under the picture to which it refers. To put it in some other position—above or beside the picture—is to force the reader to search for it and perhaps to lose interest.

The good caption may simply identify the illustration, or it may give a message or news story suggested by it. The latter is being used more and more with the increasing popularity of the "picture story" of the variety shown in *Life*. A good caption should complement the information given by the picture, not duplicate it.

A good way to decide upon a type face and style for captions is to look through some illustrated publications and find captions that are attractive. In this way you can select a style and size of type.

The amount of copy needed for a caption is found by determining the number of characters that the type selected will permit to the pica or inch, multiplying that by the width of the caption, and again by the number of lines that the caption is to include. Generally all lines of a caption are the same length. (A caption that is 2¼ instead of 3 lines long, for example, may look unfinished.) It may require several trials to write a caption of the desired size.

The size of a caption is frequently determined not by the extent of the ideas to be expressed, but by the space allocated to a picture next to it or in a similar position on the same or facing page. Pictures occupying adjacent or related positions are usually given identical space for captions.

Captions or legends that accompany photographs, charts, cartoons, and art work should be written carefully with a view to their purpose and the space available.

Writing an effective caption takes more time and thought than its length would indicate. In addition to giving a message briefly, it must have some punch and be the proper length to fit the space limitations.

The caption writer is responsible for the line giving credit to the photographer or source of the chart or art work reproduced. (See CREDIT LINES.) This credit line may appear immediately below the picture, *i.e.*, above the caption itself, or as a final phrase in the last line of the caption. The usual form is simply such an acknowledgment as "Acme photo."

**carbon copy** A few extra copies of a typed, written, or drawn item can be easily made with the aid of carbon paper. Four or five carbon copies usually present no problem. Up to 20 carbon copies can be produced on a hard-hitting electric typewriter with the right combination of papers.

To improve the legibility of carbon copies, thin hard paper and thin carbon paper are best. A thin sheet for the original will increase the legibility of the copies. The undermost copy may be on heavy hard paper, but the use of a regular-weight letterhead for the original will reduce the legibility of the copies.

Some find that several additional legible carbon copies can be made if the message is typed *without a ribbon*. The original will then be completely illegible, but the carbons will be much sharper. In fact, an effective way to get crystal-sharp typing for offset reproduction is to type without a ribbon directly on the back of a piece of carbon paper.

Carbon paper is obtainable in red, yellow, blue, and other colors as well as in black, and in larger sizes as well as the standard 8½ by 11 in.

A layer of carbon can be applied to any paper. Business forms requiring multiple carbon copies are often simplified by eliminating separate sheets of carbon paper, and putting the carbon on the underside of the forms themselves. The whole area need not be carbonized. The carbon can be applied only to selected areas, so that one carbon copy will receive only the shipping information, and another the full discount and billing information, etc. Such work is done by printers specializing in business forms. (See BUSINESS FORMS.)

A recent development produces carbon images without conventional carbon paper. A colorless chemical coating on the underside of a sheet interacts with another colorless coating on the top side of the next sheet to make the image.

Carbon paper is available in ribbon form for use in typewriters, especially electric typewriters, and yields a sharper result than cloth ribbon.

**car cards** See TRANSPORTATION ADVERTISING.

**cardboard** See also PAPER; PAPER SIZES AND WEIGHTS.

Under "cardboard," the term most used by the layman, will be discussed those paper products that are thicker and stiffer than paper.

Cardboard is bought like paper: by the pound and in the same range of prices, grades, and finishes. Therefore, much of what is said about paper is not repeated here. The basic sizes, however, are not the same.

The average user of printing is most likely to be interested in three items: (1) cover paper, for pamphlet covers, (2) Bristol board, for post cards, etc. (3) crude board for protecting the contents of envelopes, for mounting posters and pictures, etc.

The table accompanying the entry on PAPER SIZES AND WEIGHTS is arranged to show the comparative weights and basic sizes of the various papers and cardboards. It shows, for example, that 94-lb. post-card Bristol is about equivalent to what would be 140-lb. book paper if such heavy paper were made.

The terms used in the paper trade are so numerous as to be confusing, but they may be roughly organized as follows:

After the heavy-weight papers, the ledger papers, and the cover papers, come the Bristol boards and then the binders' boards, boxboards, etc. There is a limit to how thick paper can be made. Heavier weights of stock are produced by combining two or more webs of paper, either without paste while still wet or with paste.

Cardboard can be obtained in the same finishes as paper. When the surface must take ink and stand erasures, index Bristol is used. When a good smooth printing surface is all that is required, printing Bristol, mill Bristol, or wedding Bristol is used. A cheaper grade is called "bogus Bristol." Bristols are 0.006 in. (6 pt.) thick, or more. (The Bristol used in government postal cards is about 6 pt.) Basic weights for Bristols are 90, 100, 120, 140, 160, 180, 200, and 240 lb. for a ream of 500 sheets, 22½ by 28½ in.

It is possible to get coated Bristol, coated-one-side Bristol, colored Bristol, and Bristols designed to take lacquer, lithography, waxing, lamination, etc. Extra-tough Bristols made of manila rope, jute, or kraft pulp are available for tags, etc. The so-called "tag boards" can also be very cheap. The word "manila" alone does not indicate the presence of rope fibers.

Since cardboards are usually built up out of several plies, it is quite common to use a cheap filler, together with a better grade of lining. "Lining" in paper-trade terminology means the outside layer.

Cardboards over 0.012 in. thick are often grouped under the general name "paperboards." These include binders' board (the strongest grade, 0.030 to 0.300 in. thick), chip board (a cheaper grade), strawboard, boxboard, millboard, pulpboard, newsboard, pressboard, corrugated board, etc.

The cheapest cardboards are made from reprocessed newsprint and are not bleached white. Special cardboards are obtainable as artists' drawing board, mat board (for mounting pictures), etc. Artists' drawing board can be surfaced for water color, ink, etc., and is obtainable for special art techniques under such names as Ross board, scratch board, etc. (See DRAWING TECHNIQUES.)

**carding out** Carding out a column of type means to insert strips of cardstock, Bristol board, paper, etc., between the lines to make the column a bit deeper. This might be done, for example, in order to make 12 lines occupy the same space as 13 lines in an adjoining column. The smallest metal spacing material is the 1-pt. lead, which is about 0.014 in. thick. Post-card stock is less than half as thick. Carding out doesn't look very well, but it is about the only thing a *printer* can do when faced with uneven columns, unless authorized to do what an editor would do under the circumstances, namely find a way to cut or add copy to get even columns.

**caret** See also PROOFREADING.
Proofreader's mark ∧ to indicate that an insertion is to be made.

**cartoons** See also ART WORK; DRAWING TECHNIQUES.
Appropriate cartoons add to the effectiveness of almost any printed material. They help get it read and put important points across.

Sometimes good and relevant cartoons can be found in already pub-lished form. Newspapers and magazines often grant permission to reprint cartoons that have appeared in their pages, provided credit is given. For nonprofit purposes such reprint permission is often given free. However, in reproducing a two- or three-column newspaper cartoon, care should be taken not to reduce it to a size that is illegible.

Usually it is necessary to have special cartoons drawn. This has the advantage of permitting continuity of style and flexibility of layout.

To make a cartoon two things are necessary: the idea and the artist.

Thinking up cartoon ideas is not easy, but it is a job the editor should accept and not wish on the artist. It is not easy for an artist, either, and he may have the additional handicap of knowing very little about the subject matter.

The best way to work out ideas for a cartoon is to make a list of the main points that need emphasis and then try to convert these points into visual form. Once the important points are clearly stated, the artist is much more likely to be able to help in visualizing them.

*How to create cartoon ideas.* Cartoons need not always be funny. Some are straightforward pictures of ordinary people taking the action that the writer desires. The artist's way of drawing people can add the necessary warmth or sympathetic appeal.

Some cartoons make their points by contrast—perhaps introducing a character who does everything wrong. Some base their humor on exaggeration—the caption giving good advice but the characters taking that advice too literally. Some take the author's figures of speech and illustrate them with disarming literalness.

Even the little gnomes who merely crawl about some pages or charts and point at things may help nurse the reader along through pages that he would otherwise skip. (For suggestions on choosing an artist, see ARTISTS.)

When a cartoon is ordered, the artist should be told (1) the age and interests of the audience to be reached, (2) the editorial slant of the publication in which it will appear, (3) the specific idea to be put across, (4) the proportions desired, (5) the size in which the cartoon is to be printed, and (6) whether he must deliver a line drawing or may use the wash-drawing technique.

Care should be taken to use a cartoon style that the audience likes. Some groups appreciate subtle, sophisticated caricatures; others prefer their humor simple, realistic, and slapstick. A good editor uses discretion in imposing his own tastes on his readers.

For many purposes stock cuts are useful. (See STOCK CUTS.)

**cartouche** A flourish with pen or brush made to serve as a decorative scroll or border.

A cartouche.

**case** 1. Hand type is kept in compartmented trays called "cases." The capital letters used to be kept in the upper case, the small letters in the lower case. This explains the terms "upper case" for capital letters and "lower case" for small letters. The so-called California job case accommodates both, side by side.

2. The case of a book is its cover. In case bookbinding, also called "edi-

A pair of type cases.

tion bookbinding," a book's cover or case is manufactured in a separate operation from the book itself. The process of gluing a book inside of its cover is called "casing in." In hand bookbinding a book's cover or binding is built around the book itself, not assembled as a separate case to be glued on later. (See illustration under BOOKBINDING.)

3. A case of paper weighs about 500 to 700 lb., the exact amount depending on the dimensions and thickness of the kind being packed.

**case in** See CASE and illustration under BOOKBINDING.

**Caslon** See Appendix 1, Type Faces.

**cast off** See also COPY FITTING.

To estimate the number of columns or pages a manuscript will make when set in type.

**catalogue** See also PAMPHLETS; BOOK MANUFACTURING; BINDING; MECHANICAL BINDINGS.

Producing a catalogue differs very little from producing a pamphlet or a book, so the discussion printed under those headings will not be repeated here.

Important elements to consider in planning a catalogue are as follows:

1. *Size.* Is the catalogue to fit in a pocket, sit on a shelf, go in a file, or lie in a desk drawer? Will it get more attention or less if it differs from the other catalogues used by the recipient? What envelope will be used?

2. *Need for durability.* Must it withstand hard wear? Or exposure to water or grease? This may determine the nature of the cover, binding, or paper to be used.

3. *Ease of reference.* A catalogue needs to be well organized and indexed, so that information will be easy to find and complete.

4. *Postal regulations.* Catalogues of 24 pages or more can be mailed for a lower rate than smaller ones. The use of thin paper and compact typography will, of course, save mailing weight and expense. (See Appendix 4, Postal Information.)

5. *Typography.* (See also Appendix 1, Type Faces.)

In many catalogues a large amount of detailed technical information must be presented. The material must be compact and yet each kind of information must stand out and identify itself for ready reference.

The best way to attack this problem is to examine other catalogues whose designers faced similar problems; to pick a style that would be satisfactory; and then to encourage several printers to bid either on this style or on any simplification of it that they might suggest.

Slight changes in catalogue design to fit a printer's equipment can mean big savings. However, a printer who suggests changes should be asked to set a sample page or entry in the style that he suggests.

Complicated catalogues are often set in Monotype, since in that method it is possible to mix three faces as easily as two can be mixed in Linotype and Intertype, and since small price corrections, etc., in standing type are easily made.

The best printing process to use in producing a catalogue is, of course, determined by the number to be run, the nature of the illustrations, and the style of typesetting desired. (See PAMPHLETS; CIRCULARS.)

In an effort to make an expensive catalogue have a longer life, it is common to omit prices from the main descriptions and give them only in dated price lists. For a method of issuing revised price lists at frequent intervals with a minimum of cost and effort, see FLEXOPRINT.

Catalogues are often supplied in mechanical binders for ease of substituting revised pages (see MECHANICAL

BINDINGS), and may be thumb-indexed, step-indexed, tab-indexed, or edge-indexed (see INDEXING).

**center spread**  See also LAYOUT.

The pair of facing pages in the center of a magazine or pamphlet, so bound that they are on a single sheet of paper. This means that photographs and art work may be spread across the two pages without difficulty.

On spreads (facing pages) other than the center spread, it is inadvisable to have headlines or photographs "bridge the gutter," *i.e.*, run across from the left-hand page to the right-hand page, because poor alignment in the bindery may ruin the effect.

It is customary to lay out pages in pairs, however, so that on each double-page spread the left page will harmonize with the right page.

**centered**  Placed in the exact center of an area; said of a caption, illustration, or block of type. Material that is not centered is indented, or run "flush left" or "flush right." Too great a reliance on centering makes for a disorderly page. It is better to use the flush-left or indented style when there are many elements to be organized.

**certified mail**  See Appendix 4.

**character count**  The length of a piece of copy is usually expressed in terms of the number of characters (letters and spaces) that it contains. (See COPY FITTING.)

**Character Counter**  Trade name of a transparent plastic gadget for quickly counting typewritten characters. It is available at $1 postpaid from Cobb Shinn, 721 Union Street, Indianapolis 25, Ind.

**charts**  A useful line of special materials for making charts is offered by Chart-Pak, Inc., 100 Lincoln Ave.,

Stamford, Conn. This firm supplies the makings of charts—bars, dotted lines, symbols, etc.—in tape form ready to stick down where required. See also TRANS-ADHESIVE IMPRESSIONS for another useful aid to chart-making.

**chase**  The steel frame in which pages of type are "locked up" for placing on the printing press or for making duplicate plates. (See illustration under TYPE.)

**chemical pulp**  Paper made from wood by the sulphite, sulphate, or soda process is said to have been made from chemical pulp. It is superior in strength and permanency to paper made from groundwood pulp, though likely to lack the permanence and strength of a paper made from rag pulp.

**chip board**  A cheaper grade of binders' board. (See CARDBOARD.)

**circulars**  Definitions may differ, but for the purposes of this book it is assumed that a circular is a piece of printed matter of from one to six pages, whether it is called a leaflet, a folder, a broadside, a dodger, a flier, a package insert, an envelope stuffer, or what not. Larger items are discussed under PAMPHLETS. (See also POSTERS and LETTERS.)

Circulars can effectively be run on the mimeograph, spirit duplicator, Multigraph, Multilith, or on job printing equipment. All these processes permit the use of more than one color of ink and the use of line drawings. If there are to be photographs or wash drawings, then the choice narrows to Multilith, letterpress, and offset, or perhaps photography.

One of the first decisions in planning a circular is whether or not to set type. Typesetting may cost $5, $10, or even $30 a page. It is possible to buy 1,000 completed copies of a mimeographed circular for less than the cost of setting the type alone. On the other hand, type composition is generally more attractive than typewriter composition (see TYPEWRITER) although the latter can be very attractive, especially when done on the Varityper (see VARI-TYPER) or on the IBM electromatic proportional-spacing typewriter.

Here are some general suggestions on printing circulars:

1. A very small, one-page job might be most economically done by a label printer. (See LABELS.)

2. If the budget allows only $10, the possibilities are probably limited to mimeographing, spirit duplicating, or multigraphing. A well-designed mimeographed job, making use of spot drawings or diagrams and using headlines done with a lettering guide, can be very attractive. (See also COMBINATION RUN for a way of getting 1,000 sheets of white bond paper, 8½ by 11, printed in black ink on one side with any copy for as little as $6.60.) Multilithed jobs generally cost more than $10 unless the plate is prepared by hand instead of by photography.

3. If the budget allows up to $25, it may still be necessary to stick with one of the above processes in order to get the quantity required, but it also becomes possible to use the Multilith (thus opening the door to photographic reproduction of drawings, lettering, etc., with special ink, on special paper). On simple one- or two-page jobs, a $25 budget may allow type to be set for letterpress or offset reproduction. Perhaps an ad or clipping can be reproduced by offset.

4. A $50 budget for a one- to six-page circular generally makes type composition feasible and permits letterpress printing if desired.

When circulars are ordered in large quantities, it is common to print them "2-up" or "4-up." For example, a simple mimeographed receipt, size 4¼ by 5½ in., can be run 4-up on an 8½- by 11-in. piece of mimeograph paper, and later cut apart. Circulars can be printed several-up on newspaper presses or comic-book presses and then cut apart.

There is a minimum charge below which letterpress and offset printing cannot go, but these processes can easily underbid even mimeographing on a per unit basis when the quantities begin to exceed 5,000. (For illustration of different ways to fold and trim leaflets, see BINDING.)

**clip book**   See STOCK CUTS.

**clipping bureau**   A clipping bureau is a firm which watches almost all national publications and a wide selection of local ones and clips items of interest to its clients. Two established firms are Burrelle's Press Clipping Bureau, 165 Church St., New York 7, and Romeike Press Clipping Bureau, 220 W. 19 St., New York 11. A clipping bureau will watch for the name of a firm or individual, a product name, the treatment of a particular subject, or what you will. Such clippings can be helpful in verifying the effectiveness of a publicity campaign or in getting leads for salesmen or names for mailing lists.

A clipping bureau charges by the item, with a minimum monthly retainer. Sometimes a new client may be startled by the thoroughness of the coverage given by a clipping bureau, as when he gets a bill for several hundred clippings of a single syndicated item.

**clip sheet**   See also CAMPAIGN PLANNING; COPY WRITING.

Where wide publicity is sought in a big campaign or drive, a whole packet of publicity aids may be distributed to the press in advance as a clip sheet, in a form suitable for the editor to clip out and reproduce forthwith.

A clip sheet may contain news stories, feature articles, personal interviews, editorials, fillers, cartoons, ads, photographs, "quotable quotes," in fact anything that a newspaper can carry.

Pictures and cartoons are more likely to be reproduced if cuts or mats are sent or offered free on request. (See CUTS and MAT.)

A clip sheet is usually designed like a newspaper page. It may be an 8-column or 7-column page or a 5-column tabloid page, or a series of miniature newspaper pages approximately 9 by 12 in., assembled and stapled together for convenient handling. It is printed on one side of the paper so that every item is ready to be clipped and pasted.

The editor who does not use "canned" copy can still use the clip sheet as an "idea hatcher" and send out his reporters for local news and interviews related to the drive.

A few years ago the authors produced a 9-page clip sheet (8⅞ by 11¾ in.) which was printed and distributed to all daily newspapers, one weekly newspaper in every county seat, and the weekly magazines at a cost of $3,240. This included a two-color cover (black and red), eight 4-column pages of black-and-white copy, and 3½ full newspaper columns of mats for immediate use.

Western Newspaper Union, 210 S. Desplaines St., Chicago 6, is equipped to print and distribute newspaper clip sheets and to furnish cuts, mats, and mailing lists.

**cloth printing**  Textile printing is a field of its own and will not be discussed here. However, buyers of the printed word occasionally need to buy printed flags, pennants, arm bands, insignia, cloth book covers, etc.

Cloth can be printed by the same methods used for paper. Pennants are often printed by silk screen since this process lends itself to putting a thick layer of pigment on the felt.

Cloth book covers are usually stamped with specially cut brass dies (specially cut because the space between the letters and lines must be cut away more deeply than for printing paper). If ink is used, two "hits"

are recommended to ensure coverage. Metal foil or colored foil can also be used instead of ink since it adheres to the cloth where heated brass dies have pressed down on it.

Cloth for book covers and for other purposes can also be printed by the offset and gravure processes. Even photographs can be imprinted on cloth by these processes.

Insignia for sweaters, flags, pennants, etc., can be embroidered or woven effectively instead of printed. Even complicated designs in several colors can be embroidered by automatic machine at comparatively reasonable rates.

To locate firms doing this kind of work, look in the Classified Telephone Directory under Labels—Fabric.

**coated paper**  See also PAPER.

Paper is coated to make it suitable for the letterpress reproduction of fine-screen halftones. It can be "brush-coated" or "machine-coated" and can be finished as dull-coated or glossy-coated.

Machine coating, sometimes called "process coating," is a recent development. The coating is applied at the wet end of the papermaking machine instead of afterward as a separate operation. Machine-coated paper is, therefore, cheaper and is much used for large circulation picture magazines.

When coated paper is ordered, it is important to specify how it is to be used, whether in lithography, for varnishing, for precision register work, for gumming, or what not. Paper coated on one side only is available for labels, box coverings, etc. "Folding coated" is specified for covers and where extra durability is needed. Coated papers come in creams, India tints and colors, and also in "duplex" finishes (a different color on each side).

**COD**  See Appendix 4, Postal Information.

**coin cards** These devices for facilitating the sending of coins through the mails are obtainable from die cutters generally, including (to name two sources) the Dennison Manufacturing Company, Framingham, Mass., and Freedman Cut-outs, 34 Huber St., New York City.

**cold gold** See GOLDMARK.

**cold type** A term coined to distinguish Varityping, IBM typewriter composition, Justowriting, and ordinary typing from type composition done by the older "hot metal" methods such as Linotype.

Properly speaking, work done on the Fotosetter or Photon is cold type too, since hot metal is not involved. However, there is a tendency to reserve the term "cold type" for the somewhat cruder "typewriter" methods, where the images are created by having type strike through a carbon ribbon.

Cold type is used basically for just one reason: to save money. Very attractive work can be done, and the layman may not be able to distinguish it from conventional printing, but the claims made for cold type dwell on its economy and utility, not on its beauty.

Some of the advantages of cold-type composition are as follows:

1. *The machines are cheaper.* For the price of one Linotype you can get a dozen IBM Executive Electromatic typewriters or standard Varitypers, or perhaps four Coxhead DSJ Office Composing Machines (improved Varitypers), or two complete Justowriter installations. One publisher of a big directory turned to IBM composition because speed required the use of six keyboards simultaneously and he couldn't find a printer who could make six Linotype machines available when he had to have them.

2. *Wages are lower.* Cold-type compositors aren't unionized, and are paid less. This situation may change.

3. *Output is higher.* This is partly because of the simpler keyboard, partly because of the faster keyboard action, and partly because the slowdown tactics that plague union composing rooms haven't yet taken hold in the cold-type field.

4. *Correction costs are lower.* More mistakes are caught as they are made instead of later because the operators can see better what they are doing.

5. *Composition that is difficult with hot type is often easy with cold type.* For example, wide lines divided into many columns are difficult in hot type but easy on the typewriter. Composition involving chemical formulas and mathematical equations or special symbols often shows tremendous savings when done in cold type. (Note that the white space in and around an equation is just white space in cold type, but is a mosaic of metal spaces and quads in metal type.)

6. *Editorial costs can be shaved.* Sometimes compositors can be given editorial responsibilities—and a typewriter doesn't mind being kept waiting while something is being looked up. One directory publisher composes directly from his source material and saves keyboarding an interim manuscript. He also puts his information into type as fast as he gets it because his "type" (being only slips of paper) can be alphabetized after being set which would not be so easy with hard-to-read metal slugs.

7. *Type can be "kept standing" at negligible expense.*

Of course, cold type is not without its disadvantages. Lines can be justified only by typing twice, and thus the greatest savings can be expected on jobs (like directories and price lists) where justifying isn't required. Work to be done on IBM typewriters or the Justowriter must avoid the use of italics or small caps. The available type faces, though fully adequate to many uses, are generally inferior in both variety and design to those available in hot metal, and aren't likely to catch up. (In Linotype, a character can be designed to any width the designer wishes; in the Coxhead DSJ it must be fitted into one of three widths.) A really *bold* boldface simply isn't available in cold type. The making of proofs of cold-type composition poses special problems: beyond perhaps one carbon copy, extras have to be made by some photocopying or whiteprint method. And finally, comparatively few printers use cold-type methods as yet, or know anything about them, and of those who have entered the field, by no means all maintain very high standards of craftsmanship.

The techniques of cold type are still in flux and many short cuts probably remain to be devised. Present procedures are roughly as follows:

The best combinations of carbon ribbon and paper and impression are worked out by experiment, and then great pains are taken to maintain uniformity in these things. Unless the material is very simple, it is not typed directly in pages, but is typed in galleys for later pasting up in page form. Typed material is *lightly* sprayed with some fixative like Krylon to prevent smudging during proofreading, correcting, or paste-up.

Corrections are "patched in" by placing the galley face down on a glass-topped table illuminated from underneath. The new material (also face down) is positioned over the old, then both error and correction are cut out with a *sharp* razor blade which cuts through both layers at once. The error is now discarded; the correction fits neatly into the resulting hole and is secured in place with a strip of Scotch mending tape. When this is expertly done, the patch can scarcely be detected from the face of the galley, alignment is perfect, and the work goes rapidly. Corrections for errors noticed during the typing are usually typed in the right margin, or a faulty line can be marked and then retyped correctly, the bad line being cut out during the correction process or during paste-up. Chinese white and India ink are also used as required during the correction process, also white Scotch tape. Special marks or accents which are not available on the machine can be added by pen or by some process like Artype. (See ARTYPE.)

The basic tools of the paste-up operation are, of course, the drawing board and T square or parallel rule, triangle, rubber cement, etc., often in conjunction with mounting paper on which special guidelines have been ruled. Laps are avoided unless they can all face one way because they cast shadows, though shadows that are not too close to type can easily be opaqued out on the negative. Another paste-up technique calls for the use of a light table or Camera Lucikon or Lacey-Luci. Here the guidelines are visible through the typed galleys being pasted down. Another method is to project the guidelines down from above, a procedure that is necessary when working with nontranslucent materials.

Where proofreading is done from the master copy, care must be taken that editors do not mark or soil the type itself; often a tissue overlay is used to protect the type and make it possible to mark corrections more readily.

In directory work, it is possible to type each entry or even each line on a separate card and to change the sequence of the cards at will prior to "shingling" them in page form. The typing is carefully placed on the card near the upper edge. Each successive card in a column is so placed as to cover all of its predecessor except the typed line or lines. Cards can be either lightly adhered or mechanically held by some such method as Remington Rand's Flexoprint process. (See FLEXO-PRINT.)

A machine called the Listomatic has

been developed by the makers of the Justowriter which will accept a series of cards, each containing from one to three lines of a directory and automatically photograph them one at a time onto film in galley form. The work goes at the rate of several hundred cards a minute. The cards can be punch-coded for automatic sorting like ordinary IBM cards. The Listomatic sells for about $30,000. A similar machine has been under development by the makers of the Varityper.

One firm which is experienced in cold-type composition by all the methods mentioned above is The Science Press, P.O. Box 749, Lancaster, Pa. An example of their work which shows its flexibility is the annual "Editor & Publisher Yearbook."

**collating** Examining the gathered signatures (see SIGNATURE) of a book to see that all are included and in the proper order. (See BOOKBINDING.) Verifying the number and order of sheets as a way of checking on completeness. Sometimes used to mean the actual gathering of such sheets or signatures or even putting together of type from different machines.

**collotype** See PHOTOGELATIN.

**color** See also COLOR PRINTING; DESIGN.

Color science is a complicated field in which artists, chemists, and physicists all claim the right to speak and do not always understand each other.

There are, however, a few general considerations that may help the layman avoid mistakes even if they do not show him how to create masterpieces. Intelligent use of color can add a great deal to the effectiveness of printed material.

To understand color, it is best to discuss it purely as a sensation and leave any technical analysis of it to the physicists and chemists. It is with color as a sensation that the artist and printer are concerned. They are more interested in its psychological impact than in its physical composition. Color can get attention. It can create a mood. It can please or irritate.

Color is used both realistically and abstractly. Realistic color, used the way the mail-order catalogues use it, can greatly increase sales effectiveness. The only products that the mail-order companies do not advertise in color are those which color does not help sufficiently to justify the cost.

Abstract (decorative) color, well handled, can also increase the pulling power of a printed message. People, like bees, are simply attracted by color, at least when it is handled so as to have pleasant associations for them.

The color combinations with the highest attention value are those with the greatest contrast—white on red, orange-red on black, yellow on black, white on black, and black on white. (However, the attention value of a sign depends not alone on the sign itself but also on its relation to its setting.)

When a job is to be run in black and one other color on white paper, red is an easy favorite for the extra color.

Note that the above-mentioned color combinations differ both in hue and in brightness. The lightness of orange-red contrasts better with black than would a darker red. Contrast is desirable when type or lettering of one color is to be run on a background of another. The degree of contrast determines the legibility.

Photographs should always be printed in black or very dark colors, never in red or blue or any other light color unless a washed-out effect is sought deliberately.

Vermilion is the best color to use in combination with photographs as shown on the cover of *Life*. Yellow is also good with photographs.

There are times, however, when low contrast is preferred to high contrast.

There must be high contrast between type and background, but there may be low contrast between the background and other elements.

Harmony in color selection is a subtle thing, but a few hints on how to achieve it may be helpful:

Colors are not attractive or unattractive in themselves; everything depends on how they are used. The person who does not like a green tie with a blue suit, likes green trees against blue water or sky.

People really have no "favorite" colors. They may think they do, but they will turn against the color of their choice when it is badly handled (they may not even recognize it), and they will likewise be attracted toward any colors effectively used.

It is not possible to say that two or more colors do or do not harmonize, without knowing how they are to be arranged on the page. Certain colors may clash when equal masses are used, yet go beautifully together when a small area of one is used to accent a large area of the other. Bright colors may fight each other and give a "dazzle" effect when used side by side, yet look well when separated by an area of white, gray, or some other color.

When intense colors are combined with toned or tinted colors, it is common to use larger areas of the latter.

Any color is a mixture of white, black, and a color; or at least it can be analyzed as if it were. When white is added to a pure color, the result is a lighter "tint" of that color. When black is added to a pure color, a darker "shade" of that color results. When both white and black are added to a pure color, that color takes on a grayer "tone."

Bright, intense colors are much harder to combine successfully than the same colors with a slight amount of gray added.

Two colors tend to harmonize better when they have the same white content or the same black content, or both. Harmony between gray and a color can be established in the same way, either by choosing a gray with the same white content as the color, or by choosing one with the same black content as the color.

Gray and black and white should be handled like colors in layout work. The use of middle gray areas in a black-and-white job often adds as much as an extra color. Black type on white paper produces an effect of gray, and type masses should be regarded as blocks of gray.

Modern color theory, as developed by Munsell and Ostwald, depends on a "hue circle" of the type shown on p. 48. The basis of this hue circle is that opposite colors, if pure, should form a neutral gray when mixed.

Red, orange, yellow, and brown are regarded as warm colors. They also give the effect of thrusting themselves forward. Green, blue, and gray are regarded as cool colors, giving the effect of distance.

Paper is part of the color scheme. A yellow-red that is pleasing on buff paper may be disappointing on blue-white paper.

In working with color, it is extremely helpful to have as many color samples at hand as possible. It may be worth while to keep a scrapbook of interesting color combinations. Certainly most printed jobs will be more interesting (and very little more expensive) if the printer is required to match carefully chosen colors instead of using any red that he happens to have ready mixed.

There are a number of books on color theory, but on the whole they are more confusing than helpful to the layman. Color samples are much more useful than color theories. The printing buyer who wants to choose and use color intelligently should equip himself with (1) sample books of colored papers from the paper merchants and paper mills, (2) some ink sample books

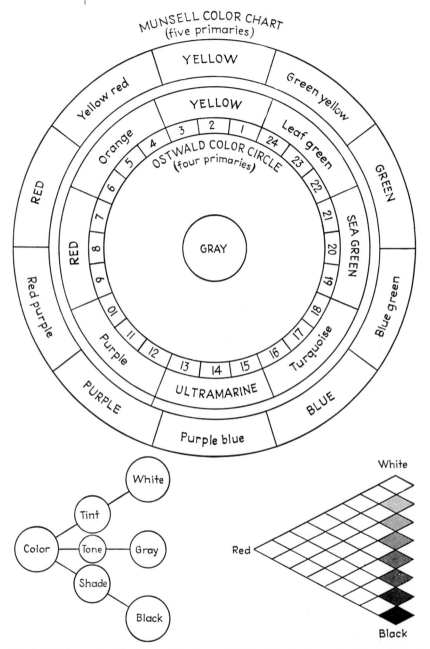

MUNSELL COLOR CHART
(five primaries)

OSTWALD COLOR CIRCLE
(four primaries)

A color can be most easily described in terms of its "hue" (red, yellow red, etc.); its "value," meaning its gray content; and its "chroma," meaning its intensity. Imagine that the above circle is really a geometric solid, the colors intense along its equator and graying toward the core, and the core ranging from white at the top to black at the bottom. At lower right is a cross section of such a solid.

from printing ink firms, (3) paint swatch books put out by paint companies and obtainable at paint stores, usually at 10 cents each, (4) a generous assortment of pastel chalks (available in any art supply store), and, best of all, (5) the $3.75 color swatch book put out by the Color-aid Co., 329 E. 29 St., New York City.

This last item is especially helpful since 18- by 24-in. sheets of paper of any selected color may be ordered from it by number at 25 cents a sheet. Some 202 colors and shades and tints are available—6 basic hues and 18 intermediate hues, each in 4 tints and 3 shades, plus 8 grays, 1 white, and 1 black. Larger "TV boards" (22 by 28 in.) are also available at $1 each.

These swatches are much more useful than the ink sample books since often the right color for a job is not to be found ready mixed. It must be mixed to order, a simple enough procedure (not expensive either) if the buyer can supply a sample of the color wanted together with a specimen of the paper it is to be printed on. The color-aid sheets are also invaluable for showing tint blocks and color areas on dummies.

For samples of printing-ink colors, write to the ink manufacturer with whom your printer deals. For samples of colored papers, inquire of the various paper merchants and paper mills. See also BOURGES COLOR SYSTEM.

**Color-aid** See COLOR.

**colored paper** See also PAPER.

Paper can be obtained in almost any color. The usual colors are, of course, the light ones, since dark ink is not very legible on too dark a paper. Printing with light ink on a dark paper is impractical since two impressions are usually required to get opacity. The same effect may be obtained by printing a reverse plate in dark ink on a light paper.

"Duplex" paper shows one color on one side, and another color on the other side.

Colored paper costs more than plain paper, often considerably more. On very short runs, the cost of the paper is a relatively unimportant item, and colored or duplex papers can provide the effect of an extra color at little extra cost.

On longer press runs it is usually cheaper to run an extra color of ink on white paper than to use colored paper. The extra color of ink can be used to tint the entire surface of the paper if desired, thus giving the effect of colored paper.

**color engraving** See COLOR PRINTING.

**Coloron** Coloron sheets are transparent sheets printed in a variety of colors and tints of colors. They are used to determine in advance what the effect will be if (for example) a certain tint of blue is printed over another color— and whether type surprinted on the combination will be more legible in white, in black, or in one of the tints or solids. Each sheet shows one color (the process colors as well as the basic colors are available) in a series of panels ranging from a solid of that color through all the tints, 90 per cent, 80 per cent, etc., down to 10 per cent. In each panel is shown type in reverse on the tint, type in reverse on the solid, type in the solid on the tint, and type in the tint on white. Coloron sheets are sold in sets by the Delta Brush Manufacturing Corp., 119 Bleecker St., New York City, or by art stores.

**color photography** See also PHOTOGRAPHY.

Any photographer using any camera can take pictures in color simply by loading his camera with color film. However, color photography makes exacting demands as regards illumination and exposure, and good results require skill and experience.

The films most used commercially are Kodachrome (now available only in 35mm. size), Anscocolor, Anscochrome, Ektachrome, Ektacolor, and Kodacolor. The latter as improved in 1956 can be used with good results.

The first four yield positive transparencies that should be viewed against a diffused white light or projected on a screen.

Ektacolor, like Kodacolor, produces a *negative* transparency in which each color is represented by its complementary. Prints on paper can be made from Ektacolor and Kodacolor negatives and in the latter case can now be made with the simplest darkroom equipment.

Printing plates can be made direct from a transparency, either positive or negative. However, it is common practice first to make a color print on paper from the transparency, both because it is easier to retouch on paper and because photoengravers may charge extra for working from transparencies. If the photoengraver charges $500 to make printing plates from an oil painting, he may charge $520 to make plates of the same size from a transparency. However, the buyer may have secured a color transparency for only $100 as against $350 or more for the oil painting, so he realizes a net saving by using the transparency.

Color prints on paper can be made from any transparency. Good ones, however, are rather expensive.

A remarkable method of converting a black-and-white photo into a full-color photo has been introduced under the name of Kodak Flexichrome Process.

Duplicates of color photographs, whether transparencies or color prints on paper, can be had at many prices and in many qualities, ranging from the under-a-dollar variety offered to amateurs in photofinishing stores, to first-quality prints for advertising or exhibition purposes worth several hundred dollars. One company, Bebell and

Bebell Color Laboratories, 2531 Church Ave., Brooklyn 26, N.Y., offers color prints on paper at prices ranging from 50 cents for a 2¼ by 3¼ to $25 for a 16 by 20—with quantity savings amounting to about one-third on lots of 25. The same company will make duplicate transparencies at rates ranging from $3.50 for a 4 by 5 to $50 for a 16 by 20. Other companies equipped to do processing of color photographs of all kinds are Pavelle Color, Inc., 533 W. 57 St., New York City, and Color Print Laboratories, 342 Madison Ave., New York 17.

For information about printing color photographs, see PROCESS COLOR.

**color printing**   See also COLOR; FLAT COLOR; PROCESS COLOR; COLOR PHOTOGRAPHY; COLORED PAPER.

Multicolor printing can be done by sending the same paper through the press as many times as there are colors. Color means added attractiveness. It also means added cost and special care in handling in order to obtain the best effects.

In most processes it is necessary to "wash up" the ink fountain and the ink rollers, and substitute ink of the desired color. Since wash-ups take time, even printing in a single color other than black is usually more expensive than printing in black.

The use of a second color on a printing job (black being considered the first color) requires an extra press run, an extra make-ready, extra washing-up, and an extra form of type or cuts. But this is not all. It also poses the problem of "register."

If a black-and-white impression lands on a page within ⅛ in. of where it is supposed to go, no one is likely to object. If a red image that is supposed to be the rouge on a lady's cheek lands ⅛ in. away on her nose, there are likely to be complaints. Two or more colors must "register." (If the design is such that close registration of the colors is not important, the printer need not charge for the extra care that close registration implies.)

To illustrate one problem of register: a 50-in. piece of paper can stretch or shrink as much as ¼ in. during a change of humidity. If it does so between impressions, the printer is in trouble.

Flat color is the simple form of color printing in which there is usually no attempt to print one color over the other in order to get some other shade. Red is red and blue is blue. However, in many cases one flat color is printed over another to give the effect of a third color.

However, full-color paintings, color photographs, and scenes from actual life do not limit themselves to any given number of colors. These can be reproduced only in process color using black and the three primary colors (red, blue, and yellow) and mixing these colors to get the full range of browns, grays, greens, purples, etc. (See PROCESS COLOR.)

All printing processes can handle flat color, *i.e.*, nonprocess color. Process color can be done in letterpress, offset, gravure, and photogelatin. Fake process work (see FAKE PROCESS) can be done in these ways and in silk screen.

In mimeograph work, color may be added by cleaning out the black ink and substituting another color, but it is easier to buy an extra drum for each color that is to be used and just switch drums. It is also possible to fit a pad inked in color over the black-ink drum, but such a pad has to be removed and re-inked frequently. To get two colors on a single sheet, the sheet must be run twice (a different drum or a newly inked drum for each color), or the pad may be so inked that certain areas produce one color and the rest a second color.

In multigraph work, changing the color is as easy as changing the ribbon.

In spirit duplicating, the master can

be made in several different colors, and these colors will then print simultaneously.

Process color plates are relatively expensive. Making them is basically photomechanical (see PROCESS COLOR), but skilled handwork is almost always necessary before acceptable proofs are produced. (See FLUORESCENCE PROCESS.)

The illustration above is a proof of the black plate of a two-color ad.

This is a proof (in black) made from the red plate of the same two-color ad.

When the black plate is printed on paper which has previously received an impression from the red plate, the result is a two-color effect as shown here.

There is also a process known as "fake process color," less expensive and sometimes quite satisfactory, which amounts to having a black-and-white original hand-colored by the platemaker. (See FAKE PROCESS.)

If it is decided to use a second color on the first page of a 16-page pamphlet, for example, this probably means sending all the 16 pages through the press a second time, and opens the possibility of using color on other pages besides the first one at little extra cost. The printer is able to tell which other pages can have the extra color without additional presswork. (In a 16-page pamphlet it may be pages 4, 5, 8, 9, 12, 13, 16, or it may, under certain circumstances, be all of them.)

A second color can dress up a pamphlet, circular, or car card enormously. On short runs, an inexpensive way to get a touch of color is to use colored paper, to paste on a colored label or illustration, or even to hand-color a line illustration. Just one splotch of water color can spruce up a black-and-white piece.

In any job containing a process color illustration it is possible also to use the process colors flat—the blue, the yellow, and the red. It should be noted, however, that process blue is a pale, robin's-egg shade and that process red is closer to magenta than to vermilion. Process yellow is a good solid canary, but the others do not always look well when used by themselves. Process colors are balanced one with another for process color printing and cannot be changed to be used "flat" without completely destroying the fidelity of the reproduction.

Photographs can be run effectively in sepia as well as in black, but light colors are to be avoided for single-color photographic reproduction. Photographs printed in a flat blue or red, etc., always lack contrast and should be used only where a washed-out effect is desired.

On the other hand, photographs can be given added depth by being run in black and a color by the so-called "duotone" process, especially in offset. (See DUOTONE.)

In the foregoing paragraphs it has been assumed that each extra color means another press run. From a cost point of view, this is approximately correct. However, there are two-color presses and even presses that can print in four colors on both sides of a piece of paper in one operation. These are economical only for long press runs.

There are some special problems involved in seeing proofs of color printing. If the work is being done in letterpress, the engraver will furnish color proofs, made on a proof press. If the work is being done in offset, gravure, or photogelatin, proofs usually are made on the presses that are to do the actual printing, though offset plates may also be proved on a proof press.

In either case, the proofs can be compared with the original, corrections can be made if any are necessary, and revised proofs pulled. Proofs should always be pulled on the paper to be used in the final run in order to assure a better comparison.

However, the final result may not duplicate the proofs, and it is difficult to check on this by demanding press proofs, especially if the first color must be run and the press washed up before subsequent colors can be added.

Even if all the colors are to be printed simultaneously on a multicolor press, it is expensive to keep big presses idle while proofs are rushed back and forth by messenger. Production men who get good color results often spend a lot of time looking over the pressman's shoulder while a run is getting underway.

**color proofs**  See COLOR PRINTING.

**color separation**  See also COLOR PRINTING.

Color printing requires a separate plate for each color—red, blue, yellow, and black in process color (see PROCESS COLOR) and the selected tints for flat color (see FLAT COLOR). Color separation is the technique by which the colors of the original art work—drawing, photograph, or oil painting—are sorted out so that all the reds appear in the red plate, the blue and the shades of blue in the blue plate, etc.

Color separation may be done by the artist or by the printer, by hand or by photomechanical processes. An artist, for example, may make a black-and-white drawing with a flag in it and ask the printer to make a plate of the flag only and run that in red, and then to make a plate of the whole thing, but without the flag, and run that in black.

An artist may also make a "key drawing" in black and white, and then put a piece of translucent acetate over it and fill in, in black on the acetate, the areas that are to print in red. The printer then makes his black plate from the key drawing, and his red plate from the red separation on celluloid. (See BOURGES COLOR SYSTEM for another overlay technique.)

Another way in which the artist can make the color separation requires work in two stages. First he makes a "key drawing" showing only the part to be printed in black. The engraver makes a cut of this and pulls a proof in very light blue ink. On this the artist then paints in India ink the part that is to be reproduced in color. Since the engraver's camera cannot pick up the pale blue, it will photograph only the part in black. A cut is made from this to print in color with the first cut which prints in black.

The printer can also handle the color separation work. Flat-color jobs present no problem, for each color goes on unmixed with any other color. Full-color originals are more difficult. Here the printer may do his separations by the fake process method or by the proc-ess-color method. (See FAKE PROCESS and PROCESS COLOR.)

The latter is basically photomechanical, but handwork is also almost inevitable. In fact, the handwork necessary in improving a photomechanical set of plates to the point where they can give an exact reproduction of the original is often greater than the handwork needed to make free-hand separations without mechanical aid. The difference is that the former offer an exact reproduction, and the latter offer at best an approximation.

**combination halftone and line plate**
See also CUT; HALFTONE; LINE CUT.

When two kinds of art work are to be combined in one cut—one of which requires halftone treatment, and the other line treatment—the cut costs at least twice as much. An example is when lettering is surprinted over a photograph.

**combination run** Some printers offer 8½- by 11-in. leaflets, printed *on one side* on 16-lb. white bond and in black ink, as low as $3.50 per hundred. This does not include typesetting, hand-lettering, or photos, but applies to black-and-white material that can be copied photographically (same size, reduced, or enlarged) to print on 8½- by 11-in. paper. Jobs 11 by 17 or 17 by 22 are twice or four times the price.

Such prices are possible when a printer can use a so-called "combination run." The process is as follows: The printer has a big offset press (see OFFSET), say, size 17 by 22 or 35 by 45. He waits until he has 4 or 16 different jobs, each 8½ by 11 and each for 100 copies. Then he runs all the jobs at once and later cuts them apart.

Offset printers handling work of this kind usually ask at least five working days. Extra copies ordered at the same time run about 50 cents a hundred. (Thus, the first 1,000 cost $8.) Strip-ins cost about $1.50 each additional. (See

STRIP.) Pages cannot bleed (see BLEED) unless trimmed smaller than 8½ by 11. Work to be run on both sides cannot be estimated on quite the same combination-run basis, and work on special paper cannot be combined at all.

Sometimes Multilith prices are very little higher than combination-run prices. (See MULTILITH.)

Printing in combination run is usually done by offset lithographers who also advertise their work under Planographing. Local combination-run printers may be located under Lithography or Planography in the Classified Telephone Directory.

**Composalist**  A machine developed by the Ralph C. Coxhead Corporation of Newark, N.J., which will accept a pile of cards each carrying one line of a directory, and photograph the cards automatically in sequence in such a way as to produce galleys of type in film form.

**composing room**  See also TYPE.

Typesetting or type composition is done in a composing room, usually separate from the pressroom and often under another roof entirely.

**composing stick**  See STICK.

**composition**  See also TYPE.

The setting of type from which to print. This may refer to the setting up of metal type by hand or on the Ludlow, Linotype, Intertype, Monotype, etc., or to setting directly on film as in the Hadego, Headliner, Fotosetter, Linofilm, and Photon. It may also refer to the product of machines like the typewriter, Varityper, and Justowriter (see TYPEWRITER).

**compositor**  See also TYPE.

The person who sets type and spaces and justifies the lines.

**comprehensive**  In the language of the art directors, a "comprehensive" or a comprehensive drawing is a handmade, approximate facsimile of what the finished job will look like in print. As much work can go into comprehensives as into the final art work, but ad agencies still prefer to show them to their clients instead of roughs (see ROUGH) both because beauty tends to sell itself and because two men looking at the same rough may, unknown to each other, have quite different ideas about how it is to be developed. (See illustrations under LAYOUT.)

**condensed**  Term used to describe a type face that is narrower and hence more compact than the usual type of the same height.

### This is 10-pt. Gothic.
### This is 10-pt. Gothic condensed.

**Constat**  See PHOTOCOPYING.

**contact screen**  A new halftone screen, also called the magenta screen. (See HALFTONE.)

**container printing**  Boxes, cartons, cans, collapsible tubes, etc., are almost always printed by the manufacturer, since the problems are specialized and the printing may have to be done during manufacture. Although every known process of printing is used, offset and silk screen are favorites because of the ease with which they print on uneven surfaces.

Container labeling, as distinct from container printing, can of course be done anywhere, although special adhesives may have to be used for some surfaces.

For the names of container suppliers look in the Classified Telephone Directory, under Boxes, Package Development, etc., or consult the "Packaging Catalog" listed in Appendix 2, Bibliography.

**Contak shading film**  See SHADING TINTS.

**Copi-Counter** In this device the well-known "map measure" has been adapted for graphic arts duty, and reads in inches, picas, and agate lines instead of in inches, miles, and kilometers. It looks like a double-faced pocket watch but with a little wheel sticking out one edge. When you roll the wheel along typed lines, the hand moves to indicate the number of picas or the number of lines.

As an example of its use, suppose you have too much type for the space and have been cutting, and you want to know whether you have cut enough. Just roll the wheel down your galleys, jumping over excisions, and then up the dummy page. If the hand gets back to zero, you have cut enough; if not, the amount by which it failed to return to zero tells you how much more to cut. The Copi-Counter is available from Arthur H. Nellen, Jr., Box 106, Broomall, Pa., at $4.95.

**copper engraving** See also HALFTONE.

Fine-screen halftone engravings are usually made on copper, while coarse-screen halftones can be made on the coarser-grained but less expensive zinc.

The term "copper engraving" also refers to the plate on which an artist has hand-engraved a picture, or to the print made from that plate.

**copy** See also COPY FITTING; COPY PREPARATION.

To a printer, copy means the manuscript to be set in type. The key ingredients of a printing job are copy, layout, and art work.

**copy casting** Determination of the number of words or characters in a given manuscript or piece of copy. See COPY FITTING.

**copy editing** See also COPY WRITING; COPY PREPARATION; EDITORIAL WORK; STYLE SHEET.

In this handbook the term "copy

editing" is assumed to include rewriting, revising, and polishing. These are jobs for a person of experience who can make decisions and set policy regarding a manuscript.

Once this basic, structural editing has been done, there is still a very important job—preparation of the copy for the printer. This latter process, sometimes also considered "copy editing," is more generally called "copy preparation," and is so referred to in this book. Copy preparation means putting the accepted editorial material in shape for the printer by making it accurate as to facts, grammatical, consistent as to style, and correct in spelling and punctuation, and by marking it for type. (See COPY PREPARATION and STYLE SHEET.)

The copy editor takes over after the writer has, presumably, done his best work on a manuscript. This is probably the most ticklish and exasperating stage, for the writer is usually convinced that he has done a satisfactory job. And yet, in view of the needs of the publisher and the interests of his audience, it may not be entirely appropriate. At this point the copy editor must take over, conferring with the author and working on the manuscript so that the final copy will be read and will have the desired effect on the reader.

A good writer, thoroughly familiar with the purposes and policies of a publication, will edit his own copy and thereby win the blessing of the editor. Many a writer, either through inexperience or incomplete instructions, submits a manuscript that is illogical, unclear, or uninteresting, or all three. Despite these faults, it may be a "must" for the publication because it carries the by-line of a big name, because it is technically accurate and significant though unreadable, or because it is newsworthy and unique. If this is true, the manuscript is worth the editing required to make it acceptable.

Copy editing may include complete rearrangement, revision, or rewriting. Or it may mean only slight polishing and pepping up. How far to go in copy editing will depend upon the state of the original manuscript, the policy of the publication, and the initiative and fortitude of the copy editor. If he goes too far, he may offend the holy of holies in his trade or staff; if he does not go far enough, he may be accused of passing on dull, unreadable copy. Hitting the proper balance between these two comes from long experience with reviving dead copy and close acquaintance with the policies and personnel of the publication for which it is being prepared.

"Is it logical?" is probably the first test to put to a manuscript to be copyedited. All too often a manuscript suffers from the disorderly thinking of the writer who has omitted some step in the argument, back-tracked or repeated, or wandered around without any plan or logic. A good check on this is to list the topic of each paragraph (since a paragraph should be unified around one central theme) and trace the writer's thinking—or lack of it. This will be a good guide as to what to omit, what to rearrange, what to add.

"Is it clear?" may be the next test. Are the words understandable and vivid? Are the sentences short enough to be clear? Is each paragraph unified and arranged in the best relation to the other paragraphs? When the copy editor has finished, the answer should be "Yes" to each of these.

Finally, "Is it interesting?" Obviously it must be both logical and clear to be interesting, but being interesting requires more than orderly reasoning and clear wording.

To be interesting a manuscript must have a good lead which will hold the reader's attention, and must treat the subject from the point of view of what will interest and help the reader. The lead may be that of the news reporter who often starts out with one or more of the five W's—who, what, where, when, why. Or it may be the lead of the feature writer who piques the reader's curiosity by some provocative statement or pertinent incident. It is seldom the lead of the dry historian who reviews the whole history of his topic before he gets to that topic, or even announces what it is. It is not the lead of the apologist who throws up several paragraphs of explanation and qualification, before he plunges into his subject. With manuscripts from such writers (and there are many in the professional and technical fields) the copy editor may do well to up-end the whole job, putting the history at the end and the explanation or apology in a footnote if it is really needed.

The big test of a manuscript's being interesting goes beyond the lead to the words, figures of speech, and details of the whole thing. Interest is created by strong, colorful nouns and vigorous verbs which carry the action or thought forward. Specific details, actual quotes, and sharp incidents should replace the fuzzy verbiage, vague generalizations, and blurred images of the dull writer.

The importance of copy editing assumes greater proportions every day as new publications and new communication media compete for the reader's time. The day is past when an editor could complacently approve dull copy with the explanation or apology that "Our readers have to read this even though it is dull because it is authoritative in their field." That may have been true when reading material was so scarce that the reader could not be selective. Today every piece of copy has to compete for the reader's time. It must compete with films, radio, television, color photography, digest magazines, pocket-size books, comic books, 25-cent whodunits, and the general magazines. Whether it gets read or not will depend in part on the copy editing.

**Copy Fitter** Trade name for a sort of slide rule which juggles such factors as line lengths, characters per pica, number of lines, etc., and produces answers without the need for paper work. It is supplied at $2 postpaid by Cobb Shinn, 721 Union St., Indianapolis 25, Ind.

**copy fitting** See also COPY PREPARATION.

The problem of making the copy fit the space arises in even the simplest publications and has to be solved somehow, whether by cutting copy, adding copy, or changing the kind, size, or leading of the type—or by a combination of these measures.

The easiest method of copy fitting avoids mathematics entirely and requires only the use of a typewriter. Suppose, for example, the problem is to write just enough copy to fill 10 lines of type as used in this book. Put a piece of paper in the typewriter and start to copy a few lines from the book, line for line, as shown in the illustration. It will soon become apparent about how long a line of typewriting will make one line of printer's type. It is now only necessary to write enough to fill 10 typewritten lines of the indicated length. It can be assumed that this amount of copy will also fill 10 lines when set in type, give or take a line.

The same method can be applied to caption writing. Just type up an old caption of the desired style and length, and then compose a new caption that will have the same number of typed characters. It will fit the same space as the old caption when set in type.

The trial line or lines can be taken from a back number of a magazine, from a printer's type book, or what you will. If you can't find a sample of the right width, there's no harm in using fractions of lines. For example, if you want the kind of type used in this book but in a 3-in. width (18 picas), copy one full column (13 picas) plus 5 picas from the adjoining column for your trial lines.

The reason why this system works is because typewriters always write the same number of characters per inch. Some have pica type and write 10 characters per inch; others have elite type and write 12 characters per inch, but whichever it is, you can count on it, and count by it.

## This is pica type 1234567890

### This is elite type 123456789012

Printer's types will also average a predictable number of characters per inch, the number varying with the type. It is true that the "w" and "m" are wider than the "i" and "l," and that caps are wider than small letters, but usually these differences average out.

Suppose, for example, the problem is to write just enough copy to fill 10 lines of type as used in this book. Put a piece of paper in the typewriter and start to copy a few lines from the book, line for line, as shown in the illustration. It will soon become apparent about how long a line of typewriting will make one line of printer's type.

However, if your copy is already typed to a
different width, it is not necessary to retype
it in order to estimate the number of lines of
type it will make. Instead, rule a line vertically on your copy to show how much of each line
will make one line of type and estimate the
overage. On short copy it is easy enough to
mark off the length of your trial lines on the
edge of a piece of paper, and use this measure
to mark off the probably line breaks, as shown
in the illustration.

Therefore, if you find that your specimen lines, when typed, average 3 inches wide on an elite typewriter, and if you type your copy to that width, you need only count your typewritten lines to determine how many lines of printer's type you're going to get.

However, if your copy is already typed to a different width, it is not necessary to retype it in order to estimate the number of lines of type it will make. Instead, rule a line vertically on your copy to show how much of each line will make one line of type, and estimate the overage. Are your manuscript lines half again as long as will fill a line of type? Then you'll get half again as many lines of type as you have manuscript lines. Sometimes you can just estimate the overage, counting the full lines in each paragraph, and estimating how many additional lines will be made by the excess of words to the right of your guideline. On short copy it is sometimes easy enough to mark off the length of your trial lines on the edge of a piece of paper, and use this measure to mark off the probable line breaks, as shown in the illustration.

You can do all your copy fitting by matching typed manuscript lines to typed trial lines, as outlined above, but for some work there are advantages to the so-called "character-count" method. This method is not as complicated as it is sometimes made to sound when you realize that 1 inch is 12 characters (12 letters or spaces) on an elite typewriter, 10 on a pica typewriter.

Before plunging into character counting, however, the beginner should be warned that he *must* understand printer's measurements. He must know that a pica (besides being a kind of typewriter type) is a unit of measurement. Sooner or later he must learn to use this term in specifying column widths, etc. He must know that there are 12 points to the pica, 6 picas to the inch, 72 points to the inch. (See TYPE MEASUREMENTS). Too many beginners try to slide by points and picas. Don't do it. There are 12 points to the pica, 6 picas to the inch, 72 points to the inch. Repeat that until you know it. Don't read on until you're sure of it.

Once you are equipped to think in points and picas, you should have no great difficulty with character counting if you will take time to work through a few examples. Remember that basically all you are doing is figuring characters per line, lines per page, etc. If you get confused, forget the tables, and just count characters, taking any short cuts that occur to you.

Suppose, for example, you have a 10-page typewritten manuscript with 25 lines on each page averaging 6 inches each. A pica typewriter has been used so the typing is 10 characters to the inch. This means 60 characters per 6-inch line. Multiplying characters per line by lines per page by number of pages ($60 \times 25 \times 10$), you get a total character count of 15,000. You are now in a position to calculate how many lines this will make in any type face you like. For example, if you choose a kind, size, and width of type that assays 50 characters to the line, your 15,000 characters will make 300 lines. If you're going to get only 40 characters per line of type, you'll come out with 375 lines.

An easy way to figure out how many characters you will get per line of type is to find some specimen lines, count several, and take an average. Some think the counting goes more easily if you typewrite the lines first, after which the count can be made with the aid of a ruler.

However, there are tables from which you can learn the character count of each kind and size of type. The counts are usually given in terms of characters per pica. Suppose you're thinking of setting the above-mentioned manuscript of 15,000 characters in 9-pt. Baskerville, 13 picas wide, the same type used in this book. The tables will tell you (see page 354) that this type averages 2.95 characters per pica. From this figure, the conversion table on page 356 indicates that your 13-pica line will contain 38 characters. Dividing this into 15,000 characters gives 394 lines of type.

The next question is, how many pages will be required for 394 lines of type?

Count a full column on a page of this book and you'll find there are 51 lines per column, 102 lines per page. At that rate 394 lines will require just under 4 pages.

If you're working on a book like this one in which the type has been selected, and is not to be changed, that's your answer. Your manuscript will require just under 4 pages. If you must allow for heads and subheads you'll have to cut a few lines. However, if you're free to change the type specifications, you can, without cutting, save more room for headings in various ways. You can put more lines per column, use less space between lines, widen the lines, or choose a more compact type face.

For example, putting 52 lines into each column would gain 2 lines per page, 8 lines on 4 pages. Or you might notice that, although this is 9-pt. type, it takes up more than 9 points of space. Since there are 72 points to the inch, you ought to get 8 lines of 9-pt. type to the inch, but on this page you're getting only about 7. The reason is that this is 9-pt. type leaded 1 point, or 9 pt. on a 10-pt. body. You're actually getting close to 7.2 lines per inch, 51 per column. Change this to 9-pt. solid (unleaded) and you could have 56 lines per column (8 per inch, 7 inches). That would make 112 lines per page, 448 lines in 4 pages. Or you could widen the columns by a pica, and gain about 3 characters per line, 300 characters per page, 1,200 over 4 pages. Or you could go to a more compact type face like 9-pt. Granjon which averages 3.16 characters per pica, or about 41 per 13-pica line. At 41 characters per line, 15,000 characters would require only about 366 lines, well under 4 pages.

Probably the easiest and one of the most common jobs of copy fitting is to write "to space." Here you just copy a few trial lines of material set in the specified face, count or calculate the number of lines required, and then write the needed number of lines of new copy in the indicated width. The simplest way to do this, as noted above, is to set your typewriter to the right width of line, and then write the needed number of lines.

The problem of figuring the lines of

type required for a given manuscript to be set in a given face and size is also simple. Just see how many times one line's worth of characters will go into the manuscript.

The toughest problem is to select the kind of type, size of type, and leading that will permit a given manuscript to be put into a given space. Usually this problem is solved on a trial-and-error basis. Pick the type you'd *like* to use and estimate the space it requires. If your copy doesn't fit, at least you'll know immediately whether you're close or not, and can try again. Note that a relatively small change of type size makes a surprisingly large change in the number of characters you can get into a given space. This is because a smaller size of type will give you not only more characters per line, but also more lines per column inch.

Several devices intended to speed or simplify character counting and copy fitting are described under these headings: HABERULE VISUAL COPY-CASTER; STREAMLINED COPY FITTING METHOD; CHARACTER COUNTER; COPY FITTER; COPI-COUNTER.

For further information on copy fitting see the information given in Appendix 1, Type Faces.

**Copyfix** See PHOTOCOPYING.

**copy preparation** See also EDITORIAL PLANNING; COPY EDITING; PROOFREADING.

Before manuscript copy is sent to the printer, it should undergo a careful process known as "preparation of copy for the printer." This is the place at which a few strokes of an editor's pencil can save many dollars in type corrections later.

The essentials of copy preparation can be outlined as follows:

1. Policy O.K. The man with the deciding voice says, "Let's publish this." If he has been in on the planning from the beginning, he is likely to give the final O.K. more readily.

2. Careful scrutiny to catch any inconsistencies, anachronisms, inaccuracies, etc., and to fill in any missing data.

3. Writing or rewriting headlines, by-lines, boxed material, captions, credit lines, subheads, etc., that may have been omitted.

4. Rough "cast-off" or character count (see COPY FITTING) to determine the space required; decision on layout and type; necessary cutting or expanding of text, headlines, captions, etc., to fit layout.

5. Scrutiny for proper paragraphing, sentence structure, grammar, spelling, and punctuation. For authoritative guidance in correct forms, the University of Chicago "Manual of Style" (see the Bibliography) is excellent. In addition, many editors work out their own style sheet to be used by each staff member. (See STYLE SHEET.)

6. Retyping. The printer is entitled to clean, double-spaced copy, typed on one side only of 8½- by 11-in. paper, with ample margins at top and sides for his type markings. He charges extra for time wasted over illegible copy. The printer has no objection to erasures or xxxx's or partly filled pages, but he may have difficulty with hand-written corrections.

7. Marking for type (see TYPE). This may be the responsibility of a layout man, not the editor, but editors often do it whether or not they are their own layout men. Of course, the type to be used should have been determined when layout plans were made, taking into account whether the printer has the kind of type that is specified or will get it.

To prevent loss, manuscript copy ready for the printer should plainly indicate the job for which it is being set: issue of magazine, title of book or pamphlet, name of customer, etc. All pages should be numbered consecutively, and renumbered if pages are added or deleted. If it is necessary to insert pages 11A and 11B, be sure to

School Executive

Engelhardt

The Annual Report to the Public *) 24 pt. Bodoni Bold Ital c+ l.c. fl. left*

*10/11 Bod Bold fl. left* (By N. L. Engelhardt

*8/9 Bod. Bold fl. left* Associate Superintendent of Schools

New York City

*10/12 Bod. Bold Ital. 2 even lines fl. left* With a true sense of responsibility, the superintendent makes his annual report to the people an accounting of their children and their schools.

[ Among school administrators the term "annual report,"     *10/10 Oldstyle #1 on 20 pi*
has come to mean the report prepared for public con-
sumption.  To be sure, reporting annually to the Board
of Education on all phases of school developments is
a service rendered by all good administrators.  Such
reporting may snowball into considerable volume.

Each year the selection of material for the report
to the public results from the acceptance of certain criteria.  These include timeliness, novelty,
emergent needs, expansion requirements, maintenance
of support, arousal of interest and frequently re-

*6 pts. ld →* porting for information only.

*4 pts. ld →*             The Early Reports )            *10 pt Bodoni Bold c+ lc centered on 20 pi*
Printed annual reports are as old as formalized
public education programs in American communities.
Neale records a Boston report of 1738 and a Hartford report of 1767.  He states that seventy-one
Massachusetts communities were issuing reports by
1846.  The underlying purposes differed little

The above copy has been typed to column width and marked for the printer. Note the specific directions for every line of copy or block of copy: (1) size of type to be used, (2) type face, (3) italic or not, (4) location—centered, flush left, etc.—and (4) leading or spacing between lines.

*ok.*
*H.S.T. 4/10*

# 25—SchoolExecu

MAZEAU—NIGHT APRIL 1—MACHINE 7
SCHOOL EXEC. 10 on 10 Oldstyle 20 PICAS
SLUG—ENGELHARDT
THE ANNUAL REPORT TO THE PUBLIC

## The Annual
## Report to the Public

**By N. L. ENGELHARDT**
Associate Superintendent of Schools
New York City

*l.c.* WITH a true sense of public responsibility the superintendent makes his annual report to the people a accounting of their children and their school

AMONG school administrators the term annual report, has come to mean the report prepared for public consumption. To be sure, reporting annually to the board of education on all phases of school developments is a service rendered by all good administrators. Such reporting may snowball into considerable volume.

Each year the selection of material for the report to the public results from the acceptance of certain criteria. These include timeliness, novelty, emergent needs, expansion requirements, maintenance of support, arousal of interest and frequently reporting for information only.

### The Early Reports

Printed annual reports are as old as formalized public education programs in American communities. Neale records a Boston report of 1738 and a Hartford

FOOTNOTE.

*School Reports*
*by N. A. Neale.*
*Missouri Book*
*Co., 1921.*

report of 1767. He states that 71 Massachusetts communities were issuing reports by 1846. The underlying purposes differed little from those of today. Throughout this early school literature, certain reasons for reporting appear quite frequently. Almost invariably the reports give the number of school children, and comment on the quality of instruction, state the nature of grants and appropriations, enumerate the advantages arising from education to individuals and the public, present a written report on the conduct and condition of the schools.

For many years the desirability of having annual reports has been emphasized through legislation. In many states annual reports are required by law and their contents prescribed. Thus for certain kinds of reports, purposes are designated by law. They are usually associated with budgets and financial tions, board of education

The same copy, now set in galley 25, has been proofread and marked for correction by the printer. (See proofreaders' marks under *proofreading*.)

mark plainly on page 11 "See also pages 11A and 11B." Otherwise the added pages could get lost with nobody the wiser. Do not clip or pin corrected and retyped paragraphs to the manuscript; pasting is safer.

On the last page of manuscript copy, mark "end." This will enable the printer to know that he has lost no pages.

These precautions are necessary because manuscripts, which were once stapled, are usually unstapled while being set and may indeed be divided between two or more compositors.

It is human nature to postpone any writing until just before the deadline and to complete it while the printer's messenger is waiting, if then. Under such circumstances, the temptation to skimp on copy preparation is strong. Somehow the need to get copy freshly typed always presents itself most strongly just after the last typist has gone home for the day.

It should be remembered, however, that poor copy preparation is an expensive luxury and that a single correction in a galley may easily cost $1 or more.

Excellent pointers on copy preparation are given in Julie Eidesheim's "Editor at Work" (Rinehart, 1939).

**copyright** A notice of copyright in this exact form, "Copyright, 1955, by John Doe," must appear on a printed item, or copyright cannot be claimed. The date must be the year of publication. The name must be that of the individual or corporation in whose name the copyright is claimed. (On works of art the form © is acceptable when accompanied by the initials, monogram, mark, or symbol of the copyright proprietor.)

The only other formality required is to fill out forms, available from the Copyright Office, Library of Congress, Washington, D.C., and send them with two copies of the best edition and $4 (by certified check or money order) to the Register of Copyrights, promptly after publication.

In the case of unprinted manuscripts of lectures or dramatic material intended to be delivered or performed from a platform, one copy should be sent with $4.

In books, the copyright notice must appear on the title page or the page following.

Commercial prints and labels used in connection with the sale or advertisement of articles of merchandise may be copyrighted. Two specimens should be filed along with the proper application. The fee is $6.

Plots, titles, slogans, ideas, and news cannot be copyrighted.

Copyright is good for a period of 28 years renewable during the last year for another 28 years, for a total of 56 years.

Foreign copyright presents special problems, and a request for special instructions should be addressed to the Register of Copyrights, with an explanation of the specific circumstances involved. Books and periodicals by U.S. citizens must be manufactured in the United States as a condition for full copyright protection here.

A new Universal Copyright Convention was ratified by the United States in 1955. Information concerning it may be obtained from the Copyright Office.

Leaflets containing the rules for copyright applications may be obtained from the Register of Copyrights, Library of Congress, Washington, D.C.

An invaluable book on the subject is "A Manual of Copyright Practice for Writers, Publishers, and Agents," by Margaret Nicholson (Oxford University Press).

See also RECORDINGS.

**copy writing** See also COPY EDITING; COPY PREPARATION; EDITORIAL PLANNING; EDITORIAL WORK.

Copy writing is here considered to be the initial writing of a manuscript as distinguished from the rewriting, revising, and polishing discussed under copy editing. (See COPY EDITING.)

To the editor copy means any written matter—news story, poem, editorial, advertisement, photo caption. It means written matter that is to entertain, to instruct, or to sell. Hence, the term "copy writing" could refer to any kind of writing. In printing and advertising circles it is generally used in the more workaday sense—writing in order to stimulate the reader to some definite action or new way of thinking.

Such copy is generally written to persuade the reader to a course of action. It is thus "selling" copy whether the desired action is buying certain merchandise or voting in a certain way. Only reading matter wholly paid for by the reader is likely to have amusement or instruction as its sole objective.

*General slant.* The copy writer must first know the product or idea that he is trying to sell. This idea may have been staked out in the earlier stage of editorial planning (see EDITORIAL PLANNING), but almost invariably he will have to do further research to determine the appeals that he is going to use to achieve the desired objective.

Experienced advertising copy writers, as well as fund raisers and organizers, have found that virtually every piece of copy of proved effectiveness appeals to the self-interest of the reader. It immediately answers his natural questions: "What's in it for me? What pleasure or profit will I derive from reading this or from doing or believing what the writer suggests?"

Copy writers are frequently cynics. Many of the most successful assume that no one does anything except for reasons of personal pleasure or profit. Apparent altruism is usually grounded in a desire to gain the good opinion of others, or at least to appease the conscience. The basic appeals used by copy writers are sometimes summarized as

(1) desire for personal adequacy and social recognition, (2) desire for romance, (3) desire for long life, (4) desire to make money, (5) desire to save money, (6) desire to save time, (7) desire to save energy, (8) desire for comfort.

Equally important is knowing the age level, economic condition, special interests, and prejudices of the audience. A reader is more likely to be moved by copy that seems to be written just for him, in the words that he might use himself, and with the tone that he has come to expect of his most trusted neighbor or business adviser.

*Planning the whole.* The usual construction of a piece of copy is (1) get attention so that the copy is sure to be read, (2) create interest and desire, (3) establish conviction by proving each claim or each point of the argument, (4) get action by giving an incentive, showing the means for immediate action and asking directly for that action. These ingredients are as important in general advertising as in mail-order work, even if it is more difficult to check the results.

Most copy writers begin by making a check list of points to be included in the copy. Some go further and develop a detailed outline to assure complete coverage and strategic arrangement of the salient points. The opening sentences of a piece of copy must catch the reader's interest, or he may never read further. They must convince him that here is something that will help or amuse him. A good lead puts him in a receptive frame of mind, curious enough to read on and responsive to the story that he must already anticipate. In skillful hands the lead is an integral part of the story, setting the tone and pace of that which follows.

News reporters developed a sort of formula for their leads. At one time practically every news story began with the five W's—who, what, when, where, and why. With this formula, the first sentence gives the meat of the story, and the harried reader knows whether to read on or pass to the next column.

Feature writers frequently put their lead in the form of a question or a believe-it-or-not attention getter. They may also play on the emotions and use some appealing detail as the lead. Thus they pique the reader's curiosity and at the same time set the tone for the whole story.

Digressive leads seem to offer a beguiling pitfall for the novice. He begins by passing the time of day with some irrelevant observation, apparently on the theory that his main point is not of itself interesting. This is a fatal state of mind in which to write copy. Either what he has to say is in some way of interest to the reader or his efforts are foredoomed to failure.

*Making it readable.* The importance of writing copy that will be read has led to the development of many formulas and tests for readable copy. Perhaps the best known is that developed by Rudolf Flesch and described in his book "The Art of Readable Writing" (Harper, 1949, $3). Whether or not a writer wishes to use the Flesch yardstick, he will find it helpful to check his copy on the four main points in the Flesch test: (1) the number of words in an average sentence, (2) the number of affixes per 100 words, (3) the number of personal words, and (4) the number of personal sentences. From this data Flesch proceeds to get what he calls a "Reading Ease Score" and a "Human Interest Score."

Copy suitable for 75 per cent of the adults in the United States is classed as "standard," seventh- to eighth-grade level, and typical of the digest magazines. Standard copy has 17 words in the average sentence, 37 affixes in 100 words, and at least 7 per cent personal words and 15 per cent personal sentences. In similar manner, Flesch describes six other degrees of readability from "very easy" (the comic-book level

readable for 90 per cent of the adults in the United States) to "very difficult" (the scientific level readable for only 4½ per cent of the adults). He also explains how to sample and test readability.

One farm magazine experimented with the very easy and standard versions of the same material and found that the former brought far greater readership.

In his book, Flesch points out other qualities of readable copy—qualities which are less easily measured but which are frequently dependent upon the four bases of his tests and table. His thoroughly down-to-earth comments and his emphasis on the personal and human qualities make his yardstick more than a scientific test.

One editor uses the following test on the work of his copy writers:

1. Are the words familiar?
2. Are the sentences short?
3. Are they varied to relieve the monotony of the usual subject-verb-object pattern?
4. Is each paragraph short and well unified?
5. Does everything contribute to the one big object or conclusion?
6. Is the argument so simple and logical that the reader can remember the main points?

Many editors have less formal requirements but agree that simplicity is the key to readability for the average person.

*Heads, subheads, and captions.* Writing good titles or heads is just as important as writing good text copy, for the title must sell the article to the reader. The title or head should introduce the article in vigorous, "selling" words. Current practice favors a strong, simple verb as the keynote in a title, or a few vivid nouns.

Heads and subheads may be all that the reader sees as he scans a page. If they are well written, they will give him the story in essence. They can be so provocative that he feels compelled to read the whole story. Even if they only warn him away from stories that wouldn't interest him, they have served a purpose.

Pictures get attention before printed words. The caption under a picture will be read before printed columns of copy. It merits good copy—clear, concise, and to the point. Instead of merely echoing the message of the picture, the caption should carry the reader on to the body of the story or to a pertinent point in the argument. Thus, the caption under three pictures on a page could drive home three significant phases of the central idea or message. (See CAPTIONS.)

Good copy-writing techniques are discussed in many of the books listed with annotations in Appendix 2, Bibliography. A few key pointers on copy writing are as follows:

*Before you start to write.* 1. Know your product. Use it, read it, experiment with it. You cannot do justice to a book you have not read or a product you have not used. It is hard to warm-over someone else's copy and improve it unless you know more than he did about the product. If you don't personally care for the product, find someone who does and talk to him. Talk to the author or editor or inventor or designer or engineer. Be sure you know every feature. And if it is a revised or improved product, learn about the changes and why they were made.

2. Know your audience. Do not take any mailing list on faith; run through some of the names and you may get some big surprises. Know all the lists you could be using. Write a different letter to each group if the arguments could be different. Study former buyers. Study the complaint file, if there is one. Work at a retail store or a convention booth for a while. Look over the orders as they come in. Be sure you know everything you possibly can about those for whom you are writing.

3. Know your marketing set-up. Are your prospects used to buying by mail, or in stores, or how? Will the store they might go to have the product, or know about it? Will they think they know how to get it for less than the sum you quote? Will they send cash or expect to be billed? Will you send on approval? Be sure you know where your audience will be buying what you offer so you can ask for the right kind of action.

*When you start to write.* 1. Start by asking yourself, "What's in this for the prospect?" If there are several advantages, list them all in the order of importance.

2. Now enumerate all possible objections that the prospect might raise. Be sure each objection is countered with a plus argument—and plainly so, for the prospect must not be left with any doubts unanswered. In fact, you can often answer objections without stating them and indeed can turn an objection inside out and make it seem like an advantage to the reader.

3. Prove your points. Testimonials will help, for the reader will not always take your word alone for what you claim. Use pictures if they will help. Cite statistics if you have persuasive ones, for figures make a greater impression than generalities as a rule.

4. Present the price as if it were an inexpensive alternate to some far more costly course. Guarantee satisfaction or a quick refund. Make ordering easy and quote postpaid or delivered prices.

5. Beware of the too transparent questionnaire or phony claim, *e.g.,* that the sales letter is a Gallup poll when it isn't at all.

6. Beware of claiming too much for your product or idea.

7. Emphasize sincerity above slickness. Remember that the right arguments presented to the right prospects with the ring of sincerity will get orders.

8. Strive for a conversational style.

Any style you wouldn't use in describing your item to a friend is probably wrong for a selling letter. Your purpose is not to impress the reader with your clever style, but to win him as an interested reader and a potential customer.

9. Favor the word "you." It is rarely overused. The first word of the first sentence will get more attention if it begins with that winning word, YOU.

10. Don't be too familiar. After all, your readers will probably include all kinds of people and some may be irritated if they suspect that you are trying to backslap them into buying.

11. Don't be cocksure or patronizing or pontifical. The recipient may well know more than the writer, and it will hardly increase his confidence in you or your product if he suspects you are trying to talk down to him.

12. On the other hand, don't assume too much knowledge on the part of the reader. If you try to use trade jargon or office slang, you are likely to confuse him and annoy him a bit as well.

13. Try all copy on a few guinea pigs, paying particular attention to any points over which they seem to stumble. Often a word that can be either a noun or an adjective is read wrong at first glance and requires rereading if the passage is to be untangled. Such spots are hard for the writer to find by himself because he naturally reads the correct meaning into the equivocal word.

14. Beware of phrase worship. There comes a time in the writing of a piece of copy when it may be time-saving to put away all previous drafts and try a new version away from the high-sounding phrases which seemed so deft on the first go round. Really telling phrases from your early drafts will come to mind easily, but some that sounded so fine and meant so little will usually drop out of your way once they are out of sight. Deft phrasing is always pleasant, but it can never take the place of a good initial idea, logical order, and persuasive exposition of ideas.

15. Avoid beginning a sentence with a participial clause as a weak and often unrelated part of the whole.

16. Avoid verbal clichés, but don't be afraid to ask for the order in the straight talk that customers expect.

17. Go gently with humor. Some ad writers can get away with it, but most of us lack the gift. Besides, even the best humor passes some people by or leaves them annoyed because they miss the point altogether or because it does not appeal to their taste.

18. Statistics are a good weapon, but a double-edged sword. You can prove anything with figures and many of your readers know it. If you distort, some will catch you and your rating will slip in their eyes.

19. Respect the prospect's time. Get to the point immediately and keep your copy brief and interesting.

**coquille**   A drawing technique based on the use of drawing paper that has a surface consisting of raised dots. (See STIPPLE; ROSS BOARD; for an example, see DRAWING TECHNIQUES.)

**costs**   See also SAVING MONEY; ESTIMATING COSTS.

Approximate cost figures are given in this book under several entries. (See CIRCULARS; PAMPHLETS; MIMEOGRAPH; OFFSET, etc.) All costs are based on actual prices quoted by commercial firms. It is assumed that a firm operating its own printing and duplicating equipment will find that its own costs are comparable when labor and overhead are properly accounted for. Although each figure quoted is an actual one, another buyer, in another city and at another time, may well expect to be quoted a different figure, perhaps higher, perhaps lower.

**cover paper**   See also PAPER; CARDBOARD.

Paper suitable for the covers of pamphlets. Some weights are as light as text paper but are more likely to be available in special colors and finishes. Other grades are two to four times as heavy as text paper. Cover paper comes uncoated and coated in the same variety as text paper. Basic weights for

quality reproduction proof is produced on this machine in a matter of minutes and at very low cost. The letters are printed in sequence on a strip of sensitized paper or transparent film. Any desired letter spacing is obtainable. The machine is very easy to

This picture can be improved by cropping. At present it includes several loosely connected groups and a needless amount of foreground and background. The groups on the sidelines look posed and rather uninterested in the central group—a fact that is distracting to the reader. (*Courtesy of Cincinnati Public Schools.*)

cover paper are referred to the basic size, 20 by 26. (See table under PAPER SIZES AND WEIGHTS.)

**Coxhead-Liner** A photographic composing machine for setting display type in sizes from 14 to 72 points. It is manufactured by the Ralph C. Coxhead Corporation of Newark, N.J., and sells for $750 with extra type fonts at $28.50. It sets type for price books, catalogues, newspaper ads, fliers, signs, name plates, and many other applications. The machine is designed to be operated on the top of a desk. The copy is set by merely dialing. A high-

operate, since exposure time, photographic development, and fixing are all automatic.

**Craft-Color** Thin acetate sheets in 19 bright colors with adhesive backing used for making color layouts, posters, package designs, sales charts, etc., manufactured by the Craftint Manufacturing Co., 1615 Collamer Ave., Cleveland, Ohio.

**Craftint** Trade name of Craftint Manufacturing Co., 1615 Collamer Ave., Cleveland 10, Ohio, makers of Craft-Tone Singletone and Doubletone shading tints, Craf-Type, Craft-Color, etc.

See SHADING TINTS; also DRAWING TECHNIQUES.

**Craf-Type** See ARTYPE.

**creasing** See SCORING.

**credit lines** Photo agencies require a credit line under a published photo, *e.g.*, "Acme photo," under penalty of additional royalty. Publications extending the right to reprint a cartoon or other item almost invariably insist on a credit line. Both courtesy and fair play require it in any case so that the artist or photographer will have due recognition.

The credit line is usually placed flush right immediately below the photo or cartoon, or is printed in the last line of the caption.

Since credit lines are easily overlooked, editors often train themselves to make one extra page-proof check just to see whether all credit lines are in order. They know that any omission makes trouble, while free and accurate use of credit lines, even when not actually required, makes friends.

Some magazines omit credit lines under individual pictures and print them in one paragraph on one page.

**crop, cropping** See also SCALING; PHOTOGRAPHS.

To crop a piece of art work or photograph means to indicate that only a portion of its area is to be reproduced, not the whole. The editor or designer will indicate by "crop marks" exactly how much of it is to be reproduced. The printer or engraver will follow these marks and reproduce the desired area in the desired size. (The original photograph or drawing is never physically cut, of course.)

Crop marks may be placed on the art work itself (but not within the area to be reproduced) or on an "overlay," or on both.

Since overlays may be torn off or go askew, it is safest to put crop marks on the original, mounting the art work or the photo on a larger board if extra margins are needed. A tissue overlay may still be used to help visualize the cropping called for or merely to protect the original.

This cropping of the larger photograph makes it much more effective. Distracting elements are eliminated. Attention is focused on the main action of the picture. (*Courtesy of Cincinnati Public Schools.*)

Photos can easily be damaged in cropping and scaling. (See PHOTOGRAPHS: CARE IN HANDLING.) A photograph should never be under any paper that is being written on. Even a soft pencil can make depressions in the glossy surface that may show in reproduction.

A grease pencil should be used to indicate the cropping of a glossy photographic print since grease marks will rub off with a cloth or tissue.

Most photos need cropping, either to eliminate unimportant background or to alter their proportions.

The editor or art director who indicates where a photograph is to be cropped must try to visualize a part of the picture with the rest cropped out. It is important to remember that while a photograph is not necessarily cropped to the same size as the finished reproduction, it must be cropped in the same proportions. For example, a 6 by 6 area on a photograph, when reduced or enlarged, will always produce a square cut. But if a 3 by 4 cut is needed in the final reproduction, the photo must be cropped in that proportion of height to width.

One good procedure is this: With white envelopes or file cards cover the portions of the picture that are not to be reproduced. Those placed horizontally will eliminate unwanted sky and foreground. those placed vertically will eliminate unwanted areas at left and right. In this way an 8 by 10 print may yield an essential area of perhaps 7 by 7, or even 3 by 4 in., etc.

Suppose the essential part of your picture is square, whereas a 3 by 4 cut is needed. In that case, the covering envelopes or cards may be adjusted so that some sky or foreground is restored to give the proper proportions. Then, with a grease pencil, mark as guides the four corners of the exposed area. Remove the cards or envelopes, and using one of them as a ruler, mark in the margins the extension of the four guide points. Bring the overlay down and trace the marginal guidelines. Then, lifting it from the photo, draw in pencil the rectangle that is identical with the desired area of the photo.

Draw a diagonal of this rectangle on the tissue overlay, which can then be placed on the layout to check the space required by the photo reproduction when reduced. (See SCALING for exact method.)

Where the area allotted to the illustration is unalterable, the photo must be cropped to fit that space. Sometimes, the layout requires a vertical picture when the only one available is stubbornly horizontal in shape and cannot be cropped to a vertical shape without losing vital areas. There may be no remedy but to get a new layout or a new photo. (Good layout men try to let the photos dictate the layout plan.) Sometimes tricks are resorted to, such as having the retoucher add more sky. (See RETOUCHING.)

Cropping requires an eye for balance and composition. The photographer does the first part when he crops nature by pointing the camera. He crops again when he decides whether to use all or part of the negative in making his prints. If his pictures arrive in assorted shapes, he has already indicated the cropping he suggests. If, however, all his photos are on 8 by 10 paper, it is evident that some will need further cropping since nature does not always conform to the 8 by 10 proportion.

No matter what the shape of the print, it is worth remembering that there may be more picture on the negative than shows on the print. If a layout demands a broader or a taller shape, it may be possible to go back to the negative for a print of the desired proportions.

Cropping is an art and follows the general rules of good artistic composition and balance. For example, if in a portrait a man is shown in profile, it is customary to allow a little more space in the direction in which he is looking, less behind him. If there is space between figures, it is customary to allow equal or greater space around them.

In many instances, it is better to single out one or two appealing faces in a crowd than to reproduce the entire group. Careful cropping avoids beheading people in the photos or arbitrarily making amputees of them.

To determine just how art work will look after cropping and reduction, a photostat can be made to scale, trimmed to the crop marks, and tried on the layout.

**cursive** Cursive letters are those resembling handwriting with rounded form and joining strokes.

## Lydian Italic

## Lydian Cursive

**cut** See also LINE CUT; HALFTONE.

"Cut" is a word-of-all-work commonly used to mean engraving, line cut, halftone, or even to refer to a picture printed from these. One sends art work to the engraver and orders "cuts" made, or checks page proofs to make sure that each "cut" has its credit line.

Practically speaking, only one printing process uses cuts, namely letterpress (relief) printing. (See LETTERPRESS.) The other processes print from one big plate containing both type and illustrations. Therefore, cuts are not required for offset, photogravure, photogelatin, or silk screen, nor can they be used. One can, however, send the printer art work and have him reproduce it in line or in halftone.

The simplest kind of cut explains the name. It is a woodcut with the surface cut away by an artist to leave the lines of a drawing or diagram which is to be printed. Metal, rubber, and linoleum surfaces are also used, blocked so as to be type-high. The most familiar kind of cut is perhaps the common rubber stamp. (See RUBBER STAMPS.)

Engravers formerly made cuts by copying the artist's drawing by hand on metal or wood. Nowadays a line drawing can be transferred photographically to a metal surface, after which the metal unprotected by the image is eaten away (etched) with acid.

There are two important classes of cuts or engravings: (1) the line cut and (2) the halftone, sometimes called "halftone cut" or "halftone engraving." (See LINE CUT and HALFTONE.)

Line drawings containing no grays as distinct from blacks or whites can be reproduced as line cuts. Photographs, wash drawings, and other art work containing grays or middle tones, which are neither solid black nor solid white, must be reproduced as halftones.

Line drawings include drawings done in pen and ink, in brush and ink (undiluted black ink), in ink spatter technique, etc. Halftone reproduction is usually necessary for photographs, wash drawings, pencil sketches, etc. (See illustrations under DRAWING TECHNIQUES.)

In case of doubt, a printer or photoengraver can always explain whether a given piece of art work should be reproduced in line or in halftone; in borderline cases, he may be able to suggest minor retouching to permit the making of a line cut from art that might otherwise have to be reproduced in halftone.

Halftones usually cost more than line cuts and must be ordered in the "screen" appropriate for the paper to be used. The two processes are more fully described under LINE CUT and HALFTONE.

It is true that plates have to be made in order to produce "engraved" calling cards by the intaglio process (see INTAGLIO), but these are called "plates" or "engraved plates," not cuts. In a true engraving, the design is graven into and beneath the printing surface with a "graver," and is printed by the intaglio process. In a cut, the design is brought into "relief" by cutting away all areas that are not to print, and it is printed by the relief process. However, the word "engraving" is today used loosely as a synonym for cut. For cuts, one goes to a photoengraver; for real intaglio engravings, one goes to a steel engraver.

The cost of cuts often influences the choice of a printing process. It almost always costs less to reproduce either line or halftone art work in offset than in letterpress. On the other hand, the offset process is usually inferior to letterpress on photographic work, equal on line work, superior on delicate pencil sketches. (For comparative costs of mounted cuts, line and halftone, see the table under HALFTONE.)

**cut-in head** This paragraph has been set to include a "cut-in" subhead. This style, often found in textbooks, is particularly useful in securing extra variety and emphasis in typewritten material. It is, however, a style *Example of Cut-in Subhead* that makes extra trouble for the type compositor and, therefore, costs considerably more than subheads that are centered, indented, or run flush left.

**cut-outs** See DIE CUTTING.

**cutting** See also DIE CUTTING.

Almost all printers have machinery for cutting and trimming paper both before and after printing. Paper cutters can cut paper on the square, or even make a straight angular cut. Special equipment is needed for round-cornering, punching, and die cutting into special shapes. (See DIE CUTTING.)

It is necessary to let the ink dry before printed material can be cut. Otherwise, one printed sheet may "offset" onto the back of the next under the pressure of the cutter.

There are cutters that can make a cut 70 in. long. Most printers and binders have smaller equipment, perhaps not even big enough to handle a 38 by 50 or 35 by 45 ream. Therefore, it is advisable to check before ordering paper. It may be necessary to have the paper supply house cut it before delivery to the printer, or to have the printer cut it before delivery to the binder.

**cutting copy** See COPY FITTING; COPY PREPARATION.

**cylinder presses** See PRINTING PRESSES; FLAT-BED PRESS.

# D|d

**Davidson Duplicators** A line of small offset presses similar to the Multilith (see Multilith) made by the Davidson Corporation, a subsidiary of the Mergenthaler Linotype Corporation, 27 Ryerson Street, Brooklyn 5, N.Y.

The Davidson Dual prints by both offset and letterpress, the conversion to letterpress taking about ten minutes, and permitting printing on the Multigraph principle from type, rubber plates, or curved electros. Special attachments permit perforating, numbering, and imprinting from Linotype slugs.

**Day-glo colors** See LUMINESCENT PRINTING.

**dead metal** Areas not intended to print, including those areas on a cut or duplicate plate which are to be trimmed away or routed out. The term is sometimes used to refer to the "killed matter" thrown into the "hell box" ready for remelting.

**decalcomanias** In order to print the manufacturer's name and trade-mark on a vacuum cleaner, it is not necessary to run the machine through a printing press. Instead, a piece of paper can serve as "stand-in" for the vacuum cleaner; the desired design can be printed in full color on the paper; and the inks of the finished design can be transferred from it to the vacuum cleaner later on by a simple hand operation. This is the decalcomania process.

"Decals," after transfer, are as permanent as if they had been painted by hand on the surface. Some decals adhere through the use of varnish; some carry their own "stickative" which need only be moistened, yet which will become waterproof. (All decals have some lacquer for body and tensile strength.) In both types, the backing paper slides away when moistened, leaving only the ink film affixed to the side of the truck, the vacuum cleaner, the store window, or whatever it is.

Decals can be obtained in any size, with any type of art work, and in any number of colors. For best results they should be used on smooth surfaces such as glass, metal, or enamel, or on surfaces that can be made smooth with a coat of varnish; special decals can be obtained for use on almost any surface. They can be affixed to surfaces that are

73

curved in one dimension, but not to complex curves (any more than paper can be made to take the curve of a sphere).

The cost of decals is figured by the area, quantity, colors, and art work. A simple decal, the size of a playing card, may run $12 to $20 per thousand, depending on the number of colors and quantity ordered.

Silk-screen decals tend to run a little cheaper than lithographed decals in small quantities and may be just as satisfactory unless the design is too delicate to reproduce in silk screen. Some suppliers who handle both kinds give quicker delivery on silk-screen decals. (See SILK SCREEN.)

A simple window decal is made as follows: A layer of transparent "stickative" is laid on a piece of porous paper. Many layers of opaque lacquer are then printed on top of the adhesive until a sufficiently strong film has been built up. Then the desired design is printed on this base layer, in one or more colors. Finally, another layer of adhesive finishes the decal.

If this decal is now moistened and applied to the inside of an automobile windshield so as to be readable from the outside, the wet backing paper will slide away and can be discarded. Or, the decal can be placed on the front of the windshield, and slid from the backing paper onto the glass.

Decals can also be made that are readable from both sides of the glass they adhere to.

When decals are ordered, specifications for their use should be given so that the manufacturer can get the design faced toward or away from the backing paper and can print the proper transfer instructions on the backing paper.

For the names of local decal suppliers, look under Decalcomanias in the Classified Telephone Directory. Companies handling all types of decal work include The Meyercord Com-

pany, 5323 W. Lake St., Chicago 44; and The American Decalcomania Company, 4344 W. 5th Ave., Chicago 24, Ill.

**deckle edge**    Handmade paper comes with a feathery deckle edge on all four sides, unless trimmed. Machine-made paper has a deckle edge on two opposite sides until trimmed. The deckling runs with the grain on machine-made paper and occurs when the paper fibers at the edge of the web try to flow under the rubber dam or deckle that determines the width of the paper.

Deckle edges are usually trimmed off. They may be left for their decorative value on greeting cards, limited editions, etc.

**deep-etch offset**    See also OFFSET.

For a single color and on short runs offset printers can use albumin plates, which, with care, are good for up to 150,000 impressions. For critical work, including color, and for long runs where more copies must be printed, the printer may make deep-etched plates, which cost more, but in general last longer. On a deep-etched plate, the greasy areas that carry the ink are depressed level with, or beneath, the surrounding wet surface and are thus somewhat protected from wear. Deep-etched plates usually give more dependable results, since the quality of the impression is less subject to gradual deterioration during the course of a press run.

Even deep-etched plates wear out, however, and for very long runs (up in the hundreds of thousands) the trend is toward the use of bimetal plates. (See BIMETAL PLATES.)

Deep-etched plates should be, but are not necessarily, superior to albumin plates. The printer who is taking full advantage of recent technical advances (the Cronak plate treatment, cellulose gum in place of gum arabic, etc.) may get longer and better runs from albumin than a less progressive competitor gets from deep-etch.

**Deeptone** A proprietary name used by the Donnelley Company in Chicago to describe its highest quality offset work. (See OFFSET.)

**delivery** See also SCHEDULING.

The delivery date often wanted on a job is "yesterday." Printers get used to hearing that every job is a rush job.

Generally speaking, the more time a printer has, the better and the more efficiently he can do his work. His dream is to have a backlog of nonrush work to draw on and keep his machines and men from standing idle between rush jobs. He may even bid lower on a job on which delivery will be accepted "any time next month."

A delivery promise, once given, is contingent on the customer's holding up his end of the bargain, as regards delivery of manuscript, correcting proofs, etc.

Extraordinary speed is possible, as witness the everyday miracle of the daily newspaper; but random jobs are not like scheduled magazine or newspaper jobs. If a printer is free to drop all other work, if his men are willing to stay overtime, if the typesetting can be divided among several compositors, if the customer can stay in the composing room and O.K. proofs as they are pulled, if the paper is on hand, if a press and folding machine are free, if the engravers and binders involved are also willing to cooperate fully, if there are no ink-drying problems, *then* perhaps one-day or two-day delivery can be achieved.

Normally, however, the following factors must be considered in working out a production schedule and arriving at a delivery date:

1. When can delivery of manuscript, art work, engravings, and paper be expected?

2. Considering other work already scheduled, how soon can the composing room, pressroom, and bindery start on the job?

3. How long will the composition, platemaking, press run, drying, binding, etc., actually take?

4. How much time will be consumed in getting the customer's O.K. on galley proofs and page proofs?

5. How will this schedule be affected by the fact that printers do not (without heavy extra pay) work holidays, Saturdays, or Sundays, and by the fact that "morning" to a printer means 8 A.M. while to the average customer it means any time before noon?

6. What is the added cost of overtime work for a rush job?

"Delivery in two weeks" (10 working days barring holidays) on average jobs is pretty good. One-week delivery on any job involving composition is excellent service. Magazines send off art work and copy for color work from two to four months in advance of delivery dates, and often have to be content with a month's lapse between their last editorial correction and the publication date.

**descender** See ASCENDER and illustration under TYPE.

**design** See also ART WORK; DESIGNERS; ILLUSTRATIONS; MARGINS; TYPE; LAYOUT.

The simplest way for the beginner to design a pamphlet or anything else is to adapt to his own purposes the basic design of another one which is attractive or which is known to have been effective with a similar audience.

No stigma need attach to borrowing from other designs, provided the borrowing is done creatively and not slavishly. The best professional designers will freely admit that their art is that of adapting intelligently.

Finding some good models to follow may not be easy. However, someone, somewhere, has almost certainly met and solved a problem quite like yours.

The local librarian can probably find helpful samples. Most libraries have a "vertical file" of pamphlets, posters, and clippings.

*Suggestions on design.* Use the words of the message as basic elements of the design. Borders, rules, and dots generally contribute nothing to the enlightenment of the reader and should be subordinated to the type or eliminated altogether.

Words should be taken singly or in natural groups and visualized as blocks to be moved around on the paper. How would they look if set big or small, bold or light, tall or wide, in caps or lower case, in roman or italic, in long lines or short?

Do some elements need greater emphasis than others? Good ways to get it are by setting a bold black letter against a graceful script, a sans-serif against a serif type, or (sticking to one type family) large against small, italic against roman, caps or small caps against lower case.

A few widely used display types are Bodoni (Bodoni Bold, Bodoni Ultra), Futura (also known as Spartan, Tempo, and Twentieth Century) in various weights, Memphis (also known as Beton, Karnak, and Stymie) in various weights, and Lydian (also Lydian Bold and Lydian Cursive). (See Appendix 1, Type Faces.)

A few widely used and universally liked text types are Baskerville, Caslon, Garamond, Granjon, and Times Roman.

Bold type is to be avoided in choosing a text type. The solid reading matter in books, magazines, and pamphlets is almost never set in boldface or in sans serif because people find large blocks of boldface or sans-serif type hard to read. (See BOLDFACE and SANS SERIF.)

*Avoid long lines.* Avoid text lines of more than 65 characters. This applies to typewriting as well as type. Small 8-pt. type on a 5-in. line becomes unreadable, because the reader's eye finds its way with difficulty from the end of one line to the beginning of the next.

Newspapers use 7- or 8-pt. type on a 2-in. (12-pica) line and get about 33 characters per line. A 5-in. line almost requires 12- or 14-pt. type with space (leading) added between the lines; if more words must go into the space than 12 or 14 pt. would permit, it is better to divide the space into two narrow columns which will take smaller type as has been done in this book.

For captions and subheads, a type is often selected that offers a contrast to the text type. Sans-serif types are a popular choice. However, it should be in character with the general style.

*Use color.* Color usually pays for itself many times over in added effectiveness. Even full color (process color), which is expensive, may pay its way when the product itself is colorful. Look at one of the big mail-order catalogues for a lesson in which kinds of merchandise repay the use of color. (See COLOR.)

*Use illustrations.* It is hard to think of a printed message that cannot benefit from the use of illustrations or decorations. Cartoons get quicker reader attention than any other type of printed matter. Photographs, drawings, charts, and their captions also get read before the text does.

Whether or not a printed message is read may depend on whether it looks interesting or looks dull on the first glance.

Many people say a picture is worth ten thousand words, but too few of them act on it when preparing printed matter. Perhaps this is because editors are more often writers than artists. Admittedly good pictures are hard to find (see ILLUSTRATIONS) and may seem unessential, but even purely decorative ones have an informative effect—they help attract the reader's attention and keep him reading.

Editors often make it a rule to get

some sort of break from unrelieved text on every spread with a cartoon, chart, box, photograph, or at least a display heading.

What is design? It is really the art of drawing the straightest line between two points: between writer and reader, between idea and action. A designer should be told "Help us achieve this objective," not merely "Make this pamphlet pretty."

Of course, many designers take a very limited view of their job, and would not know what to do with any except the most literal instructions. These are draftsmen, however, not designers.

A good designer deserves to be taken in on the whole thinking behind the operation. Then if he knows his stuff, he may easily see a way to get twice the results at half the expected cost.

For instance, a designer was asked to plan a mailing piece. The budget was $200 for 10,000 copies. He suggested "Let's cut the budget to $50. You're advertising these books as cut-price bargains. People will believe you more quickly if the mailing piece looks as though you had been forced to pinch pennies to get it printed." He proved to be right. The deliberately cheap-looking mailing piece outpulled an expensive-looking predecessor.

Good design is design suited to its purpose. This may mean either following tradition to gain easy recognition and acceptability, or breaking with tradition to gain attention.

A grocery ad can best concentrate the reader's attention on price if it uses familiar grocery ad typography. On the other hand, if its purpose is to say "This is the most exclusive food store in town," effectiveness may be served if the design looks like something Benjamin Franklin might have set or is otherwise unusual.

The important thing is that the design help get the message across, and not claim for itself attention that should be focused on the message.

Much good design is unobtrusive design, deliberately preferring the familiar to the bizarre, and purposely clothing the message in the familiar, the welcome, and the acceptable.

Even design intended to startle must not mislead, lest it turn away those very people who would actually be interested in the message.

The most effective advertisement is not that which makes people say "That's a good ad," but rather the one which makes readers exclaim "That's a good buy," or "That's a smart company." (See also the check list of layout pointers given under LAYOUT.)

A design service for magazine editors is offered by the Butler Typo Design Research Center, Mendota, Ill., where for a fee of $25 a magazine's design will be evaluated, and for $175 it will be evaluated and redesigned.

**designers** See also DESIGN.

Wherever possible, if the budget permits or can be stretched, hire a good designer. He will not only produce a better-looking job but may actually do it for less money.

Top-notch free-lance artists experienced in designing pamphlets, books, packages, etc., are listed in "The Literary Market Place." (See Appendix 2, Bibliography.) Their fees are likely to be at least $100 for the simplest jobs, but they can often save more than their fee by the effectiveness of their work.

Printers sometimes offer good designing service. Ad agencies may also have designers on their staff. Not all designers can do just anything, however. A "type" man or a magazine illustrator may be no good at all on posters. One designer may have a formal, classic style; another may have a modern, asymmetrical style; a third may have a friendly, free-and-easy style.

Amateurs who "know what they like" sometimes turn out to be excellent designers, once they realize how rare good taste is and acquire the courage to hold out for what they want.

The best way to explain to a printer or designer what is wanted is to show actual samples of the kind of design the purchaser has in mind.

**diazo copying**   See WHITEPRINTS.

**Dick strip**   Machine addressing is often done on great rolls of paper 2 to 3 in. wide. The rolls of addresses are then inserted in a Dick Stripper or Wing Mailer, machines for cutting off the addresses one at a time and sticking each onto a magazine or other material to be mailed. These machines look a little bit like a carpenter's plane. The roll or "Dick strip" is advanced from one address to the next by a simple thumb motion. Every time the machine is pressed down, another address is gummed, cut off, and affixed.

For information about the Dick Stripper, write to C. P. MacArthur, 137 W. Tupper St., Buffalo 1, N.Y. The Wing Mailer is made by Chauncey Wing's Sons, Greenfield, Mass. Similar automatic equipment (using perforated rolls, however) is made by Cheshire Mailing Machines, 1415 W. Altgeld St., Chicago 14.

**die cutting**   The cutting of special shapes (cut-outs) in paper, cardboard, cloth, etc., is done by die-cutting firms. Die cutters have some shapes of dies in stock. If one of these will do, the expense of having a special one made can be avoided.

There are two types of dies: high dies and steel-rule dies.

High dies look like heavy-duty cookie cutters. They cost from $25 (for small, simple shapes) on up. They can cut through many layers of material at once. Once the die is paid for, the cost of cutting is low.

Steel-rule dies are made by tracing the lines of the pattern on ¾-in. plywood, by cutting along the lines of the

pattern with a jigsaw, and by bending or cutting steel rule to fit the slots. The piece of plywood with the sharp edges of the steel rule projecting in the shape of the desired pattern is placed in an ordinary printing press. One sheet of material at a time is then fed into the press and cut. (Sometimes two to four can be die-cut at one impression.) A steel-rule die costs from $6 up for simple shapes, to $100 or more for complicated multiple shapes such as Christmas package seals.

Once the die is paid for, high-die cutting costs from 75 cents per thousand up. Steel-rule die cutting costs from $3 per thousand up—about as much as printing the job in an additional color.

For an excellent description of the die-cutting process with many illustrations see Victor Strauss' book "Point of Purchase Cardboard Displays" listed in Appendix 2, Bibliography.

**direct mail advertising**   See also MAIL ORDER; MAILING LISTS; LETTERS; COPY WRITING; Appendix 4, Postal Information.

Whenever anybody mails a sales message to anybody else, he is using direct mail advertising as distinguished from space, radio, or television advertising. The magazines themselves are heavy users of direct mail advertising to subscribers and advertisers. Sears, Roebuck, the Book-of-the-Month Club, the National Association of Manufacturers, etc., constantly use direct mail.

The term "direct mail" includes "mail order," but the latter term is more restricted and indicates that the reader sends in his order and payment by mail. (See MAIL ORDER for a discussion of this important phase of direct mail work.)

Most of this book is really about direct mail advertising, since there are separate entries about each of the tools of direct mail. (See LETTERS; HOUSE ORGANS; CIRCULARS; ENVELOPES; BLOTTERS;

CALENDARS; POST CARDS; NOVELTY PRINTING, etc.) There are many additional entries on the techniques for producing and using such direct mail materials. (See MAIL ORDER; MAILING LISTS; COPY WRITING; DUPLICATING METHODS; ADDRESSING; Appendix 4, Postal Information; etc.)

A few of the many jobs that direct mail advertising can do are as follows:

Get consumer orders direct by mail
Get dealer orders direct by mail
Get inquiries for salesmen to follow up
Pave the way for salesmen
Presell the prospect
Keep customers sold between salesmen's visits
Maintain member interest in an organization
Boost the morale and know-how of employees
Direct the activities of a member or sales organization
Bring customers into a store
Reactivate old customers
Collect accounts
Secure names of additional prospects for the mailing list

As compared to space advertising, direct mail costs a little more per reader impression. However, with targeted direct mail aimed at well-chosen lists there need be no waste circulation, and there is an opportunity to tell the whole sales story, without competition, not just a part of it.

Success in a direct mail campaign requires clearly conceived objectives, careful planning, and skillful use of the tools and techniques of the trade. Four important ingredients of a good campaign follow:

1. A good mailing list, consisting of genuine prospects, and nothing but genuine prospects.

2. A message presented in such a way as to be of genuine interest to the recipient.

3. Arrangements to make it as easy as possible for the prospect to take the desired action before he forgets or loses interest.

4. Economy and effectiveness in the use of printing, paper, envelopes, art work, postal regulations, etc.

The lessons of mail-order experience are worth studying (see MAIL ORDER) even if the campaign is not intended to bring in orders by mail.

Anyone who expects to engage in much direct mail work would do well to join the Direct Mail Advertising Association, 381 Fourth Ave., New York 16 (dues $48 with a special $16 rate for educational organizations). Membership in DMAA includes a subscription to the *Reporter of Direct Mail Advertising,* a trade journal.

There are many good books on direct mail advertising. Some of the best are listed and described in Appendix 2, Bibliography.

**displays**  See also POSTERS; SILK SCREEN; DIE CUTTING; MOUNTING AND FINISHING; SIGNS; TRANSPORTATION ADVERTISING.

If you need displays of any kind in quantity you'll get much help from a book entitled "Point-of-purchase Cardboard Displays" by Victor Strauss, Presentation Press (Box 3, Planetarium Station, New York 24, $15). There is also a trade paper devoted to the subject entitled *Spot,* published at 404 Fourth Ave., N.Y.

Victor Strauss' book will even interest those who need only one display of a kind, although it is aimed at the sales managers, artists, and printers who have to produce several hundred at a clip.

A printed display is basically a printed poster (printed by any method) plus additional processing, including mounting, easeling, creasing, die cutting, animating, etc. There are a number of firms that specialize in creating and producing displays of all kinds. A good way to get the name of one, apart from looking in the Classified Telephone Directory, is to keep an eye peeled for displays similar to your needs, and ask who made them. This applies whether you are looking at mass-produced cardboard displays, or at convention or window displays.

One warning: elaborate convention displays have a way of becoming white elephants after their first use. They are difficult to crate, ship, uncrate, and set up; and they soon begin to look frayed at the edges. Sometimes the money would be better spent on 100 printed displays.

Animation is being used more and more in cardboard displays, and there are now motion devices costing (in quantity) under a dollar that will operate for a month on a single flashlight battery cell. Two sources for motion devices are Hanks Craft of Reedsburg, Wis., with sales offices at 525 Lexington Ave., N.Y., and Haft and Sons, 95 Kent Ave., Brooklyn, N.Y.

**display type** See "Display Faces" beginning on page 362 in Appendix 1, Type Faces.

**distribution** See also the Introduction to this book; CAMPAIGN PLANNING; LETTERS; ADDRESSING; DIRECT MAIL; MAIL ORDER; SHIPPING; Appendix 4, Postal Information.

Each copy of a printed or duplicated piece of literature must be in the hands of a likely reader before those responsible can regard their work as completed.

No matter how well the editor, writer, designer, and printer do their jobs, their work goes for naught if the intended readers never see it. Distribution should never be an afterthought. It must be part of the original planning. The basic design of the material and the editorial approach must take into account the people who are to read the message and the conditions under which it will pass into their hands.

Furthermore, because effective distribution is very likely to cost more than the material itself, this must be allowed for in the budget.

How will the reader receive the material? Will the postman slip it under his door or lay it on his desk? Will he find it on his chair at a meeting? If so, will he sit on it or put it in his pocket? Will it be handed to him on a street corner? Will he pick it up on a store counter or newsstand?

Unless distribution is planned and supervised from the point of origin, there is an excellent chance that any bulk shipment leaving the office will never be unwrapped and distributed to individual readers by even the best-intentioned recipients. Distribution involves a lot of work. It costs at least 1½ cent per item if carried by the postman, and usually at least ½ cent per item if done by boy from door to door. It can easily be slighted or overlooked by people whose major concern is something else.

Organizations may be both the best and the worst agents for the distribution of materials. They are the best because people tend to trust material received through an organization that they have taken the trouble to join. They may be the worst because, unless they distribute a lot of material, they may promise to distribute and then fall down on the job for lack of experience.

It is, of course, easier to distribute free material than that which the reader must pay for. It is fair to assume that a person is more likely to read something that he paid to get, than something handed him free. For this reason, it is sometimes better to make a small charge for material than to give it away. Certainly, dealers and organizations are far less likely to waste bulk shipments that they have paid for than material that cost them nothing.

Another way to attack the same problem is to mark an item "5 cents" or "10 cents" even though it is given away free, so as to increase its value in the eyes of recipients.

Making a charge for materials will, of course, cut down the number distributed and may be undesirable for this reason. When a man writes in for something, he proves by this fact alone that he is interested.

Selling printed material is sometimes harder than it looks. However, it can be done, and the usual channels can be analyzed in terms of pamphlets, newsstand one-shots, bookstore items, mail-order items, and periodicals.

*Pamphlets.* Very few pamphlet series are self-supporting. Usually it costs far more to tell a man about a pamphlet than could be charged for it. Pamphlets must really be sold in bulk if they are to pay for themselves—perhaps to an organization which in effect will do the retail "selling" without charge, or perhaps to an individual who is buying in quantity to give out himself or who is buying assorted titles or subscribing to a series.

*One-shots.* Pamphlets or booklets that find their way to the newsstands are known in the trade as "one-shots." They are handled as if they were the first issue of a magazine, although no second issue was planned. If a one-shot promises to be a really fast-selling piece of merchandise, the American News Company (131 Varick St., N.Y.) may take it on for distribution through its 300 branches, or it may reach the "independent" local wholesalers through one of the independent national distributors or direct.

Their proposition may be somewhat as follows: "Give us, say, 250,000 copies of your pamphlet. We will place them with our wholesalers in the most promising cities and areas throughout the country. They will place them on their newsstands. We will pay you half the retail price for those which sell. Any we cannot sell we will return to you, billing you for the transportation

charges, or we will instruct the dealers to destroy unsold copies and return only the cover."

One-shots are great risks for a publisher. It is almost essential that he be able to make ends meet even if half are returned unsold. A one-shot is in competition for the reader's money with the best-known magazines in the world. It must sell itself on sight or lose out. A title as self-explanatory as "Your Income Tax—How to Keep It Down" is almost essential.

*Bookstore items.* There are only a few hundred real bookstores in the United States. On the whole they do not like to bother with low-priced items. They get a minimum discount of 40 per cent from list price, and prefer to buy speculative items on a consignment basis (to be paid for, when and if sold). It is difficult to get them to stock any item without sending a salesman to show it to them and take their order. In the case of an item that bookstores and libraries will want to order from time to time, it may be desirable to consign a supply to the major book wholesalers: the Baker & Taylor Company, 1429 North Broad St., Hillside, N.J., the American News Company, 131 Varick St., N.Y., the A. C. McClurg Company, 333 E. Ontario St., Chicago, and A. C. Vroman, Inc., 383 S. Pasadena Ave., Pasadena 2, Calif.

In general, the way to reach the bookstore market is to arrange for publication of the material through one of the regular book publishers. This is possible even if, or perhaps especially if, the authors or sponsors of the material want to order a sizable number for their own use.

*Mail-order items.* See MAIL ORDER.

*Periodicals.* The special advantage of issuing material in periodical form is that the publisher is selling a $5 or a $10 unit, not just a 25-cent item. He can thus afford to pay the relatively high cost of persuading a prospect to subscribe. A secondary advantage is the fact that periodicals may qualify for the very cheap second-class mailing privileges. (See Appendix 4, Postal Information.)

Where the publisher of a 25-cent pamphlet can spend at most 12½ cents to get one reader, the publisher of a 25-cent magazine may be able to spend up to $10 or more to get one subscriber. The economics of the operation may be illustrated by the following figures:

| | Revenue | Expense |
|---|---|---|
| Subscription | $ 2.50 | |
| Advertising | 12.50 | |
| Printing and mailing | ...... | $3.50 |
| Editorial and overhead | ...... | 4.00 |
| Total | $15.00 | $7.50 |

This allows up to $7.50 to get the subscription, but this is not the whole picture. The average new subscriber may keep his subscription 3 years and thus be worth three times $7.50.

Newsstand sales can also be profitable. Dealers get a discount of 20 per cent from wholesalers, who, of course, get more. However, since newsstand sales vary from month to month and the publisher must accept a loss on any unsold copies, publishers prefer to sell to subscribers rather than on the stands.

**distribution of type**   Type that has been set by hand has to be distributed after use if it is to be used again, *i.e.,* the pieces of type are put back in the compartmented case from which they came.

**Ditto**   See SPIRIT DUPLICATOR.

**dodgers**   See CIRCULARS.

**Doubletone paper**   See SHADING TINTS.

**drawing techniques**   In planning art work for publication, the editor and artist must decide on the drawing technique to be used. They may be influenced by such different factors as (1) the subject to be treated, (2) the editorial effect to be obtained, (3) the method of reproduction to be used, (4) the requirements of the layout, *e.g.,* heavy lines and blacks for a bold effect or delicate lines and faint shadows for a light effect, (5) the special talents of the available artists, and (6) the art work already at hand.

For purposes of comparison 10 of the major drawing techniques are illustrated (pages 84 to 85) along with a photograph, which is probably the most widely used of all illustration techniques.

The steps in reproducing art work vary with the drawing technique used and the printing process.

In letterpress printing a plate must be made for any photograph or drawing. (See LETTERPRESS.) The five illustrated on page 84—pen and ink, brush drawing, lithographic crayon on Ross board, scratchboard, and line drawing with added shading—may be reproduced by means of a line cut (see LINE CUT) since every element is either black or white with no grays. (Areas that seem gray are really made up of fine black dots or lines.)

The six on page 85—line and wash, wash, poster technique, airbrush, and photograph—require a halftone, which can reproduce grays by mechanically converting them into black dots. Line cuts are often cheaper than halftones but not always. (For comparative costs see the table under LINE CUTS.)

In mimeograph, only the first five drawing techniques can be used and then only by means of tracing with a stylus on a regular stencil or by a photochemical stencil. (See MIMEOGRAPH and STENAFAX.)

All can be reproduced by photo off-set, gravure, photogelatin, or even silk screen. (See OFFSET; GRAVURE; PHOTO-GELATIN; SILK SCREEN.) Usually the extra cost of reproducing an illustration in these other processes is less than the cost in letterpress, since a plate must be made in any case and it is very little more trouble to put an illustration on the plate than to put type on it.

Sometimes the nature of the art work determines the printing process to be used. Sometimes the printing process determines the nature of the art work.

Line drawings print well in any process on any kind of paper, except that unusually fine lines print best on a relatively smooth paper. It is desirable to match drawings and type as regards weight of line. Bold drawings do not always look well next to delicate type, and vice versa.

Photographs reproduce best in letterpress (but coated or calendered paper must be used), gravure, photogelatin, or Optak. Offset reproduction of photographs tends to be of lower quality although the best offset work can be very good. (See LETTERPRESS; OFFSET; OPTAK.)

Offset is perhaps the best process for reproducing wash drawings and pencil, crayon, or charcoal sketches.

Glossy paper can be used in any process, but is essential only in letterpress and then only for the reproduction of fine-screen halftones. If shiny paper is considered undesirable, then the other processes have a double advantage over letterpress: (1) they can use a dull paper for the finest halftones and (2) this paper can cost less. (Fine-quality halftone work can also be done on a rather expensive *dull-*coated paper.)

The drawing techniques themselves require special materials in order to achieve their distinctive features.

*A pen-and-ink line drawing* is done on smooth white paper with a pen and India ink. Every line is either white or black. There are no grays.

*A brush-and-ink drawing* is done on smooth paper with a brush saturated in India ink. Again there are no grays. *A dry-brush drawing* is done with a brush dipped in India ink, but used on the drawing only after there is so little ink left in the brush that it has to be rubbed onto the paper rather than flowed on. Because the ink adheres only to the high spots of rough paper, effects of gray can be achieved.

*The stipple-board (or coquille board) drawing*—litho crayon on Ross board— is done with crayon or ink on special stipple board which has hundreds of tiny raised dots. A light touch coats only the peaks of these dots with pigment, giving a halftone effect. One well-known stipple board is made by the Charles J. Ross Company of Philadelphia. Ross boards may combine the stipple and the scratchboard features (see below) but always have the latter.

*The scratchboard drawing* is done with India ink on a special drawing board that has a thick surface coat of white clay. The artist need not draw laboriously around white highlights. He boldly covers an entire area with India ink and later restores certain areas to whiteness by scratching off the ink and the top layer of clay coating. (See SCRATCHBOARD.) Stippled scratchboard drawings can be made on board that combines the features of both stipple board and scratchboard.

A woodcut style is sometimes carried out in wood or linoleum (see BLOCK PRINTING), but is often imitated in India ink.

*The line drawing with added shading* may be the work of the artist alone or it may be a collaboration between artist and engraver. If instructed to do so, the engraver may "lay a Ben Day" (see SHADING TINTS) on the plate when he makes a line cut of a line drawing, meaning that he will add any desired kind of shading to those areas which

## DRAWING TECHNIQUES

The most used drawing techniques are here shown applied to a single object, a Ronson table-model cigarette lighter. All the examples were prepared by I. N. Steinberg's staff, York Studios, 57 W. 69 St., N.Y. 23. The choice of technique is determined by the effect desired, the method of printing, and the kind of paper to be used. The drawings on this page are considered line drawings. Those opposite must be reproduced by the halftone process. The method of reproduction used here—letterpress on machine-finished paper—does not do full justice to the halftone renderings, which would show to better advantage in a finer screen on coated paper, or in gravure, photogelatin, etc. Wash drawings do especially well in offset.

Pen-and-ink line drawing.

Brush drawing.

Lithographic crayon on Ross board.

Scratchboard drawing.

Line drawing with added shading.

Line and wash drawing.

Wash drawing.

Poster technique.

Airbrush rendering from photograph.

Unretouched photograph.

Retouched photograph.

are entirely white on the original drawing but which the artist indicates should be shaded in the printed version.

There is an increasing tendency among artists to lay their own shading tints right on the art work, thus avoiding engravers' charges for tint laying and seeing in advance what the finished product will look like. This may be done by applying an adhesive shading film to parts of the art work that are to have the effect of gray. A similar effect is obtained by making the drawing on special Craftint paper printed with a pattern which is invisible until the artist "develops" it by applying a colorless liquid developer to the areas to be shaded. (See SHADING TINTS.)

Note that stipple board and scratchboard may give an effect similar to that of shading films and are sometimes listed with the shading tints.

*A pencil or crayon drawing* on smooth paper (not shown) is a drawing made up of gray lines, not the black lines of India ink, or the black and white of soft black pencil on rough stipple board. Hence, a pencil drawing must be handled as halftone work, not as line work.

*A wash drawing* is done with a brush and water-color paint, "washing" on the various grays between all black and solid white.

*In the so-called "poster technique,"* opaque tempera (show-card color) is used. When the drawing is to be reproduced in black and white, the artist usually works with a series of graded, ready-mixed grays ranging in tone from white to black. Being opaque, the shades usually remain distinct from each other, though an effect of blending can be achieved by means of fine brush work.

*Airbrush drawings* are made with an airbrush, with which very delicate, soft effects can be achieved. (See AIRBRUSH.)

*Photographs* really have no lines, no solid blacks and whites; everything is a blend of tones. They must be reproduced by the halftone process.

Other illustration techniques are described under: BOURGES COLOR SYSTEM; TONE-LINE PROCESS.

**drop folio**   See FOLIO.

**drop-out halftone**   See HIGHLIGHT HALFTONE.

**dry brush**   See DRAWING TECHNIQUES.

**dry mounting**   See also MOUNTING AND FINISHING.

The preferred method of mounting photographs. By this method, photographs can be affixed to a cardboard backing quickly, permanently, and without wrinkles, bubbles, or stains. Dry mounting is somewhat more expensive than paste mounting. Given the right equipment, it is easier, cleaner, and quicker.

In the dry-mounting process, a piece of specially processed dry-mounting tissue paper is cut to the size of the photograph and placed between the photograph and the backing. The photograph is then pressed down with a medium hot electric iron. The coating on the mounting tissue melts slightly and binds the photo to the backing.

**dry offset**   Letterpress printing in which the type and plates print on a rubber roller which in turn "offsets" the image onto the paper.

**dummy**   See also LAYOUT; PASTE-UP DUMMY; DESIGN.

A page-by-page layout for a pamphlet, magazine, or book. Sometimes a dummy is sent to the printer along with the manuscript. On other work, especially magazine work, the printer may not receive a dummy until after he has supplied galley proofs of the text. A dummy that has been made up from galley proofs is called a "paste-up dummy" or a "paste-up." (See PASTE-UP DUMMY.)

To a book salesman, a dummy is a prepublication imitation of a book, showing jacket, binding, table of contents, and perhaps a sample chapter.

Printers, paper merchants, and binders are usually glad to make up blank, bound dummies for the use of the layout man. However, a bound dummy is not so easy to work with as separate pages, and the actual paper to be used may be unsuitable for the erasing that layout paper must survive.

Magazine printers often supply layout and dummy paper already ruled with the margins and columns used by that magazine.

To make a dummy, get a pad of layout paper (ordinary white paper, but tough enough to take erasures). It should be as large as two facing pages of the publication. For a publication 8½ by 11, the layout paper should be big enough to hold the double-spread area, 17 by 11.

Mark off the page sizes, the margin sizes, the column sizes, etc., for, say, pages 2 and 3. If these same proportions apply to other spreads as well, transfer these markings to as many other sheets of layout paper as necessary. Pinpricks through the line intersections of pages 2 and 3 to the sheets intended for pages 4 and 5, 6 and 7, etc., will give a good guide for drawing the lines on those pages.

Use one side of the paper only. Nothing is more maddening than to decide to swap page 4 for page 12 only to discover that page 4 is on the back of page 3, and must be re-done in the new location. When facing pages of a dummy have been prepared on one side of the layout paper, it is a simple matter to cut them apart when it is necessary to join them to new partners. Scotch tape makes this joining easy.

Before a dummy is sent to the printer, certain information must be added about margin widths, folio numbers, etc. It is not necessary to repeat this information from page to page. If the margins, subheads, captions, etc., are to be the same throughout, it is enough to tell the printer how to handle them on the first text page, or the first time they occur.

**duograph**  See DUOTONE.

**duotone**  Black-and-white photographs are sometimes reproduced in two colors for added depth and beauty. This is called the "duotone" or "duograph" process. Two halftone cuts are made from the same original. One is run in blue, green, tan, or some other color. The other is printed in black right over the first. The result is to extend the range of the photograph to include not merely all the grays, but also all the tints, tones, and shades of the added color.

Somewhat the same effect may also be achieved with only one impression through the use of duotone ink. This is a special ink designed to bleed into the paper (the way a pen stroke on a blotter has fuzzy edges). The ink is and remains dark where laid on the paper; but as it bleeds away from these areas, it turns much lighter and exhibits an undertone of a different color. Photographs reproduce well in duotone ink. However, duotone ink is not so satisfactory for printing a page combining both photographs and type since the tendency of the ink to bleed or fade off has an undesirable blurred effect on the type.

**duplex paper**  See COLORED PAPER.

**duplicate plates**  It is often desirable to make duplicate printing plates of pages of type and/or cuts. The usual reasons are as follows:

1. When the job is to be run 2-up, 3-up, etc., i.e., two or three copies side by side on one sheet, duplicate plates provide an inexpensive method of exact duplication.

2. They will insure sharpness and

clarity in a long run where type will wear excessively.

3. They insure against the costly delays that would result if the original and only type and cuts were damaged during the press run.

4. They permit exact duplication of the same advertisement in several different publications simultaneously.

The cheapest duplicate plates are stereotypes. The finest duplicate plates are electros. (See STEREOTYPE and ELECTRO.) New kinds of duplicate plates are coming into use including plastic plates and rubber plates. (See PLASTIC PLATES and RUBBER PLATES.) They are made on the stereo principle, but wear longer and are less subject to stretching or shrinking in the making. One of their advantages is low mailing weight.

Magnesium plates are not strictly duplicate plates since they are not molded; each is an original plate made in the same way that zinc and copper cuts are made. However, they are often used where duplicate plates might otherwise be used and are becoming increasingly important. (See MAGNESIUM PLATES.)

**duplicating methods** Office machinery used for duplicating letters, forms, price lists, etc., is usually called "duplicating machinery" and is not designated by the name of "printing," although in some cases the same processes are used. (See STENCIL; MIMEOGRAPH; HECTOGRAPH; MULTIGRAPH; OFFSET; MULTILITH; PHOTOCOPYING; WHITEPRINT; PHOTOSTAT.)

For further information about any process, look under that process. (See also LETTERS and the chart "How to Choose the Right Printing Process" inside the covers of this book.)

Many offices will want to select a stencil duplicator as their first purchase —as good a one as they can afford. There are several brands—Mimeograph, Speed-o-print, etc. Even shops having several kinds of duplicators tend to

find that the mimeograph (the word is here used to describe the process, not the brand of machine) is the one that carries the load since it can produce from 25 to 2,500 copies cheaply, quickly, and, in the hands of a good operator, with excellent appearance and legibility.

Where quantities are likely to be small—several hundred at most—the spirit duplicator may, however, be cheaper to operate and has certain advantages of its own. Where the information to be duplicated is compact and may have to be run off at repeated intervals, Addressograph or Elliott machines may be considered. (See ADDRESSOGRAPH and ELLIOTT ADDRESSING.)

All methods handle typewritten material, line drawings, and hand lettering. However, only offset and photocopying handle photos and wash drawings.

For 1 to 10 copies, same size, of line work (no photos), see WHITEPRINTS, for which purpose, however, the original must be on one side only of translucent paper. This process will handle photos but only from specially made positive transparencies. (See also CARBON COPIES.)

For 1 to 10 copies, enlarged, reduced, or same size, of line or halftone work, see PHOTOSTAT. For highest quality reproduction of photos, however, see PHOTOGRAPHY.

For 10 to 400 copies of work that can be typed, written, or drawn in special ink on special paper, see HECTOGRAPH and SPIRIT DUPLICATOR. Work can be done in several colors simultaneously.

For 25 to 2,500 copies of work that can be typed, drawn, or traced on a stencil, see MIMEOGRAPH. Stencils can also be prepared photographically, but such work is better done on a MULTILITH if there is much of it.

For 25 to 5,000 or more copies of typewritten material that must closely resemble actual typing, see MULTIGRAPH. Drawings can be handled on the Multigraph, but special plates must be made. The Multigraph, properly equipped, can also do regular letterpress printing of price lists, menus, post cards, letterheads, etc.

For 100 to 10,000 copies of anything which can be typed or drawn, see MULTILITH.

For 100 to 10,000 or even 50,000 copies of anything that must be reproduced photographically including type, typing, lettering, line drawings, and small photographs, see MULTILITH. Multilith reproduction of photos tends, however, to be inferior to regular printing processes including offset work on larger presses.

The Multilith is now crowding the mimeograph and even the hectograph, with its introduction of several models at less than $1,000. However, it is not to be recommended as a substitute for the other processes unless there is work enough to keep it and a skilled operator busy continuously.

**Dupligraph** A machine similar in principle to the Multigraph and now owned by the same company. (See MULTIGRAPH.) Unlike the Multigraph, it is a flat-bed process using embossed metal plates instead of movable type.

The special feature of this machine is its ability to print a form letter and strike in a form address and salutation simultaneously, through the same inked ribbon, thus guaranteeing a well-matched fill-in.

The Dupligraph is no longer being made, and only secondhand models are obtainable.

**Duplimat** See PHOTOCOPYING.

# E | e

**easeling**  The work of attaching easels to the back of posters and displays is done by firms specializing in mount-

Easel glued to back of poster.

ing and finishing. (See MOUNTING AND FINISHING.)

**edge index**  For a discussion of thumb-indexing, step-indexing, and tabbing, see INDEXING. Edge-indexing is an inexpensive alternate to the above which also has the merit of adding nothing to the over-all time required for a binding job. To use a typical edge-indexed directory, bend the pages until they fan out and look for tiny black

marks resulting from printed rules that run right to the edge of the paper. If you want the section on, say, "Transportation" look down the right edge of the first right-hand page for this heading, and look for a black mark just opposite this heading. Open at that place.

The basic method is an old one and can be used by anyone, but an improvement on it—the idea of using double and single rules alternately to increase the number that can be distinguished without confusion—has been patented by Machol Edge Index, Inc., 25 Fifth Ave., New York 3, which will supply examples and useful information about the method on request.

**Edison Margin Justifier**  See MARGIN-ATOR.

**editing**  See EDITORIAL WORK; EDITORIAL PLANNING; COPY WRITING; COPY EDITING; COPY PREPARATION.

**edition**  Some books are published in several editions, *e.g.*, a de luxe edition, a regular edition, a book-club edition, a paper-covered edition, a cheap reprint edition, etc.

In a slightly different sense, a book may have a first edition, a second (revised) edition, etc.

Books are advertised as having reached their "third impression," "7th large printing," etc., when they have merely been reprinted the stated number of times without change. They are advertised as having come out in a new edition when revisions have been made, new matter has been added, or format or price has been changed.

**editorial planning**  See also EDITORIAL WORK; COPY WRITING; COPY PREPARATION.

Before any publication goes to the printer—in fact, before it is written—there should be time for editorial planning. This means working out the details of the publication itself; it also means planning the publication as an integral part of the over-all program or campaign. Without such planning, any publication, whether it is a circular, a periodical, or merely a covering letter, may miss fire or fall short of its potential.

Who participates in this planning will depend upon the nature of the organization and the publication. Major projects, such as a special brochure or series of leaflets, will probably require an official O.K. from on high—the boss, the board of directors, the policy committee, or whoever holds the purse strings. The best assurance of quick approval at the finish is to have these people in on the planning from the start. Besides, they should have constructive suggestions and ideas worth the asking.

Once the main theme is agreed upon and the potential audience is staked out, certain decisions must be reached by the editor. The following check list may help to cover the points of prepublication planning that require decision. (Note that many of these decisions are interdependent and cannot be made in the order named.)

1. *Space allocation.* Shall it be a four- or six-page leaflet? A 20-page pamphlet or a 24-page one, which mails for a lower postal rate? (See Appendix 4, Postal Information.) Shall it be a one-page letter with reply questionnaire on the bottom or a letter with separate questionnaire enclosed? Shall it be a one-page magazine article without pictures or a two-page article with pictures?

2. *Kind of illustration, if any.* Will illustrations bear the burden of the story? Or will they be attention getters for the copy? What kind of illustration should be used—photograph, cartoon, pictograph, or line drawing?

3. *Use of color, if any.* How can color be used to improve the publication? What is the added cost for each added color? Is there a cheaper way to dress up a publication? (See COLOR for suggestions.) What can be done with black-and-white printing to give variety to a publication? (See SHADING TINTS; DESIGN; LAYOUT.)

4. *Printing process.* What printing processes are within budgetary limits? Which is the best for this particular job? Consider cost, possibility of illustration and color, number of copies to be run, etc. (See also the charts inside the covers of this book.)

5. *The copy writer.* Shall he be a member of the staff? Or shall the publication be written by, or ghost-written for, a "big name" from outside, whose authority will carry weight? If an outsider, what indoctrination should he have as to general policy and to this particular publication in relation to the over-all program? How much can he be paid? Or is this to be his contribution?

6. *The artist.* What style of art work is most appropriate to the subject and the audience? (Most people prefer realistic cartoons to stylized ones.) How many pieces of art work will be needed? Of what size and shape? What should each drawing show? What reference

material should the artist have in order to draw the picture accurately? (See ART WORK.) How much will the budget allow for each piece of art work? What artist should do the job? (See ARTISTS.)

7. *The photographs.* Are the pictures to be used chiefly as attention getters? Or must they be on-the-spot news pictures? What good photographs are on hand? What others are available? (See PHOTO AGENCIES.) What photographs will have to be taken? Should they be horizontal or vertical? Who and what should be in the picture? (In specially staged pictures every detail should be worked out as to background and properties, grouping of people, etc.) Are pictures planned to supplement the copy instead of duplicating it?

8. *Distribution.* Where is the publication to go? To what kind of reader audience? Could the same piece be used effectively for other mailing lists too? How is it to be shipped—as a self-mailer, as an enclosure, or as a separate piece in envelope or wrapper? What are the comparative costs of these? (See DISTRIBUTION.)

Testing of copy is very desirable at some stage of the development of a publication. The director of one of the most scientific of the nation-wide public-opinion polls reports that he tries out the first draft of his questions on a sample group. Then, when the interviews are studied, some causes for misunderstandings always come to light and suggest that certain questions be rewritten and others added.

The same technique will help almost any piece of copy. Try it out on other staff members. Send it out to a selected list. (See MAIL ORDER.) Better still, talk it over with people who are typical of those whom the publication is to reach.

Almost any publication brings bigger dividends if it is planned in relation to other publications and as part of an over-all campaign or long-range program. (For suggestions see CAMPAIGN PLANNING.)

Good pointers for the editorial planning of a magazine are given in the books listed in the Bibliography.

**editorial work** This general term includes a multitude of activities, which are dealt with in this book under the following headings:

*Editorial planning:* laying down general policy; passing upon manuscripts; budgeting money, space, and staff effort; planning illustrations; etc.

*Copy writing:* writing copy, headlines, captions.

*Copy editing:* rewriting, revising, and polishing.

*Copy preparation:* putting accepted editorial material in shape for the printer by making it accurate as to facts, grammatical, consistent as to style, and correct in spelling and punctuation, and by marking it for type.

*Proofreading:* checking and correcting proofs.

*Dummying:* indicating which material is to go on which pages and in what arrangement.

*Illustrations:* how to select, procure, and use them.

In a large publishing operation, the staff may include specialists in each type of editorial activity. In a small operation, the person in charge can (1) be a jack-of-all-editorial-trades; (2) deal with a printer equipped to offer editorial services (whose prices, at least in the long run, will reflect the extra service rendered); or (3) hire free-lance editorial assistance. In "The Literary Market Place" (see Appendix 2, Bibliography) a number of free-lance editors are listed with addresses, telephone numbers, and areas of specialization.

An authoritative reference book invaluable in editorial work is the University of Chicago "Manual of Style" listed in Appendix 2.

**E.F.** Abbreviation for English finish.

**eggshell** See ANTIQUE.

**Egyptian** A family of type styles more frequently called "square serif." For examples, see Appendix 1, Type Faces.

**Ektachrome, Ektacolor** Color films. (See COLOR PHOTOGRAPHY.)

**electric typewriter** In ordinary typewriters the pressure of the typist's finger on a key makes the type bar strike. In an electric typewriter the key, whether hit hard or gently, merely acts as a trigger; energy from a motor-driven roller makes the type bar strike with predetermined force.

Electric typewriters make better mimeograph stencils, and can make as many as 20 legible carbon copies. They enable a typist with an uneven touch to turn out completely even and uniform work. Since the impression can be made heavy or light, "fill-in" work can be matched to form letters more easily.

The standard IBM electric typewriter with a 12-in. carriage costs about $400. Special models for handling special forms are also available. Underwood, Royal, and Remington also make electric typewriters.

The IBM electric "executive" typewriter offers all the features of the standard model plus an arrangement that allows wide letters more space than thin ones. Fourteen faces simulating book types are available. With a 12-in. carriage this machine costs about $700. (See illustration under TYPEWRITER; also VARITYPER.)

**electro, electrotype** See also CUT; STEREOTYPE; DUPLICATE PLATES.

An electrotype, usually abbreviated to electro, is a metal duplicate of a page of type and/or cuts. It is possible to print from it exactly as if the original type and cuts were being used.

Electros are used on long runs because they wear longer than type. Their use also protects expensive cuts. If an electro is damaged on the press,

another can easily be made. If an original cut is damaged, replacing it requires going back to the art work, takes longer, and costs more.

Electros are also used where an ad must be supplied to several magazines at the same time, or where a job is to be printed 2-up, 3-up, etc., to obviate the need for duplicating the typesetting and engraving.

A mounted electro made from a combination line and halftone cut.

There are several kinds of electros. In approximate order of increasing price and quality these are

Wax-mold electros
Tenaplate-mold electros
Vinylite-mold electros
Lead-mold electros

For exceptionally long runs, electros can be nickel-faced at extra cost. This is the rule in the case of lead-mold electros. (A so-called "steel-faced" electro is really faced with nickel.)

Electro prices vary somewhat from city to city. An 8- by 10-in. mounted wax-mold electro from a form containing halftones costs about $11. A mounted lead-mold electro costs about $23. These electros are used for the finest halftone work. They should be made only from unmounted original copper halftones. The high pressure used would crush type or mounted cuts. Since costs change frequently, it is well to consult your printer for current prices.

A comparison of the various methods of making duplicate printing plates is given under DUPLICATE PLATES.

The method of making a wax-mold electro is as follows. (Tenaplate, Vinylite, and lead-mold electros are made in much the same way, save that other materials are used instead of wax.)

The type and/or cuts to be duplicated are locked up "for foundry." This means that they are locked in a chase as if for printing, but with one major difference: they are surrounded with type-high "bearers" to prevent damage to the edges of the form. (See FOUNDRY PROOFS.) The compositor or printer does this and then ships the form to the electrotyper.

The electrotyper cleans the type, levels it, dusts it with graphite, lays a sheet of wax over it, and forces the wax down into the form under pressure. The wax is thus molded to an exact likeness of the type and cuts. The wax thus takes the shape of the type and cuts and constitutes a mold. Copper is then deposited electrolytically on this wax mold and is later backed with lead. If an electro is then to be used alongside type, it is mounted type-high. For some uses, however, it is left unmounted.

Minor corrections can be made in the wax. For example, rules can be joined at the corners even where they did not fit together perfectly when a proof was pulled from the type. However, there is a time charge for such work, and corrections in the wax also mean extra work for the finisher.

Color separation electros from a single original can be made, as when the border and several lines of type are to print in red and the rest in black. Curved electros can be made for use on rotary presses.

Elliott addressing machine.

**elite** See also TYPEWRITER.

Elite type is the smaller of the two common styles of typewriter type. It measures 12 letters and spaces to the inch instead of 10 as in pica style. (See PICA and samples under COPY FITTING.)

**Elliott addressing** See also ADDRESSING.

Elliott addressing machines operate on the stencil principle. A fiber frame, usually about 2 by 4½ in., holds a piece of stencil tissue which prints like a miniature mimeograph stencil.

These stencil address cards are guaranteed by the manufacturers for 10,000

A tray of Elliott addressing stencils, showing how an inverted card becomes an index card. The stencils also come in different colors for visual keying.

impressions. In the 2- by 4½-in. size, they cost about $20 a thousand. Although the cutting of the address cards can be done on any office typewriter, specially equipped typewriters are recommended. The manufacturers will put a three-line address, plus a one-line index, on their stencils for about $24

per thousand plus the cost of the stencils. Extra lines cost $3 per thousand.

Small organizations expecting to need no more than 500 address cards may obtain complete Elliott addressing equipment for less than $80.

A hand-fed office machine costs $165. A similar model with automatic feed

Elliott address stencils can be cut on any typewriter and can be keyed by means of punch marks on the frame.

costs $250. A model that can do addressing and also imprint messages on post cards costs $270.

Electrically operated models cost $475, $800, $1,900, and, for special uses, up to $18,000, and can be supplied for such specialized uses as billing, making up payrolls, dating, and numbering. Some firms, including the Literary Guild and Montgomery Ward, maintain billing information right on Elliott address cards.

Elliott address cards can be "keyed" by punching small holes in the frame. Thus an Elliott machine with automatic address-selector attachment can be set to print only address cards with holes in certain positions, or to print all except cards with holes in certain positions. Some address cards have provisions for punching in 240 different positions.

For information, write the Elliott Addressing Machine Company in your city or in Cambridge, Mass.

Advantages claimed for the Elliott addressing method include lower initial costs, the fact that address cards can be prepared on the typewriter, lower cost of address cards, less filing space required, lighter file drawers ($\frac{1}{12}$ as much as for the same number of metal plates), perfect addressing even on stuffed envelopes of varying thickness because the address card is flexible, visible addressing (envelopes put in face up, not face down), less noise both in cutting address cards and in running them, faster addressing, more durable address cards, easier indexing since the indexing line can read DOE, J. R., although the plate reads Mr. J. R. Doe. (See ADDRESSOGRAPH for the special advantages of that process.)

In general, it can be said that users of both Elliott and Addressograph machines report highly satisfactory service. Both processes can produce work of excellent appearance. Both types of plate can give more service than they are usually called upon to give.

**Elrod** A machine that extrudes melted type metal in the form of leads and rules any desired width and of indefinite length.

**em** See TYPE MEASUREMENTS.

**Embosograf** A machine and a process for producing neatly lettered and brightly colored signs in small quantities.

Special type with sharp edges is used. The type is assembled and arranged as desired on a ruled setup chart. A piece of (say) blue "top paper" is placed color side down on the type. A piece of (say) yellow cardboard is placed face down over the top paper and type.

The whole assembly is now pushed under a pressure plate, which comes down and crushes the cardboard against the top paper and the type. The type assembly is now removed from under the pressure plate, and the cardboard is lifted off. Surplus blue top paper is peeled away, leaving neat blue letters against a yellow background. The letters have an embossed effect.

Any colors can be used. After the first impression, the type adheres to the setup chart which has a waxed surface and can be used for as many more impressions of the same sign as desired. It is as easy to make every sign in a different color as to use the same color scheme consistently.

Embosografed signs are used in retail stores, on office-building directories, on college campuses, etc. Complete equipment, including press and a selection of type, costs $215 for signs up to 4 by 10 in., $480 for signs up to 8 by 22 in., and $670 for signs up to 14 by 22 in. The equipment is made by the Embosograf Corporation of America, 38 W. 21 St., New York 10.

**embossing** Producing raised letters or designs on paper or other material. The work is done with matched dies, a relief die striking from beneath the paper into an intaglio or hollow die above the paper. (See RELIEF and INTAGLIO.)

One common example of embossing is the work done with a corporation seal; another, the stamp on a post-office envelope.

The expense of embossing lies primarily in the making of the dies, and in the careful press make-ready that is required. After that, the material to be embossed is run through the printing press in the same way as for ordinary printing. One printer who regularly handles embossing work on sheets up to 38 by 56 quotes prices ranging from $12 to $20 per thousand sheets of paper; somewhat more for cardboard.

Any colors to be used are put on first, in ink, by regular printing methods. Because of the accuracy and precision required in this type of work, it is recommended that those having had no previous experience with embossing, contact the embosser for advice on layout, gripper, and other requirements before printing.

A few firms doing embossing work

are John W. Crawford Co., 160 Varick St., New York 13; Stauder Engraving Co., 4130 Belmont Ave., Chicago.

**en** See TYPE MEASUREMENTS.

**end paper** The paper pasted to the inside of the cover of a book. It is part of the same piece that forms the first leaf of the book. (See illustration under BOOKBINDING.) It is usually of a somewhat stronger material than the text pages. It may be white or colored, printed or unprinted. (The end papers in this book carry a printed chart.) End papers are sometimes called "end sheets," "lining papers," or "paste-downs."

Printed end papers add attractiveness to a book. It is sometimes possible to "gang" them up on the same offset plate with the book jacket and thus get them printed in the jacket colors at little additional expense over the printing costs of the jacket.

**end sheet** See END PAPER.

**English finish** See also PAPER.

Paper that has been calendered to a smooth finish, but not to a shiny finish. English-finish paper will take 110-screen halftones satisfactorily. It is not coated. English finish is abbreviated E.F.

**engraver's proofs** After an engraver has made a line cut or halftone, he delivers it together with an engraver's proof of it. From this proof the customer determines whether the cut is acceptable. An engraver's proof says in effect, "Results of this quality can be obtained from this cut. If your printer comes up with poorer results, it is not the fault of the cut."

Unfortunately for the printer, engraver's proofs are usually pulled on the finest coated paper. If possible, the buyer of a cut should request that the engraver pull his proofs on the paper on which the job is actually to be printed.

It is always desirable to send engraver's proofs to the printer along with the cuts, so that the pressman may know what kind of results the cuts are expected to yield. This is essential as regards process color engravings, in which case not only the finished proof is sent but also "progressive proofs" showing the pressman how the job should look after each color has been added.

Engravers usually supply two proofs and charge extra if more are requested.

**engraving** See also CUT (in the sense that one orders "engravings" or "cuts" from a photoengraver).

To the layman, the word "engraving" may immediately call to mind the engraved calling card. This is a specialized example of the process of intaglio printing. (See INTAGLIO.)

Orders for engraved calling cards, wedding announcements, social stationery, etc., can be placed with most department stores and some jewelers. This method of printing is expensive compared to ordinary printing because a special plate must be made first and because the printing process itself is inherently slow. The resulting dull-black raised lettering can be very crisp and attractive.

There are two cheaper processes which have some of the characteristics of engraving. In the process called "thermography" a calling card is printed from type in the ordinary way and then, while still wet, is sprinkled with a special powder and heated. (See THERMOGRAPHY.) The result is raised lettering. Embossing is another method of producing raised lettering. In this case the paper is indented from its underside as much as it is raised on the upper side. (See EMBOSSING.)

For genuine engraving, look in the Classified Telephone Directory under "Engravers—Steel and Copper Plate," or try John B. Wiggins Co., 638 S. Federal St., Chicago; Ross-Cook Engraving Company, Inc., 307 W. 38 St., New York. For thermography, try Ahrendt, Inc., 333 Ave. of the Americas, New York 14.

**engrossing** The hand lettering done on diplomas and citations. It is done by artists who specialize in decorative lettering and illuminating. The words "calligrapher" and "engrosser" both mean someone skilled in penmanship. The word "engrossing" applies to the lettering; the word "illuminating" applies to any added decoration.

A good engrosser can turn out from 10 to 30 high-school diplomas an hour, in any desired style of lettering. The letters flow from his pen with amazing speed. Rates vary with the amount to be engrossed, the area to be covered, the style of letter desired, and the degree of perfection required.

Perhaps the best way to locate a near-by engrosser is to ask a local high school or college for the name of the man who does their diploma work. A few engrossers and illuminators are J. R. Rosen, 80 Boylston St., Boston; Ames & Rollinson, 50 Church St., New York 7; Harris Engrossing Studio, 53 W. Jackson Blvd., Chicago.

**enlarging** Three methods of enlarging are by camera lucida, pantograph, and photography. The first two are mechanical. (See CAMERA LUCIDA; PANTOGRAPH; PHOTOGRAPHY.)

A much-used application of the photographic principle for enlarging is, of course, the Photostat. (See PHOTOSTAT.)

The invention of photography has made possible and simple the faithful reproduction of any illustrative material in enlarged or reduced size. Everyone who has used a Brownie box camera is familiar with the process of making a reduced-size copy. To enlarge requires only a very big camera, or its equivalent, moved very close to the object to be copied.

The object to be copied can be illuminated from in front; or, if it is transparent like a photographic negative or a Kodachrome transparency, it can be illuminated from behind.

Photographic enlargements can be made in any size. The process is the same as if a lantern slide should be projected upon a big piece of sensitized paper instead of the usual screen with the paper then being developed and fixed.

Standard sizes for photographic paper are 4 by 5, 5 by 7, 8 by 10, 11 by 14, 14 by 20 in.

To make a very rough enlargement or reduction, artists frequently use a camera lucida.

**envelopes** It pays to buy standard-size envelopes and to order them well ahead of the need for them from an envelope mill or envelope jobber. Envelopes can be imprinted at very low rates by companies specializing in this work. Regular printers can supply and imprint envelopes but may have to charge for the use of presses, which are more costly than those necessary for envelope printing. Printers are also justified in charging more than minimum prices for rush work or work of unusually high quality.

It is particularly important to plan for and order envelopes at least as soon as the material to be mailed in them is planned. Many an otherwise well-planned mailing has been held up, either because standard envelopes were not ordered in time or because the job required a nonstandard envelope which took longer to make than expected. Low prices and overnight delivery do not go together on envelopes any more than on anything else.

Careful planning and stock control are necessary to keep envelopes on hand. A single exceptional mailing may

## ENVELOPES—THE MOST COMMON SIZES

Commercial
No. 6¼ (3½ × 6)

Official
No. 10 (4⅛ × 9½)

Baronial
No. 5½ (4⅜ × 5⅝)

Spot-of-gum postage saver
No. 6¾ (3⅝ × 6½)
No. 10 (4⅛ × 9½)

Two compartment
(6½ × 9½)

Booklet
No. 7 (6¼ × 9⅝)
No. 063 (6½ × 9½)
No. 090 (9 × 12)

clean out a supply intended to last for several months.

The No. 10 (4⅛ by 9½) and the No. 6¾ (3⅝ by 6½) envelopes are the most commonly used for letters. Those who use less common sizes usually do so expressly to make their communication stand out as distinctive in the addressee's pile of mail. (See illustration for other standard sizes.)

Large envelopes are sometimes purchased without printing, since an imprinted label can be affixed to them to carry an address. This makes for flexibility since the envelopes can never become obsolete and can be ordered well ahead. (Labels are more quickly procured and less costly to scrap.)

There are many specialized kinds of envelopes. Window envelopes have the advantage of making it unnecessary to fill in the recipient's name on the envelope as well as on the enclosure. Bills sent out in window envelopes cannot be inserted in the wrong envelope by mistake.

Business reply envelopes (see Appendix 4, Postal Information) have come to be a necessary enclosure in mail-order work.

Through the use of a special double envelope, a letter stamped with first-class postage can go out along with heavy enclosures on which only third-class postage is paid, although a 1955 change in postal regulations also makes it permissible to stamp "first-class message enclosed" on a package, and put the extra postage on the outside.

Many specialty envelopes are obtainable, some of which combine into a single piece a sales letter, an envelope, an order form with coin pocket, and

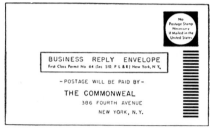

With the window style of this Combine-velope, the subscriber's name and address can be imprinted from a plate or stencil right on the order form, or it can be typed or written in.

When the reader tears off the right half of the Combine-velope (see below, left), he has this business reply envelope in which to return his subscription and remittance promptly.

When opened up, the Combine-velope shows the new or renewal subscription message on the left. On the right are the handy order form and the pocket side of the reply envelope. These features make it easy to subscribe and send remittance.

An order form or questionnaire form can be made to do double duty as a reply envelope, as shown above. No pocket is used in this case, since no remittance is expected. Instructions on how to fold and seal should be given the recipient.

a prepaid reply envelope. (See illustration.)

One firm that specializes in such mailing devices and will send a useful catalogue on request is the Direct Mail Envelope Company, 15 W. 20 St., New York 11. Many lettershops offer one or more such specialties.

Penny-saver envelopes (see PENNY-SAVER) are obtainable which seal like ordinary envelopes but have one unsealed flap. They can be mailed third-class. Some postage meters can seal and stamp envelopes twice as fast if the envelopes are made with the flaps on the opposite side from usual. Cata-logue envelopes are made on the penny-saver principle, and are then called "booklet" envelopes.

The U.S. Post Office sells envelopes at very low rates and will imprint them with return name and address. (See Appendix 4.) However, post-office envelopes require a considerable investment in postage (unstamped envelopes are not supplied); names are imprinted in only one standard style; and delivery of printed envelopes may take four to five weeks.

Note that envelopes are not actually required for all mailings. The Post Office permits almost anything that will not fall apart in transit to be sent as a self-mailer without envelope. (See SELF-MAILER.) Where self-mailers can be used, the saving on envelopes, handling, and perhaps postage may be considerable. Periodicals are frequently handled as self-mailers.

The classic example of the self-mailer is the post card. This is one of the great bargains of the postal service. It is first-class mail, it costs only 2 cents, and Uncle Sam throws in the paper stock, free. Where large quantities are to be imprinted, the Post Office will supply them in large sheets of various sizes so that they can be imprinted in one impression and cut apart later. (See Appendix 4.)

In designing the form in which a return address is to be imprinted on an envelope, it should be remembered that many envelope-imprinting machines do not carry enough ink to permit the use of reverse blocks; and some do not give sufficiently accurate results to permit halftones.

For the names of envelope supply houses, consult any city Classified Telephone Directory, under "Envelopes." For a useful "Handbook of Envelope Products and Purposes" write to the United States Envelope Company, Springfield 2, Mass.

**estimating costs**   See also SAVING MONEY.

A certain amount of price information is given throughout this book as part of the discussion of methods. It should be remembered, however, that an estimate on one job can never with certainty be applied to another job, no matter how similar. The authors do not present this price information to suggest that the reader need not pay more. He may have to pay more for entirely legitimate reasons. They feel, however, that he will want to know that rotogravure jobs usually start at $2,000 or so and that there is no use asking for bids in "roto" on a $100 job.

A printer's estimates vary according to (1) his equipment and its suitability to the job, (2) his desire to get the job, and (3) his standards of work and service.

All printing costs should be seen as the sum of two costs: fixed costs and running costs. The fixed costs—design, typesetting, art work, engravings, plates, press make-ready, and bindery make-ready—must be added to the price whether the edition is to be 1,000 or 1,000,000 copies. Thus, 1,000 copies of a job may cost $100 and 2,000 copies cost only $105. Fixed costs loom large on small runs but become a negligible factor in the unit costs of very long runs.

The cost of a great many jobs (neither very large nor very small) comes to about three to five times the cost of the paper. On long runs, this can be reduced to twice the cost of the paper. This rule of thumb will turn a printer's hair gray. He will at once begin to point out that everything depends on the number of colors, the length of the press run, the number of illustrations, the type of binding, etc.

Nevertheless, any job that seems likely to cost ten to twenty times the cost of the paper may well be studied to see whether the extra expense is really justified. It may or may not be.

A printer's estimate may be entirely justified, and the only way to reduce the ratio may be to redesign the job for another process, perhaps silk screen as against lithography, or mimeographing as against letterpress work.

A rough (very rough) way to predict the cost of a letterpress or offset job follows. (See also DUPLICATING METHODS.)

This method of rough estimating may be very misleading. It is not recommended to any printer. However, it may be helpful to customers whose plans are only in the formative stages. On 9 jobs out of 10, it will prove to be right within 50 per cent, one way or

## Typical Printing Charges * by Letterpress Printers

*Display composition,* any size, 50¢ per line, $10 per page †
*Linotype composition,* 6–14 pt., about $3 per 1,000 ems (or per 2,000 characters) plus $2 setting-up on machine (straight matter)
*Page make-up, proving, and press lockup,* about $3 per page or column
*Make-ready and presswork:*

| Size | Make-ready on press | Presswork, one side, per 1,000 |
|---|---|---|
| 9 x 12 | $ 5–$10 ‡ | $2.50–$3.00 |
| 17 x 22 | 8– 15 | 2.50– 3.25 |
| 19 x 25 | 12– 20 | 3.50– 4.00 |
| 25 x 38 | 20– 40 | 5.00– 7.00 |
| 35 x 45 | 35– 70 | 7.00– 9.00 |

*Folding,* about $2 per 1,000 signatures (any number of folds) with small paper sizes; $2.50 per 1,000 with large paper sizes; plus $3 to prepare machine
*Binding* (saddle-wire, including folding and trimming), per 1,000 (add $5 to prepare machines)

| Size | Self-cover | Added cover |
|---|---|---|
| 8 page, any size | $5 | $7 |
| 16 page, any size | 6 | 8 |
| 32 page, any size | 7 | 9 |
| Extra signatures, each | 4 | |

*Cutting paper,* 2¢ per pound

* Advertising typographers, whose charges must include the expense of supplying reproduction proofs, may charge considerably more.

† Prices vary from one region of the country to another, depending on local material, labor costs, etc.

‡ For fine work and where there are halftones, extra care must be taken, and printing costs are higher.

the other. There is often that much variation between printers' bids.

1. Using any paper of the approximate weight desired, make up a dummy in the proposed size and number of pages. Weigh it. Then multiply by the number of copies to be printed and add 10 per cent for waste and another 10 per cent for trim (if any). This will give the approximate number of pounds of paper that should be ordered. Multiply by the price per pound if known (15 cents is about minimum as a contract price with small buyers often paying 25 cents and more).

2. Allow $8 per page for type composition, make-up and lockup, and $5 per cut. Double both figures if the pages are as large as 8½ by 11. These are round figures. Simple book composition can cost $3 per page, and 8½ by 11 cuts can cost $40 or more.

NAME OF CUSTOMER_____

ADDRESS_____

TITLE AND DESCRIPTION OF JOB_____

_____

_____

_____

_____

_____

*Date* _____

**SPECIFICATIONS**

No. of Copies_____

No. of Pages_____

Trimmed Page Size_____ x _____

Untrimmed Page Size_____ x _____

Printing Sheet Size_____

**STOCK**—TEXT _____

_____Sheets_____lbs._____lbs. at_____per lb.

STOCK—COVER _____

_____Sheets_____lbs._____lbs. at_____per lb.

Add _____ % for Profit.

**CUTTING**_____

**COMPOSITION**

Linotype _____

Monotype _____

Add _____ % for Profit.

Hand _____

Make-up _____

Break for Color _____

Foundry Lock-up _____

Press Lock-up _____

**ENGRAVINGS**_____

Add _____ % for Profit.

**ELECTROTYPES**

_____ Size _____ x _____ inches _____

Routing for Color _____ Fixing _____

Add _____ % for Profit.

**MAKE READY**

_____ Forms _____ hours each _____ hours at _____ per hour _____

**RUNNING**

_____ Forms _____ pp. _____ Imp. Each _____ hrs. at _____ per hour

**INK** (Allow for Overrun)

Color _____ Amount _____ lbs. _____

Add_____ % for Profit.

**BINDING** See Details "Over"_____ M at _____ per M.

Add_____ % for Profit.

**CARTAGE** _____ lbs. _____ Pkgs. at _____ per Pkg.

TOTAL

DISCOUNT

PER M FOR ADDITIONAL COPIES

One printer makes all estimates on the above form to make sure he allows for every important cost factor. The columns allow him to figure a job several ways.

3. Allow a minimum of $5 for make-ready, or $1 per page—whichever is larger.

4. Allow 75 cents per page per 1,000 copies for ink and presswork with a minimum of $2 per 1,000. Over 16 pages, allow 30 cents per page per thousand.

5. Allow $5 per 1,000 copies for folding, saddle-stiching, and trimming a self-cover pamphlet of up to 32 pages; $7.50 per 1,000 if it has a separate cover; $3 per 1,000 additional for each additional signature. Add $5 to total cost to cover make-ready on the binding machinery.

In general, the rates for printing a periodical are lower than for commercial work because the periodical with standardized format can be set up more easily after a few issues.

**etching**   To etch means to eat with acid, as when an artist scratches a picture on a paraffined copper plate and then uses acid to etch or eat away the copper where his strokes have gone through the protecting paraffin. Proofs taken from such an etched plate (see INTAGLIO) are also called etchings. Had the artist removed the metal himself, instead of exposing it for the acid to remove, he would have been making an "engraving."

Etching is also done by photoengravers, who prepare their plates photographically instead of by hand. (See LINE CUT.)

**expanded**   Type that has been designed to make the letters wider than usual (as compared to their height) is said to be "expanded" or "extended." Exceptionally narrow type is called "condensed" type. This sentence is set in 9-point Century Expanded.

**express**   See RAILWAY EXPRESS.

**extended**   See EXPANDED.

**eyeleting**   The process of reinforcing a punched hole. Often calendars are fitted with a metal-reinforced eyelet so they can be hung on a nail. The work is done by firms specializing in mounting and finishing. (See MOUNTING AND FINISHING.)

# F|f

**facsimile** As generally understood, an exact copy. Old books and documents are sometimes reprinted in facsimile editions which reproduce not only the exact type arrangement but also discoloration of the paper, any marginal notes, etc.

Any halftone printing process will do this type of facsimile work, but the best method is probably photogelatin (because screenless), with gravure as next choice. (See PHOTOGELATIN; GRAVURE.)

A photographic copy is a facsimile. In certain legal work, a photographic copy or a Photostat of a document is acceptable where other types of copies would not be.

The word "facsimile" is also used to describe some newly developed methods of sending pictures, drawings, or written material by wire or radio, to be reproduced at the receiving end.

**Fairchild engraver** See SCAN-A-GRAVER; SCAN-A-SIZER.

**fake process** See also PROCESS COLOR; COLOR PRINTING.

Full-color reproduction by the process-color technique is potentially exact but expensive. If approximate results will do, considerable saving can be made by using the fake process technique.

Regular process color printing begins with some high-precision photographic "color-separation" work. In fake process work this stage is much abbreviated, and the platemaker (who must also be something of an artist) makes the separations by hand.

By the fake process method, a black-and-white original can be converted into a colored picture; or a full-color original can be copied though not reproduced.

Fake process work is recommended only where slight changes in color values are not objectionable. It may do complete justice to the picture of a package or a sunset, while failing utterly to give satisfactory reproduction of the close-up portrait of a steaming beef stew. Any attempt to achieve too much in fake process would boost the cost up above the cost of genuine process color.

Both genuine process-color methods and fake process-color methods are used in offset, gravure, and photogelatin as well as in letterpress. Printers can advise on when to use which.

**ferromagnetography** If finely divided magnetic powder is dusted over a tape recording, the pattern of the recorded sound becomes visible. If a different kind of recording head is used—one designed to magnetize the tape in patterns of letters or numbers—a legible image can be brought out with the dusting powder. This image can be printed by touching the tape to sticky paper, and in other ways.

This principle has been found useful in connection with high-speed digital computing machines which can spew forth figures far faster than most devices can take them. Ferromagnetic printers have been constructed which can record figures on high-speed drums at rates of thousands of characters per second. Printing by magnetic methods is in its infancy, but work of fair definition has already been achieved, and the method may yet find wider use in the graphic arts field.

**fill-in** See also LETTERS.

When name, address, and salutation are typed in at the top of a form letter, this is referred to as a "fill-in." Fill-ins can also occur within the body of the text, especially when the work is done on an automatic electric typewriter. (See AUTOMATIC ELECTRIC TYPEWRITER.)

Fill-in work is also known as "personalizing."

**film** See also MOTION PICTURES; FILMSTRIPS.

The word "film" is generally applied to transparent sheeting such as the cellulose acetate on which photographic film is based, cellulose nitrate (celluloid), cellophane, polyvinyl acetate (Vinylite), polyethylene (Pliofilm), etc. Sometimes the word "foil" is given the same meaning.

Transparent film can be obtained in various thicknesses, at most art supply stores. Sometimes it is given a slight grain (making it frosty in appearance) so that it will accept pencil and ink markings.

It is possible to draw on smooth film by using special inks, by mixing some soap with water colors, or by using paints with a turpentine base.

**Filmotype** A device for composing display type by exposing one letter after another from a master film onto sensitized photographic paper. It is similar in its operation to the Coxhead-Liner. (See COXHEAD-LINER.)

A filmstrip.

**filmstrips** See also MOTION PICTURES.

The term "filmstrip" is generally used synonymously with "slidefilm" to describe a continuous strip of 35mm. movie film containing 20 to 100 frames of still photographs, diagrams, or charts. These pictures are projected upon a screen, one at a time, like lantern slides.

Filmstrips may be in color or in black and white. Some contain printed captions right on the pictures, some are intended to illustrate or be accompanied by a talk, and some are made to be used with narration and sound effects recorded on a 12- or 16-in. phonograph record or on tape.

The term "slidefilm" is more properly applied to a set of individual slides, usually 2 by 2 in., either glass or film mounted in cardboard.

There are a few machines that will handle both 2 by 2 slides and a filmstrip; most machines handle only one or the other.

Filmstrips are much cheaper to make than movies. For some purposes, they are as good or better. They are particularly valuable for educating people in the details of a subject, since

A set of 2- by 2-in. slides.

the pictures can be left on the screen as long as the instructor desires and he can adjust the pace to meet the needs of his audience. Movies are better when the objectives are to show motion or to get an emotional response.

The problem of making a filmstrip is basically that of creating or assembling the pictures in the right order. Most filmstrips consist of about 20 to 100 still pictures.

It is customary to make the art work of one uniform size, namely, 6¼ in. high by 8¼ in. wide, so that all pictures can be photographed in the same focus. This *proportion* must be adhered to, although the size may vary if necessary. (See SCALING.)

Photographs are usually carefully retouched (see RETOUCHING) both to emphasize important detail and to correct flaws. Even minor flaws become prominent when a picture is enlarged upon the screen.

Drawings may be used. However, if drawings in black ink on white paper are used, the result may be to throw a blinding amount of white light on the screen, and it may be better to reverse these, black for white, or to make the drawings in black on gray with white highlights.

Photographs for filmstrip use should be low in contrast, since they will gain in contrast when copied onto the master negative and again onto the positive projection print.

An ordinary black-and-white filmstrip print need cost only 75 cents or so, since it consists merely of 3 to 5 ft. of 35mm. movie film.

Making the master negative from finished art work will cost approximately $1 per frame.

The art work, however, will run up the cost, perhaps to $10 or $35 per frame, *i.e.*, per picture.

Silent filmstrips may be distributed with a printed or mimeographed narrator's text. Most silent filmstrips are prepared with short captions printed below, above, or directly on each picture. A good technique for putting captions on photographs is to draw or print white letters on transparent film (cellulose acetate) and then airbrush in black behind the letters on the underside of the film so that the letters will stand away even from white parts of the photo. These so-called "embossed titles" may be secured from Q Q Motion Picture Titles, 1243 Ave. of the Americas, New York 19. Many printing companies using the "hot press" technique are equipped to print such captions. The film is laid over the photograph and both are copied together.

Sound filmstrips employ a 12- or 16-in. record or a tape to carry the narration and musical accompaniment. Usually a gong sounds to tell the operator of the filmstrip projector when it is time to turn to the next picture.

The use of sound increases the effectiveness of a filmstrip and also its cost. The narrator, the music, the studio, and the sound crew all cost money.

The preparatory work on a set of separate glass or paper-bound slides is the same as for film. A set of slides costs a little more and has the advantage that the pictures can be rearranged at will; the disadvantage that they can accidentally get into the wrong order. If there is time, it is very easy also to make changes in a filmstrip, simply by rearranging the original art work and then shooting a new negative and positive.

Filmstrips or slidefilms can be made in color. A simple way is to shoot the art work with an ordinary roll of 35mm. color film, as many times as there are sets to be made, and have these films finished in 2 by 2 slides.

Most color filmstrips are prepared from original drawings in color or from color transparencies. The preparation of art work for color filmstrips is similar to that for black-and-white filmstrips. The use of transparencies poses a different problem, for transparencies cannot be retouched easily and therefore should be of excellent quality if they are to be used for filmstrips.

Several firms equipped to make color filmstrips to order are: Cinéque Color-film Laboratory, 424 E. 89 St., New York; Manhattan Color Laboratory, 254 W. 54 St., New York; and Slide-O-Chrome Corp., 108 West End Ave., New York.

Charges run approximately $2 or $3 per frame for preparing a master copy from color art work or transparencies. After that the reproduction charge ranges from 45 cents a foot for less than 100 feet to 25 cents a foot for 1,000 to 2,000 feet, and 20 cents a foot for 5,000 to 10,000 feet.

There are estimated to be about 100,000 filmstrip projectors in the United States, a much smaller number having a sound attachment. These are owned by schools, colleges, sales organizations, etc. They may also be rented, with or without operator, from many local film-projection services listed in the Classified Telephone Directory.

Firms that are organized not only to make filmstrips to order but also to undertake the distribution of them include the Society for Visual Education, 1345 W. Diversey St., Chicago, and the Jam Handy Organization, 2792 E. Grand Blvd., Detroit, Mich.

An automatic projector to use in displaying slides in windows and convention booths is obtainable from Picture Recording Co., Oconomowoc, Wis., at $165. It shows 2 by 2 slides for six seconds, each on a built-in 8- by 12-in. screen, and can handle 12 slides in continuous cycle or on a demand cycle initiated by push button.

Those who plan to buy or use films or filmstrips will get valuable suggestions from the books on films listed in Appendix 2, Bibliography.

**finishing** See MOUNTING AND FINISHING.

**first-class mail** See Appendix 4, Postal Information.

**flat** In order to make an offset plate, film negatives or positives are first stripped into place on a large yellow sheet of paper which holds them in the proper arrangement. This assemblage of film and paper is called a "flat." It is somewhat easier to store flats in case of a rerun than to store plates, although both may be done.

**flat-bed press** There are flat-bed presses and there are rotary presses. In the former, the printing surface of the type and the cuts is flat; in the latter it is cylindrical.

Rotary presses should not be confused with cylinder presses. Curiously enough cylinder presses are flat-bed presses since the printing surface is flat although the paper is wrapped around a cylinder. (See PRINTING PRESSES.)

**flat color** See also COLOR PRINTING.

Color printing is either flat-color work or process-color work. Flat color is cheaper because simpler. (See PROCESS COLOR.)

In flat-color work red is red, blue is blue, and yellow is yellow; and the three are not blended on the page to give effects of purple, violet and magenta, green, orange, etc.

A pamphlet having red headlines and black text is a flat-color job. It remains so if blue borders and yellow tint blocks are added. If a green panel is needed, it is possible to get the effect of green by running blue over yellow, and the job is still classified as flat color.

If, however, it is necessary to reproduce a full-color photograph or painting, with all its shades and tones, then the job falls into the process color category.

Cuts and plates for flat-color work are purchasable singly at ordinary rates, just as if they were all to print in black. Cuts and plates for process-color work are made only in matched sets and cost considerably more.

Flat color does not necessarily mean full-strength color—the color can be made to appear much lighter than full strength by printing it in a dot or line pattern. (See SHADING TINTS.)

Silk screen work is usually done in flat colors, as are many posters and children's books. (See TINT BLOCKS.)

**Flexichrome** See COLOR PHOTOGRAPHY.

**flexographic printing** What used to be called "aniline printing" is coming to be referred to as "flexographic printing" since the former term had come to be somewhat of a misnomer. The flexographic printing industry specializes in printing paper bags, envelopes, food wrappers, etc. It has learned to print on such normally difficult surfaces as cellophane, wax paper, polyethylene (Pliofilm), etc. Originally aniline dyes were the basis of the quick-drying alcohol-base liquid inks that gave the process its former name. Now many kinds of ink are used, but the presses used are all web-fed rotaries printing fast-drying inks from rubber plates. The process is comparatively low in cost and, although once low in quality, new methods have greatly improved it.

The process is of no great interest to most buyers, since ordinarily they will be buying not flexographic printing, but imprinted paper bags, etc.; they can let the paper-bag manufacturer take the responsibility for getting the printing done. However, if you want to avoid unpleasant surprises, you have to design with the limitations of the process in mind. Insist on seeing samples comparable to what you are ordering, and do not expect better quality than you are shown. The process itself may not have serious limitations, but some flexographic printers have because they try to sell price, not quality, and may insist that what looks terrible to you is of generally acceptable quality in their industry.

**Flexoprint** A method of setting up price lists, directories, etc., in visible file panels in such a way as to permit overlapping typed entries to be photographed direct from the panels for the purpose of making offset printing plates and running off copies. Each card is slotted to ride on rails in the visible file panels and to space itself from the cards that precede and follow. Insertions and deletions are made simply and rapidly. Means are provided for sliding cards from one column or tray to the next. The equipment is made by Remington Rand, 315

Fourth Ave., N.Y. Somewhat similar equipment is also made by Acme Visible Records, Crozet, Virginia.

**fliers** See CIRCULARS.

**flock printing** Also called "frost printing," "flock application," and "glitter application"; often used to apply special velvet or frosted finishes to Christmas cards, boxes, etc. Instead of printing ink, sticky glue or varnish is applied to the paper and then sprinkled with rayon fibers, cotton lint, metallic powders, frosting powders, etc. The flocking material adheres only where the glue or varnish has been left by the type or cuts.

The glue sizing or adhesive is printed by either letterpress or silk-screen process. The latter is often preferred, since by this process a heavier layer can be deposited on the paper. One firm that specializes in flock printing is Screen-Flock Industries, 5545 N. Clark St., Chicago 40.

**flop** A picture can be flopped, left for right, during the process of reproduction, if the engraver or printer is so instructed. This is often desirable when a person faces out of the layout and should face in. (See discussion and illustration under NEGATIVE.)

**fluid duplicator** See SPIRIT DUPLICATOR.

Flexoprint visible file panel.

**fluorescence process** The Kodak fluorescence process offers artists a method of making full-color, water-color paintings that are much easier to reproduce faithfully than similar paintings done with ordinary paints.

A booklet entitled "Kodak Fluorescence Process" is available at $1 from the Graphic Arts Sales Division, Eastman Kodak Company, Rochester, N.Y.

The artist simply uses special Kodak fluorescent paints instead of ordinary paints, handling and mixing them as he has always done. The resulting pictures cannot be told from ordinary water colors under ordinary light. Under ultraviolet light, however, the colors glow with fluorescent light. The character of this glow is carefully worked out to help the printer (who must have special equipment) make color separation negatives and printing plates on which the usual hand corrections will be almost entirely unnecessary.

**fluorescent printing** See LUMINESCENT PRINTING.

**flush** As used in printing, this means "even with." Headings are often run flush left, *i.e.*, flush with the left margin. Headings that are not run flush left or flush right, are indented, centered, or run "full measure" (flush with both margins).

The word "flush" when used alone means flush left, unless a mark on the layout or proof shows that it should be interpreted as meaning flush right.

A "flush-mounted" cut means one on which the printing areas run right to the edge of the block, no room being left around the edges for nailing. Flush-mounted cuts are either nailed through nonprinting areas within the design or fastened down with adhesive or by "sweating." (See SWEATING.)

**folding** See also BINDING.

A single leaf of paper has two sides, hence two pages. Folded once, it makes a four-page leaflet. Folded again it makes an eight-page leaflet, etc.

Thus, 4, 8, 16, and 32 pages are standard units for booklet work; larger books are made in multiples of 16 or 32 pages. 6-, 12-, and 24-page units can also be handled on some folding machines.

Note that an 8-page unit must be trimmed before pages 2, 3, 6, 7 can be read. Before trimming this is called a French-fold leaflet. (See illustrations under BINDING.)

Trick folding and folding other than that outlined above may have to be fed through a folding machine a separate time for each fold, or even involve handwork, so it may cost more.

Many small printers have no folding machines but send out all folding and binding operations to a binder. Many have folding equipment, however, either integral with certain presses or separate.

Some folding machines put a thin line of paste down the fold of an 8- or 12-page leaflet, thus making separate stitching unnecessary.

Machine folding can be obtained for as little as $2 per thousand pieces, whether one, two, three, or even four folds are called for. (See ESTIMATING COSTS.)

**folio** (1) A page number. (2) A sheet of paper that has been folded once. (3) A large book, about 12 by 15 in.

A drop folio is a page number placed at the bottom of the page.

**font** Complete assortment of types of one face and size, including capitals, small capitals, small letters, numbers, punctuation marks, etc. Most Linotype, Intertype, or Monotype fonts contain also matching italic *or* bold letters.

Occasionally a proofreader will find that one letter has slipped in from a different font—a different type face or different size, for example. He must watch for this "wrong font" and mark it (w.f.) for the printer to correct.

**footnote** In a manuscript, footnotes may be typed either at the bottom of the page or immediately following the reference. They are often separated from the rest of the typed page by a line.

The word in the text requiring a footnote should be followed by a superior number with a corresponding one preceding the footnote. Using an asterisk or dagger in place of a superior number is not recommended except in scientific or algebraic matter where superior numbers might be mistaken for part of a mathematical expression. In tables, however, symbols are commonly used to avoid confusion with exponents. If the number of footnote references is large and superior numbers are not desirable, superior letters may be substituted for the asterisk and dagger series.

Footnotes throughout a single article, chapter, or section are usually numbered consecutively in manuscript. This is done both because many publishers prefer to follow this method in the printed book and because in any case there is small likelihood that each typed page will make up into one printed page.

**foreign-language printing** Setting type in a foreign language is a highly specialized business, not only because of the different accents and special type faces required, but because of the many proofreading pitfalls that await the unwary.

Many feel it is not enough merely to have proofs read by someone who "knows" the language in question. That someone must (1) know the language, (2) know it on a highly educated level and have a journalist's competence in using it, and (3) be an experienced proofreader.

Almost any good printer who knows where to find a proofreader with these qualifications can set material in those languages which use the roman alphabet, at least in French, Spanish, German, Italian, etc.

Others have found that it is satisfactory to proofread a foreign language by comparison, depending on the original to be correct and having experienced proofreaders who know simply the alphabet and the accents of the language.

In any case, the safest policy is to give foreign-language work of any kind to a printer who does work of that kind regularly. He will have the type and the accents. He will know how important it is to get a qualified proofreader and will have one of proved competence on the staff or have his telephone number.

Two of the most versatile of the foreign-language printers are International Press, 121 Varick St., N.Y., and King Typographic Service Corp., 330 W. 42 St., N.Y. 36, which give typesetting, proofreading, and printing service in virtually any language including Chinese, Russian, Hebrew, Arabic, etc.

**form** See also BUSINESS FORMS.

To a printer a form is the assemblage of type pages or cuts that are to be printed on one side of one piece of paper. A 96-page job may consist of three forms of 32 pages each. (For illustration, see TYPE.)

**format** The shape, size, and style of a book, pamphlet, magazine, or other publication. For example, a book may be published in a cloth-bound, 5 by 8 format for sale at $3 and later in a paper-bound, 4 by 6 format for sale at 25 cents. The format must be determined before layout and dummy can be made. (See also LAYOUT; DUMMY.)

**forwarding of mail** See Appendix 4, Postal Information.

**Fotosetter**  See INTERTYPE FOTOSETTER.

**Fototype**  The Fototype method of setting type utilizes letters that are printed on separate slips of white cardboard. These letters can be assembled to form headlines, using a special composing stick. Once a headline is set, it is backed

Setting Fototype.

How Fototype is backed with scotch tape. The letters that will be photographed are on the underside and duplicate those seen here.

with scotch tape and is ready to be photographed.

Fototype is most often used in combination with typewritten or Varityped text for offset reproduction. (See VARITYPER.) A line of Fototype can be pasted down alongside other material, or it can be enlarged or reduced photographically and "stripped in" alongside other material in its enlarged or reduced size.

Fototype comes in approximately 300 sizes and styles. It is sold in kits consisting of 100 of the most frequently used characters and 50 each of the others. The average kit costs about $8 for a set of capital letters, and $5 more for the small letters. Refill pads of any letter cost about 35 cents each.

"Reverse" alphabets (white letters against black) are available, but the ordinary alphabets can of course be reversed by getting a negative photostat.

For full information write the Fototype Co., 1414 W. Roscoe St., Chicago 13.

The following lines were set in Fototype:

**ANYONE CAN SET FOTOTYPE**

*for Emphasis*

# EASY TO USE

## COMPLETE KITS

Also available is transparent Fototype which is designed for use with positive-working offset plates. It is possible to "burn" Fototype transparent lines directly into this kind of offset plate without first making a negative. Almost any exposure frame and light source may be used for this purpose. Transparent Fototype is also used in the various blueprinting processes now on the market as well as for visual aids.

**foundry proofs**  See PROOFS.

Foundry proofs are easily recognized by the broad black bands like bands of mourning around each page of type. These bands are from the "bearers" that lend support to the type page when the foundry makes stereotypes or electrotypes. (See the illustration on page 114; also STEREOTYPE; ELECTRO.)

The editor or purchaser of printed

matter will receive proofs in the following order: galley proofs, revised galley proofs, page proofs, revised page proofs, and (if duplicate plates are to be made) foundry proofs and plate proofs.

Foundry proofs are supplied, not for corrections, which should have been completed in the page-proof stage, but to show that the corrections indicated on the final page proofs have been made. In the absence of instructions to the contrary, the printer may order duplicate plates without waiting for O.K.'d foundry proofs to be returned by the customer.

**foundry type**  See also TYPE.

Foundry type is hand-set type, cast in individual characters, and kept in a "type case" (see CASE), each character in its own compartment.

**four-color printing**  See PROCESS COLOR.

**fourth-class mail**  See Appendix 4, Postal Information.

**freight**  See RAIL FREIGHT; SHIPPING INFORMATION.

**French fold**  See FOLDING; BINDING.

When a piece of paper is folded

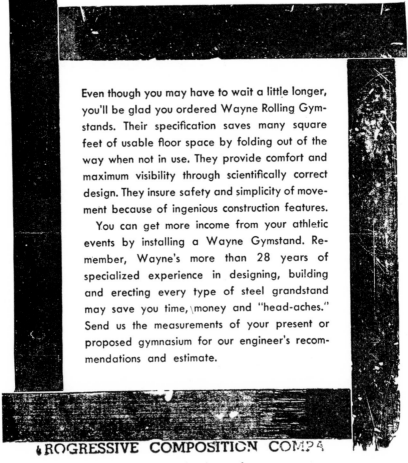

Even though you may have to wait a little longer, you'll be glad you ordered Wayne Rolling Gymstands. Their specification saves many square feet of usable floor space by folding out of the way when not in use. They provide comfort and maximum visibility through scientifically correct design. They insure safety and simplicity of movement because of ingenious construction features.

You can get more income from your athletic events by installing a Wayne Gymstand. Remember, Wayne's more than 28 years of specialized experience in designing, building and erecting every type of steel grandstand may save you time, money and "head-aches." Send us the measurements of your present or proposed gymnasium for our engineer's recommendations and estimate.

PROGRESSIVE COMPOSITION COMP4

A foundry proof.

twice, the second fold at right angles to the first, an uncut eight-page folder is formed. The result is a French-fold

A French-fold leaflet.

leaflet, which handles like a four-page leaflet, although actually printed on only one side of the paper.

**frisket** See MASK.

**frost printing** See FLOCK PRINTING.

**full measure** To set a line of type "full measure" means to make it the full width of the column, flush with both margins. The instruction is not needed unless the printer might otherwise assume that some kind of indention or centering was intended.

**furniture** Printer's term for the wooden or metal spacing material used to separate type pages from each other or to fill the space between the type and the metal chase in which it is locked up for press.

Leads, slugs, and furniture are all used for spacing. Leads are 1, 2, or 3 pt. thick, slugs are 6 to 12 pt. thick. Furniture is the biggest of all. (For illustration of furniture in use, see TYPE.)

**Futura** See the two charts entitled "The Futura Family," in Appendix 1.

# G | g

**galley, galley proof**  A galley is the shallow metal drawer or tray in which type is kept after it has been set. Each galley normally holds enough type to make two or three pages (book size) although at first the type is not divided into pages. (See illustration under TYPE.)

Proofs that are pulled before the type is divided into pages are called "galley proofs." They are usually about 6 to 8 in. wide by 24 in. long. Each one shows whatever lines happened to fit on that particular galley. Each is marked at the top with a galley number, so the printer can identify that particular tray of type.

Galley proofs should show only one column of type and are made with wide margins to provide room for proofreader's marks.

Printers normally supply three sets of galley proofs, one marked "Return this set with corrections," another to be used in the paste-up dummy (see PASTE-UP DUMMY), the third to be kept by the customer. If extra sets of galley proofs are needed, perhaps for the author, they should be ordered in advance and will be charged for at the rate of 2 to 3 cents for each proof of a single galley.

Some editors order one set of galley proofs pulled on colored paper to distinguish it from the master set, and use this one for paste-up purposes. (These are occasionally called "pink proofs" or "pinks.") Others prefer to paste up with a white set of proofs, since it is then easier to see from the dummy how the finished page will look. If revised galleys are necessary, they are usually pulled on colored paper to avoid confusing the two sets.

In some instances the printer can be instructed to skip galley proofs and go directly into page proofs. This is practical only when each page is self-contained with no carry-overs and when the copy has been written to fit the page. The danger in skipping galley proofs is that corrections on one page may affect succeeding pages and thus greatly increase the cost in both time and money.

Reader's galleys (master galleys) are sacred. They must not be cut up or marked except with necessary corrections to the printer.

It is very important that all the original copy be kept with the master proofs when these are sent from printer to customer, or from customer to printer. Such material (manuscript, art work, layout) is almost sure to be needed for reference when working with proofs.

**Garamond, Garamont** See Appendix 1, Type Faces.

**gatefold** When an illustration bigger than the printed page is to be inserted in a book, magazine, or pamphlet, this can be done by means of a gatefold insert as illustrated.

A gatefold insert.

In a slim pamphlet or magazine, it is better to run such an illustration across the center spread; if a center spread is not available, or if, as in the case of a bound book, the nature of the binding conceals the center fold, then the gatefold insert may be necessary. If a gatefold insert is added before trimming (see BINDING), it must be narrow enough so that the outer fold escapes the trimming knife.

**gathering** When a book or booklet consists of several units or signatures, these have to be gathered into the right sequence as part of the binding process. (See illustration under BOOKBINDING.)

**gelatin printing** There are two important techniques in gelatin printing: the hectograph and the photogelatin processes. (See HECTOGRAPH; PHOTOGELATIN.)

The hectograph process is used for duplicating office forms and communications when the quantities needed are between 10 and 50.

The photogelatin process, also called "collotype," is used for reproducing paintings, large photographic illustrations, facsimiles of old documents, etc., in quantities up to several thousand. It has the special advantage of reproducing halftone subjects without the use of the halftone screen required in other processes.

**glassines** See BRONZE PROOFS.

**glossy** A photographic print on glossy paper. Photographic prints intended for reproduction are usually made on 8 by 10 glossy paper.

Glossies are not easily scratched or soiled in handling. A glossy print has a greater range of tonal values; the blacks are blacker, and the whites are whiter than in dull prints. However, it is perfectly possible for a printer to reproduce from a photographic print made on dull or mat (sometimes spelled "matte") paper.

**Goldmark** Gold leaf prepared in a form which permits gold writing or decorating to be done without the heat usually required. If you lay a piece of Goldmark (also called "cold gold") on a leather, plastic, paper, wood, or metal surface and write your name on it with a ball-point pen, or a pencil, a genuine 23 K. gold facsimile of your signature will be transferred to the article. Goldmark is made by Hastings & Co., Inc., 2314 Market St., Philadelphia 3, Pa.

**Gothic** See Appendix 1, Type Faces.

**government printing** The U.S. Government Printing Office is the largest printing plant in the world. As far as the Federal government departments are concerned, it is the only source from which they may order their printing, for Congress has given it a monopoly over public printing and binding, except for certain requirements outside Washington. In the fiscal year 1945, at the peak of wartime demand, it handled $80,000,000 worth of government printing and did a gross business of $68,900,000 in the fiscal year ending June 30, 1954.

To those who have the privilege of dealing with the Government Printing Office, generally known throughout the Federal establishment as the "G.P.O.," and those who are interested in its operations, the following paragraphs are addressed.

The G.P.O. is equipped to do almost every type of printing and binding, including forms, pamphlets, books, periodicals, posters, and other color work. It grants waivers for direct procurement of some stock-item specialties, and it contracts on open bid for other printing that it cannot produce economically.

The major divisions of the G.P.O. that serve the various Federal departments and agencies, including, of course, the Congress itself, are as follows:

*Planning Divisions.* These are headed by a planning manager. The Division of Planning Service receives all requisitions and copy, provides production and delivery schedules, answers inquiries on progress of work, acts as liaison for other office departments, follows up the back-and-forth transmission of proofs, issues waivers for direct procurement of printing, writes specifications for work to be procured from commercial sources, and in general is the equivalent of the sales staff or the public-relations office in a commercial plant.

*Division of Plant Planning.* This sets up the specifications or production plan, makes the estimates, and fills orders for blank paper and supplies.

*Division of Typography and Design.* This furnishes layout service, advice on typography and standards, casual art work, retouching, and photographic service. (The National Archives Photographic Department can also serve other government agencies on a reimbursable basis, and does good color work.) This division is also charged with the maintenance and supervision of quality standards.

*Composing Division.* There are several composing rooms in the G.P.O. which make up the Composing Division. These are the Linotype section, the Monotype section, the Job section, the Patents section, and the Hand section. The division has 100 Monotype keyboards, 135 casters, 152 slug machines, 4 strip casters, and 2 Ludlows, with a sufficient variety of type faces to afford good typographical effects for selected jobs. Naturally, since the purpose of government publications is utilitarian, it is best equipped in a few standard text faces. Some of the Monotype faces available at G.P.O. in a wide range of sizes include Alternate Gothic; Baskerville; Bodoni; Bodoni Bold; Bodoni Ultra; Bookman; Caslon O.S. 336; Caslon 37; Caslon Bold; Garamond; Garamond Bold; Franklin Gothic; Kennerley; Kennerley Bold; Sans Serif Medium, Bold, and Extra Bold; and Stymie Light, Medium, Bold, and Extra Bold.

Some of the Linotype and Intertype faces available at G.P.O. in a wide range of sizes include Baskerville, the Bodonis, Century Expanded, Futura Demibold with italic, Garamond, Garamond Bold, Granjon, Ionic, Memphis Medium and Bold, Vogue Bold and Oblique, Vogue Extra Bold and Oblique.

*Platemaking Division.* The G.P.O. probably has more extensive platemaking facilities than almost any other printing plant. It is equipped to produce every kind of printing plate. This division has long been in the foreground of research and experiment on plastic plates and plastic electrotype molding.

*Presswork Division.* The G.P.O. has every type of letterpress equipment from platens to web-fed rotaries. Some of its rotaries will print, perforate, fold, and paste or staple up to 64-page units at speeds up to 12,000 per hour. Its post-card presses produce 2½ billion post cards annually. Its three specially built *Congressional Record* presses run at a speed of 20,000 impressions per hour. Between congressional sessions these presses usually run the tremendous income-tax printing program.

The G.P.O. also operates a full range of offset equipment. Supplementing the press equipment are all necessary photographic and platemaking facilities. Because of limited need, no installations of gravure, rotogravure, or photogelatin have been made. The G.P.O. contracts for work of this nature.

*Binding Division.* This has 250 major pieces of machinery and is capable of taking care of any binding problem that its Federal customers require— anything from padding or simple pamphlets to heavy case-bound books.

*Offset Division.* This is responsible for the processing of all jobs or publications produced by offset lithography. It includes the offset copy preparation, offset negative, offset platemaking, and offset press sections.

*Division of Tests and Technical Control.* This is responsible not only for testing and research on all materials used by the G.P.O. but it also manufactures printing and writing inks, press rollers, and adhesives. It provides technical and scientific counsel to the production divisions as well as to other government departments that require it. This division has worked closely with the Bureau of Standards and with commercial printing and printing supply research organizations.

*Documents Division.* This distributes and mails Federal publications for the originating Federal departments, and maintains a sales organization for documents that have general public interest. This division generally uses mailing lists furnished by the Federal department, but it has also built up many accurate lists of its own for the purpose of promoting sales. Certain departments have specially classified lists which are often made available to other agencies.

Any government publication that is of sufficient interest to create a public-sale demand is printed, stocked, and sold by the G.P.O. Superintendent of Documents. The originating department pays all preparatory costs and the Superintendent of Documents is charged only the additional rate for paper and material, presswork, and binding.

To this cost he adds 50 per cent, as required by law, to establish a sale price, this margin allowing for overhead and expenses. He makes a discount of 25 per cent for quantity orders, and any profit that he accumulates is turned back to the general funds of the Treasury. Under this arrangement, the public can buy, at low cost, either by mail order or at the bookstore maintained in the G.P.O. Documents Division, valuable government reports covering a wide range of subjects. The advantage to the departments is that this method of distribution gives cost-free circulation to their publications.

The G.P.O., of course, maintains all the other divisions and sections necessary to any well-organized production plant. It also operates five duplicating plants formerly under the jurisdiction of the Treasury Department's Procurement Division. These plants, including a shop in Washington, D.C., have a fine record of quick service on Multigraphing, mimeographing, and Multilith jobs considered too small for the G.P.O. big presses. Many government agencies also have their own equipment for such work.

Every user of the G.P.O. should purchase from the Superintendent of Documents a copy of the G.P.O. "Style Manual" and also a copy of the G.P.O. "Type Book." The "Style Manual" is a mine of information on how to prepare copy for the printer.

Editors who do not feel competent to design their own publications can ask the G.P.O. Division of Typography and Design to assist in designing their publications.

One way in which nongovernment groups can enjoy the privilege of having their material printed by the G.P.O. is to have a congressman read that material into the *Congressional Record* and then order reprints. Such reprints are available at very low rates. Sometimes a congressman is willing to go still further and send material out under frank.

**grain**  In all machine-made paper, the fibers tend to align themselves in the direction in which the pulp flows, despite mechanical shaking intended to minimize this. (Handmade papers have no grain.) It is harder to tear or fold paper across the grain. The pages of a book turn more easily when the grain runs parallel to the binding edge.

Paper for a 6 by 9 book to be printed on 25 by 38 stock would therefore be ordered with grain long, *i.e.,* the 38-in. way. This is sometimes abbreviated as 25 by 38, the underlining indicating the way the grain is to go.

**graphotype**  See also ADDRESSOGRAPH; ADDRESSING.

The graphotype is a machine for embossing letters in the thin sheet metal used in Addressograph plates.

**gravure**  Photogravure or gravure printing is the most important commercial application of the intaglio (pronounced in-tal'-yo) principle. (See INTAGLIO.)

Printing is done from large copper plates or copper-covered cylinders. These plates are relatively expensive, but once they are made, the cost of running them is comparatively low. The process lends itself to high-quality reproduction of photographs and other halftone illustrations, even on the most inexpensive paper. Its reproduction of type is not quite so good. The letters have slightly fuzzy edges, because all reproduction by this process necessitates the use of a cross-line screen. Type reproduced in gravure is entirely legible, but it is best not to use small sizes, certainly not below 8 pt., nor to use a text type with very thin serifs, like Bodoni. A booklet containing a good statement of the technical details of gravure printing is available free on request to Alco-Gravure, Hoboken, N.J.

The two important divisions of the gravure industry are sheet-fed gravure and rotogravure.

Small runs, from 10,000 to about 100,000, are best handled on a sheet-fed gravure press. Larger runs of 100,000 and up (monotone) and 250,000 up (four-color) may be handled economically on a web-fed rotogravure press, although it should be noted that many rotogravure presses handle the equivalent of 15,000 sheets per hour, each as big as 44 by 70 or more—sometimes in four colors, on both sides—so that a job has to be pretty big to warrant the attention of these giant presses. In general, very few monotone jobs are done on rotogravure for sums less than $1,000 to $3,000. Large color jobs range higher, but in long runs unit costs are very low. (See the charts "How to Choose the Right Printing Process" inside the covers of this book.)

The minimum cost of making a plate in sheet-fed gravure is about $250 for an area 25 by 38. Once made, the sheet-fed gravure plate can be kept for a rerun; *i.e.,* gravure plates can be run again for gravure printing, but cannot be used in any other printing process.

The approximate cost of making a plate for rotogravure is $300 to $500. A rotogravure cylinder may also be kept for a rerun for a reasonable length of time.

Rotogravure is a high-quality process for reproducing black-and-white photographs, and is beautiful as a color process.

Relief halftone (enlarged).

Gravure plate (enlarged).

Rolling ink onto the surface areas of a relief halftone plate.

Flooding ink into the depressed gravure cups, then scraping surface areas clean.

The relief engraving prints only from ink on raised areas; the gravure plate prints only from ink in its depressed areas. The relief dots vary in size; the gravure "ink cups" are of uniform size, but of varying depth. The shallowest carry barely enough ink to soil the topmost fibers of the paper, or none at all. The deepest carry enough ink to soak the paper to the point where the squares run together.

A special adaptation of the gravure process is used in large-run color work, and is known as the "News-Dultgen process." (See illustration.)

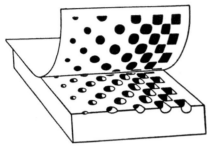

In the News-Dultgen gravure process, used for long-run color work, the ink cups vary *both* in depth and in area, not just in depth. (*Drawing courtesy of Interchemical Corporation.*)

The gravure principle has been widely adapted for such special purposes as printing paper bags, cartons, labels, etc. Presses for these purposes often take a web of paper only a few inches wide.

Firms doing sheet-fed gravure work include Beck Engraving Co., Philadelphia; R. R. Donnelley & Sons, Co., 350 E. Cermak St., Chicago; Photogravure & Color Co., 207 W. 25 St., New York 1.

Firms doing rotogravure work include Alco Gravure Co., Hoboken, N.J. (plants also in Baltimore, Chicago, and Los Angeles); Cuneo Press, Inc., 2242 So. Grove St., Chicago (affiliates are the Neo Gravure Co., Weehawken, N.J., and the Pacific Neo Gravure Co., 325 Minna St., San Francisco); R. R. Donnelley & Sons, Co., 350 E. Cermak St., Chicago.

Special gravure service to advertisers is provided by Intaglio Service Corp. of Chicago and New York, and by International Color Gravure, Inc., 39 W. 60 St., New York. Both will convert art work into film positives, make trial plates and pull proofs, do any necessary correcting of the positives and then make duplicate positives to send to as

many magazines as are to run the advertisement. The magazines make their rotogravure cylinders from these sets of positives.

**green copy** One of the first copies to come off a printing press. An editor who catches a serious error in a green copy may still have time to stop the presses before a whole edition has been run off. Green copies often contain defects of inking and make-ready, since they are printed while the pressman is still making final adjustments.

**greeting cards** Greeting cards are widely used for semicommercial and business purposes as well as for personal mailing. In fact, they have become a specialized form of direct mail advertising. Christmas cards, birthday cards, etc., are obtainable in considerable variety from most department stores, stationers, printers, and photographic stores, either plain or imprinted with the buyer's name and message.

Most of the imprinting of customers' names on stock cards is done by the ordinary letterpress method. The little job printer around the corner can do it as well as anybody else. Most cards are imprinted at the point of sale, by the printer or the stationer.

Those who wish to have their own custom-made greeting cards can furnish their own art work and design and have the cards printed to special order. (See DESIGNERS; ARTISTS; ILLUSTRATIONS.) The soft illustrations so often used, are best reproduced by the offset process. (See OFFSET; see also CIRCULARS for information on how to choose the right process for small work such as greeting cards.)

Photographs are best reproduced as actual photographic prints on photographic paper. If the quantity does not exceed 100 or 200, the cost of doing them this way will be less than the cost of making halftones and printing them. Type or lettering can be made a part of the photographic print by techniques with which every photographer is familiar.

Special blank cards and envelopes are available from most paper supply houses and photographic stores.

**gripper edge**  It is often impossible to print anything within ½ to 1 in. or so of the gripper edge of a sheet of paper. This amount of room must be allowed for the metal fingers, called "grippers," that draw the paper into the printing press. The requirements vary between printing presses, but the factor must be considered in laying out a printing job, especially if it is to bleed on all sides.

**groundwood pulp**  See also PAPER.

Newsprint is made from groundwood pulp, sometimes known as "mechanical pulp" to distinguish it from the "chemical pulp" used for better quality papers.

Groundwood pulp is made quickly and cheaply and produces a sheet of good printability and opacity. It is used for regular newsprint, supercalendered rotogravure paper, the cheaper book papers and coated papers, and the cheaper kinds of Bristols and boards.

Paper made from groundwood pulp yellows on long exposure to light, because the deteriorating agents in the wood are not removed during manufacture. It lacks strength owing to its short fibers. Because of these factors, it is not used where permanence is important. Paper free of groundwood content is called a "free sheet."

**gummed paper**  Paper can be purchased already gummed, or it can be gummed to order. (For gummed labels, see LABELS.)

**gutter**  See also MARGINS.

The gutter of a book, magazine, or pamphlet is the inside margin where facing pages join.

# H|h

**Haberule Visual Copy-caster**  A desk book that combines all the following in one unit: one-line showings and alphabets of all the most used type faces; character counts for these and for virtually all other type faces in all available text sizes; tables for figuring characters per line without arithmetic; and a special rule for determining (again without math) how many lines of which sizes and leadings will fit in a given space, or how much space will be required for a given number of lines. It is priced at $7.50 and is available from art stores or from Haberule Company, Wilton, Conn.

**Hadego**  An ATF machine of Dutch origin for setting display type. It somewhat resembles the Ludlow, except that its letters are photographed instead of being cast in metal.

**hairline**  This is a hairline rule:

A 1-pt. rule (½2 in.) is wider than a hairline. (See RULE for comparison of different kinds.)

**halftone**  See also CUT.
There are two kinds of cuts (engrav-
124

ings): the line cut and the halftone. (See LINE CUT.) Halftone cuts, also called halftone "engravings," must be used to reproduce photographs and drawings that contain grays (middle tones or halftones) which are neither jet black nor pure white. (See DRAWING TECHNIQUES for an explanation of when to use a halftone. See the following chart for comparative costs.)

A special technique had to be developed to reproduce grays because of the fact that printing ink is black, not gray. If ink is rolled onto type or a cut and then impressed into the paper, the paper either becomes black or stays white, with no halfway measures.

Early engravers overcame this problem by engraving by hand closely spaced fine black lines to get the effect of gray. For a light gray, the lines were lighter and farther apart, so that the paper would be only 10 to 20 per cent covered with ink. For a dark gray, the lines were heavier and closer together, so that the paper would be perhaps 50, 70, or even 90 per cent covered with ink.

The same results can be achieved with dots. The ink-spatter technique (see SPATTER) can produce grays of vary-

Diagram of copying camera showing art work, lens, halftone screen, and film negative. The coarseness of the screen is greatly exaggerated. The image on the film negative is shown as it will appear after development.

## Approximate Cost of Mounted Cuts *

| Size | Line cut | Zinc half-tone | Ben Day line cut † | Copper half-tone |
|---|---|---|---|---|
| 1½ x 2 | 5.11 | 5.18 | 6.37 | 7.00 |
| 2 x 3 | 5.88 | 5.53 | 7.00 | 7.84 |
| 3 x 4 | 7.14 | 6.30 | 8.47 | 9.38 |
| 4 x 6 | 8.82 | 7.70 | 10.71 | 12.39 |
| Approx. cost per add'l sq. in.‡ | .12 | .12 | .12 | .24 |

Note: Zinc halftones are made in screens up to 100 lines to the inch. Copper halftones are made in 110, 120, 135, 150, 175, and 200 screen. (See Cut for further explanation of other columns.)

* Figured on a rate of 7 cents a unit.

† This does not include cost of laying Ben Day on plate.

‡ Costs are not actually figured on a square-inch basis. However, these figures will give a rough idea of prices until a photoengraver's scale can be consulted.

ing tonal values, depending on the size and number of the dots produced by the spattering.

By the halftone technique, any desired gray tone can be manufactured out of tiny black dots with white space between them. (See illustration.)

Halftone cuts are produced commercially by photomechanical methods, without handwork, as follows:

Art work is put before a photoengraver's camera. A special screen is put into the camera just in front of the film and a fraction of an inch away from the film. The screen is like a window screen, except that it is much finer, having from 50 to 200 lines to the inch, and except that the lines instead of being wire are blackened scratches in plate glass.

The film is now exposed and developed, and becomes a negative duplicate of the original photograph or drawing, except that the outline of the screen appears on the film in the form of white (unexposed) lines, and thus breaks up the image into dots.

The action of the screen is such as to produce large dots where the light was strong, and small dots where it was weak.

A zinc or copper plate is now sensitized, placed in a vacuum frame in direct contact with the screened negative, and exposed to strong light. The surface hardens where light gets through the negative. The unhardened surface is washed away, exposing the bare metal. The bare metal is etched (eaten

10%

20%

30%

40%

50%

60%

70%

80%

90%

Solid

10 screen          65 screen          110 screen

How the halftone process mixes black dots with white paper in varying proportions to get any desired gray. Colored inks can be thinned with white in the same way. The so-called "10 screen" shown here is not actually used in printing—it is a fivefold enlargement from a 50 screen. The halftones in this book are 100 screen.

away) with acid. Where much light fell on the original negative, all of the surface is eaten away, save very tiny dots. Where only dim light fell on the original negative, very little of the surface is eaten away. This surface will carry lots of ink and print as dark as the original art work was in that place.

The recent development of "powderless etching" eliminates much handwork. One large engraver serving many small accounts by mail has now shifted entirely to powderless etching and offers halftones of up to 120 screen at rates below the usual for 100-screen zincs. For example, he offers a flush-mounted, type-high halftone in 100, 110, or 120 screen at $2.48 for 4 square inches, $5 for 20 square inches, and at about 8 cents a square inch beyond that. His name is Basil L. Smith, P.O. Box 8169, Philadelphia 1, Pa., also 14 W. 45 St., New York 36.

With conventional glass screens it is difficult, short of additional manipulation, to get a complete "drop-out" of the dots in the areas which should be pure white, but this is easy through use of a "magenta contact" screen. This Eastman Kodak product is now gaining acceptance, particularly in the offset field. The magenta screen, or contact screen, has dyed lines, not black lines, and its opacity can thus be manipulated with the aid of filters.

Other methods for dropping out the halftone dots in the highlights require that an artist use special paints to distinguish between areas to be held and areas to be dropped. (See KEMART PROCESS; also HIGHLIGHT HALFTONE.)

Halftone cuts of 50 to 100 dots to the linear inch (50 to 100 screen) are called "coarse-screen" halftones and are usually made on zinc. Halftones of 110, 120, 133, 150, 175, and 200 screen are called "fine-screen" halftones and are usually made on copper.

Coarse-screen halftones are used for printing on rough papers like newsprint.

The finer halftones must be printed on smooth paper. 100- and 110-screen halftones can be printed on English-finish, machine-finish, or supercalendered paper. Finer screens really demand coated paper.

Coarse-screen halftones can be printed on smooth paper, but fine-screen halftones will not reproduce well on rough paper.

It is not good practice to make a halftone from the proof of another halftone. The result is likely to be a *moiré* effect somewhat like watered silk or herringbone patterns. This is caused by one screen pattern crisscrossing the other. (See illustration under MOIRÉ.) A good halftone must be made from the best possible original copy.

Photographs are often printed so as to "bleed." (See BLEED.) Halftones that are to bleed must be ordered wider or deeper (by at least ⅛ in. for each edge that is to bleed) than they will be after trim.

Halftones that are cut square, with no special vignetting, surprinting, or other handwork, are least expensive. As it happens, the ordinary, simple, square halftone is probably the least confusing to the reader. It pays on both counts to avoid special trick layouts with photographs.

The halftone process is used for the reproduction of middle tones in almost all printing processes, not merely in letterpress (relief) printing as discussed above.

The steps in making ready a halftone for offset reproduction are substantially identical to those outlined above, except that the type is transferred to the printing plate at the same time the halftones are.

See SCAN-A-GRAVER for a description of a new electronic process for making newspaper halftones.

See GRAVURE for a description of the slightly different way in which the halftone technique is adapted to gravure printing.

See PHOTOGELATIN for a description of a screenless method of reproducing halftones. (It is not really screenless, but the screen occurs naturally like a grain in specially treated gelatin.)

For help in choosing the right printing process where there are photographs or other halftones, consult the charts inside the covers of this book.

An ingenious "Halftone Screen Determiner" is made by Arthur H. Gaebel, Inc., of Larchmont, N.Y., price $2.50. It is simply a piece of heavy transparent acetate sheet imprinted with a graded pattern of fine lines. When laid over a halftone, the fine lines interact with the lines of the halftone to form a *moiré* pattern in the form of converging lines pointing to the number of the screen being measured.

**hand addressing**  See ADDRESSING.

**handbills**  See CIRCULARS.

**hand-lettering**  See LETTERING.

**hanging indention**  See INDENTION.

**head**  See HEADINGS.

**headband**  The decorative tape at the top and bottom of the spine of a book,

Headband

just inside the cloth of the binding itself. Headbands serve no structural purpose—they are merely glued on to give the book a more finished appearance. Most of the books manufactured today have no headbands.

**headings, heads**  See also DESIGN.

Skillful use of headings and subheads can increase the legibility and attractiveness of any piece of printing and its editorial effectiveness.

Because readers frequently scan a page quickly, heads and subheads assume tremendous editorial importance. They should give the basic essentials of the story so that the 6-second scanner will get the main points even though he may never read the body of the article. Having these basic facts, he knows what the article is about and is more likely to go back and read the whole carefully. With subheads that are simply teasers, he may not get enough meat to interest him or to remember.

The simplest way to get good attention value for a heading is to use type as large as possible. If the heading is too long to be set in large type, then the key word alone can often be set large.

Hand-lettered headings may be attractive but are hardly essential, considering the great variety of type styles and sizes available. (See Appendix 1, Type Faces.)

Variety in headings can be achieved by using italic or sans-serif type for contrast with roman, caps in contrast with lower case, light with bold, etc. Headings can be run across one or many columns and set flush left or right, or centered in a black or white space, or boxed, etc.

*Flush-left Subhead*

The flush-left subhead is one of the most useful and economical. The line of the text that follows it is usually indented.

*Centered Subhead*

The centered subhead is also popular, although not so easy for the eye to find. A wide centered heading sometimes looks as though an inaccurate attempt had been made to indent it or set it flush left.

*Run-in Subhead.* One of the best headings for saving space is the heading that is run in. It is economical if set in the italic or small caps of the text type, or in some other face that the compositor can mix with the text face without undue trouble.

---

*Boxed Heading*

---

The boxed heading has a certain display value, but it adds to the expense because cutting and mitering rules is more expensive than setting type. The cut-in heading (also called a "cut-in side note") has good atten-
*The Cut-in Heading* tion value and is often used in textbooks; it also adds to the expense of the typesetting. Marginal headings, often called "side notes," also have their virtues, but cause a lot of extra work for the printer and are wasteful of space.

The term "sidehead" is used to mean either a cut-in heading or a marginal heading.

Headings are often set in the *italic* or *ITALIC CAPS* or the CAPS AND SMALL CAPS of the text type, and in the same size. Alternately they may be set in **boldface** or in **Bold Sans Serif,** or perhaps in LIGHT SANS SERIF CAPS. Caps are regarded as slightly less legible than small letters and are, therefore, not used quite so much.

Many editors make it a rule to break every column with at least one subhead. Some like to use a subhead every three column inches or so, feeling that solid text looks less readable than text broken by frequent subheads.

**headliner** See COXHEAD-LINER.

**headlines** See HEADINGS.

**head to come** Meaning that the headline or title will be supplied later, after the printer has set the text matter in type.

**hectograph** See also SPIRIT DUPLICATOR; DUPLICATING METHODS.

A hectograph is an office duplicating machine which can produce from 10 to 50 (under some circumstances, up to 100) copies of typed, written, or drawn material at very low cost. Beyond 50 copies on the hectograph, the copies grow faint and progressively harder to read. To get more, it is necessary to prepare a new master. (See SPIRIT DUPLICATOR for a similar process that will yield up to 400 copies.) Hectograph machines are made in both flat-bed and rotary forms. Their printing characteristics are the same.

Up to four colors can be reproduced simultaneously from the same master. Black, however, is not used. A purple ink gives the maximum number of copies. The best results are attained when special hectograph paper is used.

The hectograph (gelatin) process works as follows: The item to be reproduced is typed, written, or drawn on a hard-surfaced paper master. Special hectograph ink containing an aniline dye is used. This is obtainable in the form of writing ink, printing ink, pencil, ribbon, or carbon paper, and in four colors. This master is now laid face down on the gelatin surface. The dye is dissolved and transferred to the gelatin within a few seconds. The gelatin will now release some of the dye, when blank paper is pressed against it, thus duplicating the message. Within 24 hours the same gelatin can be used again since by that time the dye will have sunk into the gelatin and will no longer print.

Flat-bed hectographs with very large beds are used to copy mechanical drawings, maps, operating reports, statistical charts, etc.

Machines operating on the gelatin hectograph principle are marketed un-

An office hectograph duplicator.

der the trade names Ditto, Speedograph, and Vivid.

**Heyer Addresser** A low-cost portable addressing machine operating on the spirit duplicator principle. In operation it is held in one hand and rolled across the item to be addressed with a rocking motion that first moistens the surface with quick-drying alcohol, then rolls on an address. The price, including enough materials for a list of 270 names, is $9.95. For more details of the process, see Master Addresser. For information write the Heyer Corp., 17 E. 17 St., New York City.

**highlight halftone**   See also HALFTONE.

A highlight halftone is one in which the white areas are really white instead of being slightly grayed by tiny dots as in an ordinary halftone. (As an example, see the highlight halftone of a mimeograph lettering guide under MIMEOGRAPH.) Highlighting is required to get the best reproduction of most pencil and crayon sketches and wash drawings. Some, but by no means all, photographs benefit by it.

A highlight halftone engraving for letterpress printing costs three times as much as an ordinary halftone. The methods of getting highlight halftone effects at less than highlight halftone prices are described under VELOX and KEMART PROCESS.

Highlighting is done by painting out the highlight areas on the film negative with opaquing fluid, or by etching faint dots until they disappear. Similarly, near blacks can be made solid black by painting over these blacks on the metal after exposure but before etching. This must be requested specially if wanted, and is charged for at time rates.

A "drop-out" halftone is the same thing as a highlight halftone. The high-light dots are dropped out. This can be done in the camera as well as afterward as described above.

Highlight effects can also be obtained in offset and other processes. The extra cost varies but is usually competitive with letterpress.

**Hooven letters**   See AUTOMATIC ELECTRIC TYPEWRITER.

**hot type**   Type which is set with hot metal as in Linotype and Monotype composition. See also COLD TYPE.

**house organs**   See also PERIODICALS.

Many companies issue house organs, or magazines, for the benefit of their employees or customers. Thousands of such publications are issued every month. Companies not wishing to handle the editorial and production work within the staff sometimes have their publications edited outside, perhaps by their advertising agency or by a firm specializing in the editing and production of house organs. One such firm is The Gebbie Press, 19 E. 48 St., New York, which also publishes a directory of house magazines, as does *Printers' Ink Magazine*.

One source for a monthly art clipbook is Multi-Ad Services, Inc., 720 N. Jefferson, Peoria, Ill.

# I|i

**IBM Executive Typewriter**  The IBM Executive electric typewriter made by the International Business Machines Corporation writes in type styles that can hardly be distinguished from book type. Such styles can be used because this typewriter gives wide characters more room than narrow ones. For example, there are 10 characters in each of the following lines, but the "i" is getting two units of space, the "a" three units, the "A" four units, and the "M" five units. Such "proportional spacing" is automatic.

The work of the
IBM Executive Typewriter
iiiiiiiii
i i i i i i i i i i
aaaaaaaaa
a a a a a a a a a
AAAAAAAAA
A A A A A A A A A
MMMMMMMMM
proportional spacing
PROPORTIONAL SPACING

By reason of its attractive type styles the IBM Executive machine, priced at

132

around $700, is widely favored over ordinary typing for preparation of price lists, bulletins, directories, etc. (See COLD TYPE.)

More than 15 styles of type are available on the IBM Executive, but the face specified at time of purchase cannot later be changed. In this respect the machine is less versatile than the Varityper (see VARITYPER). However, certain of the type bars are demountable, permitting a shift in seconds from, say, a dollar sign to a pound sterling sign, and from certain little used mathematical signs to certain others, and to special symbols that can be made up to order. Seventeen of the keys on late model IBM's are demountable.

The standard IBM Executive has a 12-in. carriage and can write a 10-in. line on paper 11 in. wide. Also available are 16-in. and 20-in. carriages. Special card-holding platens are also available, including one (for recent machines only) which holds a Flexoprint card flat and permits writing at the very top edge.

Carbon ribbons are most used for reproduction, and come in various weights and hardnesses, acetate-backed as well as paper-backed. For consistent work it is important to get the right combination of ribbon, platen, and paper and to stick with it—even to watch the *age* of the ribbons since fresh ones often write blacker than those that have been kept for a time.

**illustrations**   See also ARTISTS; ART WORK; CARTOONS; CUT; DRAWING TECHNIQUES; PHOTO AGENCIES; PHOTOGRAPHERS; PHOTOGRAPHS: HOW TO SELECT; PHOTOGRAPHY.

Illustrations can be reproduced in every printing process but in some better than in others. Sometimes the kind of illustrations to be used determines the printing process. Sometimes the printing process to be used determines the kind of illustration.

Illustrations are of two kinds: line and halftone. (The distinction is made clear under CUT and under DRAWING TECHNIQUES, and is further described under HALFTONE.)

Line drawings can be reproduced by any process. Halftone illustrations have been reproduced by every printing process, but it is uncommon and undesirable to attempt to reproduce them in the hectograph, mimeograph, Multigraph, or silk-screen processes, Some small presses such as the Multilith offset presses lack the ink capacity to print large halftones.

The best methods of reproducing halftone illustrations are letterpress on smooth paper, gravure, and photogelatin. (See LETTERPRESS; GRAVURE; PHOTOGELATIN; also OPTAK.) Offset is excellent for wash drawings and pencil sketches but tends to be slightly inferior to the other processes in its reproduction of photographic halftone illustrations.

The cheapest method of reproducing halftone illustrations is offset. It is usually the cheapest method of reproducing line illustrations, too, although on quantities under 1,000 it competes with silk screen and with processes of inferior quality like mimeograph or spirit duplicating. (See OFFSET; SILK SCREEN.)

It has been proved that a well-illustrated piece of printed material will be read more thoroughly and by more people than the same material in unillustrated form. This is true whether the illustrations are informative or merely decorative. In that critical moment when a reader has glanced at a piece of printed material and is deciding whether to read it or put it down, the material that is attractive to the eye gets read most often.

Many editors, therefore, make it a rule to get some kind of illustrative material on every page or on every pair of facing pages. They may use photographs, cartoons, spot drawings, graphs, charts, or maps. If appropriate material is not available, they may insert an unrelated cartoon or an illustrated news item. In a pinch, they fall back on typographic display, featuring headlines, boxed material, etc. These are often given extra attention value by printing them on gray or colored tint blocks.

Artists should always be told how their illustrations will be reproduced, so that they may prepare their illustrations in the right way. On all but the simplest jobs, it is a good idea to have the artist talk to the printer or engraver since artists and printers are prone to pass the buck back and forth when things go wrong.

It is common practice to prepare art work the same size as it will appear in print, or a third larger, or perhaps twice as large. The artist must know the final size since he must prepare his work so that its details and the thickness of its lines will look right after reduction.

Line drawings can be reproduced from clippings without difficulty if the clipping has clean, crisp lines.

It is not good practice to reproduce halftones from a newspaper or magazine clipping, because they have already been "screened," *i.e.,* broken up into tiny dots, and any attempt to re-screen such a clipping may produce a final result with a *moiré* or watered-silk pattern across it. However, if the original photograph is unobtainable and the clipping must be used, the *moiré* effect can be minimized (see MOIRÉ). Offset printers are sometimes willing to reproduce "in line" from a halftone clipping without rescreening. They attempt to reproduce each dot in the halftone as if it were a line drawing, and sometimes succeed very well.

**imposition** The operation of bringing together and arranging all the type pages that are to be printed on one side of a sheet of paper. These must be so spaced and arranged that they will come in the right order and have the right margins after the sheet is folded to page size. The imposition for any job will vary according to the folding machine that the binder proposes to use. (See illustration.)

**impression** (1) A printing press is said to be capable of delivering 3,000 impressions an hour when it can impress inked type against paper at that rate. (2) A book is said to be in its "3d impression" when the publisher has had to order three successive printings of it to keep up with the demand. (See also EDITION.) (3) A pressman must carefully control the depth of impression of his press; the type must not hit the paper too heavily and punch through, nor must the impression be too light to fully impress ink into paper.

**imprinting** Printed catalogues are often imprinted with the name of the dealer who is to distribute them. Christmas cards can be imprinted with the sender's name.

Imprinting can be handled by any letterpress printer by stopping the presses every so often during the original run, to change the imprints. However, on high-quality, close-register

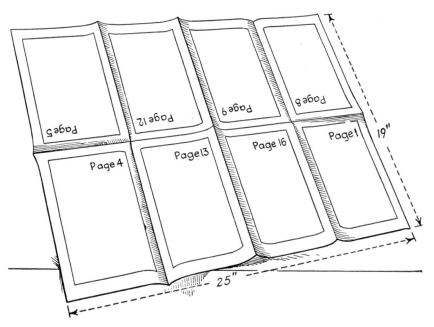

Imposition for one 8-page form of a 16-page 6 x 9 pamphlet.

work on expensive presses, this can be more work than it is worth.

Imprinting during the original press run is still more difficult for the offset, gravure, or photogelatin printer, although some presses are equipped for it.

Imprinting is most easily and cheaply done on small presses especially designed to facilitate quick changes of imprints. Some imprinting presses do not pretend to do high-quality work and usually cannot handle halftones or reverse plates satisfactorily. They are, however, quite adequate for their job of striking in a name and address.

Printers who specialize in imprinting material that was originally printed elsewhere include Hansen & Dean, Inc., 405 Broome St., New York 13; McKenzie Service, Inc., 95 Morton St., New York 14; International Label Co., 2340 W. Division St., Chicago.

**indention**  See also PROOFREADING.

The first line of a paragraph is usually indented 1, 2, or possibly 3 ems. This paragraph is indented 1 em.

### Purpose of Indention

THE PURPOSE OF INDENTION is to help the reader's eye catch the beginning of each new paragraph. Therefore, the first paragraph in an article or chapter is often not indented, at least if it follows a centered or indented heading. If it follows a flush-left heading, it is better indented. This paragraph has not been indented, and the first phrase has been set in small caps to provide a sort of squared-off beginning following the centered heading.

Every line of the following quotation from "The Bookman's Glossary" is indented 2 ems:

"*Indention*—The setting of lines of type to a measure that is narrower than the full width of the type page or column. Quoted matter is often thus set."

The following further quotation from the same source has the first line flush left and the rest indented 2 ems:

"*Hanging indention*—A form of typesetting having the first line set to the full width of the measure, while the succeeding lines are set one or more ems from the left edge. This paragraph shows the hanging indention."

Directions for indention should be specified on the original manuscript when it is marked for the printer.

**index**  See EDGE INDEX; THUMB INDEX; INDEXING.

**indexing**  Indexing and tabbing are binding and die-cutting processes and include the making of the dictionary type of thumb indexes, index cards, looseleaf pages, address books, etc. (See BINDING; MOUNTING AND FINISHING; also EDGE INDEX; THUMB INDEX.)

Indexing is also, of course, an editorial operation. (See EDITORIAL WORK.) Any book that will be used for reference should have an index.

The task of indexing is usually more tedious than difficult. It requires a definite plan in advance, consultation with the publisher to avoid typographical difficulties, and painstaking attention to details. The steps in indexing are usually as follows:

1. Go through duplicate page proofs, underlining all words that should go in the index *as words;* and write in the margin all subjects (not merely words) that should be indexed.

2. Enter each of these words and subjects with the page number on a 3 by 5 card, being consistent in form and style of entry (only one entry to a card).

3. Alphabetize the entire group of cards.

4. Combine all references to the same entry in the proper order on one card.

5. Number the cards in sequence so that none will be lost by the typist or the printer.

6. Read all entries to be sure that the wording is correct and in uniform style.

7. Use these cards for printer's copy, or type from them to sheets of typewriter paper.

For good suggestions on indexing see the books listed in Appendix 2, Bibliography.

Authors usually hate to make indexes and, through lack of skill, often make very poor ones. It is possible to get indexing work done by professional indexers on a free-lance basis. (See EDITORIAL WORK.) To locate free-lance editorial assistants who specialize in indexing, consult the "Literary Market Place," listed in Appendix 2.

**inferior characters** Scientists have a virtual monopoly on inferior characters (often called "subscripts") for such notations as $H_2SO_4$ and $X_a$. See PROOFREADING for a chart showing how to indicate to a printer that inferior characters are to be used.

**initials**

Decorative initial letters are often used at the beginning of an article or chapter. Such initials which stand above those that follow are called "standing" initials. Sometimes they lend a note of interest to an other-

wise plain page. Alternately, they may be the one thing too many on a cluttered page.

THE ALIGNMENT of initial letters must be watched carefully if they are to look well. The base of the initial letter should align accurately with the base of one of the lines of text. If the initial is handled as in this paragraph, it should also align at top if possible. If exact alignment is not possible, then it should project above the top line, never sink below it. The first word or phrase of a paragraph following an initial is often set in even small caps, as in the first two words above, to give a squared-off start to the block of type.

The "T" above projects into the margin because this departure from mechanical alignment makes for better optical alignment.

Many initial letters are too heavy for the type they accompany. This can be remedied by using outline letters, or by printing them in red or blue or some other color.

Note that a 36-pt. initial cannot be assumed to equal three lines of 12-pt. type, as the accompanying illustration will show. Careful measurement is necessary in specifying sizes for initials.

The standing initial shown in the word "Decorative" (at left) is easier to use and more legible than the set-in style (fourth line in this column). In the latter, the reader is sometimes confused by trying to read the initial letter with the second and third lines as well as with the first line, even when

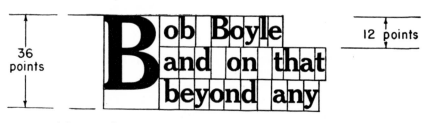

A 36-pt. initial cannot be assumed to be as tall as three lines of 12-pt. type.

these lines are slightly indented to minimize this danger.

**inks** In addition to regular inks in black and all colors, specialized inks are available—gloss inks, safety (bank note) inks, perfumed inks, invisible inks, carbonizing inks, metallic inks, cold inks, heat-set inks, and moisture-set inks, Printers can obtain all of these through their regular suppliers or, to name one source, from Interchemical Corporation, Printing Ink Division, 67 W. 44 St., New York 36.

Printing ink can be prepared for any kind of surface, and one ink will by no means suffice for all kinds of work. The inkmaker should be told by the printer, who must in turn be told by the customer, if there are any unusual problems involved.

For instance, is the printed product to be enclosed with any product such as food which it could affect or which could affect it? Is it to be varnished or pasted, or exposed to strong fumes, strong sun, or rain? If so, a modification in the ink may be indicated.

Inks can be made to print successfully by any process on cedarized bags, soap wrappers, cellophane, moisture-proof cellophane, cotton, nylon, burlap, book cloth, plastics, rubber, tin, aluminum, glassine, jute, newsprint, and on manila, kraft, machine-finished, coated, and bond paper, but the inkmaker must be given full particulars.

Note that there are several kinds of mimeograph and hectograph inks for those duplicating processes.

All ink manufacturers issue catalogues showing samples of some of the colored inks that they can supply. Some of the catalogues show not only how each color will look when printed solid, but also how it will look in a 25 per cent tint, a 50 per cent tint, etc. (See TINT, COLORON.)

In selecting colors, there is no real need to limit the choice to those shown in the sample book. Some of the catalogue colors are not kept ready-mixed

anyway. A color mixed to order may even be less expensive than one picked from a catalogue, if the pigments involved prove to be less expensive than those which make up the catalogue shade. Note that some colors are much more expensive than others, and some have very poor fading characteristics.

Ink colors may be ordered by submitting a swatch to be matched (as big as possible—1 sq. in. is not enough) or by giving a Color-aid number. (See COLOR.)

**inserts** See also BINDING. (Inserts in the sense of envelope stuffers are discussed under CIRCULARS and PAMPHLETS.)

Most pamphlets and books are put together in even units of 16 or 32 pages. Each unit or signature is folded out of one sheet of paper. If the signature as a whole is printed in black ink on antique paper, each page in it will be in black ink on antique paper.

It is often necessary to add an insert, perhaps a halftone on coated paper, perhaps a colored illustration. Inserts can be added anywhere, but money may be saved if their placement is decided with the binding problems in mind.

Inserts can be added as tip-ins or wraps. Tip-ins are simply given a narrow coating of paste along the inside edge and placed between two other pages. A wrap is wrapped around one of the signatures before binding, so that it is sewed into the binding as securely as any other page. (See illustration on page 138.)

**insured mail** See Appendix 4, Postal Information.

**intaglio** One of the five basic methods of printing. (See PRINTING.) The major commercial applications of intaglio printing are gravure, rotogravure, and engraving, *e.g.,* engraved stationery. (See GRAVURE; ROTOGRAVURE; ENGRAVING.) An etching is also an example of intaglio printing.

Outside wrap between
pages 32 and 33

Outside wrap between
pages 16 and 17 and 32 and 33

Single center insert
between pages 24 and 25

Double inside wrap
between pages 20
and 21, 28 and 29

Method of inserting
inside wrap within
16-page signature

Tip-in between
pages 26 and 27

Methods of fastening inserts into books and pamphlets.

The word "intaglio" (pronounced in-tal'-yo) is from the Italian word for "engrave," "cut," or "carve." Intaglio printing is done from depressed areas. In an engraving, the lines that are to

Intaglio printing is done from the ink caught in depressed areas.

print are cut below the surface of the plate. The whole plate is flooded with ink, and then wiped clean again. Although the surface is clean, ink remains in the engraved lines and will print when paper is pressed against the plate. (The process of preparing intaglio plates by photographic methods is described under GRAVURE.)

**interleave** Interleaving, also called "slip-sheeting," means inserting a leaf of paper between two newly printed sheets to prevent one blotting or "offsetting" on another. Although this is time-consuming, it is necessary when mimeographing on nonabsorbent paper and in some other printing operations.

**Intertype** See LINOTYPE.

The Intertype is a keyboard composing machine substantially identical to the Linotype. There are slight differences, however, between the Linotype version of a Garamond or a Caslon type face and the Intertype interpretation of the same basic design. (See Appendix 1, Type Faces.)

**Intertype Fotosetter** The Intertype Fotosetter is a recently developed composing machine that turns out type on film instead of on metal slugs. The film can be used directly for the making of offset or gravure plates, thus eliminating the whole process of making reproduction proofs from metal type and photographing these proofs to get film.

Regular Intertype faces are being made available on this machine. The work produced is of the highest quality. Since the process is photographic, a

single set of matrices can be used to set type in a variety of sizes. Procedures have been developed that make it easy to make corrections in the film.

The matrices resemble standard matrices but have a photographic image of the letter embedded in their side. After a line has been set and justified, the matrices are automatically exposed one by one in a sort of camera, and sensitized film receives the image.

Full kerning of characters is possible on the Fotosetter. Line widths up to 51 picas can be handled, justified. The range of available type sizes is from 4 to 36 points, with the possibility of getting still larger sizes by enlargement.

See also the other illustrations on page 140.

Intertype Fotosetter.

Fotosetter matrix showing photographic image of letter to be duplicated on film.

Matrices are exposed one by one in a sort of camera.

Close-up of Intertype Fotosetter.

**ital.**   Abbreviation for italics. (See ITALIC; PROOFREADING.)

**italic**   See also Appendix 1, Type Faces.
*This sentence is set in italic type.* This sentence is set in roman type.

Words underlined in manuscript copy will be set in italic unless the printer is instructed otherwise.

Italic is regarded as slightly less legible than roman and is, therefore, used for occasional emphasis rather than for entire texts.

In many type faces, there is no italic larger than 36 or 48 pt., even though the type faces are available in roman up to 72 pt. or larger.

# J|i

**jacket** The decorative and protective paper wrapper for a book. Fees for jacket designs start at about $100. Artists who have made a reputation as jacket designers are listed in "The Literary Market Place," available from the R. R. Bowker Co., 62 W. 45 St., New York, and the Directory issue of *Art Director and Studio News,* 43 E. 49 St., New York.

**justify, justification** See also LETTER SPACING.

The lines of this paragraph have been deliberately left unjustified. Note how the lines are of varying widths, presenting a ragged appearance at the right-hand edge. To justify a line of type means to make it of predetermined width, matching the rest of the column. Type lines are justified by putting more or less space between the words.

The lines of this paragraph, like the others in the book, have been justified. Short lines of less than 30 characters are difficult to justify. They sometimes make it necessary to choose between having an undesirable amount of space between words, and letterspacing a word or two, *i.e.,* spacing between letters as well as between words. Letter spacing is to be avoided.

**Justowriter** See TYPEWRITER.

# K | k

**Kemart Process**   A technique for making drop-out halftones from specially prepared art work by purely photomechanical procedures. Either the art work is prepared originally on special Kemart Illustration Board, or the white highlights are painted in with Kemart Highlight White instead of with ordinary Chinese white. Either way, the areas that are to drop out are brighter-than-white when illuminated by the special purple lights used in the process, and the halftone dots that would otherwise appear on the negative in these areas are burned away entirely. Kemart materials are available from art supply stores or from the Kemart Corporation, 340 Front St., San Francisco 11, Calif.

**kerned letter**   A type letter that extends beyond the body on which it is cast, so as to overhang the body of the next letter. Italic and script types have a larger number of kerned characters than the ordinary roman types. Kerned letters must be handled carefully to avoid breaking.

**kill**   Direction to the printer to discard type matter that has been set but is not to be used.

A kerned letter.

**Klischograph**   See SCAN-A-GRAVER.

**Kodachrome**   A color film. (See COLOR PHOTOGRAPHY.)

**kraft paper**   See PAPER.
   Kraft paper and kraft board are made from wood fibers by the sulphate process. Sulphate pulp makes paper of good strength and durability but will not bleach so white as sulphite or soda pulp. Kraft paper in its brown unbleached state is primarily used for wrapping purposes.

**Krylon**   See SPRAY.

143

**Kwik framer and proportion scale** A device to facilitate the cropping and scaling of pictures. It consists of a 10-by 12-in. celluloid sheet marked off in ¼-in. squares over an 8 by 10 area, and is opaque white along two edges. With a separate piece of L-shaped cardboard (supplied) any photograph up to about 8 by 10 in. can be framed. A movable diagonal pointer helps in working out reductions and enlargements. It is available at $3 postpaid from Cobb Shinn, 721 Union St., Indianapolis, Ind.

# L|l

**labels**  See also DECALCOMANIAS; TAGS; SEALS.

Label printing can be done most economically on special machinery developed for the purpose. For example, the Ever Ready Label Corporation, 117 E. 30 St., New York 16, N.Y., offers 5,000 gummed and perforated labels, 1¼ by 2 in., printed with any message in blue or red, for $3.95. The price includes typesetting. Any printer not specializing in labels would be justified in charging double that price or more.

The Ever Ready catalogue, available free on request, gives prices on specially printed labels of all sizes and shows a wide variety of stock labels.

For the names of companies specializing in label work, look under Labels in the Classified Telephone Directory.

**Lacey-Luci**  See CAMERA LUCIDA.

**lacquering**  See VARNISHING.

**laid paper**  Paper which, when held up to the light, shows finely spaced parallel lines and more widely spaced cross lines. The pattern arose naturally out of the screen in the frames used in making paper by hand. In machine-made paper, the pattern is added like a watermark for decorative purposes. Paper lacking the laid pattern is said to have a "wove" finish. Laid paper has no advantage over wove paper except its unique appearance.

**laminate**  See VARNISHING.

**layout**  See also DESIGN; DUMMY; PASTE-UP DUMMY.

The layout is the designer's blueprint for the printer to follow. It is a drawing of the job to be printed, page by page, showing margins, blocks or columns of type, illustrations, headings, photo captions, etc., drawn to exact size. Every item is carefully identified and marked for size, down to the page numbers and credit lines.

A multipaged layout, having the same number of pages as the finished job, is also called a "dummy." This becomes a paste-up dummy when proofs of the type and illustrations have been pasted into place for the printer's guidance. (See DUMMY; PASTE-UP DUMMY.)

A comprehensive layout or just a "comprehensive" is a layout made with great care to show exactly how the finished job will look. Headlines are let-

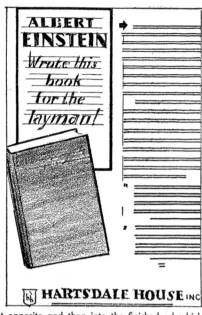

The above trial sketches developed into the layout opposite and then into the finished ad which is shown below.

tered in with a pencil in the exact style of type to be used. Lines of text type are ruled in. Some comprehensives are even more beautiful than the finished job.

A rough layout or "rough" is a layout designed for utility and not beauty. It can tell the printer everything he needs to know, but it would not be a good kind of layout for an advertising agency to show to a client's board of directors.

Although the layout is intended primarily as a guide for the printer, it also becomes a working plan which may be torn to shreds and revised before the opus goes to the printer. In this respect the layout serves as a preview of what is to come later from the printer in the form of proofs.

The layout must be planned, at least in broad outline, before any typesetting is done, since it controls or is controlled by the manuscript, the type selection, and the illustration. Whether layout should come before text, however, is a

# Relativity
## by ALBERT EINSTEIN

eAlbert Einstein wrote this book for the layman.

Its title is RELATIVITY: The Special and General Theory. Its purpose: to explain Einstein's theory so that anyone with the equivalent of a high school education can understand it. The book has had a curious history. Einstein was not yet the Nobel prize winner when he wrote the book in 1920. Only THE LONDON TIMES, in England and THE NEW YORK POST in the U.S.A. carried reviews. Because of the lack of reviewers' comments, and because at the time the real significance of the theory was not appreciated, the book soon went out of print. So for about twenty years this important work — one of the bases for the understanding of atomic energy — was unavailable to the general

public except through libraries. Now Hartsdale House re-publishes this great lost book in a more attractive form in a regular trade edition. June 2.                    $2.50

That Einstein did not overestimate the simplicity of his presentation may be seen from the reviews below; the only two that the book received.

"The book is intended to give an exact insight into the theory for those who are not conversant with the mathematical apparatus of theoretical physics. In the opinion of this reviewer, in this attempt he has been eminently successful."
            —London Times

"Written in an unpretentious, straight-forward style. The trend of his exposition can be followed in the main by any attentive reader." —New York Post

**HARTSDALE HOUSE INC.**
220 WEST 42nd STREET, NEW YORK, N. Y.

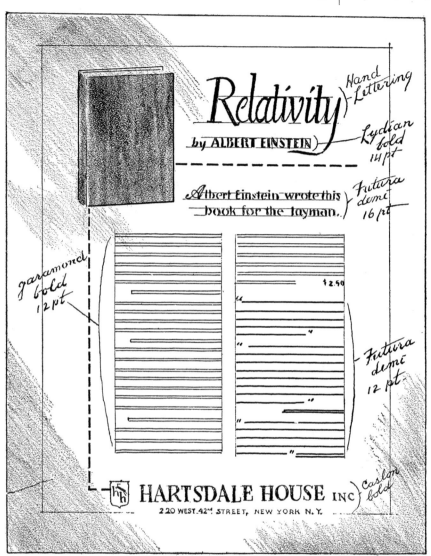

question as controversial as the one about the hen and the egg.

The layout for a book is almost always made after the manuscript is written. The publisher and his designer make it their business to adapt the design of the book and the illustrations, if any, to the manuscript.

In a heavily illustrated book, it may prove easier to subordinate the text to the illustrations and design, and rewrite when necessary.

The layout for an ad or handbill may come before the text. To begin with, the copy writer and the layout man have to know what space is available. The sequence then is as follows: decide what idea is to be put across; determine the approach as regards headline and illustration; decide the other required elements such as trade-marks, coupon, etc.; plan the arrangement or layout; decide on the number of words of text. Copy writing and layout must proceed hand in hand, so as to assist each other, not strait-jacket each other.

In a magazine or pamphlet there are at least three different ways to answer the question, "Which comes first—layout or writing?"

1. Write the copy. Then make a layout to fit the copy.

2. Make the layout. In an eight-page pamphlet, for example, allot a single page to each of eight phases of the subject. Then write the copy to fit the mold that has been prepared.

3. Conceive the copy visually. In writing each heading, caption, and paragraph, visualize its position and weight on the printed page. Then prepare a rough layout and write the final copy to fit. This means that copy and layout are being designed as an integrated job. It means that editor and designer must be the same person or else they must work and think as a team.

To make a layout, it is necessary first to study carefully the raw material—copy, art work, and illustrations, if those are at hand. Then it is well to evaluate their relative importance in achieving the object desired.

The next step is to try a few rough thumbnail sketches, arranging and rearranging pictures and copy to get the most pleasing design and the one that will present the message most effectively. (See DESIGN.) Whenever a job consists of more than one page, page layouts should be made in pairs so that the two-page spread is used as a single design unit.

Experience shows that it is safer to use only one side of the paper in making a layout. If page 4 is laid out on the back of page 3, and it is later decided to move one of the two pages to some other position in the book, one of the page layouts may have to be duplicated.

When a layout is being made, the margins are drawn in and the page numbers noted first. If a page is to be divided into columns, these must be drawn in as well.

Headlines and illustrations are the controlling elements in a layout and should be added next. However, the space requirement for the text may be calculated first, and the remaining space allotted to headings and illustrations.

Since text has a way of crowding the illustrations out of the book, the illustrations are sometimes handled as a "must" and cutting, if any, is done in the text. Some editors require one illustration per page to keep the pages looking interesting, whether or not a particularly relevant one can be found.

Illustrations must be cropped (see CROP) and scaled to size (see SCALING) so that the layout may show the exact space that they will occupy after reduction or enlargement. It is sufficient to draw a box on the layout and write in it "photo A," marking the appropriate photo with the same letter.

Captions for the photographs should be indicated as well, so that the printer may know exactly the size and space to be allotted to each one. (See CAPTIONS.)

Headlines may be "roughed" in or sketched in, letter by letter, in the kind and size of type desired so that the designer, editor, and author may have a more complete picture of the page as a whole.

Marginal notes on the layout give the printer exact type and spacing information or refer him to the manuscript for more complete directions.

Type specifications are also given on the typewritten manuscript which carries reference to page numbers on the layout.

Excellent suggestions for layout and the basic principles of design are given in publications listed in Appendix 2, Bibliography.

Additional basic layout pointers for beginners are as follows:

1. First of all, learn all you can about time limits and mechanical requirements such as printing process, color limitations, etc., on this job.

2. Use the tools of the trade—a layout tracing pad for ease of rearranging trial layouts by tracing, a variety of pencils for ease in getting desired weights quickly, a drawing board and T-square.

3. Check off elements to be included, both the "musts" and the "maybes." This will include head or heads, subheads, copy blocks, illustrations, logotypes, testimonials, order forms, etc. Be sure you know enough about each—see the photo or illustration if there is to be one, know the length of the copy, know the exact wording of the heads.

4. Evaluate the various elements. If necessary reduce them to a manageable number or expand them by pulling heads or subheads or lists out of the text.

5. Avoid nonselling heads. Kill them and try starting with the first really hard-hitting sentence of the copy. Or, if you are not allowed this liberty, play down the poor head and play up the meat of the message. (For example, the top of the page or the position *above* an illustration has far less attention value than the optical center or space below the illustration, although it may seem important to the layman and is a good place to bury a necessary evil.)

6. Strive for at least one major design theme or highlight in any layout— headline treatment or picture of product or use of product. Smack it across the optical center and then build around it. You can find something to emphasize in the most monotonous message.

7. Show intended margins. Ignoring margins is a very common error on the part of beginners.

8. Try to indicate various weights of type in your layout by changing pencils or by going from straight to wavy lines, etc. Don't just draw a box to indicate a photo—get a photostat to size or clip magazine photos to show tone values on the page. But do not get too meticulous too early or you will be reluctant to try other arrangements.

9. Try various reductions of photos, illustrations, and logotypes. Don't get hypnotized by the happenstance of the size the art happens to come in.

10. Crop freely. Most photos need it. Never butt photos, avoid montages, keep adjoining photos in scale. Be sure to see the photos you are working with.

11. Never print black-and-white photos in a color, unless you deliberately want a washed-out effect.

12. Never run type across photos, for it is more often done badly than well. Certainly never run small type. Likewise, never run type across any distracting drawing or pattern or device.

13. Favor tint blocks over boxes. These may be solid blocks, if the color is not too heavy, or screened blocks. It is often perfectly satisfactory to run type through the edge of a block as this may help to unify a layout, but there are problems. Remember that black type on a dark block will lose legibility. White reverse type on a light block loses legibility. Never run a photo into a color block unless the color is removed from under the photo.

14. Never divide a layout into unrelated sections—provide bridges to carry the eye from one part to another.

15. Keep captions under the illustrations. That is where people are used to looking for them.

16. If you cannot use color, remember that you can get some of the values of a two-color job with black and white and gray. Remember that plain white paper, unprinted and unillustrated, may add a valuable accent of white. Gray may be attained by screening the black or a gray area may be attained

by the use of a block of smaller type. A touch of black used massively will add contrast.

17. Avoid running type in color. If you do use color, go to a bolder weight than you would use in black. A far better way to emphasize type with color is to print in black on blocks of color, something the beginner often forgets to try. Think a long time before running all your type in a color other than black. If there is to be color in your job, use the same color in your layout to insure against surprises in the finished job.

18. Avoid tempting Providence by asking for deviations from the norm— eccentric borders, critical bleeds, hairlines in reverse, critical register problems, etc.

19. Get contrast into your type— black vs. light, large vs. small, italic vs. caps.

20. Never combine two similar type faces or two scripts. Rather contrast heavy with light, sans serif with old style, etc. Avoid needless changes in text sizes.

21. Unjustified lines (lines of uneven length) are entirely readable, but go easy on flushing them right. This may be effective for occasional lines, but it makes hard reading when it is applied to a whole paragraph. The same objection does not hold for flushing uneven lines left.

22. Letterspace caps, if you like, but do not use varying amounts of letter spacing in the same layout. Never letterspace lower case.

23. Never capitalize entire words within blocks of text. Use small caps instead.

24. Do not use decorative initial letters. They are definitely old hat today.

25. Indent paragraphs. Without indention you need at least a line of space to separate paragraphs, and usually you don't want to break up the unity of your text block in this way.

26. Take time to do careful copy fitting. Anticipate problems of word break and line break. By altering words now you may solve a problem which would be insoluble for the compositor.

27. Specify every detail. Never leave it to be guessed whether you want roman or italic, caps or lower case, indented or flushed lines. Specify lengths of lines, amount of leading, etc. Be sure that your layout and copy agree. All instructions must be in writing.

28. Never use a line longer than 65 characters nor shorter than 35. Select your sizes of type and lengths of line so as to stay within these limits. If you run shorter than 35 characters per line (about six words), you get bad word breaks and word spacing. If you run longer than 65 characters, the eye will have difficulty finding its way back to the start of the next line, although this difficulty can be lessened by increased leading.

**layout paper**  See also LAYOUT.

An opaque paper on which a layout may be drawn to size. Stationers and art suppliers can furnish suitable paper, strong enough to take erasures, in large pads, 9 by 12, 13¾ by 16¾, 18½ by 23½, etc.

*Layout tissue* is thin translucent paper suitable for tracing and often used for making layouts. Sometimes layouts are drawn or traced on tissue, which is then pasted down on opaque layout paper.

Magazine editors needing many layouts of the same size usually have their own layout paper printed in very faint blue with guidelines for margins and columns. One particularly good plan is to have actual columns of type printed in this light blue just as the lines and columns appear on a typical pair of facing pages. This facilitates the counting of lines and measuring of columns. Occasionally layout paper is also printed with an all-over pattern of graph squares in very light blue to facilitate placement of engraver's proofs, photostats of art work, headings, and special boxes.

**l.c.** Abbreviation for lower case. (See PROOFREADING.)

**ld.** Abbreviation for lead. (See LEADING; PROOFREADING.)

**lead** See LEADING.

**leaders** See also RULES.

A leader (rhymes with "feeder") is a row of dots or dashes used in tabular work to lead the eye across a space, as shown in the accompanying table.

| Type of leader | Dots per inch | |
|---|---|---|
| | 8 pt. (shown) | 12 pt. |
| 2 dots per em............. | 18 | 12 |
| 4 dots per em.......... | 36 | 24 |
| 6 dots per em | * | 36 |
| 2 strokes per em.............. | 18 | 12 |
| 4 strokes per em................ | 36 | 24 |

\* Not furnished below 10 pt.

Leaders are also used instead of rules to provide dotted lines where people are expected to sign and fill in.

Leaders serve no essential purpose in index work. Many prefer the first style shown below to the second.

Leaders, 901–904
Universal dot leaders, 902

Leaders....................... 901–904
Universal dot leaders......... 902

**leading** Leading (rhymes with "wedding") is a term referring to the spacing between type lines and paragraphs. When type lines are too close together on the page and seem to need air, they probably need leading. This means the insertion of thin strips of lead between them. Like the bulk of this book, this paragraph is set in 9-pt. type and is leaded 1 pt.

A lead is a thin strip of sheet metal 1, 2, or 3 pt. thick. Unless otherwise specified, the word "lead" refers to a 2-pt. strip. This paragraph is set in 9-pt. type and is unleaded, *i.e.*, set solid.

This paragraph is leaded 2 points. In Linotype, Intertype, or Monotype composition, the effect of leading can be most easily achieved by adjusting the machines to cast, say, 9-pt. type on an 11-pt. body. Hence, instructions to the printer can be written on the manuscript as follows: "Set in 9 pt. (name of type face) leaded 2 pt.," or "Set 9 on 11" or simply "9/11 pt." (See illustration under TYPE.)

**leaf** A single sheet of paper, each side of which is a page. Thus, a leaf consists of two pages.

**leaflets** See CIRCULARS.

**legend** See CAPTIONS.

**Leroy** A mechanical device used by draftsmen to assist them in keeping their lettering neat and even. It is of value chiefly to those who are not skilled in lettering. A professional show-card writer could work better and faster without it.

Using a Leroy lettering set.

A Leroy lettering set (see illustration) consists of a template on which the selected letters or symbols are incised, a pen, and a scriber to hold the pen and trace the guide letters on the template. Leroy templates are priced from $5.25, pens from 85 cents, and scribers from $4.75. A less expensive line, the Doric Lettering Set, offers three templates, two pens, a straight-edge, and a scriber for $7.50. For catalogue write Keuffel & Esser Co., Hoboken, N.J.

Similar work can be done through the use of Wrico and Wricoprint lettering guides, made by the Wood-Regan Instrument Co., Nutley, N.J.

**lettering**   See also PHOTO LETTERING; Appendix 1 on Type Faces.

Often there are times when hand-lettering is required despite the number of type styles and sizes in existence. However, type is always preferable to poor or mediocre hand lettering, even if it is necessary to set type in one size and then enlarge it by photostat, retouch it, etc. (For a comparison of the basic methods of lettering and type composition, see the chart under TYPE.)

Few artists are expert at lettering. Some will attempt it. Others prefer merely to rough in any lettering that must be part of their work and leave the finished lettering to be done by a specialist or to be set in type and "stripped in" by the printer. (See STRIP, STRIP-IN.)

Hand-lettering can be done in two ways—fast or slow. A really good calligrapher or sign painter can make letters flow out of his pen or brush almost as fast as the layman can write—not finished letters, but attractive ones.

The slow way is laboriously to sketch the outline of each letter and fill it in, trying to get every curve and hairline "just so." Lettering of this sort is likely to cost at least $1 a letter.

A recent development is photo lettering, a technique that might be described as mechanized hand-lettering. (See PHOTO LETTERING.)

There are several mechanical lettering aids for special jobs, as follows:

For putting display lettering on

mimeograph stencils, excellent cut-out lettering guides are available. (See MIMEOGRAPH.)

For simple sans-serif lettering with either pencil or pen, a Leroy or Wrico lettering set permits work that is neat, rapid, and nearly foolproof, if not inspired. (See LEROY.)

For maps and charts, one can buy individual letters or words printed on self-adhering transparent adhesive acetate. These can be adhered where needed, and cut apart and shaped to the required curve or line. (See MAPS; TRANS-ADHESIVE IMPRESSIONS; also FOTOTYPE, REDITYPE, and ARTYPE for methods of "setting type" in the office or art department.)

Hundreds of samples of hand-lettering are shown in the books on lettering listed in Appendix 2, Bibliography.

Three-dimensional cut-out letters which can be pasted to any background or held in slots in molding are available. See MITTEN'S LETTERS.

**letterpress**   The most common form of printing as differentiated from offset or gravure printing, etc. It is the oldest printing process and is used for practically all newspapers and a great many magazines and books (including this book). Letterpress printing is done on the relief principle whereby raised surfaces are inked and then pressed against the paper. (See RELIEF.)

There are two steps in letterpress printing: (1) setting the type and/or making the cuts for illustrations and (2) printing from them. (Sometimes electrotypes or stereotypes are made too.)

For the setting of type see TYPE and Appendix 1, Type Faces. (Setting type and taking a proof from it by the letterpress method are usually the first steps in other printing processes, too.) Making cuts is discussed under CUT. Printing from type and cuts will be discussed in this section.

The letterpress printing process is

capable of producing both very fine and very cheap results on either very short or very long runs. It is used for printing the highest quality of photographic books as well as for the daily newspaper.

This process offers a printer more control over his presswork than the other printing processes do. On the other hand, extra control implies extra work.

Cheap letterpress printing is done with a minimum of make-ready. (See MAKE-READY.) A printer sometimes cuts corners and does not use his opportunities to control the process. High-quality letterpress printing is done with very careful make-ready, high-quality inks, and good paper, and the pressman may spend hours adjusting and watching the press to get the most out of both type and cuts. Even magazines whose inside pages are printed by rotogravure or offset sometimes do their covers by letterpress because of its dependable quality.

Letterpress printing may be regarded as the norm against which to compare other processes. It is the one to use unless there are reasons for preferring some other process.

The letterpress process gives sharper, cleaner reproduction of type than any other process. (Practically all books are done in letterpress unless the illustrations are such as to require another process.)

Letterpress is almost always to be preferred when printing is done on glossy paper—and only glossy paper takes varnish well.

Some common reasons for using other processes are as follows:

1. On the cheapest jobs, it may be advisable to reproduce from typewritten material, instead of from type, in which case mimeograph, spirit duplicating, Multigraph, or offset may prove cheaper.

2. When there are many line illustrations, offset may be cheaper. Photographic illustrations, however, cost

very little less in offset unless quality is sacrificed.

3. When photographs must be reproduced and the quantity is very small, making the requisite number of copies by photography may be cheaper than making cuts for letterpress. (See PHOTOGRAPHY: AS A PRINTING PROCESS.)

4. Reprints are often cheaper in offset, if the type has not been kept standing. The letterpress printer will have to reset the type, while the offset printer can simply photograph the first edition.

5. Posters are usually cheaper in offset or silk screen unless they are unillustrated, plain type jobs, using type that the printer has on hand. This is because very large cuts for letterpress, whether line cuts or halftones, are considerably more expensive than offset plates or silk-screen frames.

6. In order to print halftones of higher than 120 screen, the letterpress process must use expensive coated paper. Other processes can use less expensive paper with no shine. Offset, gravure, and photogelatin surpass letterpress in their reproduction of soft pencil work, fine line work, soft color effects, etc.

7. It is necessary in letterpress printing to use a screen for halftone illustrations. If this is objectionable, as it may be in facsimile work, then the choice may fall on photogelatin which has no screen, or on the gravure or Optak processes in which the screen is practically invisible.

8. Buyers of printing often have to use the available press capacity instead of that which would be ideal, a fact that has dictated many a choice of printing process.

A comparison of letterpress and other printing processes is given on the charts inside the covers of this book.

For an analysis of the cost of letterpress printing, see ESTIMATING COSTS. For a discussion of the importance of matching the printing press to the job, or vice versa, see PRINTING PRESSES. For a discussion of how type and cuts can be duplicated for longer letterpress runs, see DUPLICATE PLATES. For a description of a specialized application of the letterpress principle, see MULTI-GRAPH.

**letters** See AUTOMATIC ELECTRIC TYPE-WRITER; PROCESS LETTERS; DIRECT MAIL ADVERTISING; MAIL ORDER.

Form letters are often much more effective than printed leaflets and pamphlets, whether they can be mistaken for personally typed letters or not.

For perfectly "personalized" form letters, indistinguishable from a hand-typed letter, see AUTOMATIC ELECTRIC TYPEWRITER. For personalized form letters that will fool experts but that are not typed out word by word, see PROCESS LETTERS.

The Multigraph is perhaps the most widely used method of imitating type-written letters, though a practiced eye may notice that its work is too even to be genuine typewriting. (See MULTI-GRAPH.)

All these methods permit typing in name, address, salutation, and perhaps additional personalizing data.

The mimeograph duplicates form letters neatly and efficiently without, however, attempting to imitate the distinguishing imperfection of typewriting, namely, the faint, fuzzy edge on each character left by the typewriter ribbon. (See MIMEOGRAPH.)

The Multilith can do any letter work that the mimeograph can do; in addition it can duplicate both letterhead and typewriting at the same time and handle small photographs, diagrams, etc. (See MULTILITH.)

Form letters can also be duplicated by regular printing processes as, for example, when reproduced on the first page of a circular.

In all large cities there are letter-shops and mailing services equipped to produce letters by one or several of the above methods.

Price estimates on the same 30-line, 1-page letter are given in the accompanying table. The cost of addressing envelopes is not included in these estimates. It is desirable, however, to have them addressed by the same people who do the fill-in work on personalized letters, so that styles will match. It is a waste of money to put an expensively personalized letter into an obviously machine-addressed envelope, especially if the letter is going to a home address where the recipient himself will open the envelope.

A specialty letter, often used to get inquiries, is made by the Reply-O Products Co., 7 Central Park West, New York. On the letter itself there is a window where the address ought to be, and the address which is seen through this window is on a prepaid reply card, held in place in a special pocket. All the recipient needs to do is pull out this reply card, initial it (his name is already on it), and drop it in the mail. (See also ENVELOPES for information about other specialties combining letter, envelope, order form, and reply envelope in a single piece.)

**lettershop** See DUPLICATING METHODS; ADDRESSING; LETTERS.

In all large cities there are lettershops equipped to handle mimeographing, addressing, folding, stuffing, and mailing work. They may be found under Letter Service and Addressing in the Classified Telephone Directory.

Some have little more equipment than a mimeograph machine and a few typewriters. Others have a wide variety of the latest automatic duplicating, addressing, and mailing machinery.

The duplicating and mailing costs mentioned in this book are typical lettershop charges which, of course, include labor and overhead.

Firms doing much mailing work sometimes save time, if not money, by

## Comparative Cost of Duplicated Letters *

| | Person-alized | Cost of letters without signature | | | | Kind of signature † | Cost of signature |
|---|---|---|---|---|---|---|---|
| | | 25 copies | 100 copies | 1,000 copies | 5,000 copies | | |
| Mimeograph | No | $ 2.75 | $ 2.75 | $ 6.00 | $ 17.50 | Same ink as letter | No additional cost |
| Multilith | No | 6.00 | 6.00 | 9.00 | 18.50 | Same ink as letter | No additional cost |
| Multilith (printer supplying pa-per) ‡ | No | 6.25 | 6.25 | 12.00 | 33.50 | Same ink as letter | No additional cost |
| Multigraph | No | 9.00 | 9.00 | 11.00 | 23.00 | Blue ink sig-nature from plate | $5 for signature plate;§ $1.50 per 1,000 for running it |
| Multigraph with fill-in | Yes | 11.00 | 11.00 | 31.00 | 123.00 | Blue ink sig-nature from plate | $5 for signature plate;§ $1.50 per 1,000 for running it |
| Process | Yes | 15.00 | 20.00 | 70.00 | 260.00 | Blue ink sig-nature from plate or hand-signed | $5.00 per 1,000 for signature from plate; $20 per $1,000 for tracing signature; $10 per $1,000 for hand-signed signature, not traced |
| Automatic elec-tric typewriter | Yes | 10.00 | 18.00 | 130.00 | 550.00 | Hand-signed | $20 per 1,000 for tracing signature; $10 per 1,000 for hand-signed signa-ture, not traced |

\* These estimates for a letter of about 150 words do not include cost of stationery (except as indi-cated), folding and stuffing, or stamping, sealing, and addressing envelopes. Lettershop prices vary widely. Those quoted are based on prices in a number of New York lettershops.

† Hand signing is possible in all processes, of course.

‡ Note that in Multilithing, the letterhead can be photographed and reproduced when the body of the letter is reproduced so that no printed letterhead paper needs to be supplied. (See also *combina-tion run*.)

§ This price is for a Multilithed signature which some consider neater and less like a rubber stamp than a Multigraphed signature. For a Multigraphed signature, the quoted price for running the plate is $1 for the first 1,000, 50 cents for each additional 1,000.

buying and operating their own letter-shop equipment.

**letter spacing** The compositor has let-terspaced the last word in this s e n - t e n c e . He has put a thin space after each letter. Small (lower-case) letters are not often letterspaced except when there is no other way to justify a very short line. (See JUSTIFY.) German print-ers letterspace words that they wish to emphasize instead of using italics.

Headings set in capitals are often let-terspaced slightly to make them more legible; thus, C A P I T A L S. A thin space has been added between each two letters except between "T" and "A," where there was already enough space because of the design of the letters.

To instruct a printer to add letter spacing, put a diagonal stroke [/] where the spacing is to go and write "letter space," "letter #," or "insert thin spaces," etc. Note the various amounts of letter spacing which can be indicated:

LETTER SPACING
(Set tight)

LETTER SPACING
(1 pt. spaced)

LETTER SPACING
(2 pt. spaced)

LETTER SPACING
(3 pt. spaced)

**ligature**   Two or more letters cast as one piece as "fi" and "fl."

**lightface**   See also Appendix 1, Type Faces.

This sentence is set in lightface type, which is used for the body or text of a printed job. **This is set in boldface type, which is used generally for emphasis.**

**line cut**   See also CUT.

Cuts (the word is used synonymously with engravings and includes photoengravings) are of two kinds: line cuts and halftones. (See HALFTONE.) Line cuts may also be referred to as zinc etchings, line etchings, line engravings, line blocks, and line plates.

Pen-and-ink drawings are typical of the kind of art work that may be reproduced by line cuts; photographs are typical of the kind that must be reproduced by halftones. (For an understanding of the distinction between art that can be reproduced in line and art that must be reproduced as a halftone, see HALFTONE; DRAWING TECHNIQUES.)

Line cuts are required only for letterpress (relief) printing, not for offset or other processes. These other proc-

esses have their own ways of reproducing line drawings, either at no extra cost, or at a charge of only a dollar or so for stripping. (See STRIP.)

The familiar rubber stamp is a kind of line cut. Wood cuts and linoleum blocks are handmade line cuts. (See BLOCK PRINTING.)

Line cuts for commercial printing are made by photoengravers by a

A mounted line cut held with nails driven through the nonprinting areas, which have been routed out.

photomechanical process. The design is transferred photographically to a zinc or copper plate. Then acid is used to etch (eat away) the metal surface that is not protected by the design. The metal is then mounted on a wooden block so as to be type-high.

When lines of type are to be run within a line drawing, the cut can be mortised (see MORTISE) to leave a notch, slot, or hole for receiving the type. However, it is difficult to wedge type into a mortise (particularly an inside mortise) securely enough to safeguard against work-ups in printing. It is safer to have an electro made from the combined cut and type, then print from the electro. Of course, it is possible to take type proofs (or photostats of them to same scale as art work) and paste them down as part of the art work, and make a line cut from the combination; this is probably the easiest procedure by far, and the one most commonly used. The electro method, however, will give better reproduction of the type; type always loses some crispness when reproduced by line cut.

If the type or lettering must run across and through the lines of the drawing then the photoengraver can be instructed to surprint the lettering on the drawing (at extra cost). Just give him both and put an overlay on the art work to show placement of the type, Alternately, have the type proofed on transparent acetate and lay it over the art work, so the engraver can photograph type and drawing at once.

Line cuts are usually made on zinc or magnesium; they may be made on copper (at double the cost) for fine work.

Prices for mounted line cuts are about as shown on the accompanying table of typical costs. Of course large users of engravings pay less than occasional users. The rate for Ben Day

**Approximate Cost of Mounted Cuts ***

| Size | Line cut | Zinc half-tone | Ben Day line cut † | Copper half-tone |
|---|---|---|---|---|
| 1½ x 2 | 5.11 | 5.18 | 6.37 | 7.00 |
| 2 x 3 | 5.88 | 5.53 | 7.00 | 7.84 |
| 3 x 4 | 7.14 | 6.30 | 8.47 | 9.38 |
| 4 x 6 | 8.82 | 7.70 | 10.71 | 12.39 |
| Approx. cost per add'l sq. in.‡ | .12 | .12 | .12 | .24 |

Note: Zinc halftones are made in screens up to 100 lines to the inch. Copper halftones are made in 110, 120, 135, 150, 175, and 200 screen.

\* Figured on a rate of 7 cents a unit.

† This does not include cost of laying Ben Day.

‡ Costs are not actually figured on a square-inch basis. However, these figures will give a rough idea of prices until a photoengraver's scale can be consulted.

line cuts applies to any cut containing fine shading, whether this shading has been added by the engraver on the Ben Day principle or has been added on the art work by an artist's shading tints. (See SHADING TINTS.) If added by the engraver, there is also an additional time charge. Two proofs of any cut are ordinarily supplied without extra charge.

An additional 33 per cent is charged for a reverse plate, where the black lines on white of the original art work are reversed to white lines on black. This charge may be avoided by supplying a reverse photostat to the engraver instead of the original art.

A line cut is fastened to the mounting block with nails, or (increasingly) by adhesive. If it is to be nailed, ordinarily a shoulder about ⅛ in. wide is left. However, when the cut is to run closer than ⅛ in. to other material, this shoulder must be omitted and the cut may be "blocked flush" on any or all four sides. The nails are then driven through any white space that may be left within the design. If there is no such space and if it is necessary to block flush on three or four sides, then the cut can be "anchored," or fastened with solder to anchors, in the wood mount. Cuts that are full column width are often ordered blocked flush on the sides to aid the printer in making up his pages.

Line drawings, like other art work, can be reversed left for right by the engraver so that objects that were facing left, face right. This, of course, turns lettering into looking-glass lettering and makes cars drive on the wrong side of the street.

To reverse a drawing left for right, but not black for white, the engraver is asked to flop his negative. (See FLOP.)

The prices of cuts are ordinarily figured by a standard scale supplied by photoengravers from which the "unit" value of any cut may easily be figured. Thus a minimum-sized zinc line cut has a unit value of 73 on the scale. The cost per unit is a matter for negotiation between engraver and customer, and depends on volume, quality demand, etc. At 7 cents a unit, the above-mentioned cut would cost $5.11.

There are some mail-order engravers specializing in magnesium cuts (a metal which may yet displace zinc as the preferred metal for line cuts) who price their cuts by the square inch instead of the unit. One is Cut Rate Cuts, P.O. Box 3142, St. Petersburg, Fla., charging 11 cents a square inch for unmounted line cuts, with a minimum of $1. Another is Basil L. Smith, P.O.

A Linotype slug.

Box 8169, Philadelphia 1, Pa., charging about 13 cents a square inch for *mounted* line cuts, with a minimum of $3.29. (Write for detailed scale.)

**line drawing**  See DRAWING TECHNIQUES.

**linen finish**  See PEBBLING.

**line plate**  See LINE CUT; CUT.

**lining**  (1) In the paper trade the lining of a piece of cardboard is the outside ply, not the inside as one might expect. It is often of a better grade than the "middles." (2) In bookbinding the lining is the material that is glued to the back of a book, after sewing and backing, to add strength to the binding. (3) In typesetting, figures that have no descenders, *i.e.*, that do not extend below the printed line, are called lining

figures: 1, 2, 3, 4, 5, 6, 7, 8, 9, 0. (Old-style figures: 1, 2, 3, 4, 5, 6, 7, 8, 9, 0.)

**Linofilm**  The Linofilm is Linotype's entry into the field of phototypesetting, just as Fotosetter is Intertype's and the Monofilm is Monotype's. In operation, a keyboard unit of the Linofilm produces a perforated tape, which is fed into a separate photographic unit. The keyboard is that of an actual typewriter and produces a typed draft (for proof-reading) of what has been simultaneously punched into the tape. In this respect, it is like the Justowriter. Unlike the Justowriter, however, the Linofilm is designed for easy mixing of many faces and any variety of extra characters in the same line.

**linoleum block**  See BLOCK PRINTING.

**Linotype**  The Linotype and its substantially identical competitor, the Intertype, are typesetting machines that cast each line as a solid metal "line of type." They are used almost universally for newspapers and share the periodical, book, and job printing field with the Monotype. (See MONOTYPE.)

There are just these three methods of machine composition of metal type— Linotype, Intertype, and Monotype. The first two are, for practical purposes, the same.

Setting type by machine is far cheaper than doing it by hand if there is much of it. For this reason the smaller sizes of type (4, 5, 6, 7, 8, 9, 10, 11,

12, and 14 pt.) are almost always set by machine. However, a hand compositor can set half a dozen lines in the time it would take a Linotype operator to adjust his machine to a new size and kind of type and length of line. (A printer may have to charge $1 or $2 merely to set one line on the Linotype, in order to cover the cost of setting up the machine.) Linotype machines will handle sizes as large as 18, 24, 30, 36 pt., and even larger, but, because it is uncommon for printers to have these sizes on the machine, they are frequently set by hand. (See LUDLOW.)

The operator of a Linotype machine sits at a keyboard somewhat like that of a typewriter. When he touches, say, the letter "L," a matrix (mold) for that letter drops into place in the line being set. When the line is complete, molten type metal is forced against the matrices, and the result is a Linotype slug, ready for printing.

matrix back in its own compartment in the magazine, ready for re-use.

The invention of the spaceband solved the first problem. When a Linotype operator pushes the space bar, a spaceband drops into place at the end of the word just set. This is simply a

Spaceband: Linotype and Intertype.

space made out of two opposed wedges. When these wedges are pushed together, the spaceband gets wider. When a line is nearly full, the spacebands are expanded until it is exactly full.

Matrix: Linotype and Intertype.

Two great problems had to be solved before the Linotype could displace the setting of type by hand. First, there was the problem of spacing between words so as to "justify" (fill) each line. (See JUSTIFY.) Second, there was the problem of automatically putting each used

The problem of getting the used matrices back in the magazine ready for re-use was solved on the latchkey principle. Each matrix has a built-in key, like the key to a Yale lock, which will unlock the door to its own compartment and no other. The used matrices are automatically pushed, one by one, past each compartment in the magazine, but each can drop off the distributor bar only when over its own proper compartment.

Most Linotype matrices are two-letter matrices, like those shown, and carry an italic as well as a roman version of the same letter, or perhaps a bold (instead of italic) with roman. If the matrices for any word are raised a notch, the line will be cast with that word in italic (or bold).

A phantom illustration of a Linotype machine. A touch of a key at the keyboard (1) releases one of the matrices stored in the magazines at (2). It falls (3) and joins other matrices and spacebands at (4). The completed line of matrices is moved to (5) where melted type metal is forced against it, and a line is cast. The used matrices then move to (6), are slid on to the elevator bar (7), are lifted to (8), and travel along the distributor bar (9) until each returns (10) to its proper compartment in the magazine. (*Photo courtesy of Mergenthaler Linotype Co.*)

Thus, a Linotype operator who is using two-letter roman-with-italic matrices can set italic as easily as roman. If he is using roman-with-bold matrices, he can set bold as easily as roman. He is not able to set all three without extra trouble and extra cost, unless the machine he is using is a "mixer" designed for such special work.

Extra trouble and extra expense are also involved in setting SMALL CAPS. As there is no special section on the Linotype keyboard for small cap keys, they are scattered about under characters that have no italic (figures, punctuation, etc.),

In order to change from one kind or size of type face to another, the Linotype operator must change magazines. For example, the 9-pt. Baskerville matrices with which this book was set are kept in one magazine. The 8-pt. Spartan Heavy matrices used for the headings are kept in another. It is possible to put as many as four main and four auxiliary magazines on some Linotype machines at the same time, but the operator must shift from one magazine to the other as his copy may require.

If typesetting on the Linotype or Intertype is desired, the following points should be kept in mind:

1. In consultation with the printer try to choose a font of type that is available; *i.e.,* one that is not tied up all the time on another job. Note, however, that the busy fonts are usually the most desirable ones. Printers will buy fonts specially for important cus-

A line of Linotype matrices and spacebands. The upper of the two rows of characters casts unless some or all the matrices are lifted a notch so that the lower (italic) characters cast. The spacebands are wedge shaped. Pushing them up increases the space between the words until the line is full. *(Photo courtesy of Mergenthaler Linotype Co.)*

tomers who plan to use them a lot.

2. If the selected font combines roman and italic, avoid the use of boldface; if it combines roman and bold, avoid the use of italic.

3. Most Linotypes will not set a line longer than 30 picas without considerable extra expense for setting each line in two parts. Some Linotypes will handle a 42-pica line.

4. In checking corrections make sure that the changed line replaces the faulty one, and not some other line. Read two or three lines before and after the change.

5. Where possible, make corrections of such a length that only one line need be reset, and not an entire paragraph.

See also LINOFILM.

**liquid duplicator** See SPIRIT DUPLICATOR.

**list broker** See MAILING LISTS.

**litho** Abbreviation for lithography. Litho coated paper means coated paper suitable for use in offset lithography. (See OFFSET; OFFSET PAPER.)

**lithography** See OFFSET for a discussion of how and when to use lithography commercially; see PLANOGRAPHY for an explanation of the principle employed in this type of printing.

"Photo-offset lithography" is the full name of the modern commercial application of lithography, which may be referred to as "offset" or "photo offset" or "offset lithography."

Lithography (literally, stone writing) is an example of the planographic process. Some fine artists still work on stones, but in commercial work, stone has given way to metal as a material for making printing plates.

The word "lithography" is sometimes used in connection with fine color reproduction work as though the process were somehow superior to mere offset. The ten-dollar word has a loftier ring but it means the same.

**Lithure** See BIMETAL PLATES.

**lock up** To lock up pages of type or cuts means to clamp them into a steel frame, called a "chase," ready for putting on the printing press. (See TYPE.)

**logotype** A piece of type that carries, not just a letter, but one or more words, such as the name of a firm or a product.

Logotype and adcuts.

Many firms adopt a special style for their name and have logotypes made so that this style can be followed whether or not the printers they deal with have this style of type.

Logotypes that are made from hand-lettering or a drawing instead of from a standard type style are sometimes called "adcuts."

Logotypes and adcuts are made to order by American Type Founders, Elizabeth, N.J.

The words "ligature" and "logotype" are sometimes confused. The former refers only to a combination of two or three letters that have been designed to overlap each other, as fi, ffl, etc.

**loose-leaf binding** See MECHANICAL BINDINGS.

**lower case** See also PROOFREADING.

Lower case, designated "l.c.," is the printer's term for small, as opposed to capital, letters. Hand type for small letters used to be kept in the lower case, that for capital letters in the upper case. (See illustration under CASE.) Hence, "u. and l.c." (upper and lower case) has the same meaning as "c. and l.c." (caps and lower case).

**lucy**  See CAMERA LUCIDA.

**Ludlow**  See also TYPE; Appendix 1.

The Ludlow Typograph or Ludlow is a machine for casting lines of type in a range of sizes from 4 to 96 pt., and up to 240 pt. for special advertising figures. It and a similar machine called the "All-Purpose Linotype" (APL) are used primarily to handle type sizes from 18 pt. up; sometimes also lines of smaller type too few in number to be worth setting on the big keyboard Linotype and Intertype machines.

Ludlow composition is really hand composition, except that the compositor sets matrices (molds) instead of actual type and casts a line of new type from these matrices. (See illustrations on page 164.)

Ludlow matrices.

The choice between using foundry type and using Ludlow or APL types depends in the first instance, of course, on the type styles available. Some types are available only in the form of foundry type.

Where the customer is willing to use either a foundry type style or something that is "on the machine," printers usually favor the latter. This is because Ludlow and APL faces are cast up new for each use, whereas foundry types wear out with use.

Sometimes foundry type is used and then melted down to prevent mixing the worn letters with unused type. Foundry type fonts that have been thinned out in this way can be replen-

ished, but this is a more costly procedure than to use Ludlow or APL slugs. See FOUNDRY TYPE. There is, of course, no disadvantage to melting down hand type that has been used only once if the printer has Monotype equipment with which he can cast more hand type. (See MONOTYPE.)

A special advantage of using Ludlow or APL composition occurs when the same line must be set many times. This is the case, for example, with the running heads in books. In such cases, the line need be "set" only once; as many lines as needed can then be cast from the one line of matrices.

Ludlow slugs have a distinctive T-shape, the body being the same thickness for virtually all sizes, and the type being molded in a "shoulder" which extends beyond the body.

What interests the buyer of composition is the fact that a printer who has certain Ludlow faces usually does not have similar faces offered by other typefounders.

Some popular Ludlow faces and some similar faces offered by other typefounders are as follows:

| Ludlow | Corresponding Face by Other Typefounder |
|---|---|
| Eden | Corvinus |
| Radiant | Lydian |
| Coronet | Trafton |
| Mayfair | Liberty |
| UMBRA | SHADOW |

Ludlow slugs.

A Ludlow slug, a proof taken from that slug, and the line of Ludlow matrices from which the slug was cast.

**luminescent printing** Luminescent, phosphorescent, and fluorescent qualities can be obtained by dusting wet ink with special powders, by using special paper, or by using special ink.

*Autoluminescence, i.e.,* the property of giving off visible light indefinitely, depends on the use of radium or some other radioactivated element mixed with a fluorescent salt which will glow under the radiation from the radioactive material. Watch dials are an example.

*Phosphorescence* is the property of giving off visible light for a limited period after excitation by exposure to an external light source. The period can be from a few minutes to 12 hr., depending on the chemical used.

*Fluorescence* is the property of giving off visible light under excitation by external radiation of a different wave length. A number of chemicals give off visible radiation while exposed to invisible ultraviolet radiation.

Luminescent printing was developed for several war uses, notably to make airplane instruments and maps visible under "black light" (ultraviolet radiation) invisible to the enemy.

In general three methods are used to obtain a luminescent effect: (1) The printing is done with tacky varnish, and luminescent powder is dusted over the surface and adheres to the varnish. (2) Luminescent paper is used, and printed lines show against this glow. (3) A luminescent chemical is mixed with the ink. When a substantial thickness of ink must be applied, the silkscreen process is often used. (See SILK SCREEN.)

Day-Glo fluorescent pigments are made by Switzer Brothers, Inc., of 4732 St. Clair Ave., Cleveland, Ohio. This Cleveland firm and other manufacturers licensed under Switzer patents use these pigments to make inks and other daylight fluorescent color materials. These "brighter-than-bright" colors are finding increasing use on 24-sheet posters, car cards, point-of-sale materials, and other promotional pieces. The Day-Glo fluorescent colors are available in silk-screen-process printing paints, letterpress and gravure inks, paints for brushing and spraying, solidly coated papers and paper products, banner satin, flock and bronzing powders.

Generally, the fluorescent colors have only a limited life when exposed to sunlight—60 days for screen-process printing paints and 120 days for bulletin paints. A thick color film of approximately 1½ mils is recommended for outdoor exposure. Very effective results can be obtained by letterpress and offset printing in reverse with conventional inks on Day-Glo coated paper stock. Unusual light and color effects are obtainable at night by using the combination of "black light" (ultraviolet) lamps with incandescent lights that flash off and on. When the conventional lights are on, the Day-Glo elements are quite colorful, and when the incandescent lights are off the Day-Glo colors glow with exceptional brilliance against the background of darkness.

Companies specializing in the manufacture of Day-Glo fluorescent materials under Switzer license include: Sherwin-Williams; Dennison Mfg. Co., Crocker, Burbank Papers, Inc.; Fred'k H. Levy Co.; Mid-States Gummed Paper Co.; Kleen-Stik Products, Inc.; Lawter Chemicals, Inc.; American Crayon Co.; Craftint Mfg. Co.; Rayon Processing Co. of R.I.; National Card, Mat & Board Co.; Wrenn Paper Co.; Rexford Paper Co.; and Dane & Co., Ltd.

**luminous printing** See LUMINESCENT PRINTING.

**Lumitype** See PHOTON.

# M | m

**machine-coated paper**  An inexpensive grade of coated paper. It should not be confused with machine-finish (M.F.) paper, which is not coated. (See PAPER.)

**machine-finish paper**  See also PAPER. A machine-finish paper (abbreviation M.F.) is an uncoated paper that has been calendered until it is smoother than an antique, not so glossy as a supercalendered paper, and not quite so smooth as an English-finish paper. It will take 85- to 100-screen halftones.

**Machol Edge Index**  See EDGE INDEX.

**magazine**  To Linotype and Intertype operators the word "magazine" means the heavy metal container in which the matrices are kept. A magazine contains a complete font of matrices for one size of one type face. (See LINOTYPE.)

**magazines**  See PERIODICALS.

**magenta screen**  See HALFTONE.

**magnesium plates**  Line cuts and halftone engravings are now being made on magnesium as well as on zinc and copper. Magnesium is a metal that is

lighter than aluminum, fine-grained, easily etched, and very long wearing. Magnesium engravings can be made on automatic etching machines by methods which eliminate the need for the repeated powdering and burning-in required by traditional methods of etching zinc and copper. Magnesium plates made in quantity by automatic methods are said to compare favorably in cost with offset plates, a fact of great interest to newspapers and other letterpress printers who had feared that they might be unable to use their present equipment for work composed on the Fotosetter, Varityper, Photon, etc. In some applications, magnesium engravings are being used in place of electros, both on a cost-comparison basis and because magnesium plates are of more dependable thickness and do not deform under pounding as lead-backed electros may do. Magnesium is also being used for binding dies. (See DIE CUTTING.) A drawback to magnesium is a tendency toward pitting while in storage.

**magnetic recording**  See RECORDINGS.

**mailing information**  See Appendix 4.

166

**mailing-list corrections**    See MAILING
LISTS; also Appendix 4, Postal Information.

**mailing lists**    Mailing lists of every con-
ceivable description can be obtained
through professional list brokers, or list
compilers, or direct from list owners
at rentals ranging from $10 to $25 per
thousand names. Currently available
lists include such specialized groups as
the former subscribers to magazines
and book clubs, buyers of merchandise
by mail, expectant mothers, doctors,
licensed pilots, etc. Usually such lists
are rented for one-time use, addressed
on envelopes supplied by the renter
and returned to him for mailing, with
the understanding that the names will
not be copied.

*Procuring mailing lists.* Some mailing
lists exist in published form and can
be obtained from trade directories and
other reference books. However, many
—particularly buyers and former buyers
by mail—have not been published and
exist only on cards or stencils in the
hands of the firm that compiled and
maintains them. They are generally
procurable direct or through list brokers, on a rental or exchange basis. List
buyers generally ask the right to test an
alphabetical or geographical cross section of the names on a large list before
renting the whole. (See MAIL ORDER.)

A firm's most valuable mailing lists
are usually its own lists. Lists of customers, prospects, publicity outlets, etc.,
can become invaluable tools for supplementing the work of salesmen and
spreading information.

*Building and maintaining mailing
lists.* Good lists are built with care.
Each addition is checked, each card is
dated, every stencil is proofread when it
is cut, all lists are checked against orders received or reviewed at intervals
by salesmen and field representatives.
Good lists are also "cleaned" regularly
to correct changes of address, to remove the deceased, and to substitute

current officeholders and business executives for any who have left. (See
Appendix 4, Postal Information, for
methods of enlisting post-office aid in
cleaning lists.)

It is easy to forget that a mailing list
is nothing but a list of living, breath-
ing individuals; however, it must be
maintained as such. List maintenance
cannot safely be left in the care of unskilled help. At least once a year and
preferably oftener every list should be
reviewed by some responsible executive. Salesmen should be encouraged to
review regularly the mailing lists of
their customers. They will seldom fail
to catch errors or omissions.

Some firms rent out seldom-used lists
for the primary purpose of keeping
them up to date. Changes can run as
high as 50 per cent a year, rarely less
than 20 per cent.

One firm, dealing with schools, used
to address each principal by name. It
now uses the title "Principal" instead
of the name, after finding it impossible
to keep up with name changes.

Lists that will be used from eight to
twelve times in two years are usually
put on stencils. (See ADDRESSING.) Often
the cards or stencils are tabbed or
keyed, so that it is possible to address
only certain groups within the list.
Tabbing has one disadvantage: it may
be necessary to run 10,000 stencils
through the machine to address 2,500
of them. One answer is to keep proof
cards, made from the stencils, in one
master file, but to maintain the stencils
as several separate lists. Since postal
regulations require that third-class bulk
mailings be sorted and tied geographically, there is also an argument for
keeping the stencils in one geographically arranged list.

Edward N. Mayer, Jr., author of
"How to Make More Money with Your
Direct Mail," defines a "prospect" as
"a man, woman, company, or institu-
tion who under normal conditions will
have a definite use for your product

or service, who has sufficient money to pay for it, and in whom a desire can be created for it." He offers the following pointers on sources of mailing-list information which are valuable in checking or building prospect lists:

1. *Commercial List Houses.* There are many concerns that compile local or national lists; some that specialize in lists of doctors, dentists, nurses, etc.; others that handle only lists of teachers or lawyers or automobile owners. Most, if not all, of them are thoroughly reliable and can be depended on to furnish the best list within the limits of available information to suit your own particular specifications.

2. *Trade Directories.* Practically every trade or industry has a directory published once a year or even more often that you can buy for only a few dollars. These directories contain full information about every organization in the industry and in most cases include a list of the top personnel of each company.

3. *City Directories.* Many cities issue annual or semiannual lists of all residents and business organizations. In some cases the information goes so far as to list the occupation and employer of the individual, making it possible to compile company employee lists.

4. *Credit Rating Books.* Dun & Bradstreet, for example, has lists of practically the entire business community of the country. Most of the credit rating books do not list local addresses, but they can be checked against telephone directories for this information.

5. *Telephone Directories.* Practically every telephone book (complete with classified section) published in the entire country is available for a ridiculously small fee through your own local telephone company.

6. *Membership Lists.* Fraternities, sororities, chambers of commerce, Rotary, Kiwanis, Lions, professional and technical societies, religious, labor, and political organizations, trade associations, social and golf clubs—all have membership lists, some of them are for sale, and some may be procured free of charge.

Although many lists are available for the asking, many others are carefully guarded. Lists are private property and you had better check before you buy to be certain

you are not paying for a piece of stolen property.

7. *Voting Lists.* State, city, county, and village clerks or other officials frequently have lists or will compile them for you from voting, tax, license, permit, or even real-estate or building records.

8. *Trade and Consumer Magazines.* The name of advertisers in various magazines may serve your needs as an industry or general list.

9. *Clipping Bureaus.* A good news-clipping bureau can give you, particularly from small city or suburban newspapers, lists of engagements, marriages, births, deaths, new businesses or organization changes, fire damages, building permits, moving notices, etc.

10. *Government Lists.* The United States government publishes more directories than any other known source. A list of these directories will be mailed to you free of charge by the Superintendent of Documents, Government Printing Office, Washington 25, D.C.

11. *List Brokers.* Many organizations rent their lists to noncompeting organizations through brokers, who are organized into the National Council of Mailing List Brokers.

12. *Subscription and Circulation Lists.* Many publishers, particularly in trade lines, rent or sell all or part of their lists. Some of them allow their lists to be used only by advertisers in their own publications. It may be worth while to advertise in order to secure the use of a particular list otherwise unavailable.

13. *Company Records and Personnel.* Ledger records, sales slips and c.o.d. orders of your own company are profitable mailing list sources. Remember your customers, past and present, are your competitors' best prospects. Your own salesmen and service representatives can, if properly trained in the job, add the best possible prospects to your list.

14. *Enclosures in Your Mailings.* Many a good prospect has been added to a list by leaving space on order blanks, etc., for your customers to list the names of friends or business associates.

15. *Contests, Coupons, Fan Mail.* These names can be valuable as well as those on the stubs of admission tickets to conventions and exhibits and names in guest books at exhibit booths.

Among the firms that act as brokers for mailing lists are Archer Mailing List Service, 140 W. 55 St., New York 19; George R. Bryant Co., 75 E. Wacker Drive, Chicago 1; Walter Drey, Inc., 257 Fourth Ave., New York 10; Guild Co., 160 Engle St., Englewood, N.J.; Lewis Kleid Co., 25 W. 45 St., New York 36; Willa Maddern, Inc., 215 Fourth Ave., New York 3; Mosely Mail Order List Service, 38 Newbury St., Boston 16; Names Unlimited, Inc., 352 Fourth Ave., New York 10; D. L. Natwick, 932 Broadway, New York 10; James E. True Associates, 419 Fourth Ave., New York 16.

The major list compilers, who will supply useful "lists of lists" on request, include W. S. Ponton, Inc., 50 E. 42 St., New York 17, and R. L. Polk & Company, 244 Madison Ave., New York 16 (also Detroit). A more comprehensive listing of list sources is given in "The Literary Market Place." (See Appendix 2.)

List compilers specialize. School lists, for example, may be obtained from the Educational Lists Co., Inc., 17 E. 72 St., New York 10. A good source of information on where to find specialized lists is the office of the trade paper of that field.

A national directory of mailing-list sources is published by B. Klein and Company, 27 E. 22 St., New York 10.

For further information on mail-order techniques and mailing lists, see the books listed in Appendix 2, Bibliography.

**mailing tubes**  See also SHIPPING INFORMATION.

Mailing tubes are expensive compared with envelopes, but there is no cheaper way of shipping maps and other items that must not be folded. Even when many copies of an item are to go to one address, it is sometimes desirable to ship each copy in its own mailing tube, for the recipient may need the tubes for his own single-copy distribution.

When inquiring about mailing tubes, give specifications as to length and diameter desired, and whether paper cuffs are needed for tucking in to keep contents in place.

For suppliers: look under Mailing Devices in the Classified Telephone Directory, or write to Hudson Paper Tube Co., 537 W. Broadway, New York; The Cleveland Container Co., 4925 S. Halsted St., Chicago, and 4900 Valley Blvd., Los Angeles.

For a 27-in. mailing tube with 2-in. diameter and paper cuffs, the following prices are typical: 6 cents each for 100, 5.5 cents each for 500, 5.25 cents each for 1,000, plus shipping charges.

**mailings**  See DISTRIBUTION; ADDRESSING; DIRECT MAIL; LETTERS; MAIL ORDER; Appendix 4, Postal Information.

**mail order**  See also DIRECT MAIL ADVERTISING; MAILING LISTS.

The mail-order industry is a specialized one existing on sales made entirely through the mails. The giants in the field are of course Sears, Roebuck and Montgomery Ward. Their catalogues offer an object lesson in how to prepare persuasive, explicit advertising copy and illustrations. Their operations are not typical of the mail-order field, however, since they can keep costs lower than is possible in most mail-order operations.

Selling by mail is not quite so simple as the novice sometimes assumes. Under certain circumstances it can be extremely effective, but only in the hands of someone who has studied the accumulated know-how of the business. There are no "tricks of the trade" in the shady sense. Actually the mail-order business is operated almost invariably on the money-back-if-not-satisfied basis. There are, however, many tricks of simple salesmanship.

Before venturing into this field, outsiders should ponder these principles, considered basic by mail-order men:

1. The product or service being offered should be something that is, or can be made to seem, unique—unobtainable elsewhere.

2. Success depends on a good mailing list. (See MAILING LISTS.)

3. The best prospects are people known to be in the habit of buying by mail.

4. If possible, a large mailing list should be tested before the whole of it is used.

5. It is hard to make ends meet on units of sale of less than $3 to $5 unless repeat business is to be expected.

6. Many mail-order men count on apportioning gross income about as follows: 50 per cent to cost of sales, 30 per cent to overhead, and 20 per cent to manufacturing costs. Some magazines are content if subscription receipts equal the cost of the subscription campaign!

7. Since the difference between a 2 and a 3 per cent return may make all the difference between loss and profit, little things should be watched. The prospect should be asked to order, ordering should be made easy for him, and inducements should be offered for prompt action.

It would be difficult to overstress the importance of a good mailing list. Practically nothing can be sold profitably to a list of names taken uncritically from a telephone book. Good returns are difficult to get from any list of people not known to have the habit of buying by mail. (See MAILING LISTS.)

It is customary to test every large list before using the whole of it. If, for example, a list of 25,000 names seems promising, 2,000 names can be taken from it and tested. These people should receive the exact material that is proposed for the whole 25,000. If 2 per cent of the 2,000 respond, it may be assumed that approximately the same percentage of the remaining 23,000 will

respond when the same mailing is sent them under similar conditions.

Considerable reliance can be placed on such a test if certain rules are followed. The statisticians can prove that, in the above instance, there are 95 chances in 100 that the results for the remaining 23,000 will fall between 1.37 and 2.63 per cent, and that there are 997 chances out of 1,000 that the results for the 23,000 will fall between 1.06 and 2.94 per cent.

The rules for planning and evaluating tests are as follows:

1. The names being tested must be a true random sample of the whole list. They must not be weighted geographically or as to age, income, or any other factor. The best way to get a true random sample is to take every tenth, twentieth, etc., name. Another way (if the list is arranged alphabetically by name) is to take all those whose names begin with "L" and "R," for example. In actual practice, of course, it may be impractical to take every tenth name, because there would be no way to skip the test names in a subsequent mailing. A common compromise, where lists are arranged geographically, is to take one or more states assumed to be typical.

2. The material mailed in the test must be identical in every way with the material to be mailed to the whole list —identical as to method of addressing, envelope, enclosures, paper, method of printing, etc. By rights, the date of mailing should be identical too. This is of course impossible, but it is possible and desirable to mail on the same day of the week and to reckon with such factors as the season, weather, current news, and holidays.

3. The test mailing must be large enough to give results of the desired accuracy. Surprisingly enough, the size of the whole mailing list has nothing to do with the size of the test sample. A sampling of 2,000 names will give just as reliable information about a list of 1,000,000 names as about a list

of 10,000 names. On the other hand, a sampling of 100 names will tell little about a list of any size.

4. The mathematical laws of probability make it possible to predict with assurance the "probable error" in the results of any test mailing. The accompanying table shows how much reliance may be placed on a given return from a sample of given size.

The unit of sale is very important in mail-order work. If the cost of addressing, printing, postage, materials, and labor on each letter mailed is 5 cents, or $5 per hundred, then each 100 letters mailed must bring in at least this $5 plus adequate payment for the merchandise, usually at least a total of $10. On a $1 item this would necessitate a 10 per cent return (which is unusually high); on a $2 item, a 5 per cent return would suffice; on a $5 item, a 2 per cent return would be acceptable.

Anyone who is contemplating mail-order work should by all means read at considerable length in some of the very excellent books on the subject. These are listed and described in Appendix 2, Bibliography.

*Mathematics of the law of probability.* The table is a guide to the reliability of test mailings of various sizes. The mathematics underlying it need not concern the layman, but for those interested in working out the problem themselves, the formula is

$$\text{Probable error} = \pm \sqrt{\frac{PQ}{N}}$$

where $P$ is the number of positive responses, $Q$ is the number of negative responses, and $N$ is the number in the test mailing $(P + Q)$. In the example given earlier, a 2 per cent return on a 2,000 test mailing may be evaluated as follows:

$$\text{Probable error} = \pm \sqrt{\frac{40 \times 1,960}{2,000}}$$
$$= \pm 6.3$$

This means that there is a fifty-fifty chance that returns on the whole list will equal the test result plus or minus 6.3; *i.e.*, they will fall between 33.7 and 46.3 for each 2,000 mailed, or between 16.8 and 23.1 per thousand, or between 1.68 and 2.31 per cent.

## Law of Probability as Applied to Evaluation of the Results of Test Mailings

| Size of test mailing | If the return on the test mailing is: | | | | | | |
| | 1% | 2% | 3% | 4% | 5% | 10% | 20% |
|---|---|---|---|---|---|---|---|
| | then 95 chances out of 100 the return on the identical mailing to the whole list will be (in per cent) between | | | | | | |
| 100 | 0–2.99 | 0–4.80 | 0–6.41 | 0.08–7.92 | 0.64–9.36 | 4.00–16.00 | 12.00–28.00 |
| 250 | 0–2.26 | 0.23–3.77 | 0.84–5.16 | 1.52–6.48 | 2.24–7.76 | 6.20–13.80 | 14.94–25.00 |
| 500 | 0.11–1 89 | 0.75–3.25 | 1.48–4.52 | 2.25–5.75 | 3.05–6.95 | 7.32–12.68 | 16.42–23.58 |
| 1,000 | 0.37–1.63 | 1.12–2.88 | 1.92–4.08 | 2.76–5.24 | 3.62–6.38 | 8.10–11.90 | 17.48–22.52 |
| 2,000 | 0.55–1.45 | 1.37–2.63 | 2.24–3.76 | 3.12–4.88 | 4.03–5.97 | 8.66–11.34 | 18.21–21.79 |
| 5,000 | 0.72–1.28 | 1.60–2.40 | 2.52–3.48 | 3.45–4.55 | 4.38–5.62 | 9.15–10.85 | 18.87–21.13 |
| 10,000 | 0.80–1.20 | 1.72–2.28 | 2.66–3.34 | 3.61–4.39 | 4.56–5.44 | 9.40–10.60 | 19.20–20.80 |
| 100,000 | 0.94–1.06 | 1.91–2.09 | 2.89–3.11 | 3.88–4.12 | 4.86–5.14 | 9.81–10.19 | 19.75–20.25 |

*Note:* The size of the test mailing, not the size of the list being tested, governs the reliability of the test results. The ranges given above are for twice the probable error. To get a range with a "997 chances out of 1,000" reliability, take three probable errors, *i.e.*, increase the range by one-half the given amount both above and below the test result.

Most direct mail operators, however, want more than a fifty-fifty assurance of the reliability of their tests. The law of probability provides this kind of assurance, too.

For example, there are only 50 chances out of 100 that the results of the full mailing will equal the test result plus or minus the probable error. But there are 95 chances out of 100 that the results of the full mailing will equal the test results plus or minus twice the probable error. And there are 997 chances out of 1,000 that the results of the full mailing will equal the test result plus or minus three times the probable error.

Good books on mail-order techniques, direct mail advertising, and mailing lists may be found in Appendix 2.

**make-ready** The process of adjusting the type on a printing press to give a perfect impression. The type and cuts must be set so as to print evenly and with exactly the right pressure on the paper. "Press-ready" means adjusting the press itself to the requirements of a new job. The paper guides may have to be reset. The color or kind of ink may have to be changed. Feeding and binding attachments, if any, must be adjusted. Make-ready is at best a time-consuming operation. It may take hours.

The first proof may show many flaws. The impression may be too heavy or too light. The ink coverage may be too dark, too faint, or too uneven.

After these faults are corrected, proofs will still show light or dark areas in all probability. This is because of unevenness within the type form itself. All cuts and type are supposed to stand type-high, *i.e.,* exactly 0.918 in. high. Unfortunately, absolute precision is only a goal, not an accomplishment.

To correct the unevenness of the type as shown by the light and dark areas of the proof, the pressman must build up the low spots and take down the high spots. He will add a piece of tissue paper, or cut away some packing to achieve an even effect. Sometimes this is done under the tympan, which supports the paper while it is being printed. Sometimes it is done behind the type.

Careful make-ready is essential to fine presswork. It cannot be hurried. Time must be allowed for it in every printing process, especially in color work. It is a particularly important and demanding operation when halftones are to be printed.

Make-ready is a larger factor in letterpress printing than in offset or other processes that do not print from type. This is both an advantage and a disadvantage. It gives the letterpress pressman greater control over his process, but at the same time it gives him more work.

The offset pressman has less make-ready work. On the other hand he has fewer tricks up his sleeve when proofs are not good. Part of the work that the letterpress man calls "make-ready" is the responsibility of the platemaking department in offset, gravure, and photogelatin printing.

**make-up** To make up a page is to assemble and arrange the headings, illustrations, captions, and text.

In most cases this is a joint task of the author or editor and the printer's make-up man. The former is responsible for editorial decisions as to what will go on which page; the latter is responsible for the mechanical assembly of the type and cuts in the space designated.

With a magazine, pamphlet, or broadside, the editor indicates the make-up by his paste-up dummy (see PASTE-UP DUMMY), which shows the exact spacing, allocation of copy to columns and pages, and the placing of illustrations and captions.

Some printers permit the editor or

his representative to work in the composing room with the make-up man to show him where to shove the blocks of copy, cuts, heads, etc. (By union rules editors do not actually handle the type.) This procedure is followed chiefly on newspaper and rush jobs and where the editor and the printer have had long experience with make-up and with working together. This is not recommended for the hesitant beginner.

Both men, whether working separately or together, should check on the accuracy of page numbers, date lines, page references, continuation of articles, position of ads, agreement of cuts and captions, cover and masthead data, table of contents against the location of articles listed, and finally the headings and by-lines in relation to the articles with which they appear.

**manila**  See also PAPER.
Manila has come to mean simply yellowish paper or Bristol. Rope manila is the designation for the very strong stock made from manila hemp. The addition of hemp or jute fibers gives extra strength to paper.

**manuscript**  See COPY; COPY PREPARATION.

**maps**  Map printing is a specialized department of the graphic arts; at least, the preparation of the art work and plates is specialized. Once prepared, maps can be reproduced by lithography, letterpress, or other processes.

Simple maps can be made by any artist or draftsman, but professional map makers use many techniques and skills especially developed for their work. A map draftsman can get more information across, more legibly, than can a lay artist simply because he knows the conventions and the best ways of handling the lettering.

Many maps are prepared like simple line drawings or wash drawings, and reproduced as such. Areas or parts to be reproduced in color are indicated on one or more overlays.

Lettering can be added by hand; or type can be set, proofs pulled, and the proofs pasted into place, word by word or letter by letter, if necessary, on the master drawing. A recently developed technique requires the printer to pull his proofs on a transparent, cellophane-like material called "Dulseal," which has a transparent adhesive on one side. Names, words, and letters printed on Dulseal can be pasted right over lines on the map, yet the letter remains visible. More recent still is a method of making proofs on an elastic transparent material. Words printed on this material can be curved to follow rivers, etc. Words, map symbols, numbers, etc., printed on adhesive-backed transparent material are available to order from Artype, Inc., 549 W. Randolph St., Chicago 6, which will send its catalogue and price list on request. Monsen-Chicago, Inc., 22 E. Illinois St., Chicago 11, Ill., also offers type and designs on self-adhering transparent acetate under the name "Trans-Adhesive Impressions" and will send samples on request.

Maps can also be reproduced effectively by the wax engraving process. (See WAX ENGRAVING.) This method can produce finished results of the highest quality even from very rough sketches.

Before putting a map into form for the final reproduction, the proposed printer should be consulted to determine exactly what kind of art work will be needed.

A few map printers are George F. Cram Co., Inc., 730 E. Washington St., Indianapolis 7; C. S. Hammond & Co., 521 Fifth Ave., New York 17; Rand McNally & Co., 8255 Central Park Ave., Skokie, Ill.

Arrangements can sometimes be made with map publishers to obtain the use of their plates or art work, in the event that they have already published a map of the desired area. Some publishers prefer to print an edition of maps to be bound into the customer's publication.

It is not permissible to trace or copy a copyrighted map in whole or in part, for either personal or business use, without permission from the copyright owner, and perhaps payment of royalty. This does not apply to most U.S. government maps, which are public property. (A few government maps made during the war reproduce copyright material; copying these by private concerns is illegal.) Useful information on where to find both noncopyright and copyright base maps is available in the book "Scientific Illustration" by John L. Ridgway, listed in Appendix 2, Bibliography.

**marbling** Books, especially large dictionaries, sometimes have marbled end papers or edges decorated with a variety of colors in an irregular pattern resembling the veins of marble.

The pigments are floated on a liquid surface, stirred into the desired pattern, and then the area to be marbled is allowed to touch the surface so that the colors adhere to it. The surface is then cleansed of color, and the whole process is repeated for the next impression.

**marginal head** See HEADINGS.

**Marginator** A typewriter attachment that permits typewritten material to be retyped in such a way that all lines are of equal length and align with each other at the right as well as at the left margins. It was formerly called the "Edison Margin Justifier." (See TYPEWRITER.) It is available from the Marginator Co., 1434 Broadway, Burbank, Calif.

**margins** See also DESIGN.

In conventional book and pamphlet work, the bottom margins are larger than the top margins in such ratios as 2:1, 5:3, 8:5, or 3:2. Outside margins are larger than inside margins in the same proportion.

On a 6 by 9 page, de luxe margin allowance might be divided as follows: 4½ picas inside, 6 picas top (head), 8½ picas outside, 12 picas bottom (tail).

On a 6 by 9 page, moderate margin allowance might be 4½ inside, 6 top, 7½ outside, 10 bottom.

On a single page, top and side margins may be about equal, the bottom margin larger.

Two facing pages (5½ by 8½ in.) with typical margins, larger at bottom than at top, and larger outside than inside. Page numbers and short running heads may be considered part of the margins.

Common margins on a 5½ by 8½ page are 3 picas inside, 3½ top, 4½ outside, 6 bottom.

Where space must be saved, 3 picas all around, or even 2 picas, will suffice, always with an attempt to make the bottom margin a little larger than the others.

The real limit to the smallness of margins is the danger of variation in the binding. Margins within the same book may average 3 picas, while varying from 2 or 2½ to 3½ or 4 picas. A ⅛-in. margin might disappear entirely, taking some of the type with it.

Whether or not generous margins add to readability is a matter of opinion. There are no margins around newspaper columns, yet few complain of poor readability.

In figuring margins, it is usual to count running heads (unless very short) as part of the type page; page numbers, if on a line by themselves, are counted as part of the margins.

Margins cannot be determined without reference to the type to be used. Half-inch margins around a 6 by 9 page would yield a 5-in. type line, which is too long to be readable unless set in large type, generously leaded. Space saved on small margins would be lost on big type. Where the maximum number of words must be printed on a page that is readable, it is often advisable to go to two columns, as in the *Reader's Digest.*

**Marline rate**  See footnote under AD-VERTISING.

**mask**  In the printshop or art studio, a piece of paper so cut as to prevent ink or paint from touching areas protected by it.

A retoucher who wishes to use the airbrush to lighten the background in a photograph will first mask out those areas which are not to be retouched. He may use a paper mask, adhering it with rubber cement, or he may simply use a coating of rubber cement, which he will peel off later.

The words "mask" and "frisket" are used interchangeably in the above sense, with printers favoring the latter term. With a frisket it is possible to take a proof of only certain sections of an inked form.

**Master Addresser**  A low-cost addressing machine operating on the spirit duplicator principle. There is a model at about $31 complete with supplies for a 500-name list, another with automatic tape advance at about $52. Materials for 500 additional addresses cost about $3.

The addresses are typed on a roll of paper on any typewriter, special matching carbon-paper rolls being used under the paper to create a carbon image of the address on the underside. From this master roll up to 200 impressions of each address can be taken, at a rate of about 20 per minute. On the $31 machine unwanted addresses can be skipped. Addressing can be done on any kind of material—envelopes, postcards, forms, etc. The machine automatically moistens the area to receive the imprint as the envelopes are fed in. About a pint of moistening fluid (alcohol) is used per 500 addresses, price 75 cents. (The moistening is almost imperceptible—just enough to dissolve off an impression from the aniline dye in the carbon image.)

Addresses can also be kept on cards or forms instead of on rolls—including punched cards, one card being fed into the machine along with each item to be addressed. The addresses can be placed on the cards by direct typing or by special self-adhering typed labels.

The combination of a Master Addresser unit with marginal punched cards such as McBee cards yields great addressing versatility. One large retailer codes a customer list of 20,000 under 160 headings and finds it practicable to select as few as 50 names from the 20,000 for special sales promotion based on their known interests.

For further information and the name of a nearby source of supply (the equipment is sold in many stationery stores) write to the Master Addresser Co., 6500 W. Lake St., Minneapolis 16, Minn.

**masthead**   The block of information in a newspaper or periodical that gives the title, publisher, names of editors, advertising manager, business manager, etc., address, date, volume and issue number, subscription rates, notice of entry as second-class mail, etc.

The masthead of a newspaper usually appears on the editorial page; of a magazine, alongside the table of contents.

**mat**   See STEREOTYPE; MATRIX.

**matches**   Slightly more than 10 billion imprinted books of matches are used annually in the United States for advertising purposes. Prices can be obtained from the Diamond Match Co., 600 S. Delaware Ave., Philadelphia, Pa., or Lion Match Co., Inc., 22-15 43 Ave., Long Island City, N.Y.

For advertising purposes two general methods are followed: (1) The matches are sold to the advertiser who distributes them to customers, as in hotels and restaurants. (2) The advertiser merely buys the space on the covers, distribution being handled by the match company in geographic areas specified by the space buyer. The advertiser designates the numbers of matches to be distributed in each area and the dates of distribution.

In planning mail promotions involving matches, advertisers should note that only safety matches and book matches packed in foil-lined, asbestos or metal containers are mailable under United States postal regulations.

**matrix**   A matrix (rhymes with "cat tricks" or "play tricks") is a mold. The kind of matrix used in casting Lino-

type, Monotype, or Ludlow types is described under those headings. The matrix or "mat" used in the stereotype process is described under that heading.

**mat services**   See also STOCK CUTS.

Most newspapers, both large and small, subscribe to a mat service in order to provide their advertisers with pictures of merchandise, decorative spot drawings, borders, etc.

Printers of one or more periodicals may subscribe to a mat service in own name and thus be able to offer the service to all their clients. Some department stores have their own subscriptions; specialty stores may subscribe to specialized mat services or buy a single catalogue of a certain kind of material.

The subscriber to the mat service receives both an assortment of mats, from which stereos can be cast (see STEREOTYPE) and a catalogue of proofs of the illustrations contained in the mats. Every month or so (for the specialized services, perhaps every season or every year), he receives new and timely pictorial material, copy ideas, and suggestions for campaigns built around this material.

If an advertiser needs a picture of, say, some lace curtains, he can look up such a picture in the catalogue, note its key number, and then locate the corresponding mat. In the same way he can find a picture of a pretty girl, a man painting, some Christmas holly, a roast of beef, etc.

Two mat services are Metro Associated Services, Inc., 80 Madison Ave., New York; and Multi-Ad Services, Inc., 720 N. Jefferson, Peoria, Ill. A directory of mat services is contained in the *Editor and Publisher* annual.

A monthly art clip-book for house-organ editors is published by Multi-Ad Services, Inc., 720 N. Jefferson, Peoria, Ill.

**mat surface**   A mat-surface photographic print has a dull nonreflecting finish, as opposed to a glossy print, which has a hard, shiny surface. Mat prints can be used for reproduction, but "glossies" are usually preferred because they are less subject to soiling and offer a somewhat greater range of tonal values. Mat prints are generally used for exhibition and framing purposes.

The word "matte" has the same meaning and pronunciation as "mat."

**matte**   See MAT SURFACE.

**measurements**   See TYPE MEASUREMENTS.

**mechanical**   A "mechanical" is a layout prepared for the engraver or printer, which contains the actual copy to be reproduced (or instructions for stripping in copy) and all information necessary for handling it. Reproduction proofs are pasted down clean and square, rules or reverses are drawn or pasted in, guidelines show the positioning of any art work which must be stripped in, the break for color is indicated, etc. Because the "mechanical" is usually executed in black and white even though the job is to run in color and because it is intended to be photographed, not looked at, its appearance is markedly different from that of the "comprehensive" layout (see COMPREHENSIVE) which may have preceded it.

**mechanical bindings**   A great variety of plastic and metal mechanical bindings are available. They offer the following advantages:

1. They are colorful and attractive.
2. Pages open flat.
3. Pages may be arranged in any order, may be of varying weights and sizes, and are usually trimmed on four sides. There is no need to bind in even forms, as of 8, 16, or 32 pages.
4. Service is quick. There is no need to put books under pressure as a guard against warping, as there is with a glued cloth cover.

Some of the disadvantages of mechanical bindings are:

1. They cost more than those simply wire-stitched, sometimes substantially more.
2. In some of the spiral types, the left-hand page is higher or lower than the page opposite, by half the distance between holes, when the book is open.
3. Mechanically bound books are a little bulkier to pack and ship.

Closed style      Loose-leaf style

Two ways of punching paper for use in mechanical bindings.

4. Mechanical bindings do not provide the support and protection often desired in permanent bindings. They may not last as long as case bindings.
5. Pages may be torn out or stolen more easily.

Any mechanical binder having broad rings can be made to serve as a loose-leaf binder if the pages are punched as shown in the illustration.

Most firms of binders offer one or more styles of mechanical bindings. The costs depend on style, length of binding edge, thickness, nature of cover, the work involved in gathering the pages into the proper sequence, and the number ordered at one time.

It is possible to put a good mechanical binding on an 8½ by 11 book, ¼ in. thick, for about $65 to $70 per thousand; in lots of 10,000 about $50 per thousand. A book twice as thick would cost about half again as much. This covers only punching the holes and applying the binding. It does not include the cost of any printing or the cover paper.

Mechanical bindings are frequently used on calendars, diaries, price books, memo books, catalogues, and stenographic notebooks.

**mechanical wood pulp**  See GROUND-WOOD PULP.

**metered postage**  See Appendix 4, Postal Information.

**M.F.**  Abbreviation for machine finish. (See MACHINE-FINISH PAPER.)

**microfilming**  A photographic method of making one or more low-cost, space-saving copies of literary or visual material. A researcher can gain access to a rare book located in a distant library by having that library make and send him a microfilm copy of it. The cost is about 4 or 5 cents per page, depending upon the copy. A manuscript can be microfilmed as a precaution against loss. If the original is lost, a replacement copy can be made from the microfilm. Banks commonly make microfilm copies of checks. The cost of storing bulky and seldom-used records can be reduced by microfilming them and discarding the originals.

In the microfilming process, original material is photographed on 16mm. or 35mm. film at about one-tenth to one-thirtieth of its original size. The first film copy is of course in negative form, with white letters on black background. Positive prints can be made from this original negative, if desired, though the original negative is entirely satisfactory for reading purposes.

Microfilm is read in special machines that enlarge the material to approximately its original size and project it on translucent glass or opaque screen.

To "turn the page" a lever is pressed; to turn many pages, a crank is revolved.

Information is obtainable, free on request, from the following makers of microfilming equipment: the Recordak Corporation, a subsidiary of Eastman Kodak, Rochester, N.Y.; Remington Rand, Inc., 315 Fourth Ave., New York; Diebold, Inc., 2 W. 45 St., New York; Bell and Howell Equipment Co., Chicago; Griscombe Products Inc., 132 W. 21 St., New York. The larger public and university libraries have microfilm equipment and are good sources of advice on its use. They can also supply the name of the nearest commercial firm doing this type of work. One such firm in New York City is the Microfilm Corp., 13 E. 37 St.; another is Graphic Microfilm, 112 Liberty St.

Prices for 35mm. copying run from about 3 cents per exposure, with certain minimum charges. Often two pages or more can be copied at one exposure.

Prices for 16mm. copying on automatic machines run about $7.50 to $15 per thousand exposures, depending on the size of the copy. Material to be copied in such machines must be furnished in separate sheets; bound volumes must be handled on nonautomatic 16mm. or 35mm. machines.

35mm. microfilm is preferred if the material is referred to often or if photo enlargements are likely to be required. 16mm. may be satisfactory if the copying is done for record purposes only and will be consulted only in an emergency.

Enlargements can be made from microfilm at a cost of 10 to 25 cents per 8½ by 11 enlargement, depending on the quantity ordered. Sometimes two or more pages can be reproduced on each enlargement.

Occasionally material is copied on 70mm. film or sensitized paper. If the reduction is not too great, such microfilm can be read without the aid of a special machine. Such copying service costs about 9 cents per negative exposure on paper and about 15 cents on film.

A recent outgrowth of microfilming is the development of the Microcard. Through this technique, about 40 book pages can be photographically reduced and photographically printed on one side of a 3 by 5 library index card. A book of 100 pages can be reproduced on three such cards.

When a Microcard is inserted in a special reading machine, each page is enlarged to its original size on a ground glass viewing screen. Several models of machines are available, ranging in price from $75 to $300. Hand viewers cost about $25 each.

The first use of Microcards was to make available out-of-print material that libraries have been seeking, but thousands of Microcards are now being issued daily by governmental and other research bodies for hitherto unpublished research materials.

Information on the Microcard technique is obtainable from The Microcard Foundation, University of Wisconsin Press, Madison, Wis.

The Microtext Publishing Corp., 112 Liberty St., New York, can handle material through a process essentially the same as the Microcard.

The Microlex Company, Rochester, N.Y., prepares photographic prints of microtext on 6½ x 8½ cards which will accommodate 200 pages of text on each side. This firm handles legal material exclusively.

Microprint is a printing-press microreproduction publishing process developed by the Readex Microprint Corp., 100 Fifth Ave., New York 11. By this process 100 pages, arranged in 10 rows of 10 pages each, can be reproduced on a 6 by 9 card.

**milline rate** See ADVERTISING.

**mimeograph** See also DUPLICATING METHODS.

Mimeograph was originally the trademark of A. B. Dick Company of Chicago used to identify its equipment, supplies, and accessories for stencil duplicating. The word has become part of the language, however, and is used freely to refer to the process, not the firm, even where another make of machine is being used.

Stencil duplicating is one of the most

A mimeograph stencil may carry special display lettering and art work as well as typewritten material. (*Drawing courtesy of A. B. Dick Co.*)

widely used of all office duplicating methods. With a mimeograph stencil sheet, which costs 10 to 15 cents, and a mimeograph duplicator, a few or a few thousand copies of typing, handwriting, line drawings, or ruled forms, on card stock or paper from 3 by 5 to 8½ by 16 in. in size, can be made in a short time.

Many schools use mimeographs and teach their operation in commercial classes. Many typists are taught to prepare duplicating stencils when they learn to type.

Mimeographs can be used continuously, or neglected for days or weeks at a time, and still be ready to turn out a rush job within a matter of minutes.

Mimeograph stencil sheets are made of a porous tissue covered with a coat-

STENCIL SHEET

CUSHION SHEET

BACKING SHEET

A stencil being cut in a typewriter.

Before a mimeograph stencil is put in a type-writer, a cushion sheet is inserted between the stencil sheet and the backing sheet.

TO MAKE CORRECTIONS ON CELLOTYPE K (YELLOW) STENCILS

wa  1. Burnish gently using a circular motion.

wa  2. Cover error with a thin coat of correction fluid. Let dry 30 seconds.

was  3. Retype - using normal or slightly lighter touch.

Three steps in correcting a typographical error on a mimeograph stencil. At right, a mimeo-graph stencil being wrapped around the inked cylinder.

A mimeograph duplicator.

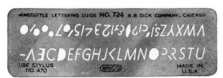

A typical lettering guide for use on a mimeograph stencil with a stylus.

*Shown two-thirds actual size*

Sample alphabets available on the A. B. Dick Co.'s mimeograph lettering guides.

Tracing, lettering, and drawing on a stencil can be done more easily over an illuminated drawing board (right) called a Mimeoscope.

### STYLI

| | | |
|---|---|---|
| 405B | MEDIUM LOOP | |
| 405C | FINE LOOP | |
| 460 | WHEEL | |
| 462 | WHEEL | |
| 467 | WHEEL | |
| 468 | WHEEL | |
| 410B | BLUNT POINT | |
| 410S | MEDIUM POINT | |
| 410XS | SHARP POINT | |
| 410XXS | NEEDLE POINT | |

Special styli are used to write, letter, rule, or draw on stencils.

To shade part of a drawing a "screen plate" having a raised pattern of dots or lines is put under the stencil. Rubbing transfers the pattern.

ing that is impervious to ink. Typing or drawing upon them with a sharp instrument pushes the coating aside and exposes the porous tissue. The stencil is wrapped around an inky cylinder, and the cylinder is rolled across a piece of paper. Ink is forced through the porous parts of the stencil onto the paper, thus duplicating the message originally typed or drawn.

Effective mimeographed work requires (1) a good stencil, properly prepared, (2) even ink distribution, (3) a duplicating machine in good mechanical condition, and (4) the right kind of impression paper.

Since mimeograph inks (except the special "hard-set" ones) dry by absorption, a paper of medium absorbency is preferable for duplicated work. When paper with a hard finish is used, a small amount of the ink may stay on the surface of the paper and rub off on the next sheet of paper that comes into the receiving tray of the duplicator. This can be prevented by slip sheeting or putting a blank sheet of paper or card stock over each copy as it comes into the receiving tray. These slip sheets are removed later when the ink is dry. (See SLIP SHEET.)

Mimeograph hard-set inks are special inks which are permanent and rubproof on hard, soft, thick, or thin papers. They dry by oxidation rather than by absorption. There is a greater danger of their drying in the machine.

There is a trend away from both kinds of oil-based inks toward quick-drying, water-soluble inks such as A. B. Dick's "Contac-Dri."

Mimeograph duplicating also may be done with colored inks. A clean ink pad is placed over the regular ink pad, and the colored ink applied to the clean pad with a protective cover or sheet of typing film between the two pads. About 50 copies may be run this way before re-inking is necessary. When there is an inch or more of space between the stenciled areas, two or more colors may be used at the same time. Colored copies are also run by the use of extra cylinders, which are kept for the particular colors used.

To keep a mimeograph in good working condition, the correct ink must be used, the ink pad must be cared for properly and changed regularly, the rubber parts of the feed table must be cleaned frequently and replaced when worn, the duplicator should be covered when not in use to keep it free from dust, and the machine should be oiled regularly according to directions.

If the paper is to feed properly, it must be uniform in size, properly centered in the machine, firmly gripped between the sponge rubber grippers, and "combed." (To comb a ream of paper means to bend it back and forth and fan the edges slightly, to be sure that no sheet is sticking to its neighbor.) After combing, the paper is squared up again before being inserted in the machine. The last 20 sheets or so are usually not fed through the machine, since they are likely to feed improperly.

Any standard typewriter in good condition may be used to type a stencil. The type keys should be cleaned thoroughly with a stiff bristle brush before beginning this work. Type-cleaning fluid should not be used as it may injure the stencil sheet. The ribbon of the typewriter is then shifted from the printing position so that the type keys strike the stencil itself. A cushion sheet (supplied with each package of stencils) is inserted between the stencil sheet and the backing, and the assembly is placed in the typewriter. The type keys should be hit with a firm, staccato touch. Characters with a large printing surface (W, #, S, M) should have a little extra pressure; small characters and the punctuation marks, less pressure. (For variety in type styles, see VARITYPER.)

A carbon copy can be made when the stencil is cut by inserting a sheet of carbon paper and one of onion skin between the stencil and the cushion sheet.

Its Mimeotype (blue) stencil sheets are recommended by the A. B. Dick Company if typing is to be combined with illustrations, lettering, or ruled forms, or if the maximum number of copies (3,500 to 5,000) will be run. Its Cellotype (yellow) stencil sheets are recommended for straight typing jobs. (The contrast of the blue stencil sheet when placed on the illuminated drawing board for tracing or lettering is better than that of the yellow stencil sheet. For typing, a blue cushion sheet is inserted with the yellow stencil sheet. The visibility while typing is high, and a proof copy is produced on the backing sheet.)

Signatures may be reproduced as part of a mimeographed letter. When a blue stencil is to be signed, the cushion sheet is removed and a flexible writing plate, signature plate, or celluloid ruler is placed under the stencil. A ball-point stylus is used for writing. Writing should be done with a firm, uniform pressure. When the yellow stencil is to be signed, the cushion sheet should be inserted between the stencil and the backing and the assembly placed on a hard, smooth surface such as a glass desk top. Do not use a wooden desk top because the stylus will have a tendency to follow the grain of the wood.

An illuminated drawing board, called the Mimeoscope, is used when tracing, lettering, drawing, handwriting, and ruling forms. It has a translucent glass top under which an ordinary 60-watt bulb gives excellent illumination with no glare. Art work to be traced is laid on the glass and covered with a protective sheet of transparent plastic. A blue stencil sheet is placed over this.

Writing, lettering, ruling, and drawing are done with styli—sharp, penlike tools, which may be obtained with various kinds of points. There are wireloop

and ball-point styli for solid lines, tracing, and drawing; wheels for dotted lines; blunt wire loops for shading; and points bent at angles for lettering. Areas may be shaded by first outlining the area to be shaded, then placing a "screen plate" (a plastic square impressed with a pattern) under the stencil and rubbing over the plate until the pattern is reproduced upon the stencil.

Lettering guides are used to make attractive lettering on stencils. They are oblong pieces of plastic pierced with letter outlines available in various styles and sizes. The lettering styli fit these openings and are drawn through them to make corresponding outlines upon the stencil.

Material too intricate to be traced upon a regular mimeograph stencil (with the exception of solid black areas and halftones) may be reproduced photochemically on mimeograph stencils. The stencil is prepared from a transparent tracing (direct method) or from a film positive (indirect method) by exposure to strong light. This work can be done in offices with special photochemical printing equipment, or by A. B. Dick Company from copy submitted, with prices dependent upon the size of the stencil and the amount of preparatory work involved. (See also STENAFAX.)

Typewritten copy cannot be added to photochemical stencils, but the two types of stencils may be used together by "patching" photochemically prepared material into a Mimeotype stencil. Pages of illustrations photochemically prepared and ready to be patched in on Mimeotype stencils are available from A. B. Dick Company at a reasonable price.

Special services of A. B. Dick Company include die impressing and form topping of stencils. Die impressing is a method of cutting standard forms, headings, typing, or designs into the stencil sheet so that the typist needs to add only the variable information.

The form and the newly typed information are duplicated at the same time.

Form topping is used when duplicated copy is run on a printed form. A facsimile of the form is printed on the surface of the stencil sheet. It guides the typist in positioning the fill-in copy, but the printing does not reproduce. Die-impressed and form-topped stencils are extensively used in business control systems where a single writing on a prepared stencil is all that is necessary to duplicate basic information on the forms needed for various functions. Part of the information on the stencil may then be blocked off when it is not needed for some of the forms. These stencils are prepared to order by A. B. Dick Company.

Also available are dual stencil sheets, two stencil sheets attached to one backing. Two stencils are typed at once, thus eliminating the rewriting of material that is needed for duplication at two points.

Used stencils may be filed in special file folders and rerun later.

Practically all lettershops handle mimeograph work. They charge from $1.50 per stencil cut, and from 30 cents per hundred for running copies.

Mimeograph machines range in price from under $100 to over $1,000, with post-card-size printers available as low as $10. The A. B. Dick machines are of top quality, and priced accordingly, as are the Gestetner machines, imported from Germany. For prices write A. B. Dick, 5700 West Touhy Ave., Chicago 31, and Gestetner Duplicator Corp., 50 McLean Ave., Yonkers 5, N.Y. Some of the lower-priced machines can be seen in stationery stores or in the Sears, Roebuck and Montgomery Ward catalogues.

For a comparison of mimeographing with other duplicating and printing processes see the charts inside the covers of this book.

**Mimeoscope**  See MIMEOGRAPH.

**mitered**  See illustrations below.

**Mitten's Letters**  A line of three-dimensional, white, molded display letters which can be pinned or glued to any background or mounted in tracks to make signs and displays. They come in many styles and in sizes from ¾ in. to 9 in. in height.

Mitten's Letters are sold at per-letter prices or in prepackaged fonts and assortments. One prepackaged assort-

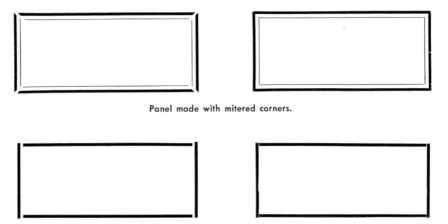

Panel made with mitered corners.

Panel made with butted corners.

ment containing 699 letters and numerals in three sizes from ¾ in. to 2 in. sells for about $53. For catalogues and price lists, write to Mitten's Display Letters, 2 W. 46 St., New York 36, also Redlands, Calif.

**moiré** When one screen pattern (see SHADING TINTS) is laid over another, the result is a *moiré* (pronounced mwa-ray) effect. This may happen when a halftone cut is made from a picture that has been printed by the halftone process and thus already contains a screen

The fabric-like texture in this photograph is a so-called *moiré* effect resulting from the fact that this halftone was made from a clipping that had already been screened once.

pattern. The resulting *moiré* effect can be highly objectionable.

If a screened clipping is all that is available, it can be reproduced with very little *moiré* effect if the engraver will experiment to find the right matching screen, and will try turning this screen at various angles to the screen in the clipping until the angle of minimum *moiré* is found. (See illustration.)

**Monophoto** The phototypesetting process being developed in England by the Monotype Corporation. Like the

Monotype the Monophoto consists of two parts. Both use the same keyboard which is operated like a typewriter to produce a perforated ribbon. In the Monotype the perforated paper ribbon guides the casting machine which automatically casts each letter singly and pushes the completed lines into a waiting galley. In the Monophoto the paper ribbon cut on a regular Monotype keyboard guides a master negative to produce letters on film in sizes from 6- to 24-pt. type.

**Monotype** One of the two basic machines for setting type. Like the Linotype (see LINOTYPE), it can set type for books, magazines, pamphlets, advertisements, etc., much faster than the work can be done by hand. Like the Linotype, it produces, for each job, fresh new type, never before used. The used type is melted down and does not have to be distributed into type cases.

Unlike the Linotype, the Monotype produces single type characters, not solid lines of type. Corrections can thus be made by hand, without the need of setting a whole new line.

Monotype composition tends to be a little more expensive than Linotype on simple material; perhaps a little less expensive on more complicated work, tabular work, etc. The Monotype can handle roman, italic, and bold as easily as the Linotype handles only two of them; and it can mix entirely unrelated fonts of type more easily. Furthermore, it can easily set lines up to 60 picas long, while most Linotypes have to cast lines over 30 picas in two sections.

The type faces available on the Monotype are substantially the same as those available on the Linotype, with only subtle differences. (See Appendix 1, Type Faces.) Printers who have Monotype equipment are less likely to have Linotype, Intertype, or Ludlow equipment; and vice versa.

The Monotype consists of two parts: a keyboard and a composing or casting

255 Monotype matrices like those above can be held in the matrix case shown at upper left—enough for roman, italic, and bold. From these matrices, the Monotype automatically casts lines of single pieces of type like those below.

The Monotype keyboard, below at left, is used like a typewriter, but it produces the perforated ribbon shown at the left. This paper ribbon, which resembles the rolls used in player pianos, guides the automatic composing machine (caster), shown below at right. It says to the caster, in effect, "Move the matrix case to the seventh row across, the fourth row down, and cast a piece of type from the letter that you find there." (*Photos courtesy of the Monotype Corp.*)

machine. A manuscript is first "keyboarded" as if the operator of the keyboard were making a typewritten copy. However, instead of a typed copy, the keyboard produces a perforated paper roll, similar to that used in a player piano. This roll is then put on the composing (casting) machine, which automatically casts each letter singly and pushes the completed lines into a waiting galley.

A device on the keyboard machine tells the operator when each line is nearly full and how much it lacks of being full. He then pushes a special key, which in effect says to the composing machine, "This line is so many ems too short. Please cast each of the spaces between words just enough wider than the minimum to take up the extra space." The composing machine is able to obey this instruction, because it casts each line *backward,* and thus gets the instructions about spacing before working its way through the line beginning with the last letter of the last word.

It is possible to use harder type metal in Monotype casters than in Linotype or Intertype machines. If a harder metal is actually used (some shops use one standardized metal in all machines), Monotype composition will wear longer. In England it is quite common to print the original edition (or even several editions) of a book from the type and then to make electrotypes from the type if still larger editions must be run. This is rarely done in the case of slug-cast composition, since even relatively small runs wear the softer metal so much that the making of duplicate plates from this worn type is undesirable.

Monophoto is the phototypesetting process being developed by Monotype. It produces type on film instead of casting it in metal. (See MONOPHOTO.)

**montage**  When several pictures or portions of pictures are combined into one to tell a story that they might not tell singly, the result is a montage.

A good montage gets its basic message across at first glance even when its elements, taken individually, repay longer inspection. It is more than just a trick way of grouping separate pictures on a page.

A montage is first sketched, often with the aid of a camera lucida. (See CAMERA LUCIDA.) Then if the negatives of each element are available, they may all be projected, one by one, in an enlarger onto the same piece of photographic paper. Some retouching with an airbrush is usually necessary. Alternately, each photo can be "blown" to size, cut out, and assembled with the others like a jigsaw puzzle.

Montage making demands considerable skill and know-how. For best results, enlargements should be made to the desired size *from the original negatives,* and these prints should be butt-joined in mounting, not lapped. Lapped edges will create shadow lines that cannot be retouched away short of making a new copy negative or a new print, and then retouching that. Lapped edges are all right if they can follow a natural line in the picture.

Something is lost every time a photograph is copied. A great deal can be lost if the procedure is from original print to copy negative, to print, to lap-joined montage, to copy negative, to final print.

**mortise**  A printing plate or cut is said to have been mortised when a hole or notch has been made in it to accommodate type. Wherever possible, it is better to paste the lettering or a proof of the type on the original art work and thus make it a part of the plate or cut, since type inserted in a mortise sometimes falls out on the press.

Letters are sometimes mortised for better fit in headlines. (See illustration on next page and under TYPE.)

A mortised cut. This is a notched mortise, open on one side. Type can be held in place more securely in such a mortise than in an inside mortise.

**motion pictures**  See also FILMSTRIP.

Motion pictures and filmstrips offer a medium of communication of tremendous and proved effectiveness. They deserve to be considered along with radio, television, and the printed word in all campaign planning.

A good, one-reel 16mm. motion picture with sound usually costs $7,500 to $25,000, or more, but it may still be the cheapest device for claiming a few minutes of the undivided attention of 1 or 20 million people. No other medium is so effective in bringing people to a new viewpoint.

A good filmstrip, consisting of approximately 50 still photographs or charts, with a 15-min. sound recording will cost from $1,000 up, but may be the most effective way of presenting and explaining certain factual information to selected audiences.

Motion-picture film comes in three widths:

8mm.—for amateur use only
16mm.—for all nontheatrical uses
35mm.—for theater use

All 8mm. and 16mm. films use a safety (cellulose acetate) noninflammable base and may be shown with portable projectors. In recent years 35mm. film has also become available for general use in cellulose acetate or safety film. However, prints around from the previous period (circa 1950) have an inflammable, cellulose nitrate base. For this reason, *all* 35mm. film must by law be projected only from specially constructed fireproof booths.

Therefore, the 16mm. size is generally used for films to be shown in schools, offices, meeting halls, etc. However, films are frequently shot in 35mm. and then printed (by reduction) in 16mm.

Films may be either silent or with sound. The trend, however, is to sound films. Except in private homes, most projectors in frequent use are sound projectors.

Sound film production costs 33 to 100 per cent more than silent, but the prints cost no more; silent pictures must be about one-third longer to allow for the titles.

Color films can be handled exactly as if they were black-and-white films. It is often not much more expensive to shoot a film in color than to shoot it in black and white, since the cost of the film is not the major part of the expense. However, making color prints is about six times as expensive as making black-and-white prints, perhaps $50 per reel for color as against $10 for black and white.

There is no getting away from the fact that good movies cost a lot of money, usually from $750 per minute of running time for simple subject matter up to $5,000 or more per minute for animation in color.

However, audiences naturally judge movies by Hollywood standards and may react adversely to any that are too obviously amateurish. Somehow, those produced at less than $750 a minute generally do look amateurish as also do some costing much more.

Some of the factors involved are as follows:

1. A movie of a man talking is usually deadly dull, even if care has been taken to change the angle of the camera frequently.

2. Live sound (out of the actors' mouths) is more costly than the kind of narration that is added afterward and merely comments on the action. "Lip sync" is the term.

3. Professional actors and narrators are usually cheaper in the long run than amateurs, because fewer retakes are necessary.

4. Although the building of special studio sets is expensive, it may be no more so than shooting on location, since the latter poses special problems of lighting and acoustics, not to mention travel and weather.

Motion pictures can in part be pieced together out of existing footage ("stock shots") obtained at $1.50 to $3.50 per foot from such stock-shot film libraries as that maintained by the National Broadcasting Co., 30 Rockefeller Plaza, New York. However, the best material is held by Hollywood and the newsreel companies, which sometimes are, and sometimes are not, willing to release it. Furthermore, available material is sometimes of low photographic quality, being made from second or third duplicate negatives.

It is difficult to use silent footage in modern pictures, since today's films run at 24 frames per second, whereas the old silent films ran at 16 frames per second.

Music costs include not only a copyright fee (or composer's fee), plus sound crew and studio, but also a narrator's fee and union rates for musicians.

For all these reasons it is impossible for a motion-picture producer to give a reliable estimate of cost in advance of completing a script. Negotiations for making a film usually are about as follows:

Producer and sponsor discuss the ground to be covered and the budget. Perhaps they screen a few films and agree that "a one-reeler like that one, which cost $15,000" is the sort of thing

a    b    c    d   *Sound track*    e

Types of motion-picture film (actual size): (a) 8mm. silent film, (b) 8mm. films before slitting, (c) 16mm. silent film, (d) 16mm. sound film (showing sound track), (e) 35mm. silent film, or filmstrip.

wanted. The producer then submits a "treatment" or general outline. If this is approved and if the sponsor authorizes the producer to have his script writer go ahead on a final "shooting script," it is usually understood *that the sponsor is obliged to pay for the shooting script, even if he decides not*

35mm. sound film, actual size.

*to use it.* Often the sponsor is asked to pay for the treatment since much research and work can go into an apparently simple treatment.

The script writer then hammers out a script. Usually this takes at least a month, perhaps considerably longer.

With a detailed and approved script in hand, the producer can now give a fairly accurate estimate of the cost of making the film, though he may suggest making the picture on the basis of charging audited cost plus overhead, rather than a flat fee.

Payment for the script and perhaps for a part of production cost is now

due. Another payment will be due when the shooting has been completed, with a third and final payment due on delivery of the final print or prints.

The buyer of a motion picture cannot see before he buys. He must buy on the basis of the seller's reputation and previous record for doing quality work, economically, on time, and at fair rates. A producer's references should be checked with care.

Reputable producers of industrial and educational films include Jam Handy Organization, Detroit; Wilding Picture Sales Corp., 385 Madison Ave., New York; Audio Productions, 630 Ninth Ave., New York; Caravel Films, Inc., 730 Fifth Ave., New York; Pathescope Productions, 580 Fifth Ave., New York; Sound Masters Inc., 165 W. 46 St., New York; Transfilm Inc., 35 W. 45 St., New York; Affiliated Film Producers, 164 E. 38 St., New York.

The distribution of film prints can be handled in several ways.

There are over 2,000 commercial and educational film libraries in the United States which lend or rent 16mm. films to owners of projectors in their area. There are estimated to be over 250,000 projectors in active use. A list of some of the commercial film libraries is obtainable from the National Audio-Visual Association, 2540 Eastwood Ave., Evanston, Ill. Another list of film libraries is available from the Superintendent of Documents, U.S. Government Printing Office, Washington, D.C.

These film libraries, which include state universities, big city school systems, etc., buy some films at $25, $35, or $50 a reel and rent for about $2 per black-and-white reel per showing (projector and operator supplied at extra cost if requested). They also accept gifts of government and other non-profit films of general interest and circulate them and may undertake for a fee to circulate commercial films of sound audience appeal.

A good film free of commercial or

one-sided propaganda may, with proper promotion, enjoy a sale of as many as 1,000 prints—rarely many more. One firm equipped to handle film distribution on a national and international scale, paying a royalty on each print sold, is Brandon Films, Inc., 1600 Broadway, New York, specialists in cultural and public affairs films. Others include Movies USA, 729 Seventh Ave., New York; Association Films, 347 Madison Ave., New York; Modern Talking Picture Service, 45 Rockefeller Plaza, New York; Encyclopaedia Britannica Films, Wilmette, Ill. (largest distributors of classroom films); and McGraw-Hill Text Films, 330 W. 42 St., New York (specialists in college text films). If distribution of this sort is contemplated, it is well to consult the intended distributor before the film is made, both to ensure that he will be willing to take it, and to get his help on giving audience appeal to the film.

Of course, television is the major user of nontheatrical films today (see TELEVISION) and, for sustaining programs, many stations depend heavily on free or cheap films that aren't too heavy on the sponsor plugs. This opens up a large field for the sponsored film.

Nontheatrical 16mm. films almost always require a subsidy. The market is still small. In rare cases, it may be possible to recover through sales as much as $5,000 or so toward production costs, but receipts from sales are almost invariably insufficient to cover production costs.

An interesting study of the sponsored film was completed in 1954 by the Association of National Advertisers, 285 Madison Ave., New York 17. It covered 157 nontheatrical sound films. Its findings include the following:

The average company spends 4.6 cents to obtain an average of 26 minutes of a viewer's time. This cost can drop to as low as 3 mills over the life of the film made for a broad, general-purpose audience. The average film has a long life—five years or so. The median cost of the films studied was $28,800. Color films were favored four to one. The typical sponsor spent 55 per cent of his budget for production, 25 per cent for prints, and 19 per cent for distribution.

Anyone contemplating the use of motion pictures or slidefilms will do well to consult Appendix 2, Bibliography, for helpful books on this subject.

**motor freight**  See TRUCKING.

**mounting and finishing**  See also DISPLAYS; DIE CUTTING.

Mounting is a fairly simple operation in which the mounting cardboard may be the major item in the total cost. Special mounting presses apply glue to the paper poster and to the cardboard backing and then squeeze both together in a sort of wringer. Sometimes a piece of blank paper identical to that used for the poster is glued to the underside of the backing to equalize the strains that might otherwise cause curling.

Firms specializing in mounting and finishing are generally equipped to do not only mounting, but also the following "finishing" operations: die cutting, creasing (scoring), varnishing, laminating, easeling, labeling, hinging, stringing, round-cornering, tin-edging, eyeleting, gumming, pebbling, paraffining. (See DIE CUTTING; SCORING; VARNISHING; EASELING; EYELETING; PEBBLING.)

There is no clean-cut distinction between "binders" and "mounters and finishers." Some binders do only book and pamphlet work; others cover also the more specialized operations.

Some printers have all the operations under one roof: printing, binding, finishing, and imprinting. Most, however, let out their binding, mounting, finishing, and imprinting (see IMPRINTING) to firms specializing in these operations. Small buyers are well advised to place the responsibility for all operations on the printer; large buyers may save by dealing directly with the firms that actually handle the separate operations. For mounting and finishing firms see the Classified Directory.

**movies** See MOTION PICTURES.

**MS, Ms., ms.** Abbreviations for manuscript. In the plural, it is MSS., Mss., or mss.

**Multigraph** See also DUPLICATING METHODS.

The trade name used by the Addressograph-Multigraph Corporation to identify its office duplicating machines. However, the company makes two basically different kinds of Multigraph duplicators. The one that operates on the offset principle is most commonly

A piece of Multigraph type, much enlarged. (*Courtesy of Addressograph-Multigraph Corp.*)

called a "Multilith," the name under which the company first introduced it. (See MULTILITH for a description of what the company now calls its "Multigraph-Multilith Process.")

The other kind of Multigraph (the one used for more than a generation before the Multilith was introduced, and the one usually meant when the word "Multigraph" is used) prints from raised surfaces on the letterpress (relief) principle, as described below.

In appearance, a Multigraph machine resembles a mimeograph machine. The printing is done from a large drum, which, however, is of very different construction. It is equipped with parallel slots running the long way of the drum, into which special metal type can be inserted. Many styles and faces of type can be used, also curved electrotypes, rubber plates, zinc etchings, stereotypes, etc. In fact, any medium with a raised surface that is used to make an impression on paper can be prepared for use on a Multigraph.

When the type on a Multigraph drum is covered with a wide inked ribbon and printed through this, form letters and other materials can be produced which closely resemble actual typing.

When the Multigraph duplicator is equipped with a printing-ink attachment, the type is inked from rubber rollers; the machine then becomes simply a small, office-size printing machine and will print cards, post cards, tickets, forms, letterheads, price lists, etc. It is frequently used to imprint dealers' names and addresses on advertising pieces.

Composition on the Multigraph takes a little more time than by other duplicating processes. Running is a little more expensive, since ribbons cost more than duplicating ink; however, the ribbon can be re-inked and used a number of times. Multigraph work tends to be a little neater than average duplicator copy and does not require an absorbent type of paper; rather, any type of paper or card stock can be used and the finished result has the special qualification of more closely resembling actual typing.

The Multigraph principle is especially valuable on duplicating jobs that require frequent partial changes of information, such as price lists and menus.

Work can be done in colors other than black by changing to another

A Multigraph flexible drum, showing how type and cuts are fastened into its slots. Nonflexible drums are also used, and work the same way, except that the whole drum is changed, not just the surface layer.

A hand-driven Multigraph machine, showing how inked ribbon is fastened over drum.

ribbon, or by changing the color of ink in the ink fountain.

Movable type is made for use in the Multigraph in practically all sizes and styles. The channels of the Multigraph will also accommodate processed Linotype, Intertype, and Monotype composition, ruling lines, etc.

With extra attachments, the Multigraph can strike in a blue signature at the foot of a letter, and do numbering, slitting, and perforating.

Sixteen cents a line is a common base charge made by lettershops for doing Multigraph work, with running charges of $3.50 to $5 per thousand impressions.

A hand-fed, hand-operated Multigraph is available at about $250, with $100 or more added for type. An automatic Multigraph is available at about $1,950, type extra.

Multigraph duplicators are manufactured by Addressograph-Multigraph Corporation, Cleveland 17, Ohio. See also DAVIDSON DUPLICATORS, combining in one machine the basic features of both Multigraph and Multilith.

See also the chart "How to Choose the Right Printing Process" inside the covers of this book.

**Multilith**  Multilith is a small offset duplicator (see OFFSET) made especially for office use. Most Multilith machines will handle paper from post-card size up to 9¾ in. by 14 in. and some are larger.

A Multilith will do anything that a mimeograph will do, and more besides. However, it costs a little more to begin with, is a little more demanding on its operator, and is at its best when used continuously rather than intermittently.

The Multilith will reproduce anything that can be written, lettered, typed, drawn, traced, stamped, ruled, or printed on the paper masters from which the machine duplicates. Photographic masters can also be prepared like regular offset plates, thus permit-

ting exact reproduction of type, illustrations, photos (*i.e.*, halftones), etc. (See also STENAFAX, XEROGRAPHY.)

However, large photographs or large solid areas of ink are to be avoided since the inking mechanism cannot handle a large flow of ink. Furthermore, it takes more skill than most operators possess to get top-notch reproduction of photographs on the Multilith in any size.

One of the special advantages of the Multilith Process is its ability to duplicate simultaneously both the letter and the letterhead, both the variable information on a form and the form itself. "Systemat" paper masters for the Multilith can be obtained on which basic forms or letterheads are already prepared in reproducing or nonreproducing ink. Any new information can be added by any composing method and the whole then duplicated.

Color work can be handled on the Multilith by cleaning up the ink rollers (a simple operation with a blotter-type cleaner sheet) and by using new ink of a desired color.

When the Multilith Process was introduced in 1932, only one type of duplicating master—a mechanically grained thin zinc sheet—was used for all Multilith Process duplicating. These masters are still being used today and are prepared by photographic process, thus permitting exact reproduction of type, illustrations, photographs, etc. In 1947, an entirely new kind of paperbase master was introduced. This new type of master is available in two ways: either plain, or with a business form or other fixed material already on it in reproducing or nonreproducing ink.

The form is, in effect, "preprinted" on the master. When nonreproducing "Systemat Masters" are used, the printed form on the master acts simply as a guide for the insertion of the information on the master with a typewriter, pen, pencil, etc. In duplicating, paper which has been printed with the same form appearing on the master is run and picks up the information that was inserted. The form itself does not duplicate.

Reproducing "Systemat Masters" have the form preprinted on the master, too. This form will duplicate onto blank paper run through the machine at the same time that the information added with typewriter, pen, pencil, etc., is being duplicated. Thus, both the form and the added variable information are reproduced together in one duplicating operation.

Another important feature of this new paper-base master is that you can run copies from it, and then file the master away for subsequent use. It is also feasible to transfer information to a new master or masters, the operation being just as simple as transferring copy to a sheet of paper. When a blank Duplimat Master is fed through the Multilith Duplicator, it becomes a copy *complete in every detail* of the original master, and it, too, can be used as a master, either to duplicate copies or to duplicate a new master. The ability to reproduce a master from a master is an exclusive feature of this duplicating process.

In common with all Multilith masters, the new masters will reproduce anything that can be written, lettered, typed, drawn, traced, or ruled on the image surface. Corrections, when necessary, are made on it with any soft pencil eraser and do not show in the reproduction.

Actually, there are two "versions" of the Multilith Process. Basically, they are the same, but there are some differences in application of the principle of Multilith Process duplicating. One version, the original and so-called "conventional" process was used on all Multilith models. In 1950, a simplified version of the Multilith Process called Simflo Control was introduced and applied to several models of the Multilith Process duplicators. Both the conventional process and Simflo Control are used today.

Simflo Control is a simplification of the "conventional" Multilith Process. The Multilith Process is based on the fact that Multilith ink and the moistening solution do not mix. This makes it necessary to apply the ink and moistening solution to the master with separate sets of rollers: one set for ink and the other for the water or moistening solution. In contrast, with the Simflo Control method both the ink and moistening solution are applied to the master from a single set of rollers.

This method of carrying both ink and moistening solution provides important advantages. The Simflo Control unit on the duplicator automatically controls the balance of ink and moisture while retaining all the other advantages of the conventional Multilith Process. This positive and automatic balancing of ink and moisture reduces operator training to a minimum. Ink used with Simflo Control makes daily clean-up unnecessary. Even after periods of inactivity, any type of Multilith master can be put on a Simflo Control duplicator and copies duplicated within a matter of seconds.

Two Multilith models are available at just under $1,000 each: one with automatic friction feed, and the other hand-fed. Both are electrically driven. A heavy-duty model, capable of doing more work, is priced at just under $2,500, including automatic, electrically controlled suction feed and other extras. With extra attachments, this model can strike in a signature and do numbering, slitting, and perforating. A larger model (14 by 20 paper size) is available at about $4,000.

Multiliths are manufactured by the Addressograph-Multigraph Corporation, Cleveland 17, Ohio. The company now calls them "Multigraph Duplicators—Multilith Process," a change from its prewar policy of calling them Multiliths. The new term is cumbersome, however, and most users of both processes continue to use the old term. (See MULTIGRAPH.)

Other office machines operating on

The smallest model of the Multilith.

the Multilith (offset) principle are made by the Davidson Corporation, 27 Ryerson St., Brooklyn, N.Y. (see DAVIDSON DUPLICATORS) and by the A. B. Dick Company, 5700 Touhy Ave., Chicago.

In determining whether to use Multilith, consult the charts inside the covers of this book.

**music printers** Music can be reproduced photographically from a handwritten manuscript; it can be set up with special music type; or it can be engraved. (See also ARTYPE.)

Engraving is the most satisfactory. Notes and symbols are punched, one at a time, into a soft metal plate, using special punches. Lettering is added in the same way. The plate is inked, the surface ink is wiped away, and a proof is taken by the intaglio process (see INTAGLIO) from the ink remaining in the depressed areas. The proof can then be reproduced in offset or any other process.

This engraving (intaglio) process gives a much cleaner result than hand notation, and gives much more flexibility than music type. It requires special skill and is relatively expensive. Music engravers include G. Schirmer, Inc., 48-02 48 Ave., Woodside 77, New York; Rayner, Dalheim & Co., 2801 W. 47 St., Chicago 32; Robert Teller Sons & Dorner, 411 W. 43 St., New York; Gilprint Co., 333 W. 52 St., New York 19. Hand autographing of music (the low-priced method) is done by the Gilprint Co. and by Robert Teller Sons & Dorner.

In ordering music engraved, autographed, or set in type, it is advisable to have the composition or lettering of the song words, if any, done at the same time by the same firm, even though it may seem that this could be done by the printer who is to do the final printing. The reason is that it may prove impossible to make the words fit unless the music compositor is responsible for seeing that they do.

# N | n

negative   The negative of a picture is a photographically transformed copy in which the white areas are shown in black, the black areas are shown in white, the light grays have become dark grays, the dark grays have become light grays, etc. (See illustration on next page.)

Photographic negatives are generally made on transparent film. Photostat negatives are made on paper and are not transparent. (See PHOTOGRAPHY; PHOTOSTAT.)

An ordinary paper negative reverses the image two ways: it turns black into white, and vice versa, and turns the image left for right, just as a mirror reverses things left for right and makes lettering read backward.

A Photostat negative, "positive negative," or "readable negative" reverses the image just one way: black for white. Lettering remains readable.

A film negative, being transparent, can be looked at from either the "positive-negative" side, or the "negative-negative" (emulsion) side.

The word "negative" is generally applied to something that exists only in order that a positive may be made

from it. A negative that is meant to remain that way is called a "reverse." Any line drawing can be converted by the engraver into a reverse plate. (See REVERSE PLATE.)

Photographs or drawings which, from the layout point of view, face the wrong way, can be flopped (see FLOP) and made to face the other way. However, any lettering contained in them will then read backward, cars will run to the left, military decorations will appear on the wearer's wrong side, etc.

newspapers   See also COPY WRITING; PERIODICALS; PUBLICITY RELEASE; ADVERTISING.

Newspaper work differs in many ways from other printing. Almost every newspaper owns its own printing plant and has it under the same roof as the editorial offices; relatively few other print users do so. The need for speed requires standardization of typography and continuity in editorial style.

In other lines, an editorial worker can get by without knowing anything of the mechanics of printing. On a newspaper, efficiency demands that every staff member know at least the

197

Photographic negative.

Positive print.

"Positive" original.

"Flopped" positive.

Photostat negative, reverse, "positive negative," or "readable negative."

Ordinary or "negative negative."

Photographic positive. (*Photo by Louise Rosskam.*)

Flopped photographic positive.

A curved stereotype plate. *(Courtesy of The New York Times.)*

elements of the paper's mechanical requirements. This fact sometimes leads newspaper people to think they know all about printing when in reality they know only one very specialized corner of letterpress printing and cannot tell one process from another.

Large newspapers are almost always printed by the letterpress process on rotary web presses. (See LETTERPRESS.) Type is set on the Linotype or Intertype, assembled with any illustrations or advertising plates, and then duplicated by the stereotype process. (See STEREOTYPE.) Curved stereotypes are made, not flat ones, to fit the cylinders of the rotary presses. The paper is fed from a roll into the rotary presses, which print it and then fold and cut it into finished newspaper sections.

For sources of information on the editorial end of newspaper work and the mechanics of newspaper printing, see Appendix 2, Bibliography.

There are two ways for outsiders to use newspapers as channels of communication: (1) through free publicity and (2) through paid advertisements.

Newspapers are glad to run any legitimate news item free of charge, and welcome publicity releases written with the reader's interest in mind, not just with the publicity man's ulterior motive in mind. (See PUBLICITY RELEASE.)

In preparing advertisements for newspaper publication, the following points are worth keeping in mind. (See also ADVERTISING.)

Newspaper space is sold at so much per *agate line*. Since there are 14 agate lines to the inch, a 2-in. ad, 2 columns wide, will occupy 56 agate lines.

Agate-line rates vary in the same newspaper as between national advertisers and local advertisers, between amusements and food, etc. Certain preferred positions cost extra. Many advertisers buy two-thirds of a page, or a full page lacking one column, in preference to a full page, feeling that they get the same attention at a lower cost, plus the advantage of being next to reading matter.

Newspaper ad rates include the setting of the type, but many advertisers have their material made up by independent typographers and supplied to the newspapers as complete plates, because they find it easier to get exactly what they want in this way. Many newspapers subscribe to a mat service in order to be able to provide their advertisers with pictures of merchandise, spot drawings, etc. (See MAT SERVICES.)

Halftones finer than 65 screen cannot be used in most newspapers, nor can plates containing extra-fine shading. Solid black areas, including giant type, must be broken up by the use of a shading tint. (See SHADING TINTS.)

Borders are used in newspaper ads more often than elsewhere, since the problem of keeping an ad distinct from its neighbors is more acute.

Some good sources for information on the preparation of advertisements for newspaper publication are listed in Appendix 2.

**newsprint**   See GROUNDWOOD PULP; PAPER.

**news release**   See PUBLICITY RELEASE.

**nickel-faced plates**   Both electrotypes and stereotypes can be faced with nickel for extra wear. (See ELECTRO; STEREOTYPES.) In the case of stereos, the nickel is deposited on the plate only after the plate is made. There is thus a slight loss of detail. Nickel (or chromium) facing costs extra. So-called "steel-faced" plates are really faced with nickel.

**nixie**   A piece of mail which cannot be delivered because of incorrect or obsolete address.

**novelty printing**   See also BADGES; BALLOONS; BLOTTERS; CALENDARS; PENCILS; MATCHES.

Many printed messages can be distributed advantageously in novelty form on pencils, balloons, blotters, calendars, badges, matches, pennants, caps, buttons, fans, mirrors, tape, beer coasters, cigarettes, etc.

Printing can be done in invisible ink, in perfumed ink (any scent), in ink that is later given a "velvet" or "frosted" finish (see FLOCK PRINTING), and on any surface, including sandpaper, cellophane, metal, foil, cloth, wax, and luminous paper. Anyone can do his own printing on almost anything through the use of decalcomanias. (See DECALCOMANIAS.)

In general, the firm selling the novelty will know about printing messages on it. When a sample suitable for duplication is found, the manufacturer can be located through the firm that issued the sample.

A few firms offering novelty services are as follows:

*Cloth caps.* Advertising Mfg. Co., 127–133 Jackson Ave., Ripon, Wis.

*Paper caps.* Economy Novelty & Printing Co., 225 W. 39 St., New York 18

*Fans.* Skinner & Kennedy Co., 416 N. 4 St., St. Louis, Mo.

*Badges, buttons, and lapel pins.* Green Duck Metal Stamping Co., 1520 W. Montana St., Chicago 4, Ill.

*Banners.* Fair Publishing House, New London, Ohio

*Beer coasters.* Campbell Press, Inc., 344 W. 38 St., New York 11

*Coin cards.* Freedman Cut-Outs, 34 Hubert St., New York 11

*Coin envelopes.* United States Envelope Co., Springfield, Mass.

*Paper clips with imprinted ad.* Green Duck Metal Stamping Co., 1520 W. Montana St., Chicago 14, Ill.

*Playing cards.* United States Playing Card Co., Norwood, Cincinnati, Ohio

*Tape* (advertising tying tape). Neuer & Hoffman, Inc., 132 Green St., New York

*Perfumed and invisible inks.* Interchemical Corp., 67 W. 44 St., New York 36

*Luminous paper.* See LUMINESCENT PRINTING.

**numbering**  Numbering of tickets, membership cards, books, etc., can be done in letterpress during the regular press run at virtually no additional expense. Special numbering devices are available which can be locked up with the rest of the form. The pressure of the paper against the device causes the number to advance after each impression.

In offset and other processes, numbering requires an extra attachment or extra operation. (See also entry under TICKET PRINTING.)

# O | o

**oblique** *This sentence is set in Futura Oblique.* In the sans-serif type faces the term "oblique" is often preferred to "italic" in describing inclined letters, since true "italic" type has serifs.

**offset** Photo-offset lithography is commonly called "offset" or "photo offset." It is the important commercial application of lithography (a "planographic"

Diagram of an offset press.

process). (See also LITHOGRAPHY; PLANOGRAPHY; DRY OFFSET.)

The Multilith is a small-size offset printing press.

202

Firms that advertise planographing and emphasize "no plates required" do the work on an offset press.

Offset tends to be cheaper than any other process

1. whenever many line drawings are to be reproduced;
2. whenever type need not be set, as when it is done on the typewriter or when, in a reprint, an earlier edition can be photographically copied;
3. whenever large illustrations (larger than book or magazine size) are to be used. (See SILK SCREEN and PHOTO-GELATIN which also compete here on the small runs.)
4. on process color work or fake process work. (Photogelatin may be cheaper on small quantities.)

Offset has the following advantages over letterpress:

1. It can use either coated or uncoated paper, but the paper must be "sized for offset." It is not committed to glossy paper for halftones.
2. It is cheaper when many illustrations are involved.

Offset has these disadvantages:

1. Its reproduction of photographs

is sometimes inferior in quality to letterpress, gravure, or photogelatin.

2. The cheaper grades of offset work often have a gray look that is worse than the worst letterpress.

Offset is not really a plateless process. On the contrary, the whole job is put on a plate—type, illustrations, and all. But since the plate has to be made anyway, it costs no more to put line drawings on it than to put type on it. It does cost about 10 cents per square inch extra (with a $3 minimum) to put each halftone on it; more if the highest quality of halftone reproduction is demanded.

To make an offset plate, the printer sets up his "copy" in front of a big camera and photographs it on film. He reduces or enlarges it so that the *film* will be of the exact size the final result is to be. He may photograph the type "same size," and an illustration in reduced size. If so, he must then take these two separate negatives and "strip" them together in the proper position. (See STRIP.) He will charge extra for each strip-in.

The film can now be retouched to remove paste marks and other imperfections, although smudgy type can never be fixed by retouching.

The film is then placed over a sensitized grained metal plate, and both are exposed to strong light. The image is transferred to the plate by photochemical action. The end result is a plate that is receptive to greasy ink wherever it is supposed to print, and receptive only to water where it is supposed not to print.

The word "offset" comes from the fact that the inked surface does not print directly on the paper—instead it prints on a rubber-covered cylinder, and from the rubber the image is offset onto the paper.

The rubber blanket presses the ink firmly into the paper; hence it is possible to print halftones on rough-surfaced papers.

Offset printing can be of very high quality or of very low quality. For reproducing a wash drawing, for example, it is unexcelled. For photographs, it tends to be less satisfactory than other processes and is often very poor indeed.

Probably the cheapest of all ways to print a leaflet is by offset in a combination run. (See COMBINATION RUN.) Prices may be as low as $4 for the first 100 copies, size 8½ by 11 in., printed on one side.

Almost anything can be printed by offset: books, booklets, posters, bottles, decalcomanias, toothpaste tubes, pencils, even sandpaper. The process is economical in runs from 1,000 to 500,000 or more. Press sizes vary from 9 by 12 (see MULTILITH) up to 50 by 68, or more.

There are basically five different kinds of offset plates: paper, albumin, presensitized, deep-etch, and bimetal. Paper plates can be prepared by being typed upon in a typewriter. They are used only on the Multilith or similar small offset presses and are good for about as many copies as a mimeograph stencil. (Recent improvements may extend their life.)

Albumin and deep-etch plates are prepared photographically. Albumin plates are used mostly for short runs though with care they can stand up to 100,000 impressions or more; deep-etch and bimetal plates are made for longer runs and cost more to make. (See DEEP-ETCH OFFSET.)

Presensitized plates are supplied already coated with special coatings which do not deteriorate on standing. These plates are very simple to make and print with very good quality because they are ungrained. Their greatest use is in the smaller sizes. Small offset plates can also be made on Verifax equipment (see PHOTOCOPYING) and on Xerox equipment (see XEROGRAPHY).

The paper used should be surface-sized for offset. (See SIZE.) When type is required, the offset printer sends out to a type composition house that sets type in the ordinary way and returns a "reproduction proof." The offset printer photographs this proof. The type itself is not used again. Cuts are of no use to an offset printer.

For a simple offset job, write, draw, or type neatly in black ink on a piece of white paper. The offset printer will duplicate it about as neatly as the original but no more neatly, unless an extra fee is paid to have his art department improve on your work.

(For a discussion of when to use offset and when to use letterpress, see LETTERPRESS. For a discussion of costs, see ESTIMATING COSTS. A comparison of all printing processes is given on the charts reproduced inside the covers of this book.)

**offset paper**   Any type of paper can be printed by the offset lithography process, including antique, machine-finish, English-finish, super, and coated. However, because moisture is used in offset printing, it is desirable to know that the finish used will not give trouble, whether by picking, by refusing ink, or by unreasonable expansion or contraction on close-register jobs.

Paper merchants can supply paper that has been "sized for offset," or otherwise treated to give good results in offset, if asked for offset book paper, offset or litho-coated, litho-English-finish, etc.

**Old English**

𝔗𝔥𝔦𝔰 𝔰𝔢𝔫𝔱𝔢𝔫𝔠𝔢 𝔥𝔞𝔰 𝔟𝔢𝔢𝔫 𝔰𝔢𝔱 𝔦𝔫 𝔒𝔩𝔡 𝔈𝔫𝔤𝔩𝔦𝔰𝔥 𝔱𝔶𝔭𝔢, 𝔞𝔩𝔰𝔬 𝔠𝔞𝔩𝔩𝔢𝔡 𝔊𝔬𝔱𝔥𝔦𝔠, 𝔚𝔢𝔡𝔡𝔦𝔫𝔤 𝔗𝔢𝔵𝔱, 𝔞𝔫𝔡 𝔗𝔢𝔵𝔱.

**old style**   The type faces most commonly used for text matter can be classified as follows:

Old style — *e.g.*, Caslon Old Style
Transitional — *e.g.*, Scotch Roman
Modern — *e.g.*, Bodoni

The difference lies largely in the handling of the serifs and the thick and the thin strokes. Old-style figures, 1234567890, differ from modern (lining) figures, 1234567890. (See Appendix 1, Type Faces.)

**one-shot**   In magazine-distributing parlance, a magazine of which there is only one issue; in other words, a book or pamphlet as opposed to a periodical. (See also DISTRIBUTION.)

**onion skin**   A light, thin bond paper.

**opacity**   Opacity in printing papers is expressed in percentages. A lightweight bond paper may have an opacity of 79 per cent, meaning that 21 per cent of the light that falls on it goes through. A 24-lb. bond paper of high opacity (the cheaper sulphite bonds are of higher opacity than pure rag-content bonds) may have an opacity of 93 per cent.

Opacity, important in lightweight printing paper, is sometimes achieved by the addition of such fillers as titanium dioxide.

**Optak**   An improved photogelatin printing process developed and used by Edward Stern & Company, Inc., Sixth and Cherry Sts., Philadelphia 6. It was formerly called "Aquatone."

Optak differs from photogelatin or collotype in that it employs a screen. This factor is responsible for the longer press runs and greater uniformity possible with Optak plates. It differs from offset, letterpress, and gravure in that no etching or mechanical treatment of the printing plate is necessary—a feature that permits the use of a screen as fine as 400 lines to the inch.

The Optak process lends itself to unusually fine reproduction of photographs and facsimile work on virtually any kind of paper.

**outdoor advertising**   See also POSTERS; TRANSPORTATION ADVERTISING.

Posters and signs offer a means of

putting a picture with a short message where people living and working in any selected area will see it repeatedly and where travelers will see it both coming and going in the course of their activities. Outdoor advertising is widely used on a national basis for such products as food, soft drinks, automobiles, gasoline and oil, accessories, beer, movies, and cigarettes. It is used locally for political campaigns, hotels, restaurants, banks, food products, community drives, etc.

In the trade, outdoor displays are classified as posters, painted displays, and "electrical spectaculars." When quantities are very small or when the "copy" is to change with each locality, outdoor posters are hand-painted. This is one of the few fields of advertising where the use of color does not cost extra.

When quantities are larger (10 to 1,000), the silk-screen process of reproduction is generally used. (See SILK SCREEN.) When quantities exceed 1,000 or so, the work is usually done by offset lithography. (See OFFSET.)

The best way to arrange for a local poster campaign is to get in touch with the outdoor advertising company whose name appears in small letters beneath local poster panels.

Most outdoor advertising space (apart from signs on an advertiser's own property) is controlled by firms that specialize in maintaining this space for use by national and local advertisers. Most such firms are members of the Outdoor Advertising Association of America and have accepted the standards of size, construction, public safety, and convenience worked out by that group.

The space cost of outdoor advertising depends largely on the number of people who pass that space. The better the location and the larger the community, the more valuable the space. In cities of over 50,000 population, a poster 12 ft. high by 25 ft. long costs about $34 a month. The national average cost is $23.50 a month. Poster advertising space, however, is sold in units called "showings." A showing consists of a sufficient number of panels to provide coverage of the entire market.

Outdoor advertising companies can handle the design and painting or printing of outdoor displays for local use, or they can advise regarding it. Outdoor Advertising Incorporated, the national sales representative for the industry, with head office at 60 E. 42 St., New York, helps national advertisers and agencies in preparing campaign plans and in seeing that the advertising is most productive.

There are two standard sizes of printed posters: the 24-sheet and the 3-sheet. The former is most used. In a 24-sheet poster the lithographed advertisement is 8 ft. 8 in. high by 19 ft. 6 in. long. The over-all size of a 3-sheet

Typical "24-sheet" posters showing how sheets are actually positioned.

poster is 8 ft. 7 in. high by 4 ft. 10 in. wide. (A 24-sheet poster is not actually printed as 24 separate sheets each 28 by 41 in. It is usually printed as 10 sheets, but it is still called a "24-sheet poster.")

Art work for posters is usually done by artists who specialize in such work, and their sketches vary in cost from $100 all the way to $1,000 each. Posters are usually printed by lithography from the artist's finished sketch.

There are about 25 offset lithographers in the United States who specialize in 24-sheet posters, and many more printers (offset, silk screen, letterpress) who handle 3-sheet posters.

Typical prices for lithographed 24-sheet posters are given in the accompanying table. A so-called 24-sheet poster is actually printed as 10 sheets. To put an average of three colors on each of these 10 sheets requires a total of 30 printings. Usually there is no need to print every sheet in every color; some sheets require more printings than others. Prices are per complete poster.

**Prices of 24-sheet Lithographed Posters**

| Quantity | 30 printings | 50 printings |
|---|---|---|
| 500 | $4.55 | $7.04 |
| 1,000 | 3.05 | 4.58 |
| 2,000 | 2.35 | 3.27 |
| 10,000 | 1.43 | 1.77 |

Fluorescent (Day-Glo) ink is being used increasingly on outdoor posters because it is up to four times as bright as the ordinary ink colors and makes a poster glow in the daytime as though illuminated. Day-Glo ink is applied by silk-screen process. The cost is estimated as an additional printing for each color covered, plus 10 cents per poster for each square foot of Day-Glo coverage.

For excellent information on how to plan, design, and buy outdoor advertising consult the books included in Appendix 2, Bibliography.

**overlay**  Editors and artists use overlays of paper, tissue, acetate, etc., to protect art work and photographs. Sometimes markings are placed on the overlays to show how the art is to be cropped, or to show the break for color, *i.e.,* which areas are to print in which

Photo with crop marks and protective overlay.

colors. The art for different colors is often executed on or pasted onto separate plastic overlays. (See COLOR SEPARATION.)

Printers also use the terms "overlay" and "underlay" with reference to the thin sheets of tissue placed under the paper or under the type during the make-ready process. In this way they control the amount of pressure with which the ink is pressed into the paper.

**over matter**  See OVERSET.

**overprinting**  The overprinting of circulars and posters to show a local advertiser's name is called imprinting. (See IMPRINTING.)

Firms that do imprinting are also well equipped to block out wrong prices, etc., and overprint them with the new information. It is difficult to block out printed characters so that they positively will not show through, but the use of metallic inks sometimes helps, as does the use of the silk-screen process.

**overrun** Printing-trade custom permits a printer to deliver a slight overrun or underrun and to modify his contractual price accordingly. (See PRINTING-TRADE CUSTOMS.) Thus, a printer who has contracted to print 10,000 copies of something for $100 may deliver 10,500 copies and charge $105, or 9,500 copies and charge $95. The same custom prevails when paper is made to order.

Overruns or underruns are unavoidable since it is impossible to predict in advance exactly how much to allow for spoilage during make-ready, handling, and binding. A printer must always start with a little more paper than the finished job requires, to allow for spoilage.

**overset** Material that has been set in type ready for use and then not used is referred to as "overset matter" or "over matter." When a magazine is finally closed for the press, there are generally some items that have been crowded out, and these may be kept as overset for possible use in the next issue.

Page proofs of circulars, ads, etc., may carry a paragraph or two of overset wordage in the lower margin if there was too much type for the allotted space. It is up to the editor to decide how to make room for the overset material, or to authorize "killing" it.

**Ozalid** See WHITEPRINT.

**Ozalith** Positive-working sensitized paper and aluminum offset plates, manufactured by Ozalid, Division of General Aniline and Film Corporation. They can be made from any translucent original in the same way as a whiteprint (see WHITEPRINT) plus additional fixing, and permit the making of plates for small offset presses in less than two minutes.

# P | p

**packages**  See CONTAINER PRINTING; WRAPPING AND PACKAGING.

**padding**  A very simple and inexpensive binding operation. To convert plain paper into pads of paper, the paper is trimmed to the desired size, padding cement is brushed across one edge, and cloth may be applied. If the pads are to be backed with cardboard, the board is interleaved with the paper at the desired intervals before trimming. It is customary to back at least 10 pads at once and cut them apart after drying.

A ny printer or binder can do padding. It is not only a way of making printed forms easy to handle but a good way to convert wastepaper into useful scratch pads.

**page**  One side of a sheet of paper. Page numbers, also called folios, in a booklet or pamphlet always begin on the right. This means that the right-hand page always has an odd number, the left an even number.

A booklet or pamphlet is made from folded sheets of paper, each sheet making a unit of two leaves or four pages. Hence the pages of any pamphlet, booklet, or broadside should be planned as a multiple of four, *i.e.,* 4, 8, 12, 16, etc.; preferably in units of 16 or 32. (See BINDING.)

**page proof**  See PROOFS.

**pamphlet binding**  See BINDING.

**pamphlets**  See also CIRCULARS; DESIGN.

For the purposes of this book, a pamphlet is assumed to have eight pages or more. Smaller printed items are discussed under circulars, posters, and letters. (See CIRCULARS; POSTERS; LETTERS.)

In planning a pamphlet, the points outlined in the Introduction should be checked. Only after that should decisions be made regarding (1) budget, (2) format (see DESIGN), (3) method of type composition, (4) printing process, (5) illustrations, and (6) paper.

For a pamphlet, type is usually set although the text may be done on a typewriter (see COLD TYPE). Setting type (see TYPE) costs anywhere from $3 to $10 per page and more. The illustrations, if any, may be another cost.

A neighborhood job printer may be as well equipped to handle pamphlet work as anyone.

These factors are worth remembering:

1. One hundred copies are likely to cost practically as much as 1,000 copies. This is because printing even one copy involves a charge for type composition, art work, plates, if any, and making the printing press ready. If a color other than black is used, there may be à further charge for cleaning one kind of ink off the press and substituting another color.

2. Economies can be effected by choosing a size that can be cut and folded from the paper without waste. (See PAPER; PAPER SIZES.)

3. The pages of a pamphlet should be planned as a multiple of four, *i.e.*, 4, 8, 12, 16, 24, 32 pages, etc. A 10-page pamphlet would have a loose sheet of 2 pages in the middle, and a 20-page pamphlet would usually be either a 16 plus a 4, or a 24 with 4 pages "canceled" (wasted).

4. A 12-page self-cover pamphlet is cheaper than one that consists of 8 pages of text plus a cover on heavier paper. The effect of a separate cover is sometimes attained by using a reverse plate. (See REVERSE PLATE.)

5. Sometimes an extra color of ink is more effective and cheaper than an expensive paper. On very small runs, the reverse is likely to be true.

6. A printer should be selected who customarily turns out work of the desired quality.

Very small printed items can often be handled with great economy by a label printer. (See LABELS.) On large runs, a printer with an automatic-feed multicolor press (perhaps with a folding attachment) may be able to underbid a smaller printer. (See also IMPRINTING; PAPER; COSTS; TYPE; CUT.)

Where the flat size of an unfolded pamphlet is less than 8½ by 11 in., or even 11 by 17, the owner of an office-size Multilith offset press can often underbid a printer whose presses are larger and more expensive to operate.

Both the offset and letterpress processes are suitable for a wide variety of pamphlet work; letterpress is sometimes thought to give more consistently satisfactory reproductions of photographs.

Rotogravure becomes economical only with quantities reaching well up into the hundreds of thousands. (See GRAVURE; also the inside front cover of this book.)

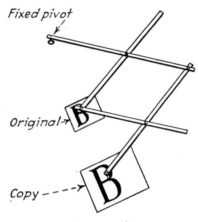

A pantograph.

**pantograph** A tool used by draftsmen and artists to make enlarged or reduced copies of maps, charts, drawings, lettering, etc. A pantograph consists of a fixed pivot, a tracing point, and a copying (pencil) point, the three held in mathematical relation to each other by a parallelogram of four bars. The device can be adjusted to enlarge or reduce by any desired proportion.

High-precision pantographs are used in making type matrices from large-scale originals, and in some steel engraving work. Much drafting work that used to be done by pantograph is now done through the use of Photostat copies or a camera lucida. (See PHOTOSTAT; CAMERA LUCIDA.)

**paper** See also PAPER SIZES AND WEIGHTS; CARDBOARD.

The easiest way to buy paper is to let the printer do it. For use on office duplicating machinery, it is safest to buy the paper recommended by the manufacturer's service agency.

However, print users can profit by knowing something about paper even if they never expect to buy any themselves. Some knowledge of paper is indispensable to the wise and economic planning of printed matter. Printing planned with standard paper sizes in mind can be cheaper all along the line —in paper, press, binding, and mailing costs.

Paper is sold by the pound, and the prices range from about 8 cents per pound for contract newsprint to 15 to 30 cents per pound for book papers. Special papers, particularly when ordered in small lots, cost 40 to 50 cents per pound and up.

Almost all paper is made of wood. Some is made of rags (cotton or linen) or has a rag content. (See RAG CONTENT.) An excellent quality of paper can be made without any rag content.

Groundwood paper is cheapest and is used for newspapers, rotogravure sections, some magazines, and some books. It has excellent opacity and printability, but turns yellow and brittle after prolonged exposure to air and light.

Sulphite, sulphate, and soda-pulp papers are made more slowly by chemically separating the wood fibers from the substances that make groundwood paper perishable. These papers tend to be stronger, whiter, free of blemishes, and durable. A sheet of paper made from pulp free of groundwood is called a "free sheet." The cost is at least twice as high as for groundwood paper.

Paper begins as a milky pulp of fibers and water, which flows onto a moving wire screen. The water is sucked out through the screen, and the limp, moist web of fibers is separated from the screen and passed between rollers. The smoothing action of the rollers is called "calendering."

If subjected to light calendering, the paper comes out as "antique" paper, like that used in newspapers or most books. If calendered longer, it becomes smoother. The steps are as follows:

| Process | Description of Paper |
|---|---|
| Minimum calendering | Antique finish, high bulking (rough, fluffy finish) |
| Light calendering | Antique finish, nonbulking (smoother finish) |
| More calendering | Machine finish (M.F.); English finish (E.F.) |
| Still more calendering | Supercalendered (Super) |

A Sunday newspaper contains both extremes of paper. Probably the rough-surfaced news section and the smooth-surfaced rotogravure section had the same start in life, but one was rolled out smoother (*i.e.*, calendered more) than the other.

The shinier papers take pictures better but are considered harder on the reader's eyes. The cost is usually about the same.

Coated papers, however, are quite different. (See COATED PAPER.) When the halftone was first invented, there were no papers smooth enough to do it justice; so coated papers were developed. Ordinary paper was brushed over with a coating of clay, casein, etc., which made it heavier without increasing its strength.

As coated paper was and is expensive, the big picture magazines wanted something cheaper. Papermakers then found a way to add the coating *during* the original process of manufacture instead of afterward. The result was machine-coated paper, also called "process-coated" paper. This takes halftones better than uncoated paper, though the highest qualities of coated paper are still made by the old brush-coated method.

Letting the printer select and buy the paper is the safest plan, since it centers responsibility. Poor printing cannot so easily be blamed on the customer's selection of poor paper. Where quantities are small, it is certainly the best plan. Printers charge a commission on buying paper for a client. This can sometimes be saved by dealing directly with the paper merchant and having him deliver to the printer.

Printers also are quite naturally inclined to use what paper they have on hand, which may not be quite so appropriate to the job (in size, weight, finish, or quality) as paper that might be obtained from a paper merchant.

In ordering paper eight qualities must be taken into account:

1. *Surface.* Antique, eggshell machine-finish, English-finish, supercalendered, glossy-coated, dull-coated, coated-one-side, etc.

2. *Finish.* Wove, laid, pebbled, etc.

3. *Proposed use.* For example, paper to be printed by offset lithography is usually ordered as offset book paper, litho-coated, etc. Mimeograph paper, hectograph paper, etc., are so designated. The paper supplier should be informed if the paper is to be used with adhesives or special inks; if it must be of a quality to accept writing ink, erasures, carbonizing, gumming, lacquer or varnish, lamination, waxing, precision register printing; if it must be weather-resistant, warp-resistant, water-repellent, colorfast, nonalterable, rigid, able to withstand repeated foldings, etc.

4. *Quality.* It is easy to buy too much quality, or too little. The important thing is to buy enough of the essential qualities, without paying for excess or nonessential quality. Good receptivity to the kind of printing process that is to be used is of first importance. Other important qualities are permanence, durability, strength, foldability, opacity. Groundwood paper offers economy, opacity, and printability. Rag, jute, hemp, and sulphate or kraft content contribute to bursting strength and folding endurance. Kraft paper excels in folding endurance. Rag-content papers offer greatest permanence, although no one has ever witnessed noticeable aging in a well-made sulphite paper. Strength sometimes has to be sacrificed to get opacity, and vice versa.

5. *Weight.* This book is printed on 70-lb. paper. (See PAPER SIZES AND WEIGHTS.)

6. *Size.* Paper can be purchased from stock in a wide variety of sizes, and it can be made to order in any size if the quantity required is large enough (at least 10,000 lb., often more). (See PAPER SIZES AND WEIGHTS.)

7. *Grain.* All machine-made paper has a grain, which makes tearing and folding in one direction easier than in the other. Paper can usually be ordered with the grain in either direction. (See GRAIN.)

8. *Color.* "White" paper comes in a wide variety of shades. Creams, buffs, India tints, etc., are available as well as all colors. Colored paper costs more than white except in the case of such unbleached papers as kraft paper and the so-called "manilas." (Manila as applied to paper means a shade, not a fiber, unless identified as having hemp content.) Paper is usually made in light colors, since it is easier to print with dark ink on a light surface than the other way around.

Extra-heavy paper is sold as cover paper or ledger paper. (See also CARDBOARD.)

Paper buyers will find detailed and authoritative information on paper in the books listed in Appendix 2, Bibliography.

**paper sizes and weights** See also PAPER; CARDBOARD.

Paper can be made to order in almost any desired weight, bulk, finish, and color, but such special orders are uneconomical unless 5,000 to 10,000 lb. or more are to be ordered at one time.

For small jobs and for rush jobs, standard sizes and weights are used. It pays to design a piece of printing so that it can be cut economically out of a stock size.

Suppose, for example, a circular is planned in size 9 by 12 in. (before folding), and the only paper available is 17 by 22. This paper will yield two circulars to the sheet, wasting one strip 4 by 17 and another 5 by 18. (See illustrations.)

Simply by changing the specifications to 8½ by 11, each sheet will yield four circulars. Half the paper will do the job. (The example cited is a very common one, although 9 by 12 is also a standard size. Many offset printers cannot print, and do not handle, any paper larger than 17 by 22 or 17½ by 22½.)

The standard paper sizes are what they are because standard-sized printing jobs can be cut or folded out of them without waste. (See the accompanying table.)

One standard article is the business letterhead, or piece of typewriter paper, size 8½ by 11. Another standard article is the book or pamphlet in size 6 by 9. Still another is the post card in size 3½ by 5½. *Remember these sizes.* Jobs designed in these sizes, double these sizes, or half these sizes, can be printed without waste on stock papers. Printing presses and envelopes are designed around these sizes too.

*Bond paper.* Business letterheads and typewriter papers come in size 8½ by 11, except in Federal government service. The sheet used by printers is just four times as big: 17 by 22. A ream (500 sheets) of ordinary bond paper in size 17 by 22 weighs 20 lb. This is ordered as "20-lb. bond." A lighter paper would be termed a 13-lb. or a 16-lb. paper, often written 13# and 16#. A heavier quality of bond would be termed 24#.

It is possible to buy bond paper in other sizes, notably 17 by 28, out of which can be cut four sheets of legal size typewriter paper. Naturally a ream of 17 by 28 paper weighs more than a ream of the same paper in size 17 by 22. For convenience, however, it is still

### Standard Paper Sizes Worth Remembering

| Use | Size | Cuts out of |
|---|---|---|
| Business letterhead | 8½ x 11 | 17 x 22 |
| Books and pamphlets | 8½ x 11 | 35 x 45 |
| Books and pamphlets | 8½ x 5½ | 35 x 45 |
| Books and pamphlets | 6 x 9 | 25 x 38 |
| Post cards | 3½ x 5½ | 22½ x 28½ |

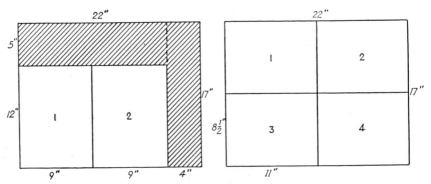

Only two 9 x 12 leaflets can be cut out of a 17- by 22-in. sheet of paper, as against four slightly smaller leaflets, each 8½ by 11 in. In the same way, a small change often permits the printing area of a printing press to be used to greater advantage.

described as a 20-lb. paper, or as being a paper of "substance 20" if it would weigh 20 lb. in the 17 by 22 size. All bond and ledger paper is described in terms of basic substance weights, referred to the 17 by 22 size. (See also BASIC WEIGHT.)

*Book paper.* The page of a printed book or pamphlet is commonly 6 by 9. This folds economically from the standard book-paper sheet size, 25 by 38. To see how this works out, visualize the folding of such a sheet: first, it is 25 by 38, then 25 by 19, then 12½ by 19, then 12½ by 9½, and finally 6¼ by 9½. When the edges are trimmed to even them and to open the folds, the final result is a 32-page pamphlet in size 6⅛ by 9¼, or 6 by 9. *Book-paper weights are always based on a sheet 25 by 38.* That size is worth remembering.

The next most common book or pamphlet size is 5½ by 8½, which is just half the letterhead size, 8½ by 11.

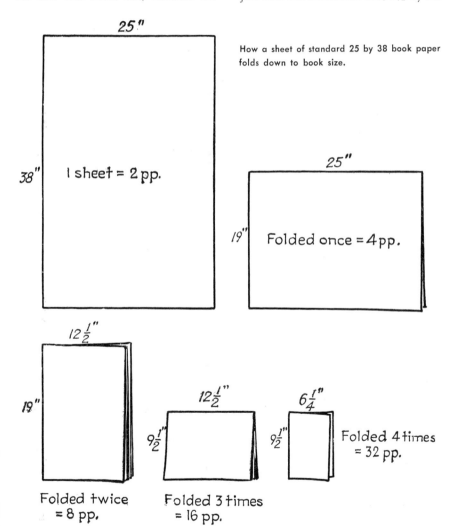

How a sheet of standard 25 by 38 book paper folds down to book size.

25"
38"
I sheet = 2 pp.

25"
19"
Folded once = 4 pp.

12½"
19"
Folded twice = 8 pp.

12½"
9½"
Folded 3 times = 16 pp.

6¼"
9½"
Folded 4 times = 32 pp.

The standard sheet of bond paper will fold from 17 by 22 to a 16-page pamphlet about 5½ by 8½. After trim, however, the finished size will be only about 5⅜ by 8¼. The full 5½ by 8½ size can be produced from another standard book-paper size, namely, 35 by 45, one-quarter of which is 17½ by 22½.

*Cover paper.* Cover paper comes just a little bigger than book paper, since the covers on many pamphlets overhang the text a little. Thus, the basic size on which cover-paper substances are figured is 20 by 26. (19 by 25 would be exactly one-half standard book-paper size.)

*Post-card stock.* The basic size on which post-card and Bristol board substances are figured is 22½ by 28½. (See CARDBOARD.)

Any given paper may come in many other sizes besides those shown above, but practically all papers come in these standard sizes.

Any size or shape at all is of course possible. There is no law against cutting paper so as to waste some. But by using standard sizes, the necessary amount of paper will be cheaper to buy, and easier and quicker to locate. The use of standard sizes helps a printer to put the job on a press that it fits instead of on a larger, more expensive press. Folding and bindery machines handle standard sizes most readily. Equally important is the fact that standard-size jobs fit into standard-size envelopes.

A printer should not be asked whether he can handle a job of a certain size. Of course he can, even if he has to print only two pages at a time. The problem is to give him a job that he can handle *most economically* and on which he can quote a good price.

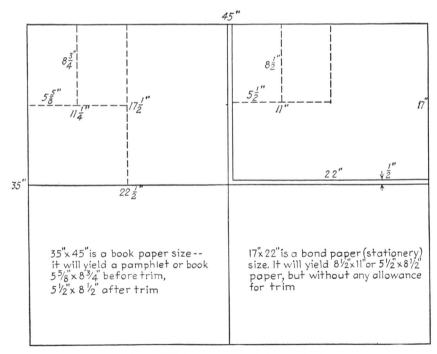

How two standard sizes fold down to standard sizes for books or pamphlets.

# Standard Paper Sizes and Weights

| Paper | Basic size, and other standard sizes | Standard basic substance weights* |
|---|---|---|
| | 25 x 38, 28 x 42, 32 x 44, 35 x 45, 38 x 50 | 30  35  40  45  50  60  70  80  90  100  120  140†  150  160  180  200  240  260  300 |
| Coated paper | 25 x 38 and as above | 60  70  80  90  100  110 |
| Newsprint | 24 x 36 (in rolls to order) | 32  35 |
| Bond paper | 17 x 22, 17 x 28, 19 x 24, 22 x 34, 28 x 34 | 13  16  20  24 |
| Ledger paper | 17 x 22 and as above | 28  32  36  40  44 |
| Cover paper | 20 x 26, 23 x 35, 26 x 40, 35 x 46 | 25  35  40  50  65  80  90  100  130 |
| Post-card Bristo | 22½ x 28½ | 94  100  105 |
| Printing Bristol | 22½ x 28½, 24 x 36, 25½ x 30½ | 100  120  140  160  180  200 |
| Blotter | 19 x 24 | 80  100  140 |

* Basic substance weights are arranged to show weight relationships between various kinds of paper. Papers of basic substance weights shown in the same vertical column at right are approximately equivalent in weight per square inch. For each kind of paper, the basic substance weight is that of 500 sheets of the size shown underscored at left.

† Paper is not made heavier than 120 lb. These weights are for comparison only.

Instead, he should be asked what printing press he would recommend for the job and what is the biggest sheet of standard-size paper it will take. If a sheet of that size is folded down (see illustration), the print user can see whether one of the resulting page sizes is desirable, and whether the resulting number of pages (or half, or double) fills his need. If this size will do, the press will be used at its maximum capacity. Without this kind of planning, double the press run may be necessary.

Paper merchants are always glad to supply dummies in any desired size, on any kind of paper. It is well to get several such dummies, to be sure that the right paper is being ordered. Things to check are opacity, mailing weight, "feel," etc. Weighing a dummy of a proposed printed piece has a special advantage: it serves as a check on the poundage of paper that must be ordered. 5,000 copies of a 2-oz. pamphlet will obviously require at least 10,000 ounces (625 lb.) of paper, plus allowance for waste, spoilage, and trim. Without this check, it is very easy, even for experts, to order double or half the right amount of paper, thanks to the always confusing phenomenon of "one leaf equals two pages."

To calculate exactly the amount of paper needed for any job, a dummy should be made to the exact size, then unfolded to show the actual size of the sheet needed. From this one can determine the number of units to be got out of the standard sheet of the nearest size; then the number of sheets needed can be calculated and finally translated into 500-sheet reams. Extra should be allowed for spoilage.

Paper is sold by the quire ($\frac{1}{20}$ ream), the ream (500 sheets), the carton ($\frac{1}{4}$ case), the case (about 500 to 700 lb.), and the skid (about 3,000 lb.). Less-than-ream lots cost more per pound than lots of a ream or more. Cutting to special sizes costs extra.

Paper should never be ordered without the printer's approval of every detail of the order. He may want the paper cut in a certain way before delivery. He knows how much extra is needed to allow for spoilage. There may be some reason why he cannot run the jobs as he is expected to, or why he cannot get so many pieces to the sheet as the buyer has figured.

**paragraph** See PROOFREADING.

**Paraliner** A mechanical ruling device which attaches to a drawing board and makes easy the accurate ruling of evenly spaced lines. A built-in micrometer can be set for any desired spacing, after which each squeeze of the spacing knobs moves the ruler by the preset amount. The Paraliner easily rules business forms, music scales, etc., and does crosshatching. A built-in protractor permits diagonal ruling. For further information write the Michael Lith Co., 145 W. 45 St., New York 36.

**parcel post** See Appendix 4, Postal Information.

**parchment** Genuine parchment is thin skin taken from a calf, sheep, lamb, goat, or other animal, and prepared to accept writing. High-grade papers imitating genuine parchment are also called "parchment." The term "vellum" is used in the same way. It originally meant a calfskin or lambskin parchment, but it is now used generally to describe smooth paper with a good writing surface.

**pasteboard** See CARDBOARD.

The heavier papers and cardboards get their rigidity and thickness by being built up out of two or more plies, which are either pasted together or pressed together wet, or both.

**paste-up dummy** See also PASTE-UP TECHNIQUES; DUMMY; LAYOUT.

The paste-up dummy shows the

printer which lines of type and which illustrations go on which pages and how they are to be arranged, spaced, etc.

As soon as galley proofs arrive on the desk of the editor or make-up man, he will have someone separate them into different kinds. Usually at least three sets of galleys are returned by the printer: (1) a master set, which has been proofread by the printer and should be proofread again by the editor and sometimes by the author, (2) a set of numbered galleys, sometimes called "pinks" because frequently printed on pink paper, and (3) an extra set for the files.

Although the second set is generally used for the paste-up, many people prefer pasting up white galleys to get an effect more nearly resembling the finished page. Each galley to be used in the paste-up is first numbered by copying the printed number at the top onto each printed paragraph. (See illustration.) Numbering the galleys tells the printer where to look for the type. It is especially helpful if an item from galley 17 is likely to appear in the paste-up alongside items from galley 5, for example.

The editor or make-up man then has someone "trim" this set of proofs for the paste-up. This means cutting away all margins surrounding each block of text and each major heading.

The make-up man then arranges the trimmed proofs on the dummy (blank pages that have been marked to show margins, columns, etc.). When he is satisfied with the spacing and fit, he pastes them in place with rubber cement.

It is not necessary to show proofreader's corrections on the paste-up dummy. Corrections must be made on the master set of galley proofs. If corrections promise to shorten a paragraph by one line, it is sufficient for the paste-up merely to snip off the last line arbitrarily. However, the paste-up

dummy must take account of corrections on the master galley proofs and allow for changes in length.

To make such a dummy, first paste in the headings, being sure that they fit as planned in the original dummy

# 22—School Exec

## Outcomes at the School

Representatives of all subject matter and area committees undertook to survey the desired and attained outcomes of the school. Where test and observational data were not already available as measures of these outcomes, standardized and teacher-made tests were administered.

A thorough investigation was made of the extra-curricular activities of the entire student body. Evidence was thus obtained as to the extent to which the school's cultural and technical training was carrying over into the pupil's after-school hours.

Evidence from concrete situations of all kinds was gathered on attitudes, appreciations, and skills at-

A galley proof, numbered and trimmed for pasting on the layout pages or dummy.

or layout or can be made to fit an altered layout if desired.

Next, paste in engraver's proofs, or Photostats of the art work (trimmed of their margins) or merely leave space for them. Then paste in the captions, checking carefully on the fit. (See CAPTIONS.)

Next try to fit the columns of copy to the space allocated. Before pasting is done, it is often best to pin down the printed columns, using pins like thumbtacks through the proofs, the page, and into the drawing board. Since the copy may not fit exactly, the next problem is to cut, or, if necessary, expand the copy so that the fewest alterations will have to be made by the printer and so that the most effective result may be obtained.

There are many tricks in fitting copy to space although, at first, it may sound like mere cutting and pasting of long strips of paper.

1. If it is necessary to cut several lines, go back to those paragraphs which have a very short last line. Perhaps by omitting a tiny phrase at the end or by substituting "often" for "frequently," a whole line of space can be saved. Whatever corrections are made here must also be made on the master proofs, which will go back to the printer as a guide for corrections. He will not follow alterations made only on the paste-up dummy.

2. Whenever possible avoid dividing a word at the end of a page since it is distracting to the reader to have to remember a syllable until he turns the page and finds the rest of the word.

3. Avoid dividing a paragraph so that the first line of it is alone at the bottom of a column or page, or the last line begins a new column. Better go back to cut out or add a line somewhere so that this wayward line can be brought back to its family. In printer's parlance the single-line carry-over is referred to as a "widow."

4. Watch out for the location of subheads. Otherwise a subhead may fall on the last line of a page or column and thus be separated from the copy that it announces. It may be well to go back and "take a tuck" in the preceding copy or, if a single line is involved, expand so that the subhead will be pushed ahead to start the next column or page.

Where a page has several columns, be sure that the subheads do not fall so as to make a distracting pattern on the page. For example, on a three-column page having just two subheads in bold type, it would be unattractive to have these come side by side like a dark streak across two columns of the page. It might be better to remove one subhead entirely or to move it to another place.

Experience will quickly sharpen the eye so that such items are brought into a harmonious whole.

Finally, when satisfactory cutting and padding have been completed, paste down the copy to make a scrapbook page to guide the printer. Rubber cement is recommended for the pasting because it does not pucker the paper and because the copy can be peeled off if alterations are necessary.

Be sure that all alterations are marked on the master proofs to go back to the printer with the paste-up dummy.

The above procedures for the handling of galley proofs and corrections are standard. However, there are a few printers and publications that follow less orthodox procedures. At least one printer encourages his magazine clients to indicate all corrections right on the paste-up dummy and to return no corrected galleys at all. (This is very uncommon.) It is possible, at least when corrections are likely to be few, to paste up uncorrected galleys, return the paste-up dummy to the printer, and then proofread the galleys. Any corrections discovered in the galleys are held and later transferred to the page proofs. This may mean extra expense, but on the other hand it may also be less expensive to make three corrections in one page proof, than to make two in galley and one in the page proof, provided the corrections in the page proof do not involve changes in other pages as well.

Extreme neatness is not necessary on a paste-up dummy, although it is helpful to the editor in visualizing the appearance of a layout. Dummies need only be clear enough to guide the compositor in "paging" the type and cuts.

There is another kind of paste-up that must be perfect. This is the one made for photographic reproduction. It is on mounting board, not on paper. Galley proofs are not good enough for this kind of paste-up. After all corrections have been made, the printer must supply reproduction proofs pulled with special care. (See REPRODUCTION PROOFS.) These must be trimmed and mounted with painstaking neatness, both to get the alignment exactly right and to avoid any smudging.

There are many tricks to paste-up technique which make the work easier and neater and which are worth learning. (See PASTE-UP TECHNIQUES.)

**paste-up techniques** See also LAYOUT; DUMMY; PASTE-UP DUMMY.

Neat, careful pasting must be done in many editorial jobs preparatory to printing, such as pasting up a dummy or mounting a photograph or piece of art work. Meticulously accurate pasting must be done on copy—either editorial or illustrative—that is to be reproduced photographically as in offset, photoengraving, or gravure.

There are several equally good ways of getting the same results, but the following paste-up techniques are practical and satisfactory.

The essential tools are rubber cement, a good flexible palette knife for applying and spreading it, a supply of mounting board, layout paper and tracing paper, scissors, photo trimmer, rulers (including pica rulers and transparent rulers), triangles, T squares, straight pins, a pricker for transferring markings from one page to another,

A good way to apply rubber cement is with a palette knife. The same knife can be used as a handle for positioning the proof on the dummy, since the proof will stick to the knife. It is easy to paste up proofs in exact alignment if guidelines are first drawn in light blue pencil on both surfaces.

a supply of pencils (hard, soft, black, blue, red, and china-marking), retouching brushes, Chinese white, ruling pen, India ink, erasers, masking tape, scotch tape—the permanent "mending" kind as well as the regular clear, black-and-white kinds.

There is no substitute for good rubber cement. It does not stretch or crinkle the paper. It does not soil the paper. When it is dry, any excess can be rubbed off easily with a soft eraser or the corner of a handkerchief. It can be used to make either a permanent or a temporary joint. Substitutes for rubber cement should be avoided. Buy only the kind labeled "rubber cement" or "synthetic rubber cement."

When pasting, it is well to have a good supply of scratch paper handy. Lay the item to be pasted face down on a clean piece of scratch paper. Smear it thinly with rubber cement. Pick it up by putting the palette knife down in the middle of the cemented area so that it sticks to the knife. Position it for pasting. Lay another piece of scratch paper over it, and rub through the back of the other scratch paper. Throw away both pieces of scratch paper rather than run the risk of smearing something else with cement left on them. (Or else put two smeared pieces of scratch paper face to face, and use them again as one piece.)

To make a temporary joint, put rubber cement on one piece of paper only, and apply when wet. To make a permanent joint, put rubber cement on both surfaces and allow them to dry before joining. (This means using great care the first time in positioning, for once stuck, they will stay stuck.)

In using rubber cement, be careful around reproduction proofs. The cement can smear the ink. When entirely dry, rubber cement can be rubbed off paper with a piece of tissue, but it may take pencil markings on the paper with it.

Trim proofs close before pasting, preferably within less than $\frac{1}{16}$ in. This helps to avoid misalignment, or apparent misalignment. Where the alignment is particularly important, rule blue lines both on proof and on the mount, and match them up in the pasting. (See illustration.)

Strive for a paste-up result that will give a good visualization of the actual printed page to come. Use proofs of the same color as the mounting board or layout paper. Reproduction proofs are always pulled on white paper, but printers often send extra proofs on blue, red, or yellow paper. This is a good enough way of distinguishing extra sets of proofs from the master set, but paste-up dummies made with colored proofs do not give the layout man much visual help.

Before pasting, it is customary to arrange the various elements in their proper positions, and pin them there, just to make sure that everything will fit.

**pasting** See also PASTE-UP DUMMY; PASTE-UP TECHNIQUES; MOUNTING AND FINISHING.

An 8- or 12-page folder can be held together by pasting instead of by wire stitching if desired. The operation is done during the folding process and does not require an extra operation, as stitching does. A thin line of paste is laid on the paper where the fold will come.

Inserts are often pasted into place in books or magazines. (See INSERTS.)

**patent base** When printing is done entirely from electrotypes or stereotypes, it is common practice to equip the bed of the press with a patent base. This raises the level of the press bed so that the plates need not be mounted on wood but can be clamped directly to the patent base. A patent base looks like a honeycomb, each of the holes providing potential anchorage for a plate clamp.

**patents** Literary and printed material may be copyrighted but not patented. (See COPYRIGHT.) A patent is a grant of the exclusive right to make, use, and sell, for a limited (17-year) period, the invention covered by the patent.

**pebbling** Paper may be pebbled either before or after printing. The word "pebble" is a general one covering special finishes such as pebble finish, linen finish, ripple finish, and imitation-leather finish. The process is often referred to as "roller embossing."

Paper is pebbled by passing it under high pressure between rollers embossed with the desired design. Since it is not so easy to print on rough papers as on smooth papers, paper is usually pebbled after printing. A fine-screen halftone cannot be put on eggshell or antique paper by the letterpress process, but it can be printed on smooth paper that is later pebbled to an antique finish.

Pebbling is often used to improve the appearance, bulk, or pliability of paper so that a less expensive paper may be substituted for more costly stock. It may be used to finish small quantities of paper that could not be purchased with that finish except in prohibitive quantity.

Among firms handling this work are The Pebbling Co., 9 Bond St., New York, and O'Brien Finishing Co., Inc., 310 E. 22 St., New York.

**pencils** A great variety of ordinary and novelty pencils can be obtained imprinted with advertising messages. Among the distributors of imprinted pencils are Ballard Pencil Co., Glenwood, N.J.; LeRoy, Inc., 2109 Summit Ave., Union City, N.J.; and United States Pencil Co., Inc., 100 Fifth Ave., New York 11. Prices on wooden pencils begin at about $4 a gross.

**pennants** See CLOTH PRINTING.

**penny-saver** See ENVELOPES; also Appendix 4.

**perfect binding** See illustration under BINDING.

**perfector press** A press that can print paper on both sides in one operation.

**perforating** Perforating is often done during a printing operation by a sharp steel rule, just enough higher than the type to penetrate the paper. The perforated line is also inked, of course, unless the printer goes to the trouble and expense of cutting away a section of his ink rollers. On cylinder presses a perforating wheel can be attached to the cylinder. Perforating can also be done as part of a folding operation.

Perforating is also handled as a separate operation on machines that punch rows of tiny holes. This is considered a finishing operation. (See MOUNTING AND FINISHING.)

**periodicals** See also NEWSPAPERS.

Periodicals of all kinds—newspapers, magazines, house organs, etc.—present the same variety of printing problems as pamphlets, books, catalogues, and posters. They can be and are printed by every known method, and the choice of a printing process can be made on the same basis as for circulars and pamphlets. (See CIRCULARS; PAMPHLETS.) Letterpress, offset, and rotogravure are the most used processes.

Where the budget is very small, one of the office duplicating methods may be indicated. (See DUPLICATING METHODS.)

Getting out the first issue of a magazine is exactly like getting out a pamphlet or a catalogue. Decisions must be made as to what process, what printer, what size, what paper, what typography, etc. Once made, however, these decisions need not come up again for months or years.

This means that the magazine editor

need not ask himself, "Would these illustrations look better in gravure?" His magazine runs in letterpress and that is all there is to it. He need not laboriously specify that a heading be set in "24-pt. 20th Cent. Ex. Bold Ital. C. & l.c. flush left on one column." He can just mark it "Style B"—one of several typographic styles worked out in advance and on file with the printer. He need not rule margins and column widths for each issue; he can have layout paper printed up in advance with this information on it. (See LAYOUT.)

Magazine distribution can also become a matter of routine. A decision can be made once and for a long time as to whether to mail in an envelope, in a wrapper, or as a self-mailer. The names and addresses of recipients can be put on plates. (See ADDRESSING.) Second-class mailing privileges can be applied for. (See Appendix 4, Postal Information.)

Only periodicals with a legitimate list of paid-up subscriptions published for the dissemination of news of a public character can get second-class mailing privileges. These are well worth having, since a pound of second-class mail (even if it consists of 25 pieces going to 25 different addressees) can be mailed for 1½ to 7 cents plus 30 per cent with a minimum rate of ⅛ cent per copy, depending on the amount of advertising and the postal zone to which it is being sent.

*Designing a magazine.* Readers are confronted with dozens of periodicals. Which one they read may be determined by the appearance or design. Seeing the same design gives a feeling of familiarity and at-homeness which is of cumulative benefit.

Since the first design of a magazine will probably be used for a long period, it is worth detailed comparison with similar publications under the guidance of an expert designer. (See DESIGNERS.)

Designing a publication involves such decisions as the following:

1. Size (see PAPER SIZES AND WEIGHTS)
2. Kind and weight of paper (see PAPER)
3. Trimmed or untrimmed paper
4. Pictures or no pictures, photographs, and/or drawings
5. Color or black and white; color on cover or text, or on both
6. One-, two-, or three-column page (professional and scholarly magazines tend to the one- or two-column page, news magazines to three columns); width of column; space between columns
7. Size of margins
8. Type face of the text, heads, subheads, photograph legends, by-lines, and credit lines (see DESIGN; also Appendix 1, Type Faces); suitable type sizes for each; alternate type styles for variety in heads
9. Type face and location of the page number, title, and issue of the magazine
10. Placing heads and subheads flush left, centered, or indented
11. Indention; decision on use of nonindented initial capital letter or small caps for the opening paragraph of an article
12. Location for masthead and copyright notice; type, spacing, and regular copy for the masthead

To avoid inconsistencies and to simplify the work, many an editor or production man makes up a typographic style sheet of such information about the design as may be needed for constant reference. It is still more useful if supplemented by pasted-up samples of the type faces, identified as to kind, size, and the average number of characters per column width for text type and one-column heads, and per pica for wider heads. The type face for legends should be marked with the number of characters for a picture of one-, one-and-a-half-, or two-column width. (Remember that a two-column picture is as wide as two columns plus the space between them.)

*Planning the contents.* A flexible, long-range plan should be worked out as to the editorial and advertising content of a periodical. This will set a policy on such questions as the relation of the cover to the content, the desirability of a direct editorial as opposed to indirect editorial comment through pictures and articles, continuing features or departments, the use of signed articles and reprints, the proportion of advertising to editorial copy, etc.

In some instances, the effectiveness of a periodical is enhanced by planning a number of issues on different phases of a single broad theme.

*Planning a single issue.* An ideal balance and variety of material can be assured more readily with a tentative page plan. This may well be in the form of an editor's dummy with a tentative assignment for every page, even to special features such as boxed announcements, cartoons, and pictures. Or it may be a written outline listing the contents page by page.

Close scrutiny of such a page plan should detect overemphasis on certain subjects; omission of other types of material; lack of balance between factual and human-interest material, between national and purely local or regional news, or between "think" copy and "how-to-do" copy. It should facilitate a closely knit publication with each item contributing to a well-integrated whole.

An annotated list of timely books on newspapers and periodicals is included in Appendix 2, Bibliography. (In addition, see COPY WRITING; COPY PREPARATION; LAYOUT; PROOFREADING; PASTE-UP DUMMY; DISTRIBUTION.)

**personalize** See LETTERS.
To make a form letter seem like a personal letter.

**phonograph records** See RECORDINGS.

**phosphorescent printing** See LUMINESCENT PRINTING.

**photo agencies** See also PHOTOGRAPHERS; ARTISTS.

Photographs on a huge variety of subjects can be obtained from one or other of the many commercial and noncommercial picture files maintained by

Commercial photo agencies
Government agencies
National associations (trade, professional, etc.)
Large corporations (care of Public Relations Director)
Advertising agencies (photos used in ads)
Libraries
Some magazines

The following commercial photo agencies will send an assortment of pictures on almost any given subject on request, usually without charge. The recipient is expected to pay for those kept and to return the others promptly. Rates vary from $7.50 per photograph up, depending on the nature of the use to be made of it. Rates for advertising use tend to be higher.

Acme News Pictures, Inc., 461 Eighth Ave., New York 1

Donald T. Ballard, P.O. Box 226, Niles, Mich.

The Bettmann Archive, 211A E. 57 St., New York 22 (historical pictures)

Black Star, 420 Lexington Ave., New York 17

Brown Brothers, 220 W. 42 St., New York

Commercial Museum, 34 St. below Spruce St., Philadelphia (lends photos on industrial, commercial, and geographic subjects)

Culver Service, 205 E. 42 St., New York 17 (historical pictures)

European Picture Service, 39 W. 32 St., New York (photos from United States and abroad)

Ewing Galloway, 420 Lexington Ave., New York 17

Fairchild Aerial Surveys, 21-21 41 Ave., Long Island City, N.Y.

Free-Lance Photographers Guild, Inc., 62 W. 45 St., New York 36 (black-

and-white photos and large collection of color transparencies)
Philip Gendreau, 369 Lexington Ave., New York
Globe Photos, Inc., 152 W. 54 St., New York 19
Graphic House, 280 Madison Ave., New York
Rapho Guillumette, Inc., 475 Fifth Ave., New York 17
Harris & Ewing, 570 Fifth Ave., New York 17
International News Photos, Inc., 235 E. 45 St., New York 17 (photos from United States and abroad)
Keystone View Co., 219 E. 44 St., New York
Frederic Lewis, 36 W. 44 St., New York 18
Magnum Photos, 17 E. 64 St., New York 21
Photo Library, 19 E. 57 St., New York
Photographic History Service, 5537 Hollywood Blvd., Hollywood, Calif. (sells material made from movies)
Pix, Inc., 250 Park Ave., New York 17
Press Association, Inc., 50 Rockefeller Plaza, New York 20
Press Illustration Service, 360 Lexington Ave., New York
H. Armstrong Roberts, 420 Lexington Ave., New York
Shostal Press Agency, 545 Fifth Ave., New York (specializes in stock color for calendars, etc.)
Three Lions, 545 Fifth Ave., New York 17 (photos from abroad)
Underwood & Underwood, 319 E. 44 St., New York
Some agencies, notably the Bettmann Archive and Culver Service, offer a service that locates any desired picture whether they have it in their own files or not.
The Federal government has many good photo files. Prints usually cost a dollar apiece. In many cases, however, lack of funds to maintain the files means that Federal departments

cannot offer the same service as the commercial agencies and that users may have to visit the files in Washington and then wait one or more weeks for prints to be made, if indeed prints can be made at all.
Good photo files are maintained by the government agencies listed below. The Director of Information for the agency is the man to approach. In some cases the agency itself will have only current material, having been forced to transfer massive collections of important older documentary photographs to the National Archives. Photos may be seen at the Archives if the inquirer knows approximately when the collection was transferred to Archives and by which agency.

Agriculture Department
  Soil Conservation Service
  Bureau of Agricultural Economics
  Farm Security Administration (their outstanding collection has been transferred to the Library of Congress)
Air Force
Army
Coast Guard
Department of Health, Education, and Welfare
  Children's Bureau
  Public Health Service
  Women's Bureau
Interior Department
  Bureau of Reclamation
  Geological Survey
  Office of Indian Affairs
  Bureau of Public Roads
  Forest Service
  Bureau of Mines
Library of Congress, Division of Prints and Photographs
Marine Corps
Navy
Social Security Board
Veterans Administration

Many national organizations, like the American Red Cross, American Library Association, and Amalgamated Clothing Workers of America, maintain files of photographs in their field.

The United Nations in New York also lends photos from their files.

Private corporations are often good sources for photographs within their area of interest. One of the most unusual collections is maintained by the Standard Oil Co. of New Jersey, at 30 Rockefeller Plaza, New York. Photographs are obtainable here free, on every phase of American life in which oil plays a part: oil production, refining, and shipping; oil workers, their homes, their towns, etc.; pictures of oil being used for transportation, etc. The only requirement is publication with a credit line.

Movie stills are another good source of pictures and are obtainable from the motion-picture producers.

Advertisers often grant permission to reprint photographs that have appeared in their ads, provided a credit line is given. Requests for permission should be addressed to the Publicity Director, giving date when the ad appeared, what publication it appeared in, and the purpose for which the picture is to be used.

Public libraries and museums can usually aid in finding good pictures, although once the pictures have been located, permission to reprint must usually be sought from the copyright owners.

An important public picture collection is that maintained by the New York Public Library. It includes millions of pictures and photographs, indexed and classified, on all subjects. The source is given on each. By its very size this collection is a clearinghouse of international importance for information on world picture sources and resources. The collection is much used, primarily by artists anxious to find out what the styles looked like at a particular period, how to draw a silo, etc. It consists of both clippings and photos which may be taken out of the

library on loan by local residents or through interlibrary request.

Pictures that appear in magazines are sometimes owned by those magazines, and sometimes not. The ownership of them is generally given in the table of photo credits printed at the front or the back of a magazine.

**photochemical stencil**  See MIMEOGRAPH.

**photocomposition**  A number of efforts have been made to perfect a method of setting type photographically, so as to produce proofs on paper or film ready for use in offset or gravure, etc., without the need for handling and inking metal types.

The HADEGO is a sort of photographic Ludlow for setting display type. The Fotosetter sets text type on film or paper. (See INTERTYPE.) Others (PHOTON, LINOFILM, MONOFOTO) are under development.

Another kind of so-called "photocomposing machine" prints an image down on an offset plate as many times as needed—as for running "two up."

**photocopying**  See also PHOTOGRAPHY; PHOTOSTAT.

Practically any kind of photographic work could be called "photocopying," but the word is most often applied to those processes that characteristically make negatives on paper instead of on film. The Photostat is thus a machine for photocopying.

A further distinction can be made, however, between photocopying machines which can make only same-size copies and those which can enlarge or reduce. The latter are described under PHOTOSTAT. See also XEROGRAPHY.

As regards the "same-size" processes there is also a distinction to be made between the whiteprint or blueprint processes (see those entries) and the "regular" photographic (silver nitrate) processes covered below. The whiteprint processes use a far less expensive kind of sensitized paper, but require that the item being copied be one-sided and translucent. (See also THERMO-FAX.)

The basic steps in photocopying are illustrated under PHOTOGRAPHY. However, the necessity for washing and drying the negatives before making a positive has been eliminated in recent years by the introduction of the so-called "transfer process" under such names as Autostat, Constat, Copease, Copyfix, Cormac, Dri-stat, Duplomat, Hecco-kwik, Photostat Copier, Photorapid, Portagraph, Transcopy (Remington Rand), Verifax (Eastman Kodak), and others.

With these processes, using equipment in the $150 to $400 price range and small enough to fit on a desk, it is possible to produce a same-size positive copy of a standard business letter, dry enough for immediate use, in less than two minutes, for a materials cost of 10 cents or less and without a darkroom or a photographer.

Same-size photocopying is done in one of two ways: (1) If the material to be copied is printed, typed, drawn, or written on only one side of paper that is not unusually thick, the light goes through this original and then darkens the sensitized paper. (2) If the material to be copied is on paper that has something on the opposite side, then the light goes through the sensitized paper first (from the back), hits the material to be copied, and reflects back from white areas but not from black ones. Thus, the sensitized paper in contact with white paper gets twice as much light as the paper that is in contact with a dark, light-absorbent ink mark.

The second technique is called "reflex" copying and produces, of course, a reverse-reading negative that cannot be read normally unless held up to a mirror. However, a positive made from this negative will be readable, and in the transfer process such a positive is made right from the still-wet negative

much as prints are made in the Polaroid "picture in a minute" camera.

The transfer process is essentially as follows: The original to be copied is placed face down on a piece of "matrix" paper which is sensitive to light but can be handled briefly under ordinary room light. Both are then exposed to strong light from underneath, the original is laid aside, and the matrix paper is activated in a special solution and then rolled into firm contact with a piece of "print" paper. When the matrix, which now looks like a negative, is peeled from the print paper, a positive image appears on the print paper. In the Verifax (Eastman Kodak) and Photostat Copier processes, the positive print can be made on any paper, and several prints can be made from the same negative. In the other processes, in which the chemistry is somewhat different, the positives can be printed only on paper which has had the proper chemical preparation.

The several companies marketing equipment for transfer copying have been introducing various refinements including printing papers of various weights, printing papers sensitized on both sides, translucent print paper as a step to making additional copies by the cheaper whiteprint process, colored developing solutions for making tinted prints, etc. Some of the equipment is adapted for copying from bound volumes, while some will copy only originals that can be passed between rollers as a single sheet.

The quality of contact or reflex photocopying is not generally quite up to the quality or permanence of Photostat copying or photographic copying but is adequate for purposes of record.

Of course, simple photocopying can be done without expensive equipment along the lines shown in the illustration under PHOTOGRAPHY.

In fact, a simple four-step way to copy a page from a book with practically no special equipment is as follows. In subdued indoor light, lay a piece of sensitized paper face down on the page to be copied. Cover it with a piece of glass (frosted or clear). Snap on a 60-watt bulb held 12 in. above the glass for about 5 seconds. Develop and fix the sensitized paper.

The resulting negative will be reverse-reading but can either be read from the back against a strong light, or in a mirror, or can be printed down to make a right-reading positive. Good results require that the sensitized paper be in perfect contact with the page. It helps to put glass under the page being copied as well as on top of it. Suitable paper can be purchased in any photo supply store by asking for high-contrast contact printing paper. (Enlargement paper is too sensitive.)

A kind of sensitive paper is available which permits making a positive from a positive without an intermediate negative. It is called Kodagraph Autopositive Paper. It must be exposed to a rather strong blue light through a yellow film. Kodak recommends using it with its "Spee-Dee" printer.

**photoengraving**   See CUT.

**photogelatin**   Photogelatin, sometimes called "collotype," is a printing process most frequently used to reproduce paintings, photographic posters, displays, and wash drawings in color.

It is a screenless process. Unlike other processes, photogelatin requires no screen for reproducing halftones, whether in black and white or in color. (See HALFTONE.) It is particularly suitable for the facsimile copying of old documents, etc., in which case it faithfully reproduces every flaw in the old paper or printing.

Photogelatin reproduction of photographs is generally superior to offset. The cost of making plates is substantially less than in letterpress or gravure. It is likely to be far cheaper than any other process where the problem is to print 100 or a few hundred copies of a very large pictorial subject. On many color jobs, photogelatin will be 90 per cent as accurate as other processes at half the cost.

There are two kinds of photogelatin work: flat-bed and rotary. The flat-bed process is not much used in the United States, though extensively used in Europe. Production is slow and sizes are limited, though quality can be excellent.

There are at least a dozen firms doing rotary photogelatin work in the United States on modified rotary lithographic presses. These presses are usually large. Most of them can handle a 40 by 60 sheet. They can deliver about 800 impressions an hour, or perhaps 5,000 impressions a day. The plates cannot be rerun a second day, though they have been run continuously for as many as 15,000 to 20,000 impressions. Reruns are possible by saving the negatives and making new plates.

Owing to the large plate size, a very small leaflet must either bear the cost of a large plate or wait its chance to be ganged up on a combination run with other small jobs. (See COMBINATION RUN.) Of course, a small job one-fourth the size of a plate could be run "4-up," thus producing 20,000 copies with 5,000 impressions.

Copy can be prepared for photogelatin in the same way as for offset. Very small type or fine serifs should be avoided.

Because of the fact that new printing plates have to be made for each day's runs, the cost of printing by photogelatin does not go down very much as quantities go up. When quantities go above 5,000 or 10,000, sheet-fed gravure (see GRAVURE) may prove to be a cheaper and equally satisfactory way of printing the same kind of material. For a comparison of photogelatin with other printing processes, see the charts inside the covers of this book.

Photogelatin printing is done on a

firm but not coated paper. It is often varnished to give it a gloss. (See VAR-NISHING.) A photogelatin reproduction of a photograph with two coats of varnish or lacquer is hard to tell from the original photographic glossy print and may be much cheaper. It is even suitable for reproduction, owing to the absence of a screen.

Photogelatin printing begins with a photographic negative made from the original copy. Then a special bichromated gelatin-coated plate is exposed to light through this negative. The bichromate hardens in proportion to the amount of light received. When moistened, the unhardened portions get wetter than the hardened portions. When inked, the wetter portions accept less ink.

Firms doing photogelatin work include Illinois Photo-Gravure Co., 466 W. Superior St., Chicago; New York Gravure Corp., 305 E. 45 St., New York 17; Black Box Collotype Studios, Inc., 4840 W. Belmont Ave., Chicago 41. The Meriden Gravure Co., Meriden, Conn., does flat-bed photogelatin work, specializing in plates for scholarly books. (Pay no attention to the word "gravure" in the titles of these firms. They specialize in photogelatin printing, not in gravure.) (See also OPTAK, a similar process.)

**photographers** See also PHOTOGRAPHY; PHOTOGRAPHS: HOW TO SELECT; PHOTO AGENCIES.

Almost every city has commercial photographers who are equipped to take portraits, banquet and wedding pictures, news assignments, etc. Usually they also do copying work and make enlargements. Some, but not all, do retouching of the sort that is necessary to make a satisfactory photograph of an advertised product. (See RETOUCHING.)

To get run-of-the-mill photographic service is not difficult. To get really good work is hard. A good photographer is one who will take extra time

and trouble and use special lights, film, and flash bulbs when necessary. When outdoor pictures are being taken he may even have to make several attempts to get the right lighting conditions.

$5 will buy a routine news shot at the studios of many commercial photographers. $25 to $50 a day plus expenses is more like what it may cost to get thorough coverage of one situation from a local photographer. The result will, of course, be a selection of pictures, not just one.

Magazine photographers who work for national magazines receive a minimum of $100 a day plus expenses. The American Society of Magazine Photographers, 1476 Broadway, New York 36, can supply names and addresses of members in all parts of the country.

Some photo agencies stand ready to take pictures on special assignment. (See PHOTO AGENCIES.) These include International News Photos, Inc., 235 E. 45 St., New York 17; Press Association, Inc., 50 Rockefeller Plaza, New York 20; Free-Lance Photographers Guild, 62 W. 45 St., New York; and Acme News Pictures, Inc., 461 Eighth Ave., New York 17. In almost any city, the photographers who service the local newspapers will accept other assignments.

Agencies specializing in magazine and advertising photography include: Black Star, 420 Lexington Ave., New York 17; Pix, Inc., 250 Park Ave., New York 17; and Magnum Photos, 17 E. 64 St., New York 21. They have correspondent photographers in cities outside New York. Robert I. Nesmith & Associates, 50 E. 42 St., New York, acts as agent for many artists and photographers throughout the country.

It is often possible to get camera clubs to undertake a photo coverage for nonprofit causes. There are such clubs in most high schools and colleges.

Those unaccustomed to working with a photographer often fail to use his time to best advantage by not planning details in advance. The photographer must know the exact nature of the assignment and the purpose for which the photographs are to be taken so that he can bring the right equipment. All properties should be in readiness, all participants wearing the right clothes.

Often a good photographer will discover picture opportunities that his client has failed to see, and he should be encouraged to do so. It is not fair to the photographer to count on this,

---

## *American Society of Magazine Photographers, Inc.*

1476 Broadway, New York City

### STANDARD FORM MODEL RELEASE

........................................................
DATE

I hereby consent that ........................................................................................................................

(Photographer) and/or assignees be authorized to use my name, portrait, picture, photograph, or any reproduction of myself for editorial and/or commercial purposes. Permission is hereby granted to make changes or alterations and/or use my name or any fictitious one for such purposes.

The undersigned warrants that he is over 21 years of age.

........................................................
SIGNED

........................................................
ADDRESS

### GUARDIAN'S CONSENT FOR MINOR

The undersigned represents that he is the parent and guardian of the minor named above, and represents that he has the legal authority to execute the foregoing consent and release.

........................................................
SIGNED

WITNESS:
........................................................

however, since the people who are to use the pictures really should know best precisely what will be most useful to them.

A photographer should be responsible for getting the correct names, positions, addresses, etc., of all the people photographed, and for getting written releases from them where necessary. (Where a photographer and a writer work as a team, the writer may do this.)

It is necessary to get written permission from every person shown in a photograph to be used for advertising purposes. A typical form of "release" is illustrated. Usually it is not necessary to get such a release when the picture is not used for advertising. However, a private citizen may bring a civil libel suit if a photograph of him is published that tends to hold him up to scorn or ridicule. A public relief agency will not want to embarrass its clients by permitting recognizable pictures of them to be taken or used for publication.

Photographers retain the ownership of the negatives of any pictures they take, unless other contractual arrangements are made when they take an assignment.

**photographs** See PHOTOGRAPHY; also the two entries which follow.

**photographs: care in handling** See also CROP, CROPPING.

A good photographic print should be handled carefully. Even if the negative is available, in case of accident, the original print may be more than just a print—it may be *better* than the negative, thanks to painstaking darkroom work.

Photographs should never be cropped with scissors. This procedure leaves no space for scaling and makes it difficult to correct mistakes. (See SCALING.) Besides, if a photo is to bleed, more of it must appear on the cut than will appear in the printed product. (See BLEED.)

A photo should always be captioned promptly before essential data are lost or forgotten. The best way to do this is to type the caption on thin paper and paste it to the back of the photo with library paste. Rubber cement will in time damage a print.

Typing or writing with a pencil on the back of a photograph should be avoided. A paper clip should be used on a photo only if it is protected by several folds of paper between the clip and the photo. Writing on a thin paper overlay while the photo is underneath is taboo. In all these ways the glossy surface of a photo may be dented or raised in such a way as to catch the light and be spoiled for use in reproduction.

When retouching is to be done on a photograph, it is well to mount it on cardboard lest it curl or crack. First, all captions and credit information should be transferred to the back of the mount before they are lost to view.

The most satisfactory method of mounting photographs is dry mounting. A piece of special dry-mounting tissue, procurable at photo supply stores, is cut to the same size as the photo and placed between it and the mount. Pressure with a hot iron, or in a special heated mounting press, binds the photo to the mount permanently.

Rubber cement is an almost foolproof adhesive since it does not permit puckering and, when dry, can be rubbed off without a trace. It should be brushed thoroughly over both photo and mount and allowed to dry before the two are pressed together. Rubber cement will in time stain a print and should not be used if the print is to be permanently filed. The print may also pucker if it is retouched.

Ordinary flour paste, rightly used, is excellent, but it requires careful handling and drying. It should be free of lumps and should be brushed thoroughly over both photo and backing in each direction, after which the two may be allowed to dry under pressure.

An overlay should always be used to protect a retouched photo. The use of masking tape to hold the overlay in place will eliminate any temptation to use paper clips.

Crop marks are best applied in the margin of a photo with a china-marking pencil or a wax crayon. (See CROP.) In case of mistakes such a mark can easily be rubbed off glossy prints with Kleenex or the corner of a handkerchief.

Photos should be filed or stored so that they will not curl or crease. Prints in active use are often kept under a heavy weight. Prints can be most safely stored in the cardboard boxes in which sensitized paper comes.

**photographs: how to select** See also entry above and PHOTO AGENCIES; PHOTOGRAPHERS; CROP; LAYOUT; PHOTOGRAPHY.

The quality of all photographic reproduction is limited by the quality of the photograph being reproduced, as well as by the printing process used. The effectiveness of a printed photograph is further determined by its size, its content, the way it is cropped, and its placement with regard to other pictorial material.

The 8 by 10 single-weight glossy print is the standard article supplied by professional photographers to newspapers, magazines, book publishers, and advertisers. It is big enough to do justice to most pictures, big enough to be retouched, and a size that engravers and printers are accustomed to working from.

Ordinarily the 8 by 10 print is an enlargement from 2¼ by 2¼, 3¼ by 4¼, 4 by 5, or 5 by 7 film. Occasionally it is a contact print from 8 by 10 film. The smaller film sizes give all the detail and sharpness that may be required for most work if exposed with care, although the 35mm. size (1 by 1⅜) is regarded by many photographers as too small to be depended upon for consistently sharp 8 by 10 enlargements.

Photographers often crop (see CROP) their photographs while making prints. They enlarge the image until the essential portion of the picture completely fills the 8 by 10 printing paper. Alternately, they may print everything that is on the negative, and let the editor crop to eliminate unessential areas. The latter procedure gives the editor more control over the proportions of a picture. Otherwise, if he wants to make a wide picture taller, for example, he may have to check back with the photographer to find out whether there is more sky on the negative than shows on the print.

A photograph intended for reproduction by any process should meet the following requirements:

1. It should be sharp. It is permissible and often desirable for nonessential background or foreground elements to be slightly out of focus, but every important detail should be "tack sharp." The vogue for soft-focus pictures has passed except in the portrait field; it is passing there too.

2. It should have a full range of tonal values, including white, black, and all the gray values between. This means that the brightest highlight in a predominantly dark picture should be white or near-white, not gray; and the darkest shadow in a predominantly light picture should be black or near-black, not gray. However, areas that should contain detail should not be allowed to go white or black. Because a photograph tends to gain slightly in contrast during reproduction, prints made for reproduction may be of slightly lower contrast than prints made for exhibition purposes. A good darkroom operator can often get a usable print from even a poor negative by using a paper of the proper contrast

and by giving some areas a longer exposure than others.

3. It should be free of unessential detail. A photograph should be cropped to eliminate unwanted sky or background, so that the essential elements will reproduce as large as possible. When distracting material cannot be removed by cropping, it can often be grayed down or removed by retouching. (See RETOUCHING.)

4. It should be natural. The people in it should not look posed.

5. It should tell a story. People should be doing something; equipment should be in use. The size of unfamiliar objects should be indicated by comparison with familiar objects. So far as possible it should get its message across with a minimum of caption.

6. It should have human interest. Good pictures of babies, animals, and pretty girls are the conventional "stoppers" because they are so high in human interest and attention value. Pictures with an emotional appeal have the greatest attention value. In general, people are less interested in a picture of the other fellow's product or problem than they are in a picture of "how this might affect me." They like to imagine themselves in the picture.

Large pictures always look better than small ones. Size does something for any picture. Too often an editor asks, "How small can we run this picture?" when he should ask himself, "How large can we run it?"

For help in finding good photographs, see PHOTO AGENCIES. For suggestions on the editorial use of photographs to tell a story, etc., see books listed in Appendix 2, Bibliography.

**photography** See also COLOR PHOTOGRAPHY; NEGATIVE; PHOTOCOPYING; PHOTOSTAT; PHOTOGRAPHERS; PHOTO AGENCIES; PHOTOGRAPHS: CARE IN HANDLING; PHOTOGRAPHS: HOW TO SELECT; MONTAGE; FILMSTRIPS.

Photography is now an adjunct to almost all the major printing and duplicating processes. It is also a printing process in its own right. Those who use printing, therefore, need to know both the basic principles of photography and the major applications of its principles. The basic principles are reviewed briefly here. In photographic printing, light instead of ink hits the paper, or film, and darkens where it hits. In the simplest techniques of photocopying, an ordinary business letter is placed over a piece of sensitized photographic paper, and both are exposed to light. The sensitized paper is then "developed and fixed" to make the image on it permanent. The result is a duplicate of the letter, but with white characters against a black background. Enough light got through the white paper of the letter to darken the sensitized paper beneath, except where the writing or typewriting held back the light. (See illustration on page 234.)

If a print is now made in the same way from this negative (white on black) copy of the business letter, the result will be a positive print which is black on white like the original.

The above process, called "contact print" copying, works the same way when sensitized transparent film is used instead of sensitized paper. In fact, film works better, since positives made through paper not only take more time, but also may show a mottled effect due to the uneven grain of the paper.

This process is much used for making same-size copies. It is the principle underlying blueprinting. (See BLUEPRINTING.) It is used in business offices for simple photocopying. (See PHOTOCOPYING.) Photographers generally make contact prints from their negatives before deciding whether or not to make enlargements.

Contact printing does not, however, permit enlargement or reduction of the size of the original. A contact print is always the same size as the original or the film negative from which it is made.

A magic lantern or film projector is a simple form of enlarger. Just as it can throw a picture of any size on a wall, so it can throw a picture on a piece of sensitized paper and thus make a photographic enlargement of the original.

A camera is essentially a magic lantern with a box built around the lens, the beam of light, and the screen. (See illustration.)

Ordinary cameras are "reducers" rather than enlargers, but large copying cameras can either reduce or enlarge.

Photostat cameras generally use sensitized paper. (See PHOTOSTAT.) Other cameras generally use sensitized film, but film and paper can be used interchangeably.

There are many different qualities of photographic film and paper. Some are very "hard" or of "high contrast,"

which means that they tend to make everything either white or black. Others are "soft" or of "low contrast" and distinguish between delicate shades of gray.

Most Photostat paper is hard and not suitable for making good copies of photographs.

Photographic films and papers differ also in their sensitivity to different colors. Those ordinarily used in Photostat and other copying work are called "orthochromatic" and are sensitive to white and blue light but not to red. They will "see" blue as white, and red as black. They should not be used in copying originals that are in color.

In order to make a faithful black-and-white copy of an original which is in full color or which contains blue or red, it is necessary to use a panchromatic film that is sensitive to all the colors.

Some good books on photography are listed and described in Appendix 2, Bibliography.

A film projector or enlarger

A camera

## PHOTOGRAPHIC CONTACT COPYING

A piece of sensi-
tized paper(in
a darkened room)

is covered by a
business letter

and exposed to light.

Developer

The exposed, sensitized
paper is put into a tray
of developer for one min-
ute

Developer

and it darkens except
where protected from
the light by the typing.

Water

It is rinsed in water
for five seconds.

Fixer

It is immersed in a
"fixer" for 10 minutes.

Water

It is washed for one hour (prints which
aren't washed enough eventually turn yellow)

Dryer

and it is
dried.

If this "negative"
(white on black) copy
is placed over another
piece of sensitized paper

exposure to light will
darken the paper where
it penetrates

and produce a
"positive" print
like the original.

**photography: as a printing process** See also main entry under PHOTOGRAPHY.

Photography is an adjunct to other printing processes whenever copying, enlarging, or reducing steps are involved. It is also a printing process in its own right. Light instead of ink hits the paper and darkens where it hits.

An example of photographic printing. The light goes through the white part of the paper and darkens the sensitized paper underneath.

Photography is not so cheap as other printing processes for large runs since it requires the use of relatively expensive sensitized paper, plus additional chemical development and fixing of the image, and drying of the paper. For a comparison of photography with other printing processes see the charts inside the covers of this book and the illustrations under PRINTING.

However, 8- by 10-in. prints can be had for as little as 5½ cents each (lots of 100 to 1,000) after an initial investment in a master copy-negative of only $1 or $2.

The photographic printing process is, therefore, relatively cheap in small quantities. It is also a high-quality process: a good photographic print with its faithful rendition of lights and shadows is the standard that other printing processes strive to equal. It is a versatile process. It can make a good black-and-white copy of anything, including type, drawings of all sorts, other photographs, and even originals in color, or any combination of these.

100 photographic copies of a photo can be much less expensive than 100 printed copies and of much higher quality. A caption that is written, typed, or in the form of a proof from set type can, at slight extra cost, be made part of the copy negative and thus print with the photo in the same operation, and can be enlarged or reduced to fit.

The photographic printing process also lends itself to specialized purposes, especially the production of transparent images for use in projection machines. (See FILMSTRIPS.)

It is possible to sensitize almost any surface and print on it photographically—paper, glass, metal, cloth, even a wall or the side of a building. (See also PHOTOSTAT.)

Firms that specialize in photocopying are Copy-Art Photographers, 165 W. 46 St., New York; Howard Photo Service, 168 W. 46 St., New York 19; and Master Photographers, Inc., 322 W. 48 St., New York. Firms which specialize in full-color photocopying include Thos. B. Noble Associates, 270 Park Ave., New York; Moss Photo Service, 350 W. 50 St., New York 19; and Pavelle Color, Inc., 533 W. 57 St., New York. (Prints in color cost a good deal more than black-and-white prints.)

Photographic Christmas cards may be made from the customer's negative for prices as low as $3 for 25, $10 for 100. One company giving this service is Pavelle Laboratories, Inc., 16 E. 42 St., New York 17.

**photogravure** See GRAVURE.

**photo lettering** Photo lettering falls between hand-lettering and the setting of display type. It is cheaper than hand-lettering and more versatile than setting type. (See also LETTERING, ARTYPE, FOTOTYPE, HADEGO.)

There are firms which specialize in photo lettering and offer a huge variety of basic alphabets and trick effects, combined with fast messenger and mail service. They include Photolettering,

Inc., 216 E. 45 St., New York; Lettering Unlimited, 110 W. 40 St., New York; and Flexo-Lettering, 220 E. 23 St., New York.

There are also several desk machines for doing simple lettering right in the art department. They include the Coxhead-Liner, Filmotype, Protype, and Typro, more fully described under these headings.

When ordering from the photo-lettering services it is not necessary to stick

*No matter how you* STRETCH *it*

*It's still*

🎄 MERRY CHRISTMAS

🎄 MERRY CHRISTMAS

🎄 MERRY CHRISTMAS

🎄 MERRY CHRISTMAS

An example of photo lettering.

to such type sizes as 36, 48, or 72 pt. They can supply any size at all, and are accustomed to working from instructions that the finished line be exactly so many inches long or high. They will also go beyond mere typesetting and provide such special effects as outline letters, letters made taller but not wider, letters made wider but not taller, letters italicized or back-slanted, letters on special backgrounds or effects, lettering on a curve or circle, and letters with perspective effects. These special effects are secured by using distorting lenses, by tilting the paper in the enlarger, by using multiple negatives, etc.

A special camera, the Fotomaster, designed for making trick derivations from original copy is obtainable from Modi-Graphic, Inc., 215 E. 9 St., Cincinnati, Ohio.

**photolithography** See OFFSET.

**photomechanical** The usual commercial methods of making printing plates are described as photomechanical, as distinct from "hand" processes. When plates were prepared by hand, the man who prepared a lithographic stone, for example, had to be an artist or at least a copyist. Nowadays lithographic plates are almost always prepared by applying photomechanical techniques, and it is sufficient if the platemaker is merely a good technician.

**photomontage** See MONTAGE.

**Photon** A photographic type-composing machine operated from a standard electric typewriter keyboard with additional controls for selecting type face, type size, line width, leading, etc. Justifying, centering, or quadding of lines is automatic. Characters are photographed on film at the rate of eight per second by flashing a strobe light through a whirling glass disc containing 16 fonts of type. Type faces and sizes may be mixed in the same line without interfering with alignment or with automatic justification.

During its developmental stages this type of machine was variously known as the Lithomat machine (after the name of the company on whose premises the first U.S. model was built), the Lumitype, and the Higonnet-Moyroud machine (after its inventors). The Photon has been developed by the Graphic Arts Research Foundation, Inc., of Cambridge, Mass., and is produced by its licensee, Photon, Inc., of the same city. The first production models went into use on a limited scale toward the end of 1954.

**photo offset** See OFFSET.

**photoprints** See PHOTOGRAPHY: AS A PRINTING PROCESS; PHOTOSTAT; PHOTOCOPYING.

**photo retouching** See RETOUCHING.

**Photostat** A photographic copying machine manufactured by the Photostat Corporation of Rochester, N.Y. It will make same-size, enlarged, or reduced photocopies. (The Rectigraph, a substantially identical machine for doing the same sort of work, is made by the Haloid Co., of Rochester, N.Y.)

Essentially, a Photostat machine is a good copying camera, capable of doing anything that the camera will do. However, it is designed to do a limited number of things more quickly and easily than the ordinary camera. It differs from an ordinary copying camera in two ways: (1) It is designed primarily to use photographic paper instead of film; and (2) it employs a prism so that its paper negatives will be "readable negatives" instead of being reversed, mirrorwise; and (3) it develops and fixes the print within the apparatus, and models may be had which will complete the washing and drying of prints and deliver them ready for use.

The paper copies produced by this machine are called "Photostat copies," "Photostats," "stats" or "photocopies." A Photostat copy made from an ordinary business letter is a negative, showing white typing on black paper. For purposes of record, this negative is as useful as a positive. If, however, a positive copy with black type on white paper is required, it is necessary to order two Photostats, first the negative Photostat, and then a positive Photostat, which is made from the negative Photostat.

Photostat copies in size 8½ by 11 or less cost from 20 to 50 cents each when ordered from commercial houses. Part of this cost is that of messenger service. A piece of 8½ by 11 Photostat paper actually costs less than 6 cents, to which must be added the cost of developing, fixing, drying, labor, overhead, and profit.

Photostating may be considered a printing process, competitive with Multilith, mimeographing, etc., when quantities are very low. It has the advantage of being very fast. It is not usually so cheap as making 8 by 10 photographic prints in quantities above 10 or so. (See PHOTOGRAPHY: AS A PRINTING PROCESS.) In deciding when to use Photostat rather than some other printing process, consult the charts inside the covers of this book.

Photostats are much used in layout and dummying work for reducing or enlarging the various illustrations or headlines so that they may be pasted

*Sensitized paper is in here*
*Print washer,*
*Print dryer,*
*Prism and lens*
*Original is put here*

A Photostat photocopying installation.

up together with the text. The Photostat technique also offers an easy way to reverse type or drawings, black for white. Other uses include copying book pages, charts, clippings, drawings, estimates, records, etc.

In one time-saving technique, photographs, printed illustrations, or even objects themselves are photocopied so that the artist may make a line drawing right over the photocopy after which the underlying photo image is bleached out.

Photostat machines will usually enlarge to twice the size of the original and reduce to one-half the size of the original in one shot. This range can be extended, but only by a skilled operator and by making time-consuming special adjustments. In two successive shots— (1) from original to negative, (2) from negative to positive—it can thus enlarge to four times, or reduce to one-fourth. With four successive shots (original to negative to positive to negative to positive) it can enlarge to sixteen times, or reduce to one-sixteenth. However, a positive copy four times removed from the original is likely to lose so much in the copying as to be unsatisfactory. It is better and sometimes no more expensive (compared with paying for four Photostats) to go to a commercial photographer when more than fourfold enlargements or reductions are needed.

Where the majority of the work is layout and dummying with reducing and enlarging, there is a Photostat unit called the Model Two Special for making prints 14 by 18 or smaller, which will reduce to 28 per cent and enlarge to over 300 per cent of original size.

Some photocopying work is of low quality. This is usually due not to any inherent limitation of the equipment, but rather to ignorance or carelessness on the part of the operator. For example, an occasional print may be out of focus in places due to curling of the paper during exposure. This kind of defect (which is prevented in litho-graphic cameras by the use of a vacuum back to hold the film flat) will be noticed by the careful operator who will then make another exposure.

While any Photostat operator can usually make copies of reproduction quality from black-and-white originals that are not photographs or drawings containing middle tones, not every operator can make good copies of photographs or of originals that are in color.

Photostat copies of photographs are usually inferior to photographic copies of photographs because standard Photostat paper is "hard" or "high-contrast" paper, deliberately designed to record near-white areas as pure white, and near-black areas as pure black. If softer paper or film is not at hand, a skillful Photostat operator can produce passable copies by "flashing" his paper before making his copies. He flashes the sensitized paper by exposing it briefly to a plain white surface. This in essence pushes the paper one-third of the way toward complete exposure while stopping just short of actually darkening it. Thus it is put in a condition where even a little more light will start it turning gray. Then he replaces the plain white paper with the photograph to be copied and makes another short exposure (again about one-third of normal).

The copying of colored originals calls for extra skill on the part of the operator because standard photographic papers are orthochromatic, *i.e.*, they see blue as white and red as black. For example, a copy of a business letter may fail altogether to show a blue-ink signature. This can be corrected by making the exposure through the yellow filter that is standard on all machines, but extra exposure time must be allowed. Originals containing red should be copied on special panchromatic paper which may be used exclusively where a good deal of the copying is to be from colored objects.

Where acceptable photocopies of photographs of colored subjects cannot be obtained because of lack of the proper materials or know-how, such work can of course be obtained from a commercial photographer.

The smallest Photostat machine will produce a finished copy as large as 8½ by 11. Other models will make copies up to 11½ by 14, 14 by 18, or 18 by 24.

A Junior Model Photostat machine, complete with accessories such as washer and drier, costs about $750, f.o.b. Rochester, N.Y. It reduces to 60 per cent of the original size but does not enlarge. The Standard Model Photostat and the comparable Rectigraph sell for about $1,800 and up; other types are available up to $9,000.

A special attachment is available for the Standard Model with which enlargements from microfilm originals can be made.

For same-size reflex copying the Photostat Corporation offers at about $250 a unit called the Photostat Instant Copier operating by the transfer process. (See PHOTOCOPYING.)

**phototypesetting** A number of machines and processes have been developed for producing type on film from which press plates or press cylinders can be made. Phototypesetting eliminates the need for casting type in hot metal, making ready on a press proof, pulling proofs, and photographing the proofs. For information on specific phototypesetting processes, see PHOTON, LINOFILM, MONOPHOTO, and INTERTYPE.

**pi, pie** Type that has been pied is type that has been spilled. Badly pied type must be entirely reset. Occasionally a printer will pi a complete form while lifting it onto the press.

**pica** See also TYPE MEASUREMENTS. Printers measure the width and depth of columns, the size of margins, etc., in picas instead of in inches. A pica is 12

points (see POINT), or almost exactly ⅙ in.

This book has been set in 9-pt. type on a 13-pica line, with 1½ picas between columns. The columns are 44 picas deep. Paper, margins, and engravings, however, are measured in inches. The page size is said to be 6 by 9 in., and the one-column illustrations have a maximum width of 2⅛ in.

This piece of type is 4 picas deep. It is therefore 48-pt. type (4 x 12 = 48).

A pica typewriter is one that writes 10 characters or spaces to the inch. Its name derives from the fact that its letters are 1 pica high, 6 lines to the inch. (What is now called 12-pt. type used to be called "pica.") A typewriter with elite type also writes 6 lines to the inch. It differs from a pica typewriter only in that there are 12 elite characters to the horizontal inch as against 10 pica characters.

A pica rule is a ruler with at least one edge measuring in picas and points. A particularly helpful ruler is one that shows picas on one edge and inches on the other with the calibration of each extended to the middle of the line to permit reading both scales instantly. A sturdy Vinylite ruler of this kind is available at $1.50 from the John Warner Co., Box 595, Ithaca, N.Y.

**picking** Papers that are too fluffy or badly made sometimes "pick" on the press, meaning that paper fibers get picked up by the inked type and transferred to the ink rollers. The same result is also caused by the use of ink that is too tacky. Picking forces the printer to wash his ink rollers frequently. The chief remedy is to avoid buying highly bulked paper. (See BULK.)

**pictograph** See PICTORIAL STATISTICS.

**pictorial statistics** When comparative figures must be given about a specific subject, many writers and editors prefer pictorial statistics to the bars, curves, or "wedges of pie" used in more conventional graphs.

Pictorial statistics have several advantages:

1. The subject is immediately apparent because self-explanatory symbols are used. A simplified drawing of a shock of wheat becomes a symbol to represent 100,000 bu.

2. Comparisons are more indelibly impressed on the reader because they are made by varying the quantities of symbols. A row of 10 easily counted shocks of wheat may represent the crop of one nation and another row of 4 shocks the crop of another nation. Two bars of different length, as used on a conventional chart, might cover the same comparison, but they might also represent a change in railroad mileage, or savings accounts, or production of prunes, since identification depends upon the accompanying caption and description.

Pictorial statistics are also used very effectively on resource maps.

Certain warnings should be given in the use of pictorial statistics:

1. Symbols should be simple, self-explanatory, and easily recognized.

2. Large quantities should be shown by more symbols representing standard units rather than by larger symbols.

3. Pictorial statistics should be used for comparative quantities not single statements of fact.

4. Only approximate details should be shown pictorially. Symbols do not lend themselves to being sliced into minute fractions.

A typical use of pictorial statistics. (*Courtesy of the Pictograph Corporation.*)

5. The spaces between rows of symbols should always be greater than the spaces between symbols within a single row.

6. Too many changes, very large changes, very small changes or differences cannot be shown effectively.

For further details read Modley and Lowenstein's "Pictographs and Graphs" (Harper, 1952).

Pictographs are available on sheets (Picto-Pak) and rolls (Picto-Tape) of pressure-sensitive paper from the Pictograph Corporation, 80 W. 40 St., New York 18, and from Chart-Pak, Inc., 104 Lincoln Ave., Stamford, Conn.

The Pictograph Corporation handles all types of graphic presentation work, including maps of all kinds, and specializes in converting statistical material into pictorial form. The company conducts research through its own staff and also works from material furnished by clients, develops graphic presentations, and executes finished art work.

**pictures**   See ARTISTS; CARTOONS; CUT; DRAWING TECHNIQUES; ILLUSTRATIONS; PHOTO AGENCIES; PHOTOGRAPHERS; PHOTOGRAPHS: HOW TO SELECT; PHOTOGRAPHY.

**pied**   See PI.

**pinks**   Pink proofs, or pinks, are sometimes submitted by printers for use in dummying. The color serves to distinguish them from the white master proofs on which corrections must be made. The color has the disadvantage of making it hard to get a visual impression of how a paste-up dummy will look when printed. (See PASTE-UP DUMMY.)

**Planofax**   See STENAFAX.

**planography**   One of the five basic methods of printing. (See PRINTING.) Its important commercial applications are photo-offset lithography (see OFF-

SET), photogelatin (see PHOTOGELATIN; OPTAK), hectograph (see HECTOGRAPH), and xerography (see XEROGRAPHY).

The word "planography" is sometimes applied to cheap offset reproduction work, as though the process in question were somehow different from offset. There is no difference.

"Plane-ography" means printing from a plane (flat) surface. Ink is applied to the entire surface, but because the sur-

An example of planography. When ink passes over the plate, it adheres only to the part showing the letter or type.

face is chemically treated, the ink adheres only where it is wanted. (Since the hectograph process does not follow this procedure strictly, it is sometimes regarded as a sixth basic method of printing, even though it prints from a plane surface. Xerography also is sometimes viewed as a separate method.)

The planographic principle was discovered by Aloys Senefelder in 1796, when he invented lithography. After drawing on a flat limestone surface with a grease pencil, he applied acid to make the stone receptive to water wherever it was unprotected by the grease-pencil drawing. Then he wet the stone and treated the image areas (which had been protected from the acid treatment) to make them receptive to printer's ink. He could now apply grease-based ink to the whole surface, and it would be refused by the wet areas and accepted only in the image areas.

Paper was now laid on the stone, rubbed, and removed. It picked up ink, exactly duplicating (looking-glass-wise) the design originally drawn on the stone in grease pencil. Senefelder thus made the first lithograph (from *lithos*, meaning stone) by the planographic process.

Artists still use this method, although in commercial work, the heavy stones have long since given way to light-weight plates of sheet zinc or aluminum, grained to resemble the surface texture of stones.

The old method of hand copying on the stone with a greasy lithographic pencil has also given way to modern photographic transfer methods. Since the plates wore out quickly when pressed directly against the paper, another improvement has been the perfection of the "offset" technique whereby the ink is first printed on a soft rubber roller, from which it is offset onto the paper.

A later application of the planographic principle came with the discovery of the photogelatin process, sometimes called "collotype." In this process, a film of gelatin is chemically treated so that, where strong light falls on it, it becomes less receptive to moisture than where shielded from light. Thus, the drier areas that received more light, accept more greasy ink. Halftone subjects may be reproduced without the use of a screen. (See PHOTO-GELATIN.)

**plastic bindings**   See MECHANICAL BINDINGS.

**plastic plates**   See also DUPLICATE PLATES.

Plastic plates are often specified instead of mats, stereotypes, or electrotypes in newspaper advertising work. Some of the advantages claimed for them are as follows:

1. They cost less than electros.
2. They give results of high quality

and do not stretch or shrink as mats may do.

3. They have a low mailing weight.
4. When they are sent out to news-papers instead of mats, the newspaper can mold its full-page mat directly from them instead of first casting a flat stereo from a mat and then molding from this.

Some printers have been slow in accepting them, perhaps through unfamiliarity with certain peculiarities such as their susceptibility to damage by heat and some kinds of type cleaners. The Government Printing Office has made very successful use of them. Now several book manufacturers are using them for printing purposes. Plastic plates can be nailed, sawed, sheared, routed, and drilled like metal plates.

The process of making plastic plates is very similar to that of making mats and stereos. However, a sheet of thermosetting phenolic plastic is used instead of the paper mat; and granulated plastic molding compound is used instead of melted stereo metal. The process compares in speed favorably with stereotyping.

**plateless engraving**   Some printers advertise plateless engraving when they really mean "thermography." (See THERMOGRAPHY.)

**platen press**   A printing press in which a flat surface bearing the paper is pressed against a flat surface bearing the inked type. Small hand presses are generally platen presses, as distinct from cylinder presses or rotary presses. (See PRINTING PRESSES.)

**plate proofs**   Proofs taken from stereotypes, electrotypes, or other duplicate plates. Usually such proofs are neither requested nor supplied; instead the customer checks only foundry proofs. (See FOUNDRY PROOFS.) Plate proofs are most necessary when the plates are complicated; for example,

243 | **Pollard Alling addressing**

when halftones and type from different original engravings are to be combined into a single duplicate plate. In such a case the chance for error makes the checking of plate proofs desirable.

**plates**  See also CUT; DUPLICATE PLATES.

All printing is done from a master surface of some sort that determines which parts of the paper are to receive ink. Except when these surfaces are made up of individual pieces of type, they are called plates. Thus there are metal and paper offset plates, gravure plates, photogelatin plates, and glass photographic plates.

There are also letterpress (relief) printing plates, but the word "plate" in ordinary letterpress printing usually means a duplicate plate (stereotype, electrotype, rubber plate, etc.). (See DUPLICATE PLATES.) Original plates for letterpress printing are usually called cuts or engravings. (See CUT.)

Some plates are made directly; for example, when an artist cuts a linoleum block or draws with a grease pencil on a lithographic plate. Others are made by more roundabout ways, often requiring that type be set, proofs pulled, proofs photographed, the photographic image transferred to metal, and the metal etched or chemically treated.

The so-called "plateless" printing is really done from an offset plate. It is plateless only in the sense that letterpress cuts and engravings are not required. Plateless engraving is done by letterpress from type, instead of by the intaglio process from an engraved plate. (See THERMOGRAPHY.)

**point**  See also LEADING; TYPE MEASUREMENTS.

In measuring type sizes, 1 pt. is $\frac{1}{12}$ pica, or $\frac{1}{72}$ in. (0.01384 in. to be exact). In measuring the thickness of Bristol board, mounting board, etc., a point is $\frac{1}{1000}$ in.

These lines are set in 9-pt. type, which means that the distance from the top of the highest ascender or capital letter to the bottom of the lowest descender is 9 pt., or $\frac{1}{8}$ in. This paragraph is set in 9 pt. solid, *i.e.*, with no space between the lines.

This paragraph is set in 9-pt. type leaded 2 pt. The same results would have been achieved if the linotyper had been asked to cast 9-pt. letters on an 11-pt. body—"set 9 on 11."

The text of this book is "set 9 on 10" meaning the 9-pt. type is leaded 1 pt. This is a 1-pt. rule:

---

This is a 6-pt. rule:

Both rules are 72 pt. long (1 in.), but it is more common to say that they are 6 picas long.

Post cards are commonly printed on Bristol board which is 6 pt. thick, meaning 0.006 in.

**point-of-purchase displays**  See DISPLAYS.

**Pollard Alling addressing**  One of the three major methods of machine addressing. (See also ADDRESSOGRAPH and ELLIOTT ADDRESSING.) Pollard Alling equipment is most used for rather large lists, or where a printer or lettershop handles the addressing of several clients whose combined lists total at least 150,000 names. Embossed metal plates are used and are linked together in long chains. One reel can hold 2,500 linked plates and weighs 9 pounds.

The cost of blank plates is about $4.50 per thousand. The Pollard Alling machines used to emboss the plates permit operators to put addresses on about 200 plates per hour. Equipment prices start at about $1,850 per machine.

Advantages claimed for the Pollard

Alling addressing equipment and methods are low cost for plates, high-speed embossing, addressing performed at speeds up to 40,000 per hour, and selective addressing methods, which permit the machine to print wanted addresses at over 1,000 per hour while skipping unwanted addresses at speeds of about 45,000 per hour. Net average production on addressing of envelopes or self-mailers is about 12,000 per hour. Averages of 40,000 per hour are maintained, however, when running on roll stock for listing or mailer strip to be used with Dick or Wing mailers or Cheshire machines.

The visual selection techniques permit an operator to see which of several mailing pieces should be addressed from any given plate. The operator can thus complete in one run an operation often requiring several runs with other systems. Plates can be added or deleted during the addressing operation or separately at speeds up to several hundred an hour. For complete information about the equipment, write to the Pollard Alling Manufacturing Co., 220 W. 19 St., New York 11.

**positive**   See NEGATIVE.

**postage**   See Appendix 4, Postal Information.

**postage meter machines**   See "Metered Postage" in Appendix 4, Postal Information.

**postage-saver**   See PENNY-SAVER.

**postal information**   See Appendix 4.

**post cards**   See also Appendix 4, Postal Information.

One good source for picture post cards in natural color or in black and white is the Dexter Press, Inc., West Nyack, N.Y., which will send samples and price list on request. The price for 3,000 natural color post cards, size

3½ by 5½, from your 4 by 5 transparency, is $84; for 6,000, $106. For giant post cards, size 6 by 9, the comparable prices are $130 and $200. The price for black-and-white picture post cards is $20 for 1,000, $30 for 2,000.

**posters**   See also OUTDOOR ADVERTISING; TRANSPORTATION ADVERTISING; CIRCULARS; SIGNS.

Posters are most often produced by hand, by silk screen, or by offset, depending on the quantity. (See SILK SCREEN; OFFSET.)

A printer having only letterpress equipment may be able to handle a small poster run satisfactorily if it is possible to use all type (no pictures) and to use only the type that he has on hand. If the poster is to have hand-lettering and decorations or illustrations, silk screen and offset firms can usually prepare the surfaces from which to print more economically than can the letterpress firm. They can usually offer more attractive results for less money.

When 1 to 10 copies of a poster are needed, it is best to consult a sign painter or show-card writer. (See SIGNS; EMBOSOGRAF.)

When 10 to 100 copies of a poster are needed, it is probably most economical to produce them by the silk-screen process. (See SILK SCREEN.) Many sign painters have silk-screen equipment.

When 100 to 1,000 copies are needed, the silk-screen process is probably the best, but offset begins to be a possibility.

Above 1,000 copies probably—certainly above 5,000—offset will be more economical than silk screen. (See OFFSET.)

For example, the car cards used in busses and trolleys are usually done in silk screen if used locally; in offset if used in bigger quantities by national advertisers.

Photographs cannot be reproduced

satisfactorily by the silk-screen method. Posters containing photographs are usually reproduced in offset. (For the highest quality of reproduction of photographs, see PHOTOGELATIN or GRAVURE.) Sometimes it pays to reproduce a photograph by offset, photogelatin, or gravure, and add additional color by silk screen.

Very small type does not reproduce well in the silk-screen process. Silk screen is unexcelled, however, for handling rich, solid colors.

Posters should be planned with regard to the space requirements at the point of display and the problem of shipment or delivery. The size should be such as to cut without waste from standard sizes of poster cardboard, 22 by 28, 14 by 22, 11 by 14, 11 by 28.

It is cheaper to print posters on paper than on cardboard if paper will do. There may be an advantage in printing on paper and then mounting a desired number of posters on cardboard with or without easel. (See MOUNTING AND FINISHING.)

For variety, posters can be built around ad reprints, photographs, Photostats, etc. They can be cut into special shapes. (See DIE CUTTING.)

Comparatively low-priced full-color posters can be made by enlargement if the art work has already been reproduced in a small size. For example, book posters can be enlarged from book jackets in this way. An offset printer makes poster plates by enlargement from black-ink proofs of the plates used for the small-size job.

For simplicity and economy, poster colors should be few, bold, and flat, i.e., not shaded or blended. A poster in full process color is usually prohibitively expensive unless the number to be ordered is very large. On the other hand, it is not very expensive to have a small color print from a circular, book jacket, or ad mounted on a poster.

Help in designing a poster can often be obtained from the firm that is to do the printing. Silk-screen houses are particularly likely to have an artist on the staff, since they make most of their printing surfaces by hand, and not photomechanically like other printers. (See ARTISTS; DESIGN.)

It is often argued that a good poster must be able to get its message across to a commuter sprinting for the morning train. That is not a bad standard to strive for, but unfortunately all messages are not that simple and brief.

A good poster ought to arouse interest at first glance and must be readable over whatever distances are involved in its display, but there would seem to be no good reason why it should not have as much small type as can be kept interesting. It is only necessary that the poster with small type should be displayed where people will have the time to read it and can get near enough to do so.

See Appendix 2, Bibliography, for books on advertising, art work, and color.

**precanceled postage** See Appendix 4, Postal Information.

**press book** See CLIP SHEET.

**press proofs** See PROOFS.

**press release** See PUBLICITY RELEASE.

**presswork** The operation of putting the ink on the paper. Most printing jobs consist of (1) composition, (2) presswork, (3) binding. The work of the pressman divides into make-ready and running time. (See MAKE-READY.)

**prices** See ESTIMATING COSTS; SAVING MONEY.

**print** See PRINTING; PHOTOGRAPHY.

**printed indicia** See "Printed Postage Impressions" in Appendix 4, Postal Information.

**printers: how to choose**  See also PRINT-
ING.

There are two important elements in
choosing a printer: (1) determining
the process to be used (see inside front
cover) and (2) finding a printer who
works in that process, who is skilled in
it, and whose equipment, prices, and
standards of workmanship are right.

The names and addresses of several
printers are given under various entries
in this book. Such mention does not
imply endorsement of the firms mentioned nor a belief that they are in
any way to be preferred to firms that
are not mentioned. Names have been
given simply for the convenience of
readers who may not be able to find a
desired specialized service in their own
town or who do not have ready access
to a Classified Telephone Directory of
one of the big printing centers.

The right printer is one who meets
the following specifications:

1. He does a lot of the kind of work
that you seek and has the right equipment for it. (There are some advantages in dealing with a printer who
does not have to give out too many
operations to other firms.)

2. His standards of workmanship are
acceptable.

3. His prices and terms compare favorably with market prices. (Allowances must be made for differences in
service, of course.)

4. He has a union shop. This is important when a union label is desired.
(See UNION LABELS.)

NOTE: Printers who run night shifts
every night can usually do faster work.

The most satisfactory way to buy
printing is to deal consistently with
one printer. Printers should be changed
no less thoughtfully than employees
are changed. If the work is varied, it
may not be possible to find one printer
who is equipped to handle all printing
processes. However, it should still be
possible to settle on one letterpress
printer, one silk-screen printer, one let-

tershop, one offset printer, etc., getting
competitive bids only occasionally in
order to be sure that prices are in line.

The practice of getting bids on every
job and taking the lowest is required
in some organizations, but it is not a
satisfactory way to work, for the following reasons:

1. Letting bids wastes time and slows
delivery.

2. In order to let bids, the buyer
must specify every detail in advance.
He thus cuts himself off from an opportunity to make those minor money-
saving changes in the specifications
which a good printer might suggest. If
the low bidder has made any changes
in the specifications, his bid must be
thrown out, or bids must be relet, or
else there was little point in getting
bids in the first place.

3. Printers do not like to do business on a basis of having to bid on
every job. Some of the best ones may
not trouble to enter such a competition.

4. Printers who get only an occasional job are less inclined to give special service when favors are needed.

5. A printer can give faster, cheaper
service to a regular customer than to
an occasional buyer for the simple reason that his men have learned that
customer's preferences and way of working. This is why periodicals can be
printed more cheaply than occasional
booklets of similar design.

A good compromise between bids
and no bids is to settle on a scale of
prices for certain recurrent types of
work—so much per page of composition, so much per 1,000 impressions, so
much per extra color, etc. This is possible only when the work is very simple and easy to define, or when the
printer has had an opportunity to handle several jobs and know his probable
average costs for future work.

**printers' measurements**  See TYPE MEAS-
UREMENTS.

**printing** This is an omnibus word. There are so many kinds of printing processes that the beginner may easily get much confused and despair of ever being able to get them all straight in his mind.

Therefore, this book has been arranged on the principle of one thing at a time. For example, the reader who has a poster problem may find by looking under POSTER that he probably should use the silk-screen process. Then he can look up SILK SCREEN and ignore the other processes for the time being.

Printing as a whole divides itself into three parts: (1) type composition (typesetting, typing), (2) printing (putting the image on paper), and (3) binding.

Type is still set in much the same way that Gutenberg did it 500 years ago. The process has been improved but is basically unchanged. There have been many attempts to find new ways to set type, but despite such recent developments as the Intertype Fotosetter, and cold type, most jobs still begin with getting type set by this one basic method—even if that type will do no more than make one perfect copy for further duplication by a new printing process that Gutenberg never heard of. (See TYPE for a discussion of how to convert a manuscript into type ready for printing. See also TYPEWRITER; COPY FITTING; COPY EDITING; DESIGN.)

Printing in its more limited sense of getting the desired image on paper (once that image, whether type or pictures, has been created) is done in five different basic ways. Each basic principle has been adapted to still further specialization. (See table on next page.)

For the five basic principles see RELIEF; PLANOGRAPHY; INTAGLIO; STENCIL; PHOTOGRAPHY. For the commercial applications of those principles—the things to remember when printing is ordered—see such headings as LETTERPRESS; OFFSET; PHOTOGELATIN; GRAVURE; MIMEOGRAPH; SILK SCREEN; PHOTOGRAPHY; DUPLICATING METHODS.

References to these processes occur under such headings as CIRCULARS; PAMPHLETS; POSTERS; LETTERS; in an attempt to suggest the best process for any given job.

The most important process for the layman to understand is letterpress (relief) printing, which might be called "ordinary printing." This is of first importance because he will probably have type set as if for letterpress printing, even if using offset or some other process.

Anyone with a clear grasp of letterpress printing will have a much easier time understanding the other processes because he will have to learn only how they *differ* from letterpress.

An elementary understanding of photography is an aid to understanding any printing process because photography is not only a printing process in its own right but is also used, or may be used, in every other process, at least in connection with the illustrations.

Information on how drawings and photographs are printed is to be found under HALFTONE; DRAWING TECHNIQUES; etc.

For binding techniques see BINDING. For books on printing and on specific processes see Appendix 2, Bibliography. For help in choosing the right printing process, consult the charts inside the covers of this book.

**printing brokers** Most printers occasionally subcontract work to other printers. They do it when they are too busy to handle a job themselves or when they lack the right equipment but want to help a good customer.

There are some printers, however, who subcontract every job and have no plant of their own. They are not so much printers as brokers. If they know their business, they have the advantage of being able to take every job to a shop ideally equipped to handle it. On the other hand, their work tends, for obvious reasons, to be uneven in qual-

THERE ARE FIVE BASIC METHODS OF PRINTING

RELIEF

*including*
Letterpress or
"Ordinary"
Printing"
Rubber stamps
Multigraph

PLANOGRAPHIC

*including*
Offset or
Photo-offset
lithography
Multilith
Photogelatin
Hectograph
Spirit duplicator
Xerography

INTAGLIO

*including*
Gravure
Rotogravure
Engraved
stationery

STENCIL

*including*
Mimeograph
Silk screen

PHOTOGRAPHIC

*including*
Photography
Photostat
Blueprint
Whiteprint

ity, and it may not be so easy for them to deliver the miracles that can occasionally be performed for a good customer by a printer having his own shop.

Before starting to deal with a new printer, it is always a good idea to visit his plant and see just what his equipment is.

**printing presses** The buyer of printing does not have to concern himself with the size, speed, and equipment of the printing presses on which his work will be done, but it may pay him to do so.

There is a perfect or near-perfect printing press for every job. This is true regardless of the printing process used. For greatest economy either the press (and the printer) should be matched to the job, or the job should be designed to fit an available press.

If, for example, a printer has a press that will take a sheet only as large as 17½ by 22½, it would be uneconomical to give him a job 19 by 25 if it could possibly be cut down to 17½ by 22½. He could handle the larger job as two sheets, each 19 by 12½, but would have twice the presswork.

If a printer has a folding attachment for one of his presses, it is well to find out what it can do and plan to use it when possible. Perhaps a 16-page, 6 by 9 unit can be folded right on the press, whereas a 24-page unit would have to

be handled as a separate bindery operation.

If a printer has a two-color press, he may be able to offer two-color printing for very little more than the price for one color.

If a printer's presses are all large, it may be foolish to ask him to stop them every few hundred impressions to change an imprint. (See IMPRINTING.) It may be better to give the imprinting work to a printer who has very small presses.

There are two important things to know about any printing press:

1. What is the largest sheet of paper that it will handle?

2. What is the largest area that the printing can occupy on that paper? (Usually, paper cannot be printed right up to the edge, at least not on the gripper edge. See GRIPPER EDGE.)

There is no reason why a small sheet of paper cannot be printed on a large press, but the press time will cost as much as for a full-size sheet. Presses are made with capacities varying from label or post-card size up to 50 by 70 in. or even larger.

"Perfector" presses will print on both sides of a sheet of paper in one operation. Multicolor presses will print in two, three, or four colors in one operation. Some big magazine presses will print in four colors on both sides of the paper in one operation.

Platen press          Cylinder press          Rotary press

A cylinder press must make two revolutions for each impression. During the second revolution no paper is fed, the cylinder lifts free of the type, and the type slides back to its starting point.

Many presses have folding attachments so that booklets can be folded and perhaps pasted or stapled as part of the printing operation, thus avoiding separate bindery work. (See BINDING.) However, trimming the edges of a booklet is always a separate operation although some folders will do rough trimming.

Some small presses are hand-fed, but most have automatic feeders. Some presses are "sheet-fed," and some are "web-fed." The sheet-fed presses accept separate sheets of paper. The web-fed presses take paper from a continuous roll and cut it into sheets only after printing it.

Presses are of three types: platen, cylinder, and rotary. Platen and cylinder presses may also be called "flat-bed" presses. Platen presses open and shut like a clamshell. They support the type on one flat surface and the paper on another, and press them together. Cylinder presses take each sheet of paper, wrap it around a cylinder, and then roll it across a flat surface that supports the inked type. Some cylinder presses hold the type on a horizontal bed; some hold it vertically.

Both platen and cylinder presses run at speeds of 1,000 to 4,000 impressions per hour, with the smaller units capable of the higher speeds.

Rotary presses pass the paper between two cylinders, one of which holds curved printing plates. Speeds are from 5,000 to 25,000 per hour.

**printing-trade customs** The prevailing printing-trade customs are listed below. Some points particularly worth noting are as follows:

A printer may decline to release type or plates for use by another printer, e.g., when another printer bids lower on a reprint (Item 6).

A printer who has furnished ideas but who later loses a job to another bidder may charge for those ideas (Item 5).

A printer may deliver 10 per cent more or less than the amount ordered, and charge accordingly (Item 11).

If there is any likelihood that a job will have to be rerun, a printer must be specifically instructed to keep the type or plates and may charge for this (Item 9). However, offset printers usually keep the "flats," from which they can make new plates, for a certain length of time without special instructions.

Printers usually store a customer's paper for a reasonable time without charge, depending somewhat on the extent of the printer's storage facilities.

PRINTING-TRADE CUSTOMS

1. *Quotations.* All quotations are based on work being performed during regular straight time working hours and conditions prevailing at date of quotation and are subject to amendment or withdrawal at any time prior to the receipt and acknowledgment by the printer of any acceptance thereof.

2. *Prices.* All prices are based on the written specifications, the work to be begun at once and carried on continuously until completion. Prices on non-estimated work and reprints of both estimated and nonestimated work are subject to change without notice.

3. *Orders.* Orders received and accepted by the printer cannot be canceled except upon terms that will compensate against loss. The customer guarantees the legal propriety of all matter submitted to the printer for printing and/or publication; and will indemnify the printer against all claims and responsibility arising from the printing and/or publication of such matter, including the legal expenses and disbursements incurred by the printer in contesting the same.

4. *Experimental work.* Experimental work performed on orders, such as sketches, drawings, composition, plates, presswork, and materials, whether or not similar to those herein specifically

enumerated, will be charged for at current rates.

5. *Sketches and dummies.* Sketches and dummies furnished by the printer shall remain the property of the printer and no use of same shall be made, or any idea obtained therefrom be used, except upon compensation to be determined by the owner.

6. *Art work, type, plates* (including lithographic plates), engravings, electrotypes, negatives, positives, and other items when supplied by the printer shall remain his exclusive property, unless otherwise agreed upon in writing.

7. *Proofs.* Proofs, not in excess of two sets, will be submitted with original copy. Corrections, if any, must be plainly written in the margin of the proof and returned with the original copy to the printer marked "O.K." or "O.K. as corrected" and signed by the one duly authorized to pass on same. If revised proof is desired, request must be made for the same when the first proof is returned. No responsibility for errors is assumed if work is printed as per customer's "O.K." Lithographic proofs of other than typeset matter will not be submitted unless specifically enumerated in the proposal.

8. *Alterations.* Time consumed by reason of author's alterations of copy, changes made in work or materials, detention of presses, and other delays caused by customer will be charged for at current rates. If, through printer's error, work has to be done over, there will be no extra charge, but if, through customer's error or change of instructions it must be done a second or third time, such extra work will be an additional charge. Such changes will be charged for at current rates for composition or any detention of presses.

9. *Standing matter for book and job work.* All standing type matter held at the customer's request longer than 30 days is subject to a monthly charge for storage.

10. *Press proofs.* An extra charge will be made for press proofs when requested unless this form of work is called for when estimate is given. Customer should be present when the form is made ready on the press so that no press time will be lost. Presses standing idle awaiting "O.K." from customer will be charged for at regular production hour rates.

11. *Quantity delivered.* As it is practically impossible to produce exact quantities, it is agreed that a margin of 10 per cent be allowed for over or short count, same to be charged for or deducted at the per thousand production price, which is the total price of the order, less the preparation expense, pro rated per thousand.

12. *Post cards and stamped envelopes.* Since the purchase of post cards and stamped envelopes involves a cash expenditure, customers must furnish these with their order. If they are not so furnished, an extra charge of 10 per cent of their cost will be made to cover additional services in securing them.

13. *Handling paper stock.* A time charge will be made for receiving, opening, and handling of paper stock supplied by the customer. An additional time charge will be made for paper that requires conditioning.

14. *Storage charges for paper stock.* A monthly storage charge will be made on all stock held by the printer longer than 30 days.

15. *Plate storage.* A monthly storage charge will be made for the storage of all customer's engravings or electrotypes.

16. *Customer's property.* All plates, cuts, paper, and other property are held at customer's risk, and printer assumes no responsibility for loss or damage by fire, water, or from any other cause, whether or not similar to those herein specifically enumerated.

17. *Delivery.* Unless otherwise specified, price quoted is f.o.b. customer's sidewalk. All estimates are based on

continuous and uninterrupted delivery of complete order, unless specifications distinctly state otherwise.

18. *Terms.* Net cash, unless otherwise provided in writing. Interest charged on past due accounts. All claims must be made within five days of receipt of goods.

19. *Agreements.* All agreements are made and all orders accepted contingent upon strikes, fires, accidents, war, unusual market conditions, or other conditions beyond printer's control, whether or not similar to those herein specifically enumerated.

20. *Arbitration.* All claims, demands, disputes, differences or controversies and misunderstanding arising under, out of, or in connection with, or in relation to any agreement entered into between printer and customer, shall be submitted to and be determined by *arbitration,* pursuant to the Arbitration Law of the State of New York, before the Board of Commercial Arbitration of the Federation of Graphic Arts and Allied Industries of New York City, or in the Tribunal of Justice known as the Court of Arbitration, established and conducted by the American Arbitration Association, and in accordance with its Rules.

**process-coated paper** See COATED PAPER.

**process color** See also COLOR PRINTING; COLOR PROOFS.

Process color, as opposed to "flat color," is the method used to reproduce true-to-life, full-color originals. Although the work is usually done with only four inks—black, yellow, blue, and red—these may be combined by means of the process-color technique to reproduce most of the browns, grays, greens, purples, oranges, etc., that may be in the original. Sometimes more than four colors are used, especially in offset.

Process color work is expensive, but there is no other way of obtaining faithful reproductions of color photographs and full-color paintings. The big expense lies in the making of the printing plates. A 4 by 5 halftone cut suitable for reproducing a black-and-white photograph may cost about $10, whereas the set of four halftone cuts necessary for reproducing a similar color photograph may cost more than $200.

Furthermore, the cost of running a job in four colors is likely to be at least four times the cost of running it in one color, although the paper may cost no more.

For process color work done by the letterpress process, coated paper (either glossy or dull) is required. Excellent process color work on either glossy or dull paper can be done by offset, photogelatin, or gravure. Great strides have recently been made in the quality of rotogravure process color, but since this work is usually done at high speed on inexpensive paper, the quality is spotty. Many magazines that print their text in roto nevertheless print their covers by the letterpress process.

A somewhat less expensive but often satisfactory substitute for process color work is fake process work. (See FAKE PROCESS.)

Special inks are used in process color work. The yellow is a bright canary shade. The blue is a rather pale robin's-egg shade. The red is rather bluish. In any form that contains a process color illustration, it is also possible to use one or more of these inks "flat," perhaps for a border, a headline, or a tint block. The results are often disappointing, however, since only the yellow is the kind of color one would deliberately choose for such purposes. To get a good carnation red or vermilion, it is necessary to print a yellow tint under process red. To get a good blue, heavy enough to use for a headline, it is necessary to add some black or a little red to the process blue.

Most process color work is four-color work. Some of it, however, is done in as many as 15 colors, or in as few as 3, omitting the black. Theoretically black is not necessary, but it gives added sharpness to the final results.

The procedure for making four-color process color printing plates is to take four photographs of the original painting, color photograph, or scene. Transparent colored "filters" are placed in front of the camera for three of the shots. One lets through all but yellow light, one lets through all but red light, and the third lets through all but blue light.

The resulting photographic negatives are called "separation negatives." From them are made four printing plates, one of which will be printed in yellow, one in blue, one in red, and one in black. (See SEPARATION NEGATIVES.)

As there are certain inherent shortcomings in this process, it is usually necessary to correct the negatives or the final plates by hand in order to get good results. This handwork, made necessary by imperfections in the color separation work, is highly skilled and time-consuming work, and is one of the major reasons why process plates cost so much.

One attempt to reduce the need for hand corrections is the Kodak fluorescence process for preparing the original art work. (See FLUORESCENCE PROCESS.)

Fully color-corrected separations are now being made electronically, notably in the *Time-Life-Fortune* research laboratories, but are not yet widely available commercially. Essentially, the process scans the original, splits the light and turns it into three electric currents representing the three primary colors, causes these currents to modify each other for correct color balance, and finally creates separation negatives.

Great strides are being made in the improvement of color-separation techniques through the use of extra "masking" and "boosting" negatives.

The Eastman Kodak Co. has introduced a three-color system for reproducing Kodachrome transparencies by offset lithography that offers new economy on short runs with results described as "pleasing" if not perfect. A very fine screen is used, masking is almost automatic, and runs as low as a few hundred are made economically. Two firms which have pioneered with this process are the Princeton Polychrome Press, 8 Charlton St., Princeton, N.J., and the Short Run Color Corporation, 6615 Tireman Ave., Detroit, Mich.

The Dexter Press, Inc., of West Nyack, N.Y., specializes in printing color post cards. (For rates, see POST CARDS.) The company will also quote on magazine covers in color, etc., and send full price list on request.

Lithographers not equipped to make their own color-separation negatives can buy them outside. The Moss Photo Service at 350 W. 50 St., New York 19, quotes $199 for a set of 11 by 14 color-corrected screened positives in 150-screen, made from your transparency.

**process letters** See also AUTOMATIC ELECTRIC TYPEWRITER; ADDRESSING; LETTERS.

A process letter is a high-quality printed form letter made to be indistinguishable from a personally typed letter.

Process letters are printed through an inked ribbon on a regular printing press. Then the name and address of the recipient and other personalizing information are added by typewriter. Great care is taken to make the filled-in material align properly with the printed material, to use a typewriter ribbon that matches the ribbon used on the press, and to use identical type styles.

Process letters are considerably cheaper than automatically typed letters (see AUTOMATIC ELECTRIC TYPEWRITER), and many users find them just as satisfactory. Furthermore, large quantities can be produced much more quickly.

The producers of process letters pride themselves on turning out a product that will fool experts. They charge accordingly. Cheaper fill-in work is procurable from lettershops having Multigraph equipment, but more often than not it will not really pass for personally typed work.

The term "process letter" denotes a standard of quality, rather than any special process. Most process letter work is done on flat-bed presses, apparently because this kind of equipment has proved more satisfactory in the long run than the Multigraph equipment used for ordinary filled-in letters. Many firms having Multigraph equipment advertise "perfectly matched fill-in work." If their work really is indistinguishable from personally typed work, it hardly matters how they do it. However, many shops that promise perfect fill-in work (also many shops that advertise "process letter" work, for that matter) do not deliver perfect work.

Many lettershops are beginning to favor the Multilith as a means of putting a facsimile blue-ink signature on a form letter. They claim improved results over the Multigraph method of using a rubber signature plate.

A few firms doing process letter work include New Era Letter Co., Inc., 495 Broadway, New York; James Gray, Inc., 216 E. 45 St., New York; Doolittle & Company, 320 N. Dearborn St., Chicago; Reuben H. Donnelley Corp., 350 E. Cermak Road, Chicago (offices also in Los Angeles and New York).

(For information on prices, see table under LETTERS.)

**process plates**  See PROCESS COLOR.

**production**  A production man, in publishing and printing circles, is one who is responsible for getting things printed, *i.e.*, produced or reproduced. The word "production" is often used interchangeably with "printing."

**progressive proofs**  See PROCESS COLOR.

In process color printing, four plates must be made, yellow, red, blue, and black. Proofs from these plates, made singly and in combination, are called "progressive proofs."

A set of four-color progressive proofs show (1) yellow plate, (2) red plate, (3) yellow and red plates printed together, (4) blue plate, (5) yellow, red, and blue plates printed together, (6) black plate, (7) yellow, red, blue, and black plates printed together.

This order is not always followed. Sometimes the black plate is omitted, especially in gravure. Sometimes more colors and more plates are used, especially in offset lithography.

**proofreading**  See also COPY PREPARATION; PROOFS.

At the various stages of setting type, making up pages, and producing cuts and plates, the printer sends proofs back to the editor for careful scrutiny, for comparison with the original copy, and for possible corrections and revision.

Usually the proofs that reach the editor have already been read carefully by the printer's proofreader and bear his marks. Proofs usually include at least (1) galley proofs, (2) page proofs, and perhaps (3) engraver's proofs of any cuts. (See PROOFS.)

If the printer is working on a close schedule, he is justified in expecting the corrected proofs to be returned promptly. However, accuracy is of paramount importance in proofreading and should not be sacrificed to speed.

With each set of proofs the printer should return (and may have to be reminded to send) either the original copy or the previously corrected proofs for comparison. When proofreading is completed, all of this same material goes back to the printer as a record of corrections and alterations. The proof-reader should be careful never to alter either the original copy or the proofs that have been the basis for the printer's last work. Corrections are made on the new proofs only.

The master set of proofs is the set that will go back to the printer with all corrections. Duplicate sets are retained by the editor for his files or, in the case of galley proofs, for use in pasting up the dummy. (See PASTE-UP DUMMY.)

*How to read proof.* Proofreading usually involves two people: one "to hold," reading aloud from the original manuscript or last proofs, and the other to make corrections on the new proofs. The experienced proofreader sees each letter of a word rather than the image of the word as a whole. This means that he is alert to the possible omission or inclusion of a single letter and catches the slightest error in typesetting.

Although the chief job of the proof-reader is to mark typographical errors, he should also be on the lookout for errors in grammar, punctuation, capitalization, spelling, word division, indention, and spacing.

An invaluable reference guide for the professional proofreader to have at his side is Joseph Lasky's "Proofreading and Copy-preparation," listed in Appendix 2, Bibliography.

If a manuscript has not had careful copy preparation before being sent to the printer, the proofreading of the galleys is more difficult and correspondingly more important. (See COPY PREPARATION.)

The proofreader is expected to note any differences between the original manuscript, or last proof, and the new proof and to call the author's attention to any unanswered queries on the manuscript. In addition, he should be on guard to correct whatever errors or inconsistencies may have been left uncorrected in the original manuscript and hence appear in the proof. As alterations in proof cost money, changes should be made only after careful consideration and in the most economical way. (See AUTHOR'S ALTERATIONS.)

*How to indicate corrections.* Anyone who deals with publications, either in preparing copy for the printer or in proofreading and make-up (see MAKE-UP), must be familiar with the indispensable tools of his trade—the standard proofreader's marks reproduced in the tables on pages 256 and 257. These are specific directions to the printer and hence must be legible, and their reference to the text must be absolutely clear. Each alteration requires two marks: one in the text and one in the margin. Textual marks should not obliterate the printing. Marginal signs should be placed at the end of the line containing the word to be corrected. Such signs should be large enough to be legible, but not so large as to invade the space beside other lines.

When two or more alterations must be made within a line, marginal signs may be made in both margins. If there are several marks side by side in one margin, they are separated by a vertical line. The first sign is placed at the edge of the printing and others in order toward the edge of the paper.

When the proofreader is satisfied that he has made all corrections and has answered all queries from the printer, he should initial each page of the proofs.

*Correcting page proofs.* The corrected galleys should be used as the first check on the page proofs to see that the indicated alterations have been made. Since the correction of even one letter or comma may mean resetting a whole line, it is necessary to scrutinize the entire line, not just a single word, and check near-by lines that may have got out of correct order. If the error is early in the paragraph, the whole paragraph should be proofread as though entirely new copy.

## PROOFREADER'S MARKS

| Marginal sign | Mark in text | Meaning | Corrected text |
|---|---|---|---|
| ℐ | Proofreading⌡ | Delete, take out letter or word | Proofreading |
| ℰ | Legibillity is | Delete and close up | Legibility is |
| *first* | the⌃requirement | Insert marginal addition | the first requirement |
| ◡ | of a proof reader's marks. | Close up entirely | of a proofreader's marks. |
| ◡ | Symbols‿should be | Less space | Symbols should be |
| ⊥ | made▪neatly and | Push space down to avoid printing | made neatly and |
| # | in⌃line with | Add space | in line with |
| eq.# | the ˅text ˅to˅which | Space evenly | the text to which |
| ¶ | they refer.⌡Place | New paragraph | they refer. |
| | marks carefully.⌐ | No new paragraph | Place marks |
| no ¶ | ⌐Paragraphs may be | | carefully. Paragraphs may be |
| ▯ | ▯ indented one em | Indent one em | indented one em |
| ▯▯ | ▯▯ two ems or (rarely) | Indent two ems | two ems or (rarely) |
| ▯▯▯ | ▯▯▯ three ems. Head- | Indent three ems | three ems. |
| ⊏ | ⊏ings are flush left | Move to the left | Headings are flush left |
| ⊐ | or flush right▬▬▬▬ | Move to the right | or flush right |
| ⊐⊏ | ⊐ or centered ⊏ | Center | or centered |
| ⊔ | Marginal‿marks | Lower to proper position | Marginal marks |
| ⊓ | are ₛₑparated | Raise to proper position | are separated |
| X | by vertical | Replace defective letter | by vertical |
| ⊙ | lines. ⊥he first correction | Invert this letter | lines. The first correction |
| w.f. | in a line of type | Wrong font; change to proper face | in a line of type |
| tr. | is⌐beside⌐noted⌐the | Transpose | is noted beside the |
| ? | nearest bend of the line. | Is this correct? | nearest end of the line |
| Sp. | and the⟨2nd⟩ next. | Spell out | and the second, next. |
| | ⟨in this way⟩ both margins are used⟨ | Transfer to position shown by arrow. | both margins are used in this way |
| b.f. | English Finish | Change to boldface type | **English Finish** |
| b.f. ital | English Finish | Change to boldface italics | ***English Finish*** |
| rom. | *galley* proof | Set in roman type | galley proof |
| ital. | is laid paper | Set in italics | is *laid* paper |

PROOFREADER'S MARKS (continued)

| Marginal sign | Mark in text | Meaning | Corrected text |
|---|---|---|---|
| *u.c.* | Book of type | Set in upper case, or capital | Book of Type |
| *Caps* | Book Papers | Set in large capitals | BOOK PAPERS |
| *s.c.* | BOOK PAPERS | Change to small capitals | BOOK PAPERS |
| *c.s.c.* | Book Papers | Initial large capitals; other letters, small capitals | BOOK PAPERS |
| *l.c.* | the first Type | Change to lower case or small letter | the first type |
| x | baseball player | Broken type | baseball player |
| *Stet* | to the editors | Retain crossed out word | to the editors |
| 𝕒 | Water, HO | Insert inferior figure | Water, $H_2O$ |
| 𝕓 | $X^2 \div Y^2 = Z$ | Insert superior figure | $X^2 \div Y^2 = Z^2$ |
| ≡ | printed | Straighten line | printed |
| ‖ | The paper | Align type | The paper |
| | The ink | | The ink |
| | The type | | The type |
| *ld* | prepare copy and submit it | Insert lead between lines | prepare copy and submit it |
| *hr. #* | PAPER | Hair space between letters | PAPER |
| ⊙ | to the printer | Insert period | to the printer. |
| ⋀ | the proof but | Insert comma | the proof, but |
| ; or ;/ | excellent it is | Insert semicolon | excellent; it is |
| : or ⊙ | to the following | Insert colon | to the following: |
| ⋎ | authors notes | Insert apostrophe | author's notes |
| ⋎/⋎ | called caps | Insert quotation marks | called "caps" |
| -/or = | halftone | Insert hyphen | half-tone |
| *em* | Robert Henderson | Insert em dash | —Robert Henderson |
| *en* | 1939 1940 | Insert en dash | 1939–1940 |
| ? | "Where" she asked. | Insert question mark | "Where?" she asked. |
| ! | "Stop" he cried. | Insert exclamation mark | "Stop!" he cried. |
| (/) | author see page 2 | Insert parentheses | author (see page 2) |
| [/] | To be continued | Insert brackets | [To be continued] |

On page proofs where the type from the galleys has been divided into columns and pages, the proofreader may have to expand or cut copy to avoid beginning a column or page with a single short line. (See WIDOW.)

At this stage he must also see that each cut is in the right position with its designated caption and credit line. Page numbers should be inserted in the cross references and in any lines "Continued from page ⎯⎯⎯" and "Continued on page ⎯⎯⎯."

Another special check should be made at this time to see that headings and by-lines have been correctly placed with their own chapters or stories. Every letter of every heading should be scrutinized with a seeing eye since typographical errors take a fiendish delight in creeping into the display lettering or large type of a title and subhead.

*Correcting engraver's proofs.* The proofreader must be sure that the reproduction is of acceptable quality, of proper screen and free from blemishes, that the size is right, and that crop marks have been followed accurately.

### 21—School Execu

School Executive —Editorial
SLUG—MORE NEWS

**Film Council Plans Year's Activities**

At a year-end meeting held in Washington, the Film Council of America planned a vigorous program of activities for 1947. Working as an overall organization and through its constituent groups the organization will

1. Continue to support strongly the use of films for international understanding both through the procedures developed by UNESCO and the United Nations.

2. Develop a program of publications and reports through the council and cooperating agencies.

3. Recommend a thorough study by the Library of Congress Motion Picture Project of ways and means to effect better and more expeditious distribution of government-made films and to recommend standardized charges.

4. Effect a close liaison relationship with local and state groups interested in the visual education and adult education fields.

Present at the meeting were representatives of national, government, and private agencies. Film Council President C. R. Reagan, Austin, Texas, was chairman of the meeting.

The careful proofreader would not afflict his printer with the above galley. He would avoid entangling guidelines connecting marginal notes to corrections within the text, and he would write legibly but small enough to get his note beside the line to which it refers. For a neatly marked galley, see *copy preparation*.

**proofs** See also PROOFREADING; DUMMY.

A proof is a trial impression taken from type or plates at each stage of the printing process. There may be

Galley proofs (of type)

Revised galley proofs

Engraver's proofs (of illustrations)

Page proofs (of type and illustrations)

Revised page proofs

Foundry proofs (if stereotypes **or** electrotypes are to be made)

Stone proofs (of all pages that are to be printed at once)

Press proofs

This is the order of business in letterpress printing, although one or more stages may be skipped. In offset, gravure, and photogelatin, page proofs are followed by reproduction proofs (perfect proofs intended to be photographed), and blueprints, or vandyke prints may be supplied instead of engraver's proofs or stone proofs if requested.

Small "proof presses" operated by hand are used for the "pulling" of proofs. Ordinarily proofs are made with just enough care to make them legible, but with no attempt to make them perfect. The quality of a job should not be judged by the preliminary proofs, except in the case of engraver's proofs and reproduction proofs, which must be perfect. Printers automatically supply a minimum number of copies of each set of proofs (usually two) and charge extra for additional copies required by the customer.

*Galley proofs.* Usually called "galleys," these are pulled from type after it has been set but before it has been organized into separate pages. They take their name from the long narrow tray or "galley" in which newly set type is temporarily stored. (See GALLEY.) Galley proofs are usually about 22 in. deep and 9 in. wide. As each shows only one column of type, it will have wide margins on both sides of it, which offer plenty of room for corrections. At the top is shown the number of the galley in which the type is stored.

One master set of galley proofs must be corrected, initialed, and returned to the printer. The duplicate set or sets may be filed, or cut up and used for dummying purposes. (See DUMMY.)

*Page proofs.* These show the type after it has been arranged in separate pages. It is usually more expensive to make changes in page proofs than in galley proofs. Sometimes the illustrations appear on the page proofs; if not, space is left for them. When halftone cuts are shown on page proofs, they usually are very poor and cause unnecessary alarm to those unfamiliar with the unfinished nature of page proofs.

*Stone proofs.* These proofs are not often taken; if taken, they show a complete form ready for the press, including all the pages that will be printed on one side of a large sheet of paper. Pages are assembled on a large flat table called a "stone," hence the name.

*Press proofs.* One of the first copies taken on the printing press that will handle the whole run is called a "press proof." The pressman makes a number of press proofs before completing his make-ready and getting a perfect press proof. A press proof is simply a copy of the finished job, though perhaps printed on only one side. This is the time to criticize inking, halftone reproduction, and other details that are not satisfactory. Printers do not like to submit press proofs, because it means holding a valuable press idle while a messenger carries a still wet proof to the customer. Customers who want to see press proofs are encouraged to come to the plant and stand by during press make-ready.

*Foundry proofs.* Made only if duplicate plates (stereotypes or electrotypes) are to be made from the type pages, a foundry proof is really a final page proof. It shows the page locked up and ready for the foundry that will make the duplicate plates. Sometimes plate proofs are made from the duplicate plates. A foundry proof has heavy black borders around it, called "bearers," which are put there so that the hydraulic presses in the foundry will not crush the type at the ends of the lines. See illustration under FOUNDRY PROOFS.

*Engraver's proofs.* These are proofs of line cuts or halftones submitted by the engraver who made those cuts. These proofs are carefully made on the finest coated paper and should be examined critically. The printer cannot be expected to improve on them in his final work, and may well get results of somewhat lower quality. When possible, the engraver should be asked to pull proofs of his cuts on the paper that is actually to be used, instead of on de luxe quality paper.

Engraver's proofs figure only in letterpress printing. (See LETTERPRESS.) In offset, gravure, and photogelatin, press proofs are the only kind of real proofs that can be shown. There are no plates at all until the one big plate is completed, ready for the press. It is possible to see blueprints or black-and-white prints made photographically from the printer's negatives. These are very useful for checking on whether pictures are cropped and captioned correctly, etc., but they do not tell anything conclusive about the quality of the printing plate that will be made from the printer's negatives. (Sometimes it is worth while to have the offset printer make a small plate and pull hand proofs—particularly in process color work—but since a new plate will be made for the press run, the result will not be identical.)

*Reproduction proofs.* Page proofs made with extreme care so that they can be photographed for reproduction in offset, gravure, or photogelatin are called "reproduction proofs." Reproduction proofs must be perfect—if anything, more perfect than would be acceptable in finished copy, since every slightest flaw will be duplicated in the

whole run. Good reproduction proofs can be pulled only on the very best proof presses, or else on regular printing presses, and only after painstaking make-ready. Corrections on reproduction proofs are costly, since all the work of making the first set is then entirely wasted.

Not every printer will take the time to make good reproduction proofs. The offset or other printer who has to use them should, therefore, be encouraged to reject any proofs that he considers of poor quality and ask for better "repros."

Repro proofs are usually pulled on white coated paper. Occasionally, however, they are pulled on transparent glassine and are then called "glassines" or "bronze" proofs. (The wet ink is dusted with bronze powder to make it more opaque.) Good glassines permit deep-etched offset or gravure plates to be made direct from them, instead of from a film positive, which has been made from a film negative, which has been made from a repro proof on paper.

Proofs on glassine or acetate are also useful in layout work. Type that is to run across a photograph can be shown doing so before the plate is actually made, if proofed on acetate and laid over the layout or the photograph. Transparent proofs for layout work need not, of course, be made with the same care that would be given glassines intended for reproduction. Proofs can be had from some advertising compositors in white or colors on clear acetate and can be ordered with pressure-sensitive adhesive on the back.

*Color proofs.* Such proofs are simply ordinary proofs rendered in the color or colors in which the job is to be printed. It is a lot of work to mix special colors just to make a couple of proofs and, therefore, expensive; so color proofs should not be requested unless necessary. On the other hand, engravers who are making matched sets of four-color process plates (see PROCESS COLOR), supply six finished full-color proofs and two sets of progressive proofs without extra charge.

*Progressive proofs.* These proofs show how a set of process color plates will print, both separately and in combination. A full set of four-color progressive proofs show (1) yellow, (2) red, (3) yellow and red, (4) blue, (5) yellow, red, and blue, (6) black, (7) yellow, red, blue, and black.

**proportional spacing** See ELECTRIC TYPEWRITER.

**Protype** A desk-size machine for setting display type photographically. With it an operator can compose about two words a minute. The necessary type fonts come in a great variety of styles and sizes and cost from $11 to $23 apiece. Both composition and the development of exposed images can be done under ordinary illumination since the paper which is used is not sensitive to incandescent light. The Protype machine is priced at $300 and is sold by the Mergenthaler Linotype Corp., 29 Ryerson St., Brooklyn 5, N.Y.

**publicity** See CAMPAIGN PLANNING; PUBLICITY RELEASE.

**publicity release** Free publicity is the best publicity if it can be obtained and is favorable. Editors and managers of radio and television stations are naturally reluctant to give away the commodity that they are in business to sell, if they think that the beneficiary can and should pay for it. But they are under constant pressure to give their audience useful and entertaining information, so they welcome publicity of real news value. They are glad to help nonprofit causes whenever they feel that in so doing they are also serving their audience.

To distribute certain information may involve (1) writing, printing, mailing, (2) writing and paying for space or time, or (3) writing only.

When someone else is bearing the entire cost of duplicating and distributing a message, he certainly deserves all possible help from the person or organization pushing that message. One way of helping is to prepare a good publicity release. The publicity release which is likely to be used is that prepared with the recipient's interests in mind at least as much as the sender's interests. There are two recipients whose interests must be watched: the editor, *i.e.,* reporter, newscaster, feature writer, etc., and the reader or listener.

The editor may ask:

1. Is it news? (Today's events must reach a newspaper today, or better yet yesterday in the form of advance write-ups. If it is not spot news, it should at least be feature material that will be new and interesting to his audience.)

2. Is it exclusive? At least is the editor protected by a definite release date against being scooped on the story?

3. Does the release clearly show the origin and the phone number to call if more details are wanted?

4. Does the release contain full background information, including complete and correctly spelled names? (Such a release is of great value to reporters who are attending a press conference even though they make their own notes.)

5. Is the release easy to handle? Is it double-spaced, on only one side of the paper, with good margins and space left for inserting a headline? Is the essence of the story put first, so that it will make sense even if later paragraphs are omitted?

On behalf of the reader the editor must also ask these questions:

1. Will this story interest, amuse, or help the reader or listener, or merely bore him?

2. Are its facts presented so as to catch his attention? Is it brief and to the point? Does it raise any questions

that it should, but does not, answer?

A publicity release must be delivered in good time. The announcement of a press conference should be delivered the day before, so that the conference can be made part of a reporter's next-day assignments.

A story marked "for release, A.M. papers, date" should be delivered as early as possible the day before. The report of an afternoon meeting should certainly be completed and delivered by the publicity man before he has supper that night. The report of an evening meeting should be phoned in, or delivered as early as possible. (It is better to send in a partial report early, than to send a full report too late.) Both tasks are made easier if an advance release giving the bulk of the information has been prepared and distributed.

The deadline for evening papers varies, but releases should arrive the evening before if possible,

It is a good plan to alternate release dates, by giving the morning papers the break on one release, and the afternoon papers the break on the next. It is poor policy to let TV and radio stations consistently scoop the press, or vice versa. To pay for publicity in one medium and ask for free publicity from the other is equally bad, e.g., when buying newspaper space but no radio time to announce an event.

Releases to weeklies or monthlies must take account of closing dates, which may be days, weeks, or months in advance of publication.

A publicity release is normally addressed to the city editor or station manager, but it may also be addressed to the feature editor, sports editor, women's-page editor, etc. If a release is sent to someone by name, a duplicate should be sent to the city editor just in case the other recipient is not at his desk that day.

Releases of national interest may also be sent to the news services, such as AP, UP, INS, and Transradio. However, news of local origin but national interest may automatically be relayed to those news services by their local member newspaper.

Several excellent books on publicity are listed in Appendix 2, Bibliography.

**public-relations consultants** Public-relations consultants resemble advertising agencies in some ways, especially since the two kinds of firms frequently expand into each other's territory.

However, large firms often hire both kinds of agency. Sometimes, the public-relations men come in at a high policy level and have a certain amount of authority over advertising and the agency that places it as well as over other matters. Sometimes the public-relations assignment is more limited.

The public-relations man seeks to shape public opinion so that it is favorable toward an idea, an industry, an organization, a product, or a man. He may use free or paid publicity. He may use the standard mass media—press, radio, TV, motion pictures, advertising —or he may work through and enlist the help of schools, churches, clubs, political organizations, trade associations, and the like. He will certainly consider every point where the firm meets the public—packaging, billing, servicing, handling complaints, answering inquiries, etc.

Public-relations services are usually considered to be distinct from advertising and publicity services. However, certain advertising agencies provide their clients with both publicity and public-relations services. In rarer instances, certain public-relations firms provide publicity and advertising services.

Public-relations men believe that the extent and content of advertising and publicity should be determined by a public-relations counselor exercising his independent judgment as to their worth and efficacy in relation to a total program.

Public-relations services are offered either by individuals or by firms, who as a matter of professional ethics do not handle competitive clients. Fees are determined by negotiation, much in the same way that financial arrange-ments are made between attorneys and clients.

**punctuation** For rules of punctuation and examples of their application, consult the University of Chicago "Manual of Style," or Lasky's "Proofreading and Copy-preparation" listed in Appendix 2, Bibliography.

# Q | q

**quad**  A metal blank used for spacing out lines of type. There are em quads, 2-em quads, and 3-em quads. (See illustration under TYPE.) The quads used for filling out the last line of this paragraph have been made type-high so as to print in black. ████████

**questionnaires**  A recognized direct mail technique. Tests show that people both read and answer a questionnaire more quickly than they read and reply to a straight letter.

The questionnaire implies that the inquirer cares what the recipient thinks; therefore, it is inherently flat-tering. By careful phrasing, the questions can impart as much information as they elicit.

The best results are obtained when a stamped return envelope is enclosed and when those who respond are promised a report on the findings of the survey.

**quire**  One-twentieth of a 500-sheet ream; 25 sheets. Formerly it consisted of 24 sheets.

**quoins**  Wedges used to lock up a form of type in a chase ready for printing. (See illustration under TYPE.)

# R | r

**radio**   See also CAMPAIGN PLANNING; TELEVISION; RECORDINGS.

Radio has an important place in many campaigns. The print user needs to understand its possibilities in order to be able to select the best medium for any given purpose.

Printed messages in the form of ads, news items, outdoor displays, pamphlets, direct mail, etc., are often strengthened by repetition through radio announcements and programs.

The different aspects of radio should be understood and evaluated before definite plans are made.

1. Radio time is of two kinds: free time and paid-for time. Free time may be obtained for noncommercial, general-information programs of all types. (For details on how to get free time, see page 268.) Paid-for time may be obtained at rates that vary with the time of day and may be used for purely commercial programs or for noncommercial, general-information programs.

2. The length of a radio program may range from chain-break announcements using 10 words or less, to spot announcements varying in length (time measured in seconds), to programs of 15, 30, or 60 min.

3. There are many kinds of programs: brief announcements, talks, plays, music, variety shows, etc.

Today more than 96 per cent of all U.S. homes are equipped with one, or more radios. For every living-room radio there are over three sets in other locations. An average family spends 2.6 hours a day listening to radios at home or in automobiles. This listening is spread pretty evenly throughout the broadcast day, and throughout the year. In fact, radio listening holds up even in summer when TV audiences fall off.

For some information campaigns, this mass radio audience is highly desirable. For more technical or specialized information, a carefully selected audience would be better. In a sense, a radio program does select its audience by the kind of material it presents. However, the radio sponsor is paying for a mass audience whether it is appropriate or not and whether he succeeds in reaching it or not.

If a company mails a covering letter and pamphlet to a select list, it can control the list and tailor the material to fit the list. If the same company uses the radio, it can select its audience in only a very limited degree as follows:

(1) by choosing the station that reaches a particular area, (2) by selecting a time when the desired audience is free to listen, and (3) by presenting the kind of program attractive to that audience.

When should radio, then, be used rather than print or films?

1. When the appeal is to large masses of people.

2. When the information is of a general nature as contrasted with that which is highly technical or specialized.

3. When the personal appeal of a big name or a friendly voice can be used and seems likely to be effective.

4. When the advertiser wants to create a feeling of public gratitude for some program in the public interest, such as a symphony concert.

Certain factors must be considered in making the choice between radio and television for advertising and for information campaigns. (See also TELEVISION.)

1. There are more radio sets in a larger number of homes than there are television sets.

2. However, 36,000,000 families average 5.2 hours a day watching television while 46,000,000 radio families average only 2.6 hours a day listening to the radio.

3. Radio reaches many people while they are working or away from home; for example, the housewife who can listen to the radio all morning but cannot sit down to watch TV, the automobile driver, the factory worker, the vacationer at the beach. (The TV audience falls off in the summer.)

4. Television reaches its audience with a double-barreled approach—through the ear and the eye. It also costs more for time and for program production. (See TELEVISION.)

Within a particular area served by more than one radio station, the user of radio must choose between stations unless the use of all of them is possible. Choice will depend on such factors as (1) signal strength of station, *i.e.,* its power, (2) policy and reputation of station, (3) its facilities, (4) competition. The choice of stations will not permit choice of one neighborhood audience over another. It will permit selectivity only in so far as the station specializes in programs that appeal to a certain type of listener and that carry that audience along to other announcements or programs.

If it is a network affiliate, it has the pull of certain network shows that have built up a nation-wide audience over a period of years, an audience that may keep tuned to intervening programs.

The time for a radio announcement or program depends largely on the audience to be reached. (See the accompanying table.)

Although the potential radio audience is tremendous, it is not a surety any more than the newspaper or magazine audience is a surety. The radio audience can tune in to any program, but it can just as easily tune out again if the program is not appealing. No audience will keep listening unless the program has something in it for them personally—entertainment, personal profit, or information of a provocative sort.

*Building a good local program.* Information in the public interest is usually put across through such programs as (1) the straight talk, (2) the spot announcement, (3) the round-table discussion, or (4) the dramatic radio play. The last is the most difficult, but if it is well done, it is also the most effective both as entertainment and as education. Nonprofessionals tend to overvalue programs (1) and (3) and to undervalue the spot announcement, which is easier to arrange for and prepare for and which can be extremely effective.

Commercial advertisers also use such programs as the sponsored newscast, the sports broadcast, the personality program with a variety of entertainment and a winning master of cere-

## Selecting Radio Time

| Time | Audience | Cost | Advantages and disadvantages |
|---|---|---|---|
| Early morning 7:00–8:30 a.m. | Family audience, particularly good for reaching the man of the house | Costs are virtually the same all day long. Some local stations give a discount after 10:30 or 11:00 p.m. | No competition with big-name programs. A good time for local announcements of interest to the family |
| Daytime 8:30 a.m.–6 p.m. | Chiefly housewives until late afternoon when children listen | | Audience mainly women who often listen for long periods |
| Early evening 6:00–7:00 p.m. | Entire family listens but frequently on different radio sets and selecting different programs of special interest | | Good time for short programs addressed to the whole family |
| Evening 7:00–11:00 p.m. | Slightly larger audience | | Good time to reach the family audience and working women |
| Middle of the night 11 p.m.–7 a.m. | A smaller audience | | Usually considered a less desirable time, but reaching a growing audience of night workers, auto drivers, etc. |

monies, the shopping program tying in specific merchandise, the dramatic serial, the give-away show, the variety show, etc.

The local radio program, whether commercial or not, has the advantage of being able to appeal to local interests and to feature local personalities. Good results have been obtained by featuring well-known citizens; local sports, plays, and concerts; the history of the city; school activities; an employee barbershop quartet, etc.

Free-lance radio script writers may be located through local advertising agencies, local stations, and neighboring college radio workshops.

A 15-min. radio program can be recorded on one side of a 16-in. transcription. Transcriptions, records, or tapes may be rented, purchased, or borrowed through transcription libraries, national manufacturers, national organ-

izations, etc. Most of the transcriptions are prepared for 15-min. shows. Some are made up of a series of 1-min. speeches or announcements, which can be incorporated into local programs. (See RECORDINGS.)

One of the largest transcription libraries is that of the World Broadcasting System, Inc., 50 W. 57 St., New York 22. Their transcribed programs are classified by type in their indexed catalogue, which is available free to the prospective renter or purchaser. (Ready-made programs with space left at the beginning and the end for an advertising message are called "open-end" programs.)

Live shows are those broadcast with performers at the microphone as contrasted with transcribed programs. The cost of such a show depends on the cost of the performers and the cost of the time.

Typical union-scale rates for commercial network radio performers are (1) for actors and announcers: $40 each for a program of ½ hr. with 1 hr. of rehearsal time required at $9.60 per hr. for the first hour; after the first hour, rehearsal time may be computed and paid for in ½-hr. periods at $4.80 per ½ hr.; (2) for a singer (soloist): $72.60 for each program of 16 to 30 min. with 1 hr. of rehearsal time required at $8.80 per hr. for the first hour and $2.20 per ¼ hr. for additional rehearsal time after the first hour; and (3) for a group of two to four singers: $50.80 per person for each program of 16 to 30 min. with 1 hr. of rehearsal time required at $7.20 per person for the first hour and $1.80 per person for each ¼ hr. thereafter.

On individual stations rates vary, depending upon size, unionized personnel, etc.

Every radio station, when it gets its license, commits itself to serving the public interest. That means giving free time for public-service programs. News of civic organizations, community drives, school projects, playground activities, the public-health clinic, city water supply, etc., would be classified as programs in the public interest. A station should feel responsible for giving free time for such programs. It is also justified in demanding that such programs be good audience holders.

Every organization and civic group should certainly have a radio chairman to work directly with station managers on the scheduling and production of programs of this nature.

When a station gets its license, it guarantees freedom of speech on the radio. That means that, on all vital public issues, equal time must be allotted to both sides of the question. Therefore, a person or organization is entitled to free time on the radio to refute the arguments of any opponents if they had free time, or to an equal amount of paid time if they had paid time. However, the organization, even

if it is given free time, will have to provide its own talent and program material, often in competition with highly paid professional talent and scripts furnished by the other side.

Any individual, company, or organization can bid for radio broadcasting time at so much per minute or per hour. Most stations ask to see written scripts in advance to eliminate libel or obscenity. Actually a station is not entitled to censor ideas simply because they differ from those of the station manager. Freedom of speech applies to the air waves as well as to the printed page.

Radio advertising rates are given in *Radio Rates and Data,* published by Standard Rate and Data Service, Inc., 1740 Ridge Ave., Evanston, Ill., at $35 a year. Rates range from about $25 per hr. on very small stations to about $720 per hr. on large stations. (For further details see ADVERTISING.)

For further reading, see the books on radio listed in Appendix 2, Bibliography.

**radio transcriptions** See RECORDINGS.

**rag content** The most expensive papers are made in whole or in part from cotton or linen rags and are identified as having 25, 50, 75, or 100 per cent rag content. Pure rag paper is strong and does not deteriorate with age. However, well-made wood-pulp paper, free of groundwood pulp, can also offer high strength and permanence.

**rail freight** See also SHIPPING INFORMATION.

Rail freight is the cheapest way to ship material weighing over 100 lb. It is slower than railway express or motor freight (truck). Although the minimum rate is for 100 lb., smaller weights may be shipped by rail freight for that price. The rail freight rate for 100 lb. is cheaper than the 50-lb. rate for railway express and parcel post. (For comparative rates see the table accompanying SHIPPING INFORMATION.) There is no maximum as to weight or volume that can be shipped by freight.

Rail freight rates per 100 lb. vary according to the kind of material being shipped, the distance to be covered, and the region through which it will travel. Printed matter takes a freight rate which is cheaper than that for breakable articles such as furniture and household goods. The rate for shipping bulk paper depends upon the kind of paper as well.

Full insurance is included in the regular rate. If the rate is over 65 cents per 100 lb., pickup and delivery service are provided at no additional charge.

For further information about rail freight rates, consult *Leonard's Guide and Service* (described in detail under SHIPPING INFORMATION) or call the local freight agent of any railroad.

**railway express** See also SHIPPING INFORMATION.

Both air and railway express are handled by the Railway Express Agency, Inc. Air and surface parcel post are handled by the Post Office. (See "Air Parcel Post" and "Fourth-class Mail" in Appendix 4, Postal Information.)

Railway express, which includes limited valuation and local pickup and delivery, generally costs a bit more than surface parcel post (fourth-class mail), which does not include any insurance or local pickup.

Air express is generally cheaper than air parcel post for parcels weighing over 4 lb. (The minimum charge for air express is $2.50; for air parcel post, 60 cents.)

Express rates include pickup and delivery in all principal cities and towns within prescribed limits, and insurance on valuations up to $50 for each shipment weighing 100 lb. or less, or 50 cents per pound on shipments of over 100 lb. For insurance exceeding these

allowances, an additional charge of 18 cents is made for each additional $100 or fraction of excess value. Since all express is insured, the recipient must sign on delivery, thus giving a record of time and place of delivery, which may be valuable in case of necessary follow-up. Express may be sent prepaid or collect.

Express or freight (see RAIL FREIGHT) must be used for material weighing more than the weight limit for parcel post, which may be 20, 40, or 70 lb. according to the class of post office and the zones, as explained under SHIPPING INFORMATION. For manuscripts, express is often cheaper than first-class postage. (For comparative costs of shipping by parcel post, express, and freight, see the table accompanying SHIPPING INFORMATION.)

There is practically no limit to the weight and size of shipments which can move by railway express.

Railway express matter is divided into three classes: (1) merchandise, (2) food, (3) printed matter.

First-class express rates depend upon the weight and distance to point of destination with a minimum rate of $1.80 for 1 lb. or fraction. There is no handy rate chart for express as there is for parcel post. Each shipment has to be worked out on the "rate scale" of the Railway Express Agency. Typical rates are given, however. (See the table accompanying SHIPPING INFORMATION.) Further information may be obtained from the local agent of the Railway Express Agency.

Third-class express rates apply to advertising and other printed matter. The rate ranges from 4 to 19 cents per lb., depending upon the distance to point of destination with a minimum charge of $1.80 per shipment.

*Air express.* Air express is a service of the Railway Express Agency and 31 scheduled airlines of the United States and Canada. Air express directly serves more than 1,800 airport points cover-

## Typical Air Express Rates
### (When volume is under 250 cu. in. per lb.)

| Between New York and | 5 lb. | 10 lb. | 15 lb. | 20 lb. | 50 lb. | 70 lb. | 100 lb. |
|---|---|---|---|---|---|---|---|
| Atlanta | $3.21 | $4.42 | $ 5.63 | $ 6.84 | $14.10 | $18.94 | $26.20 |
| Chicago | 3.05 | 4.10 | 5.15 | 6.20 | 12.50 | 16.70 | 23.00 |
| Denver | 4.49 | 6.98 | 9.47 | 11.96 | 26.90 | 36.86 | 51.80 |
| Los Angeles | 5.77 | 9.54 | 13.31 | 17.08 | 39.70 | 54.78 | 77.40 |
| Miami | 3.69 | 5.38 | 7.07 | 8.76 | 18.90 | 25.66 | 35.80 |
| New Orleans | 3.85 | 5.70 | 7.55 | 9.40 | 20.50 | 27.90 | 39.00 |
| Omaha | 3.69 | 5.38 | 7.07 | 8.76 | 18.90 | 25.66 | 35.80 |
| St. Louis | 3.37 | 4.74 | 6.11 | 7.48 | 15.70 | 21.18 | 29.40 |

| Between Chicago and | 5 lb. | 10 lb. | 15 lb. | 20 lb. | 50 lb. | 70 lb. | 100 lb. |
|---|---|---|---|---|---|---|---|
| Atlanta | $2.89 | $3.78 | $4.67 | $ 5.56 | $10.90 | $14.46 | $19.80 |
| Denver | 3.37 | 4.74 | 6.11 | 7.48 | 15.70 | 21.18 | 29.40 |
| Los Angeles | 4.65 | 7.30 | 9.95 | 12.60 | 28.50 | 39.10 | 55.00 |
| Miami | 3.85 | 5.70 | 7.55 | 9.40 | 20.50 | 27.90 | 39.00 |
| New York | 3.05 | 4.10 | 5.15 | 6.20 | 12.50 | 16.70 | 23.00 |
| New Orleans | 3.37 | 4.74 | 6.11 | 7.48 | 15.70 | 21.18 | 29.40 |
| Omaha | 2.57 | 3.14 | 3.71 | 4.28 | 7.70 | 9.98 | 13.40 |
| St. Louis | 2.50 | 2.82 | 3.23 | 3.64 | 6.10 | 7.74 | 10.20 |

ing over 115,000 miles of airways, and through closely coordinated rail-truck ground facilities it brings air service to more than 21,000 off-airline communities. Almost every important city in the nation can be reached within a matter of hours. Air express shipments are carried on all passenger and cargo flights. For example, you can air-express a 5-lb. package from New York to Chicago for $3.05 and have it delivered the same day. Pickup and delivery are included in the shipping charge. Special delivery is available at extra cost at principal points, if needed, at any hour of day or night and on Sundays and holidays. Air express shipments may be sent prepaid or collect, with insurance included for valuations up to $50; coverage for additional valuation is 18 cents for each $100 or fraction thereof. For typical air express rates, see accompanying table.

All air express rates presuppose a volume of not over 250 cu. in. per lb. When the volume is greater, the rates are increased accordingly.

The air express system directly serves Alaska, Canada, Cuba, and Hawaii and extends through connecting air carriers to Central America, South America, and Mexico.

The only other air shipping service is the post-office airmail and post-office air parcel post. (See Appendix 4, Postal Information.)

**raised printing** See THERMOGRAPHY; ENGRAVING; EMBOSSING.

**ream** Printing papers are sold by the 500-sheet ream. Formerly, some papers were sold by the 480-sheet ream, but the 500-sheet size has now become standard. (See PAPER; PAPER SIZES AND WEIGHTS.)

**recordings** Ideas can be set in motion via tape or disk recordings and transcriptions as well as via the printed page, and many who work with words are learning to exploit the rapidly multiplying techniques of sound.

(The term "transcription" is almost synonymous with "recording," although a quality distinction is sometimes drawn as between an individually inspected "transcription" for professional use on the air, and a "recording," possibly mass-produced and not individually inspected, for home use.)

A great deal of modern sound recording begins with tape even when the desired end product is a disk. (Wire recorders are virtually obsolete.) And tape itself is the preferred medium in many radio, TV, and other operations.

With tape you can record meetings, speeches, sermons, ceremonies, broadcasts, sales talks, movie commentaries, slidefilm commentaries, interviews, customer comments and complaints, sound effects for dramatic performances, telephone messages, books for the blind, business dictation, etc.

You can make tape recordings in a studio, at a convention, in or from your car, or even with portable full equipment carried in your pocket or briefcase.

Some equipment is designed for highest fidelity, some to record voices for hours without attention, some for portability. You can buy or rent equipment according to the qualities you need.

All modern tape recorders use more or less identical tape—¼ in. wide with a special coating containing minute particles of magnetic iron oxide. The essential magnetic coating can also be applied to movie film, new or old.

No visible change occurs in the tape during the recording process, but the pattern of the sound is translated into a pattern of magnetism among the oxide particles. If you should accidentally pass an ordinary horseshoe magnet over the tape, all trace of the recording would be destroyed.

Properly handled, sound-on-tape can be played hundreds of times without getting scratchy or losing its quality. When you wish to use a tape for a new recording, the old pattern of sound is automatically erased in the re-using. Until then it will retain the last sound recorded on it, and can be played back any number of times.

There is a correlation between tape speed and the quality of reproduction obtainable. A tape speed of 7½ in. per second is quite commonly used in quality recording of musical programs for radio broadcasting. For highest fidelity a speed of 15 in. per sec. may be used, occasionally even 30 in. For recording of conversation only, 3¾ in. per sec. is considered adequate. If mere intelligibility is all that is required a speed of 1⅞ in. per sec. may be used.

However, tape speed alone is not a reliable measure of the quality to be expected of a recording. Much more important is the quality of the equipment, and the skill with which it is used. In professional recording studios tape is now generally preferred over disks for quality as well as for ease of editing out "fluffs." Once a perfect tape is made, perhaps by patching together the best portions of several performances, it can be transferred to disks if desired. However, getting perfect recordings by any medium does take skill; the amateur attempting to make high-fidelity, off-the-air tape recordings disappoints himself more often than not, even when he has paid dearly for his equipment.

A very useful introduction to tape-recording techniques and equipment is "Your Tape Recorder" by Robert and Mary Marshall (Greenberg, New York, 1955). For keeping up with developments, the magazine *Magnetic Film and Tape Recording* (Severna Park, Md.) is valuable.

Studios equipped for every kind of tape and disk recording include Reeves

Sound Studios, 304 E. 44 St., New York City; the Audio-Video Recording Co., 730 Fifth Ave., New York City; Nola Studios, Steinway Hall, New York City. Most radio and TV stations are also equipped for sound recording or know where to get it done.

Well-known program producers who build shows to order and can also arrange for production and distribution of transcriptions include Frederick W. Ziv, Inc., 1529 Madison Road, Cincinnati, Ohio (with offices in New York, Chicago, and Los Angeles); Louis G. Cowan, Inc., 485 Madison Ave., New York 19, and 8 S. Michigan Ave., Chicago 3; Kasper-Gordon, Inc., 140 Boylston St., Boston 16.

Recording for home playback is, of course, still largely done on, or converted into, disks. The process of recording on a disk, whether from a live performance or from tape, involves cutting a track on a disk that has been specially surfaced with nitrocellulose lacquer, then taking a mold from this "master" by the electrotyping process. (See ELECTRO.) The first mold is taken before the master is ever played, and serves either as a "stamper" or to make a "mother" from which other stampers can be made. Records are made by impressing the stamper on warmed shellac or vinyl "biscuits."

Apart from talent, the costs involved in making a recording may include $25 to $100 in studio rental, $10 to $25 for master, approximately $15 for stamper, and then 15 to 30 cents each for 10-in. shellac pressings, 35 to 50 cents each for 10-in. vinyl pressings, 40 to 60 cents each for 12-in. shellac and vinyl pressings, $1.50 to $5 for 16-in. pressings. Recording at 33, 45, or 78 r.p.m. makes little difference in cost. Naturally rates per unit are lower when several recordings can be made at one session and when a large number of pressings can be done at one time. However, one publicity man has a rule of thumb that (apart from talent) he can make, pack,

and mail 100 12-in. long-playing records for $200.

Masters can be played, but they deteriorate slightly with each playing. Shellac is used only for 78 r.p.m. records, and even for these vinyl is preferred except as regards cost, because it produces less surface noise and is nonbreakable. It is almost a waste of time to try to mail shellac records because too large a percentage break in transit no matter how well packed.

Records wanted in quantity for promotional use can be pressed on paper. Such records are obtainable from Sight 'n Sound Enterprises, Inc., 22 Reade St., New York City. If you supply your own printed paper, they will give it a transparent plastic coating and press in a disk recording of your message or performance at a minimum charge of about $250 and a unit cost of 12 cents down to 2 cents, depending on quantity. They can impress recordings of any size and any speed on almost any material including folders, cartons, book covers, etc. The grooves of the recording can run right through the printing. Charges include perforating (to permit easy separation of the disk) and punching out the center spindle hole. One specialty is a post card you can put on your phonograph and play.

Nonbreakable records can be obtained from the Record Guild of America, 16 W. 40 St., New York 18. This firm will make small (6½-in.) double-sided records in any quantity for as little as 10 cents apiece. Each side will play for 1 min. 40 sec. on any home phonograph. Larger 8-in. records, playing 2 min., are also available. In addition to these prices, there is an initial charge of about $25 per side for making a master, a mother, and a stamper from your original studio recording. This charge can be limited to about $12 if no mother is required. A stamper made directly from the master is good for up to 1,000 pressings. The Record Guild is equipped to press records at the rate of about 100,000 a day. Records can carry printed messages on both sides at slight additional cost.

Magnetic recording of the sound track on motion pictures is coming into widespread use. Such a magnetic track can be applied to old silent movies, including both 8mm. and 16mm. at a cost of a few cents a foot. It can be applied alongside photographic sound tracks without harming the latter. One film can have several sound tracks, beamed at several kinds of audience, the appropriate one being impressed onto the magnetic track by rerecording just before a performance.

Magnetic tape recording of both sight and sound is an accomplished fact, now in use on network TV; it promises to replace kinescope film altogether, since it requires no development time and thus permits synchronous monitoring of picture and sound *as recorded,* automatic integration of the work of several cameras, instant playback, and easy erasing. Tape of ½-in. width is being used at a speed of 20 ft. per sec. Color can be recorded as easily as black and white. Home TV recorders, however, are still some distance in the future.

Several recording devices are available at a monthly service charge from the telephone company for the automatic answering of telephones and recording of telephone messages. Rentals are set by each local phone company, but one being offered in New York City at $12.50 a month gives callers your message and then allows them 30 seconds in which to leave their message for you. You can change your message as often as you wish, and play back theirs any time you return to your desk. The machine can handle 20 incoming messages. Another, available at the same monthly rental, can handle 150 incoming messages.

Recorded messages can be delivered automatically in many ways. Theaters save operator hours by playing back recorded details of what's showing and when. If you hear a sales message start when you approach an exhibit, you probably triggered the playback equipment yourself, by walking through a light beam, stepping on a foot plate, or by mere proximity. (An inductance relay will sense the mere presence of a person.)

Perhaps the most important tip on tape recording that can be given to beginners is to practice on unimportant things before attempting to record anything where failure could be serious. You cannot record just anything anywhere with any recorder and any microphone. When attempting to record a meeting, always get there at least an hour before the crowd, to give yourself a chance to set up and check your equipment and to test the room acoustics. Note that there are both omnidirectional and unidirectional microphones, and the choice of the right one for the job is important. If several people are to talk, beware of getting the microphone too close to one, too far from another. Try to keep it equidistant from all.

Devices are available for linking a tape recorder or disks with an automatic slide or film projector in such a way that the signal to change pictures (inaudible) is incorporated right in the tape so that it automatically trips a relay and actuates the change mechanism with the correct timing.

Several tape recorders have been designed especially for business dictating needs. One of the best is the De Jur Stenorette, which weighs 12 lb., draws only 30 watts (and can thus be used off a radio inverter in a car), takes 30 min. on a 300-ft. reel, and offers full control from the hand microphone-speaker, including start, stop, and repeat. The price is $169.50 from De Jur-Amsco Corp., 45-01 Northern Blvd., Long Island City 1, New York.

Many business firms are using their dictating machines to avoid typing many communications altogether. Disks made on the Soundscriber and Audograph and Mail-a-Voice, for example, can be mailed to any recipient who has similar equipment and can be filed as easily as any typed letter.

Radio programs can be recorded in a studio and sent by mail in transcription form to any number of radio stations so that those stations can put them on the air at the time agreed upon with the advertiser without the expense of a cross-country telephone hookup. In the same way, radio programs can be sent to organizations or advertisers, who can make their own arrangements for putting the program on the air locally, together with their own announcement.

A great many schools and some other organizations have facilities for playing records and transcriptions on their own public-address systems. Many business firms use transcriptions and records in employee training.

When you make any public or commercial use of recorded material, you must be very careful about such matters as copyright clearances, written releases from people recorded, and union restrictions. Assume that all book, dramatic, or musical material is copyrighted unless you know otherwise. (See COPYRIGHT.)

When a copyrighted piece of music (or a copyrighted arrangement of a noncopyrighted piece of music) is used (and practically all music less than 56 years old can be assumed to be copyrighted), it is necessary to pay the copyright owner a recording or "mechanical-rights" fee. The basic fee covers use of the music for a limited time only, usually a year. Longer use may involve additional payment.

If the recording is to be broadcast, two additional copyright factors must be reckoned with: (1) A fee of varying amounts for each commercial use on each radio station must be paid to the copyright owner. (2) The radio station must be licensed to use the music through ASCAP (American Society of Composers, Authors, and Publishers), BMI (Broadcast Music, Inc.), SESAC, or AMP, etc., whichever of these licensing organizations controls the public-performance rights in the name of the copyright owner. Not all stations are licensed by these agencies.

From those whom you record, get written permission for the use of their voices or performances, and pay at least $1 for such permission to make it stick legally. Have a clear understanding with professional performers as to what rights you are buying, and what (if any) you are not buying. Otherwise you may find yourself asked for an additional later payment for a use you thought was covered by the first fee.

In most situations you might as well reconcile yourself to paying union rates for talent, for the possibilities of getting around this are almost nonexistent. You may have to pay a union soloist $50 for one recording (less, if a royalty on sales will be paid) but you can be sure that a recording of union talent can be played on any kind of program without question.

The Musicians' Union has three basic rates for music: one for live radio and TV shows, another for radio and TV transcription work, and still another for commercial phonograph records. At the time of writing, the rate for transcription work was $27 per man for programs up to 15 min. in length. This included a total working time of 1 hr. There was a charge of $4.50 per man for each additional 15 min. of rehearsal time. The leader got double these amounts.

On commercial phonograph records, the rate was $41.25 for 3 hr. of work, per man, with the leader getting double. In 3 hr. it is possible to make four 10-in. records or 15 min. of LP or extended play recording.

The scale of rehearsal pay for radio actors, as established by the American Federation of Television and Radio Artists, was $9.60 per hr. (with a 1-hr. minimum) plus a flat fee based on the length of the program. This fee was $15 for a 1-min. spot, and $24 for a 15-min. program, no matter how long or short the actor's part might be in that program. No separate scale existed for nonradio transcription work; this one was generally used. Sound-effects men got a minimum of $20 for the first hour of work plus $7.50 per half-hour beyond this.

**Rectigraph** See PHOTOSTAT.

**recto** A right-hand page, which always bears an odd number. The left-hand page is called the "verso."

**Reditype** A system for setting type in display sizes that is especially adapted to work with small office-style offset presses. Master letters are assembled in proper sequence and arrangement on a transparent mounting sheet, and then an exposure is made through the sheet onto a piece of film so as to provide negatives or positives for use with other material in making offset plates. Reditype is manufactured by the Davidson Corp., 29 Ryerson St., Brooklyn 5, N.Y.

**register** A printed page is in register when the impression is in the correct position on the paper. In bookwork, correct register means maintaining exactly the same margins from page to page, so that the type area on a right-hand page is exactly backed up by the type area on the following left-hand page.

Jobs printed in two or more colors generally call for close register of the impressions; for example, where a red area meets a black area, there must be neither overlap nor a white space. (See COLOR PRINTING.)

**registered mail** See Appendix 4, Postal Information.

**registration of names and trade-marks** See TRADE-MARKS.

**relief** One of the five basic methods of printing (See PRINTING). In the relief process, a raised surface (which stands in "relief" above the surrounding surface) receives a coating of ink and then presses this ink onto paper. Applica-

An example of "relief" printing. When an ink roller passes over this letter, only the raised surface receives ink.

tions of the relief principle include the rubber stamp, the Multigraph, and the letterpress process. All daily newspapers and many books and magazines are printed by letterpress. (See LETTER-PRESS.)

**reprints** It is generally cheaper to re-print a given quantity of a piece of literature than it was to print it in the first place. However, this depends on the process used and on whether the possibility of reprinting was foreseen.

The cost of type, cuts, and art work are nonrecurring items if these were saved. If the type for a letterpress job was not kept standing, it may be cheaper to let an offset printer reprint by photographing a clean copy of the first edition, rather than to set new type. He can duplicate type and drawings without trouble (unless they are on dark-colored paper), but will prefer to work from the original art work if there are halftones.

Letterpress printers normally do not keep type standing unless instructed to do so, and they may make a charge for doing so. However, when they break up a form, they usually return any cuts or plates to the customer.

Offset printers do not like to keep their plates for very long, but they do keep their "flats" (stripped-up film negatives) from which new plates can easily and quickly be made.

Gravure printers (sheet-fed gravure) can and will keep their copper printing plates indefinitely.

Rotogravure printers do not keep their printing cylinders (they would be extravagantly space-consuming to store) but keep their flats.

Photogelatin printers cannot keep their plates more than a day or so, but they do keep their flats.

Silk-screen printers keep their screens only if instructed to do so. If the screens are not kept, it is usually as expensive to make a reprint as to make the original run.

Photographic services make a practice of retaining any negative that they make on a customer's behalf, unless it is understood that the negative must be returned to the customer. Some photo services are much better equipped than their average customer to file negatives and find them again, but some lose or fail to keep negatives.

Hectograph masters and mimeograph stencils can be saved against the possibility of a rerun, but are not good for a total run of more than a few hundred or a few thousand, respectively. Multilith plates can be saved in the same way.

**reproduction** The printing industry suffers from an almost total lack of creative imagination when it comes to coining needed new words. Such words as "print," "cut," "engrave," and "reproduce" positively stagger under the burden of the work that they are called upon to perform.

Printing is *produced* by means of any one of the various techniques of printing *production*. The quality of the final *reproduction* depends in part on the skill of the *production* man who selected the *reproduction* process.

**reproduction proofs** See also PROOFS.

Revised page proofs made on slick paper for photographic reproduction as in gravure or offset. "Repro" proofs should be handled with extreme care, for they smudge easily, and every smudge or mark will be picked up by the camera in the next stage of reproduction. Since they cost more than ordinary proofs, they should not be ordered until it is safe to assume that no further revisions are required.

Many typographers offer many kinds of reproduction proofs including proofs in black ink on transparent acetate, proofs in white ink on acetate or colored paper, proofs with pressure-sensitive adhesive on the back, etc.

**retouching** Photographs often benefit by some retouching. Perhaps a distracting background must be grayed down. Perhaps more sky must be added to a horizontal photo so that it may be cropped to print in a vertical position. Perhaps the details of an advertised gadget should be brought out more clearly.

Some retouching is simple, but some calls for a good deal of skill and experience, not to mention good airbrush equipment. (For an illustration of a photograph before and after retouching, see TYPE.)

Unskilled retouching is usually worse than none at all. Photographers and art studios may or may not be good at it. Photoengravers can handle retouching or recommend a good retoucher.

One branch of retouching covers the coloring of black-and-white photos. A cheap coloring job is worthless for reproduction. A printer can "fake" the color from the black and white better than he can work from a poorly tinted photo. Good coloring can be had, comparable in quality to an original painting or Kodachrome. (See COLOR PHOTOGRAPHY.) It is, of course, expensive, though less so than the color plates themselves.

**return of undelivered mail** See "Forwarding and Return of Undelivered Mail" in Appendix 4, Postal Information.

**reverse plate**  See also NEGATIVE.

Lettering or art work consisting of dark ink on a light background can be made to print light on a dark background through the use of a reverse plate. Reverse plates can be effectively

The pamphlet cover on the right uses a reverse plate made from the design on the left.

used wherever the type or drawing alone would not have enough weight or color on the page.

**rewriting**  See COPY EDITING.

**ripple finish**  See PEBBLING.

**rivers of white**  This paragraph has purposely been set· "loose" with too much space between the words. Careless typesetting like this leads to distracting rivers of white like the one encircled. Legibility and beauty are served when type is set with close spacing and when lines of less than 25 characters are avoided. When rivers of white are noticed in proof, they should be encircled and marginal instructions to the printer should be given to "reset with narrow word spacing."

**roller embossing**  See PEBBLING.

**rom.**  Proofreader's abbreviation for roman. (See ROMAN; also chart of proofreader's marks under PROOFREADING.)

**roman**  This sentence is set in roman type. *This sentence, on the other hand, is set in italic type.* Both are set in Baskerville.

**Roneo**  Trade name for a machine which resembles the mimeograph.

**Ross board**  See also DRAWING TECHNIQUES.

The Charles J. Ross Company makes a complete line of special drawing boards, all of which are scratchboards and some of which are stipple boards. (See SCRATCHBOARD; STIPPLE BOARD.)

**rotary gelatin hectograph**  See HECTOGRAPH.

**rotary press**  See also PRINTING PRESSES.

A rotary press is one in which the paper passes between two cylinders, one of which serves to support the paper while the other prints it. An office mimeograph machine works on the same principle; so do Multigraph, Multilith, and spirit duplicators and offset, photogelatin, and sheet-fed gravure presses.

However, the term "rotary press" is often reserved for rotary *web-fed* presses like the big, high-speed presses that print metropolitan newspapers, rotogravure sections, and national magazines. (See WEB.)

These rotary presses accept paper direct from a roll, and do not cut the web into sheets until after it is printed. Paper goes through some of the big rotary web presses at close to 20 miles an hour. Some magazine rotaries print the paper in four colors on both sides, cut it, fold it, put on the cover, and staple it, all in one continuous automatic process.

**rotogravure**  See GRAVURE.

**rough**  See also COMPREHENSIVE.

The first, unfinished sketch of a layout made to give the general effect rather than the exact details. (See illustration under LAYOUT.)

**rounding**  See BOOKBINDING.

**routing**  A method of removing metal from those areas of a cut that are not supposed to print. These areas have, of course, been lowered somewhat by the action of the etching acid, but routing lowers them still more until there is no possibility of the rollers or paper bulging into them and smudging the work. (See illustration under LINE CUT.)

**rubber plates** See also DUPLICATE PLATES; RUBBER STAMPS.

Rubber printing plates are like rubber stamps except that they are precision-made for use on a printing press instead of for use by hand.

Most rubber plates are duplicate plates made from metal type or cuts. Some are cut by hand like linoleum or wood where the design is simple.

Rubber plates have long been used for printing on rough paper and uneven surfaces. Because they give better coverage with less ink, they are often preferred over metal plates for printing on nonabsorbent materials, such as plastic, foil, or cellophane. They are coming into increasing use in book and job printing; fast, lightweight rotary presses have been designed that will take only rubber plates.

Rubber printing plates are made in much the same way as stereotypes, from previously prepared metal type or engravings. They can be made to give excellent results and can outlast not only stereotypes but also copper electros, much as rubber auto tires far outwear metal-rimmed wagon wheels.

The newer oil-resistant synthetic rubber plates overcome one difficulty that used to cause trouble, namely, deterioration and swelling of the rubber through contact with oil-based inks.

Rubber plates can be made of hard rubber for fine ruled work or of soft rubber for printing on uneven surfaces. They have been used for halftone work of 100 screen and higher but not, so far, with quality results. They can be printed alongside metal type and cuts.

Rubber plates are available for patent base as well as for type-high printing. They can be supplied in curved (or curvable) form to fit any rotary press. (For presses specially equipped

with smooth rotary cylinders, rubber plates can be mounted by means of a double-sided adhesive tape.)

Unmounted rubber plates can be mailed as easily and cheaply as stereo mats and can be used even by printers who do not have stereo casting equipment. They can be used in any ordinary (relief) printing press. However, there is at present no wholly satisfactory way of duplicating a rubber plate except from the original matrix or by pulling a proof and making a line cut from this.

One important use for rubber plates is for cuts that are to be run on the Multigraph.

**rubber stamps** Perhaps the simplest method of printing is rubber stamping. For a number of purposes it is the best.

Rubber stamps are often used to put a return address on envelopes, to add a dealer's name to manufacturer's literature, to sign letters, to sign or countersign checks, for dating, for receipting bills, and for imprinting such wording as "Special Delivery," "First Class Mail," "Air Mail," "Sec. 562 P. L. & R.," etc.

Special rubber-stamp inks are available in various colors for use on laundry, cellophane, metal, glass, celluloid, checks, meat, etc.

Rubber stamps made to order cost approximately 60 cents per square inch, or 60 cents per line. Simple dating devices with customer's wording plus changeable dates cost about $4 and up.

Complete rubber-stamp printing outfits can be obtained for as little as $2.50. With this the purchaser can set his own type and make up his own stamps. However, these rank rather as toys than as business tools, since setting the type is very time-consuming.

To make a rubber stamp, type is set, an impression is taken from it in a special material something like plaster of paris, the resulting mold is baked hard, and then vulcanized rubber is forced into the mold.

Customers may supply their own type if they require a style that the rubber-stamp company does not have.

Designs that cannot be set in type, such as signatures or special devices, are first made as woodcuts; then from the woodcuts, the procedure is the same as from type. Signatures should be written in ordinary ink, preferably not India ink. This is because a signature in ordinary ink can be transferred to a wooden block to guide the cutting simply by moistening it and pressing it against the wood.

There are rubber-stamp companies in all large cities. One which will send a useful catalogue on request is the Krengel Manufacturing Co., 227 Fulton St., New York 7. It lists such specialties as changeable date stamps, self-inking stamps, time stamps, fonts of loose type, pencil-cap stamps, and a self-inking roller-marker that rolls messages up to 2 by 5 in. onto cartons and crates (price about $10, type extra).

**rule** Brass rule (also made of type metal) is used for printing straight lines, plain boxes, etc. It comes in long strips, which are cut to order for the job at hand, and in many thicknesses and combinations. Some common styles of brass rule are shown at the right.

When rules are made up into boxes and borders, it is important that they fit well at the corners. Mitered corners are preferable to butted corners. (See illustration under MITERED.) Rule is expensive and is cut specially for each use. It is well to keep this in mind when correcting proofs. Corrections requiring recutting of rules cost extra.

It is difficult enough to make rules join perfectly at the corners, and practically impossible to get them to cross each other (as in columns of figures) without the joints showing. Therefore, it is well to try to avoid using both horizontal and vertical rules. However, imperfect joints can be made perfect during the electrotyping process, if electrotypes are made. In fact, one of

the most satisfactory ways of handling complicated rules is to omit them entirely during typesetting and have them added "in the wax" by the electrotyper.

| | |
|---|---|
| Hairline | No. 1402 |
| ½ pt. | No. M-5099-A |
| 1 pt. | |
| 1½ pt. | No. 5256 |
| 2 pt. | No. 5209 |
| 3 pt. | No. 1434 |
| 4 pt. | |
| 6 pt. | |

Dot leader, 2 dots per 8-pt. em

Dot leader, 4 dots per 8-pt. em

Hyphen leader, 2 strokes per 8-pt. em

Common styles of brass rule and leaders.

(See RULING.) However, when electrotypers are very busy, they can be rather slow in getting around to work of this kind.

Alternately, type can be set, repro proofs pulled, rules drawn in with a ruling pen, and a line cut made of type and rules together.

**ruling** Ruled forms can be printed in the ordinary ways: (1) from brass rule, (2) from electrotypes made by the wax-engraving method, (3) from offset or other plates prepared photographically from an original drawn up in India ink.

However, they are often produced on special ruling machines. In these machines, the paper passes under multiple ruling pens which get their ink from special fountains. Horizontal lines are ruled in one operation, vertical lines in another. The ruling can be done in more than one color simultaneously, without extra cost.

For firms doing this sort of work, look under Paper Rulers in the Classified Directory.

When ruled forms must be printed along with type or other material, they may of course be reproduced like any line cut, from printing surfaces prepared by one of the methods listed in the paragraph above. The wax-engraving method permits the most perfect results. (See WAX ENGRAVING.) To build ruled forms out of brass rule is difficult since it is almost impossible to make the lines join neatly where they cross or meet.

One device which facilitates the ruling of evenly spaced lines is the Paraliner. (See PARALINER.)

**ruling pen**  Anyone who handles much art work will find uses for a good ruling pen, even if he is no draftsman. It is often necessary to rule a plain border around a line drawing in order to change its proportions so that it will scale to the desired dimensions.

Ruling pen.

There are a few simple tricks about using a ruling pen which should be borne in mind:

1. Buy a good one (costing $1.50 or more) with polished points of equal thickness.

2. Keep it scrupulously clean, inside and out.

3. Do not expect it to write unless the points are separated by at least the thickness of a piece of paper.

4. Hold it nearly vertical, with the flat side toward the ruler.

5. Fill it with ink; do not dip it. Use the filler quill in the cork of the India ink bottle or a dropper. There must be no ink on the outside of the points.

**run-around**  There is a run-around in the text of the above article on the ruling pen. The illustration is cut into the text, and the type lines are run around it.

The use of run-arounds increases the cost of type composition and is often avoided on that account. The narrower the type columns, the less reason there is for using run-arounds. This is one reason for designing this book with a two-column page.

When run-arounds are to be used, it is customary to set galleys as if there were to be no run-arounds, until their exact location can be worked out. Then the necessary lines are reset to the narrower measure. Needless to say, a given amount of wordage will require more short lines than long lines.

**run in**  To set without paragraphs as a space-saving device; to add new copy without making a new paragraph.

**running head**  See also HEADINGS.

The heading that runs across the top of the page of a magazine, book, or pamphlet giving the title, date of issue, or chapter title.

# S | s

**saddle stitching**  See STITCHING and illustration under BINDING.

**sales letters**  See LETTERS.

**sans serif**  See also Appendix 1, Type Faces.
The words "sans serif" are French for "without serif" and describe those modern type faces that lack serifs, such as Futura, Vogue, Alternate Gothic, and Franklin Gothic. The Monotype Company puts out a type face similar to Kabel (an imported series) which it calls Sans Serif.

## THIS TYPE has serifs.
## THIS TYPE is sans serif.
## THIS TYPE has square serifs.

**saving money**  See also ESTIMATING COSTS.
There are many real economies to be made in the buying of printing, as well as a tempting array of false economies.

If a 6 by 9 pamphlet will be just as effective as one 7 by 10, if a job in one color will get the same favorable attention and results as a multicolored job, if the omission of illustrations will in no way reduce the effectiveness of the job, then these may be ways to make real savings, not just false economies.

The big economies, though, come from the kind of thinking that not only compares this printer with that, but also inquires whether a form letter might not be even better than a pamphlet, a paid advertisement better than a mailed announcement, or free publicity better than either. (In this connection see the introductory pages in this book, especially the check list on page viii, and also the entry on CAMPAIGN PLANNING.)

Now look also at the entry on PRINTERS: HOW TO CHOOSE. Next to choosing the right medium to begin with, selecting the *right* printer is more important than anything—much more important than getting competitive bids.

Work with your printer to help him help you save money in the following ways: (1) Call him in *early* enough to take advantage of his suggestions on economies, short cuts, and ways to greater effectiveness. (2) Prepare your copy *early* enough so you can make your corrections in the copy, not later in type—rewriting in proof wastes more money than any other single thing

281

print buyers do. (See copy PREPARA-
TION.) (3) Make or have made a layout
(see LAYOUT) comprehensive enough to
leave no room for future misunderstandings by anyone. Do not gamble on
anyone else "seeing" your squiggles in
the same way you visualize them. (4)
Deliver your job to the printer complete in every detail and with written
instructions, not piecemeal and with
verbal instructions. (5) Measure your
copy to fit before you send it. (See
COPY FITTING.) (6) And finally—most
important of all—allow enough time
for everybody at every step. Haste
makes waste. Rush jobs boost costs and
lower quality. A poor job of printing
is remembered far longer than fast delivery.

In any printing job there are always
two costs: the fixed costs and the running costs. The first 1,000 copies of a
simple printed job involving typesetting may cost $25, where additional
thousands if ordered at the same time
may cost only $3 per thousand. By con-
trast, the first 1,000 copies of a simple
mimeograph job may cost only $5.50 or
less, with additional thousands available at $4 per thousand.

Thus, $26.50 may buy 5,000 copies of
a mimeograph leaflet and allow $5
for an artist to make the stencil attractive; or 1,000 plain printed leaflets;
or one or two copies of an elaborate
"presentation," where the real purpose
is to reach just one man or a committee.

The unit price of printing always
drops as quantity increases. To be sure,
the second 5,000 copies of a mimeograph or silk-screen job will not be
much cheaper than the first 5,000, but
a 10,000 order might be noticeably
cheaper in offset; in quantities of 250,-
000 or so, rotogravure might offer substantial economies.

A few additional tips are:

Go to a printer who does a lot of
the same kind of work and is equipped
**for it.**

Stick to standard sizes in paper, envelopes, etc.

Avoid expensive paper. A poor job
will look better on fine paper, but a
good job will look well on any paper.
Of course, on very small runs, the cost
of the paper is not important one way
or the other.

Strive for "press delivery" of the
job, i.e., avoid separate bindery operations if possible. Binding costs are often
higher than all other costs put together,
and may not even go down as the
quantity goes up. (See BINDING.)

Use an artist or designer. This may
not sound like an economy measure,
but it often is. A couple of appropriate
drawings can do more for a job than
fancy paper or an extra color, and may
cost less. This is particularly true of the
bigger editions where running costs
bulk larger than fixed costs. But warn
your artist not to demand close register
(see REGISTER) unless he really needs it.

Know the postal regulations. A 24-
page booklet mails more cheaply, for
instance, than a 12- or 16-page job of
the same weight. (See Appendix 4,
Postal Information.)

It is worth remembering that printers
charge for their services. If you ask
them to procure paper, cuts, bindery
service, etc., you benefit by being able
to hold them responsible for quality
and promptness, but you also will owe
them a commission on the purchases
that they make for you.

**s.c.** Abbreviation for small caps. (See
chart of proofreader's marks under
PROOFREADING.)

It is also the abbreviation for supercalendered. (See CALENDERED.)

**scaling** See also CROP, CROPPING.

To scale a photograph or drawing
means to calculate how much it must
be reduced or cropped in order to fit
the layout, and to mark this information on the art work for the guidance
of the engraver or printer.

Some art work can be reproduced "same size," but usually it must be reduced somewhat; occasionally, it must be enlarged.

If, for example, a photograph 10 in. wide by 8 in. deep is to be reproduced 5 in. wide, the engraver or printer is told that the reduced width of the printed photograph must be 5 in.

This is all he needs to know, because the height will automatically be reduced in the same proportion as the width. The height will be 4 in. The formula is

$$\frac{\text{Width}}{\text{Reduced width}} = \frac{\text{height}}{\text{reduced height}}$$

$$\frac{10}{5} = \frac{8}{4}$$

There is an easier way to scale art work, however, which requires no mathematics. *Photographs and drawings always reduce or enlarge along their diagonals.*

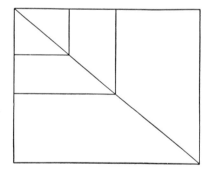

This principle of the diagonal can be applied through the use of a piece of tracing paper. (See illustration on next page.) The method is completely accurate and will work either way, *i.e.*, the proportions (the diagonal) of the layout can be used to determine the area of the picture to be used; or the proportions of the picture can be used to determine the depth required on the layout for any given width.

The method illustrated is a short cut,

in which only one line need be drawn, the edges of the tracing paper themselves serving as two other lines. If this short cut seems confusing at first, try tracing the complete rectangle and then extending its diagonal.

If the art work itself is not rectangular, draw a rectangle around it in light blue (nonphotographing) pencil, just big enough to enclose its highest, lowest, and widest points, and then proceed to scale this rectangle.

Photographs that are to bleed off the edge of the paper, offer a special problem. (See BLEED.) At least ⅛ in. will be trimmed off on each bleed edge. They must therefore be scaled to a size ⅛ in. larger than they will be after trim. Thus, a photograph that is to bleed on three sides and be 6 by 9 after trim must be scaled to 6⅛ by 9¼.

Actually, it is not impossible to reduce a 5 by 4 drawing or photograph to 5 by 3 without losing any part of it. It can be done by trick photography. It is often done to make fashion models look taller and slimmer than they actually are. However, this sort of "stretch-squeeze" service must be ordered specially like lettering or retouching. One firm offering the service is the American Blueprint Company, 7 E. 47 St., New York.

**Scan-a-graver, Scan-a-sizer** By means of the Fairchild Scan-a-graver newspapers can make 65-screen and 85-screen halftones more quickly and much less expensively than is possible with conventional methods.

The Fairchild engravings are made on a plastic and can be used for direct printing or for molding stereos and electros. The plastic is strong enough to survive up to 500,000 impressions.

About 30 min. is required to make an 8 by 10 halftone; less time for smaller units.

The machine resembles a small lathe. In operation, an electric eye scans the [*continued on page 285*]

## HOW TO SCALE A PHOTOGRAPH

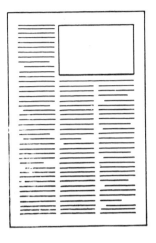

This layout, left, calls for a 2-column photograph. The photograph to be used, below, is 7½ by 9½ in., excluding the margins.

A piece of tracing paper is laid over the photo, two of its edges even with two edges of the photo. The diagonal of the photo is drawn. (It is best to mark just the corner, remove tissue to a hard surface, and then draw the diagonal.)

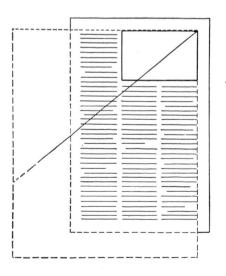

Now the tracing paper is laid upon the layout, the same two edges even with the edges of the space allotted for the photo. *The angle of the diagonal of the actual photo always coincides with the diagonal of any enlargement or reduction of that photo.* Therefore, the space left for this photo on the layout must be made deeper; or the photograph must be made shallower by cropping some sky or foreground to establish a new diagonal having the same angle as the one on the layout.

It is decided to crop the photo to fit the layout, so a new diagonal is drawn *from the layout.*

�le

The tissue is now laid back on the photo, with its right edge even with the photo as before. Its upper edge is moved down to eliminate some sky. The diagonal now shows whether some foreground must also be eliminated. ⬇

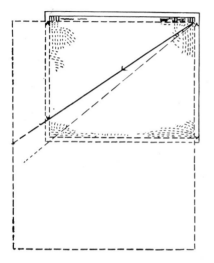

The photo as finally scaled is marked and cropped as shown at right.

➜

2 col. width

[*continued from page 283*]

picture to be reproduced and controls the motions of a vibrating red-hot needle, which simultaneously scans the plastic surface. Where the picture is light, the needle bites deeply; where it is dark, the needle burns away very little of the surface of the plastic.

To the eye, the dot formation of Fairchild halftones is very hard to tell from results obtained in the conventional way.

The company estimates that the great majority of smaller newspapers now rely on Scan-a-gravings as their primary source for halftone plates.

The Scan-a-graver will not enlarge or reduce, but this ability has been built into a later machine called the Scan-a-sizer. This latter, according to the company, will enlarge or reduce up to 4½ times, produce finished plates in a choice of screens in any size up to a full tabloid page, work 50 per cent faster than its predecessor, and even permit a photo to be reduced (or enlarged) more along one dimension so that short cars can be made longer, for example, square pictures can be made to fit oblong spaces, etc.

An attachment being installed on both old and new machines is the Variable Response Unit. This permits bringing out details that under ordinary processing might be lost in the shadows or highlights. It also permits making reverse plates. A special feature is its ability to break down a continuous tone original into five tone steps with a result resembling a poster-technique drawing.

Fairchild engravers are leased, not sold. The company estimates that if a Scan-a-graver is operated at 25 per cent capacity, the cost of the halftones it produces will be about 3 cents per sq. in. For information write to Fairchild Graphic Equipment, Inc., Robbins Lane, Syosset, Long Island, N.Y.

A machine called the Klischograph produces halftones by methods somewhat similar to those used in the Scan-a-graver except that halftones can be made on metal just as easily as on plastic.

**scheduling**  See also DELIVERY; EDITORIAL PLANNING.

Careful scheduling is necessary even on very simple printed jobs if deadlines are to be met. Schedules are usually arrived at by working backward from the date when the material must be delivered or be in the mails. A typical schedule on a sizable job might look as follows:

September 5 (Friday). All copies to be in the mails.

August 21 (Thursday). Mailing must start, since it will require 10 working days to address, fold, stuff, seal, sort, tie, and deliver to post office, and Labor Day intervenes.

August 20 (Wednesday). Completely printed and bound material to be delivered to mail room (at least 25 per cent of it), the balance to follow at the rate of not less than 10 per cent each working day.

August 20 (Wednesday). Mail room to be ready with addressed envelopes and labels, cardboard backing if needed, the necessary personnel, etc.

August 18 (Monday). Printed sheets must reach bindery, dry enough for trimming.

August 14 (Thursday). Press proofs to be O.K.'d and printing started. Printing to take two working days.

August 13 (Wednesday). Envelopes and labels must be received by mail room, together with the latest mailing-list corrections, mailing instructions as to covering letters, enclosures, lists to be used, etc., since addressing must start a week before mailing starts, if mailing is to be completed in 10 days.

August 12 (Tuesday). Final page proofs to be O.K.'d ready for press.

August 11 (Monday). Corrected page proofs to be in printer's hands.

August 6 (Wednesday). Corrected galley proofs, paste-up dummy, and all art work to be in printer's hands.

August 4 P.M. (Monday). Printer to deliver balance of galley proofs and engraver's proofs.

July 31 (Thursday). Printer to deliver first part of galley proofs.

July 31 (Thursday). Balance of manuscript copy to be in printer's hands.

July 29 (Tuesday). At least half of manuscript copy to be in printer's hands.

July 29 (Tuesday). Lettering or type proofs for art work ordered, for completion by Aug. 1.

July 25 (Friday). Artist to deliver finished art work.

July 18 (Friday). Artist to submit sketches for approval.

July 18 (Friday). Backing cardboard must be ordered, since the paper house cannot promise delivery in less than 4 weeks, and it is needed Aug. 20. August 15 delivery is specified.

July 11 (Friday). Imprinted shipping labels are ordered (see LABELS) since the work requires 4 weeks and the labels are needed Aug. 13. August 9 delivery is specified.

July 2 (Wednesday). Envelopes must be ordered, since the envelope house cannot promise delivery in less than 5 weeks, and they are needed Aug. 13. August 8 delivery is specified.

June 30 (Monday). Paper is ordered, since the mill cannot promise delivery in less than 6 weeks, and paper is needed Aug. 14. August 11 delivery is specified.

The above schedule is a tight one. On large jobs, more time might well be needed for setting type and handling proofs—perhaps a good deal more. The artist may not be able to work so quickly. Notice that the art deadline has been set for almost two weeks before it is due at the printer's to allow for corrections or for delays on the artist's part. Other deadlines have been similarly arrived at.

It is assumed that the above job is printed either on one-color or on multicolor presses. If there must be several separate press runs, more time must be allowed both for presswork and for drying between press runs.

If the job involves process color work, at least a month more must be allowed for preparing the printing plates, making color proofs, correcting the color plates, etc., regardless of the printing process used.

**scoring** Scoring is similar to perforating except that the fibers of the paper or cardboard are merely bruised with a sharp steel rule, instead of being intermittently cut through. The purpose of scoring is to make tearing easier. It is done on a regular printing press with a steel rule that is little more than type high. The rule may or may not be inked.

Creasing, on the other hand, is done to make tearing harder. A blunt rule is used, which compresses the fibers without bruising them. Creasing makes it easier to fold stiff paper or board, and increases folding endurance.

Sometimes the word "scoring" is used as if it meant the same as "creasing." If the purpose of the operation is made clear, the finisher will not go wrong regardless of the word used.

**scratchboard** See also DRAWING TECHNIQUES.

Scratchboard is a specially prepared clay-coated, white drawing board, which helps an artist achieve woodcut effects, or black-and-white-reverse effects, or highlights in dark areas.

It is possible to draw on scratchboard in the ordinary way with pen or brush. It is also possible to use it in such a way as to get white lines against a black background. When an area is flooded with India ink and then "scratched," the scratches show white. Whites produced in this way are pure and solid and easily controlled, which is not the case when white paint or white ink is used for fine work. An artist need not laboriously paint around a highlight; he can boldly rough in the whole area and scratch in the highlights later.

Some scratchboards, often sold as Ross boards, have a stippled surface (see SHADING TINTS) so that any tone can be lightened merely by scratching the tops of the raised dots gently.

**screen** A halftone is said to have a 65-line screen when it has been broken up into fine dots of which there are 65 to the linear inch. Halftones for use in newspaper work are made with 65- or 85-line screens. Halftones for use on smoother paper may be made in 100, 110, 120, 133, and 150 screen or higher. (See HALFTONE; also SILK SCREEN.)

**script** The kind of type face which imitates handwriting.

**Scriptomatic** A line of addressing machines operating on the spirit duplicator principle and especially adapted for use with original addresses on punched or Keysort cards, though any sort of master in card or roll form may be used.

The address or other information to be duplicated may be typed by any method, except that special carbon paper must be used to create an image on the underside of the paper or card stock. From this carbon image, from 100 to 200 legible impressions may be taken.

When the addresses are put on IBM or Keysort cards or the like, it becomes possible not only to make a card record serve doubly as an addressing plate, but to use machine-sort methods for selecting the addresses to be used.

Fully automatic machines are available operating at about 6,000 impressions per hr. One will handle envelopes or forms, another will put addresses on tape, Dick strips (see DICK STRIPS), etc. A special "Scriptograph" hand roller permits easy addressing of packages or addressing on an occasional basis.

Scriptomatic equipment is made by Scriptomatic, Inc., 310 N. 11 St., Philadelphia 7, Pa.

**seals** See also LABELS.

Embossed, metallic, and other specialty seals are obtainable with or without printing from the Dennison Manufacturing Co., 300 Howard St., Framingham, Mass., to name just one source.

**searchlights** Searchlights can be rented to dramatize special events from Publicity Searchlight Service Co., 52 W. 53 St., New York 19.

**second-class mail** See Appendix 4, Postal Information.

**self-cover** See BINDING.

**self-mailer** See also ENVELOPES; Appendix 4, Postal Information.

Any piece of printed matter designed to be mailed without the use of an envelope. Post cards of all sizes are self-mailers. Letters, newsletters, circulars, pamphlets, and magazines can be sent as self-mailers, provided they will not fall apart in transit. A precanceled postage stamp or gummed seal may be used to fasten the parts of a double post card or folder.

Self-mailers can be sent at regular first- and third-class rates, under the same rules as to content that govern material to be enclosed in envelopes.

**separation negatives** See also COLOR SEPARATION; PROCESS COLOR.

In reproducing any art work that is in more than one color, a separate negative must be made for each color to be used, so that from each separation negative a separate printing plate can be made.

**serif** See also SANS SERIF; Appendix 1, Type Faces.

A light line or stroke crossing or projecting from the end of a main line or stroke of a letter. The text type in which this book is set has serifs. The headings at the top of the page, however, are in a sans-serif (without serif) type.

The detached portions of these letters are serifs. Without the serifs, the type becomes sans serif.

**serrated edges** Roughly cut edges of paper, as in newspapers. The cutting is done on the press as part of the folding operation.

Substantial economies can be made by accepting newspapers, newspaper supplements, advertising broadsides, etc., with serrated edges just as they come from the press, instead of requiring them to be sent to a bindery for trimming.

**shade** See COLOR.

**shading film** See SHADING TINTS.

**shading tints** See also DRAWING TECHNIQUES; SURPRINTING.

Cartoonists, fashion illustrators, and other artists make extensive use of shading tints, or Ben Day tints, particularly in work intended for newspaper reproduction. In this way they produce work that is as easy to reproduce as a line drawing, that has the realism of a wash drawing or photograph, and that looks considerably better than any coarse-screen newspaper halftone. The shading tints are actually made of a pattern of tiny dots or lines, which give a gray effect.

There are five major ways of adding shading to a drawing:

1. The artist may rule in the shading by hand.

2. The drawing may be made on stipple board having a pattern of raised dots or lines on its surface.

3. The drawing may be made on special paper (Craftint Singletone or Doubletone) having invisible shading tints that can be made visible through the use of a special developing fluid.

4. Shading patterns printed on acetate can be adhered to the basic drawing where they are needed and removed where they are not needed.

5. The photoengraver or lithographer can add the shading in accordance with instructions from the artist, using the Ben Day or Tintograph shading mediums.

Typical shading-tint patterns are reproduced on page 290. Specimen stippled and shaded drawings are shown under drawing techniques. (See DRAWING TECHNIQUES.)

When art work is to be printed in reduced size, care must be taken to use coarse shading tints that will reduce to the desired size.

It is clear from a glance at the available shading patterns that for an artist to duplicate these by hand would be an interminable task—though it can be done.

*Stipple board.* Stipple board has two limitations: (1) Since drawing a clean pen line on it is difficult, it lends itself

better to soft effects than to line-and-shading work. (2) Only one screen pattern can be used in the same drawing. On the other hand, the artist can control the darkness or lightness of this screen pattern at will. Other techniques are less flexible in this regard.

*Singletone and Doubletone drawing papers.* These papers (made by the Craftint Mfg. Co., address below) are widely

Here the two tones of shading are produced with Craftint developer applied with a brush on Doubletone paper. The solid blacks are done with India ink. (*This drawing was done by Arys of Fairchild Publications.*)

used by cartoonists and artists doing newspaper advertising work. The papers are available in a variety of patterns and in sizes ranging from very coarse to very fine. The Craftint pattern chart gives for each style not only the number of lines per inch in actual size, but also the number of lines per inch if reduced one-fourth, one-third, or one-half during reproduction. For average newspaper use, the number of lines per inch in the printed result is usually not permitted to exceed 65.

Once the proper paper is selected, the artist first outlines the subject on

Typical shading tints available in adhesive shading film. Note the reverse patterns in the last two lines to lighten the all-black areas.

the Craftint paper. Solid blacks are added with brush or pen, using waterproof India ink. Then where shading is needed, the transparent liquid developer (furnished free with the paper) is applied with a brush or pen, and the invisible pattern in the paper appears to give a shaded effect. Singletone paper permits only one shading; Doubletone paper permits light and dark shading, each brought out by a different developing fluid.

*Shading tints in sheet form.* Such tints (sold under such trade names as those listed below) are easy and economical to use. Patterns in black ink on clear acetate are available for graying light areas. Patterns in white ink on clear acetate are available for lightening dark areas. One pattern may be laid over another if necessary for the desired effect. Several patterns may be combined on one drawing.

Some acetate shading sheets have an adhesive on one side so that they will adhere to a drawing when rubbed down firmly. To apply a tint, a piece of film somewhat bigger than the area to be shaded is laid over the art work. Then the excess film is cut off with a sharp knife, or the pattern is scratched off the areas that are to have no shading. Usually the adhesive is such that it may be peeled off without damage to the art work.

The same process is used for art work that is to be reproduced by line cut, photo offset, or mimeograph with photochemical stencil.

Well-known shading films with name and address of manufacturer are listed below:

*Ben Day Press Sheets and Shading Sheets.* Ben Day Inc., 119 Kent Place Blvd., Summit, N.J.

*Contak Shading Film.* Transograph Company, 30 W. 15 St., New York.

*Craftint Top Shading Film.* Craftint Mfg. Co., 1615 Collamer Ave., Cleveland 10, Ohio.

*Tintograph Shading Mediums and Photo-Copy Shading Sheets.* The Tintograph Company, Inc., 48 New Chambers St., New York.

*Zip-a Tone.* Para-Tone, Inc., 510 W. Burlington Ave., LaGrange, Ill.

Prices range from 50 cents to $1 for a single 8 by 12 sheet. Sheets can be obtained from almost any artists' supply shop.

"Ben Day" originally meant the process used by an engraver or offset platemaker to add shading tints in accordance with the artist's instruction. Today, however, the term is loosely used to describe any mechanical tint. The Ben Day Company offers acetate shading sheets as well as the tints applied by the engraver when a plate is being made.

 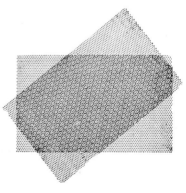

When one shading film is laid over the other, various effects may be obtained.

To have the Ben Day shading added by the engraver, the editor or his production man should write instructions to "lay a Ben Day" in the areas that have been indicated on the art work by a blue wash invisible to the camera's eye.

Since there are many Ben Day tints or patterns that approximate different shades of gray, complete instructions should indicate the desired tint by number. For a complete chart of numbered Ben Day tints, write Ben Day Inc., 119 Kent Place Blvd., Summit, N.J.

Having the printer add shading tints by the Ben Day method is not done so much as it once was, except in color comic-strip work. The work is charged for at hourly rates, in addition to the regular costs of making Ben Day cuts. It tends to be more expensive than when the shading is made a part of the original art work. The process is, however, a useful resource for the buyer of printing who does not have his own art department.

*Cost.* The cost of reproducing shaded line drawings by letterpress (but not by offset) is slightly higher than for ordinary line drawings. Both are reproduced as line cuts, but a line drawing that has added shading will take a special Ben Day rate. (See rate chart under LINE CUTS.)

Contrary to a prevailing impression, the cost of an ordinary line cut, or a Ben Day line cut, is higher than the cost of a square newspaper screen halftone of the same size. However, a Ben Day line cut is far cheaper than a highlighted, silhouetted, combination line and halftone cut, which would be the comparable thing. (See also KEMART PROCESS.)

**sheet-fed** Printing presses are either sheet-fed or web-fed, depending on whether the paper is cut into separate sheets before printing, or fed from a roll and cut into sheets afterward. Only rotary presses can be web-fed, and gen-

erally only large high-speed presses are web-fed. (See WEB.)

**sheet-fed gravure** See GRAVURE.

**shingling** A method of making a column or page of type out of many separate cards or slips of paper, each containing one or a few lines of type. The type must be positioned near the edge of each card, and the cards are then overlapped like shingles on a roof. See also COLD TYPE.

**shipping information** See also RAIL FREIGHT; RAILWAY EXPRESS; TRUCKING; WRAPPING; Appendix 4, Postal Information.

Unless printed material is shipped properly, the value of the editor's and printer's work may be jeopardized. Material must arrive on time and in good condition if it is to be most effective. That is the job of the shipper who must decide two main questions: How shall this material be shipped? How should it be wrapped for such shipment?

*Shipping methods and rates.* The chief methods are mail (including surface parcel post and air parcel post); express, both air and rail; rail freight; and motor freight. In addition, bus lines will carry on short hauls such special packages as rush shipments of cut flowers or bulk delivery of city newspapers to rural bus depots along the routes.

Airmail and air express are fastest, except to near-by cities or places without direct air service, or under poor flying conditions.

First-class mail, or parcel post "special delivery" or "special handling," can be fast also, sometimes with a speed of 1,000 miles each 24 hr. Third-class, parcel post, and railway express shipments are usually at least two or three times as long in transit. Truck schedules can be both very fast and rather slow. Rail freight is the slowest and cheapest method of shipment.

The rate for domestic airmail (weight limit 8 oz.) is 6 cents per ounce or fraction thereof, except that an air rate of 4 cents each is applicable to post cards and private mailing cards, anywhere in the United States, with the usual postal size limitations. The rate for domestic air parcel post (weight over 8 oz. and usually limited to 20 lb.) varies according to weight, zone, and character of matter. (See AIR PARCEL POST.)

Air express rates vary with both the weight and distance. The minimum charge is $2.50. Any shipment that would cost more than $2.50 by airmail can be sent cheaper by air express.

Both air services are expedited by delivering the material direct to the airfield. The Railway Express Agency will pick up matter for air express.

Aside from speed, other factors that may influence the choice of a shipping method are (1) comparative costs, (2) weight and size limitations of certain methods of shipping, (3) pickup and delivery service, and (4) insurance or need of a receipt on delivery.

In general, it is well to remember the following facts:

All mail is subject to certain size and weight limitations which vary according to the classification of the post office and the zone to which matter is being sent. The maximum limitations (70 lb. in weight and 100 in. in combined length and girth) apply to shipments to or from second- and third-class post offices. The weight limit on matter mailed between first-class post offices is 20 lb. to zones 1 and 2, 40 lb. to zones 3 through 8. (See Appendix 4, Postal Information.)

Second-class mail is for periodicals only.

Third-class rates apply only to pieces weighing up to and including 8 oz.

Fourth-class mail (parcel post) is subject to weight and size limitations which vary according to the classification of the post office. Unlike first-, second-, and third-class mail, rates de-

pend both upon the weight and the distance to point of destination. Insurance is not included in the fee, but may be secured on payment of an additional fee. No receipt is obtained on delivery of regular fourth-class mail even when insured. The post office does not provide pickup service.

Railway express has almost no limits to the weight and size of the shipments it can handle. The rate includes both pickup and delivery service as well as insurance without extra charge for valuation up to $50. (Over $50, insurance is 18 cents per $100 of valuation.) Receipts are taken for all parcels; thus time and place of delivery are recorded as well as the signature of the recipient. Printed matter receives a special third-class express rate of 4 to 19 cents per pound, depending upon distance, with a minimum charge of $1.80.

Rail freight service is provided by the railroads with rates depending on the commodity as well as on the distance and the regional rate. The minimum charge is for a weight of 100 lb. with no maximum on weight or size.

Trucking service (motor freight) has been found extremely satisfactory for large shipments between points not directly connected by railroad, and where both loading and unloading require special trucking anyway.

Shippers can get invaluable help from *Leonard's Guide and Service* (G. R. Leonard and Co., 79 Madison Ave., New York 16, and 123 N. Wacker Dr., Chicago 6). *Leonard's Guide,* a loose-leaf, indexed publication kept up-to-date by mail service, gives complete shipping information including rates and regulations for parcel post, railway express, rail freight, airmail, and air parcel post. A subscriber receives a *Guide* made up for his city, listing rates and routings that apply from that point of origin to the various cities and towns throughout the United States. Every post office and express station in the United States is listed alphabetically, by state, with keys by which to determine the shipping rates by parcel post, rail freight, and railway express. The subscription price for *Leonard's Guide* is $15 a year in New York, Philadelphia, and Chicago, $20 a year elsewhere.

The same firm publishes five motor-freight directories (New York, Philadelphia, Chicago, New England, and Boston) which give the names of the common carriers of general commodities, the location of the main office of each carrier, and a detailed list of the destinations with the carriers who serve them. Each subscriber to *Leonard's Guide* receives the motor-freight directory for his area as part of the *Guide* service. To those who do not subscribe to the *Guide*, the annual subscription rate is $5 each for New York, Philadelphia, and Chicago directories (two issues per year) and $2.50 each for New England and Boston (one issue per year). "Bullinger's Postal and Shippers Guide" (Bullinger's Guides, Inc., 303 Lafayette St., New York. $12) lists every United States post office and railroad station or nearest communication point. It is valuable for checking on addresses, since an addressee's post-office address often differs from his express or freight address.

*Wrapping and shipping.* These are really inseparable problems. For example, the decision to ship by truck may be guided by the fact that printed matter may not require heavy backing and wrapping if the shipment is at least a full truckload, carried directly from the printer to the shipping room. Wrapping a consignment of books to be shipped by parcel post may be guided by the applicable weight limit.

*Shipping time.* The method of shipping, the weather, and any number of uncontrollable factors influence the time required for shipping. In addition, a number of precautions may be taken by the shipper to expedite his shipment.

1. Businesslike arrangements for prompt wrapping, packing, and shipping frequently mean a saving of several days which not even air service could make up. (See WRAPPING AND PACKING.) The necessary labels, envelopes, and such wrapping material as paper and backing should be ready before the consignment comes from the printer. Too many times a printer is paid overtime to rush a job that is later held up, at least in part, until minor essentials like fourth-class labels or special mailing tubes can be procured.

2. Careful wrapping and proper marking of matter to be shipped will not only expedite the shipment but will help to assure its arrival in good condition.

3. Advance warning to the consignee that a shipment is on its way will give him time to clear space for it, get his money ready if it is COD, make his own distribution plans, or notify the shipper if the package is not received.

4. Efficient handling of freight receipts, parcel post insurance slips, and express receipts will assist in rapid follow-up if any part of a shipment goes astray.

Anyone who orders much printing will be forced to acquire at least a rudimentary knowledge of shipping techniques and requirements. No printing order is complete without shipping instructions, including instructions to the recipients of all bulk shipments.

It is possible for a production man to get pretty well detached from the physical bulk of the items in which he is dealing. Office boys have been sent to pick up by hand quantities actually requiring a truck. Office managers have innocently agreed to accept shipment of quantities too large to fit in their offices.

Anyone making out shipping instructions must create in his mind's eye a picture of the weight and bulk of the items being dealt with in each shipment.

## Rates from CHICAGO on Fourth-class Mail (Parcel Post), Railway Express,* and Rail Freight †

| Between Chicago and | 5 lb. | | 10 lb. | | 20 lb. | | 50 lb.‡ | | | 100 lb. | |
|---|---|---|---|---|---|---|---|---|---|---|---|
| | 4th class | Ry. express | 4th class | Ry. express | 4th class | Ry. express | 4th class | Ry. express | Rail freight | Ry. express | Rail freigh |
| Atlanta | $0.52 | $1.80 | $0.87 | $2.13 | $1.56 | $2.77 | 20-lb. limit to first-class post offices except to those in 1st and 2d zones § | $4.71 | Minimum freight rates are given in 100-lb. column | $ 7.93 | $2.25 |
| Boston | 0.63 | 1.87 | 1.10 | 2.25 | 2.02 | 3.01 | | 5.31 | | 9.14 | 2.64 |
| Cleveland | 0.44 | 1.80 | 0.70 | 1.91 | 1.21 | 2.35 | | 3.64 | | 5.80 | 1.47 |
| Denver | 0.63 | 1.88 | 1.10 | 2.27 | 2.02 | 3.06 | | 5.43 | | 9.39 | 2.71 |
| Detroit | 0.44 | 1.80 | 0.70 | 1.87 | 1.21 | 2.26 | | 3.43 | | 5.37 | 1.34 |
| Los Angeles | 0.91 | 2.16 | 1.67 | 2.83 | 3.19 | 4.18 | | 8.22 | | 14.95 | 4.92 |
| Miami | 0.76 | 1.97 | 1.36 | 2.47 | 2.56 | 3.45 | | 6.40 | | 11.32 | 3.29 |
| Milwaukee | 0.39 | 1.80 | 0.59 | 1.80 | 0.99 | 2.00 | | 2.77 | | 4.06 | 0.84 |
| New Orleans | 0.63 | 1.87 | 1.10 | 2.25 | 2.02 | 3.01 | | 5.31 | | 9.14 | 2.52 |
| New York | 0.63 | 1.84 | 1.10 | 2.20 | 2.02 | 2.92 | | 5.07 | | 8.66 | 2.52 |
| Omaha | 0.52 | 1.80 | 0.87 | 2.01 | 1.56 | 2.53 | | 4.10 | | 6.72 | 1.75 |
| St. Louis | 0.44 | 1.80 | 0.70 | 1.87 | 1.21 | 2.26 | | 3.43 | | 5.37 | 1.34 |
| San Francisco | 1.05 | 2.17 | 1.95 | 2.85 | 3.75 | 4.22 | | 8.34 | | 15.19 | 4.92 |
| Seattle | 0.91 | 2.14 | 1.67 | 2.80 | 3.19 | 4.13 | | 8.10 | | 14.71 | 4.92 |
| Washington, D.C. | 0.52 | 1.82 | 0.87 | 2.15 | 1.56 | 2.82 | | 4.83 | | 8.18 | 2.29 |

\* Railway express rates are for first class and include insurance up to $50, as well as local pickup and delivery service. For more than 100 lb., the charge is prorated on the 100-lb. figure.

† Freight rates are listed for printed matter only and are subject to a 3 per cent Federal transportation tax. Rates include local pickup and delivery as well as full insurance. Note that, although the minimum rate is for 100 lb., it is possible to ship less than 100 lb. at that price.

‡ Weight of parcel post shipments limited to 20 to 40 lb. between major cities. For details, see Appendix 4, Postal Information.

§ Milwaukee being in the second zone from Chicago has a maximum weight limit of 40 lb.

## Rates from NEW YORK on Fourth-class Mail (Parcel Post), Railway Express,* and Rail Freight †

| Between New York and | 5 lb. | | 10 lb. | | 20 lb. | | 50 lb.‡ | | 100 lb. | |
|---|---|---|---|---|---|---|---|---|---|---|
| | 4th class | Ry. express | 4th class | Ry. express | 4th class | Ry. express | Ry. express | Rail freight | Ry. express | Rail freight |
| Atlanta | $0.63 | $1.84 | $1.10 | $2.20 | $2.02 | $2.92 | $5.07 | | $ 8.66 | $2.48 |
| Boston | 0.39 | 1.80 | 0.59 | 1.83 | 0.99 | 2.17 | 3.21 | | 4.93 | 1.30 |
| Chicago | 0.63 | 1.84 | 1.10 | 2.20 | 2.02 | 2.92 | 5.07 | | 8.66 | 2.52 |
| Cleveland | 0.52 | 1.80 | 0.87 | 2.05 | 1.56 | 2.63 | 4.35 | Mini- | 7.21 | 1.94 |
| Denver | 0.91 | 2.10 | 1.67 | 2.71 | 3.19 | 3.93 | 7.61 | mum | 13.74 | 4.07 |
| Detroit | 0.52 | 1.80 | 0.87 | 2.13 | 1.56 | 2.77 | 4.71 | freight | 7.93 | 2.05 |
| Los Angeles | 1.05 | 2.33 | 1.95 | 3.17 | 3.75 | 4.87 | 9.94 | rates | 18.40 | 5.92 |
| Miami | 0.76 | 1.95 | 1.36 | 2.42 | 2.56 | 3.35 | 6.16 | are | 10.84 | 3.18 |
| Milwaukee | 0.63 | 1.87 | 1.10 | 2.25 | 2.02 | 3.01 | 5.31 | given | 9.14 | 2.52 |
| New Orleans | 0.76 | 1.95 | 1.36 | 2.42 | 2.56 | 3.35 | 6.16 | in | 10.84 | 3.22 |
| Omaha | 0.76 | 1.96 | 1.36 | 2.44 | 2.56 | 3.40 | 6.28 | 100-lb. | 11.08 | 3.26 |
| St. Louis | 0.63 | 1.88 | 1.10 | 2.27 | 2.02 | 3.06 | 5.43 | column | 9.39 | 2.75 |
| San Francisco | 1.05 | 2.35 | 1.95 | 3.21 | 3.75 | 4.94 | 10.12 | | 18.76 | 5.92 |
| Seattle | 1.05 | 2.33 | 1.95 | 3.17 | 3.75 | 4.87 | 9.94 | | 18.40 | 5.92 |
| Washington, D.C. | 0.44 | 1.80 | 0.70 | 1.83 | 1.21 | 2.17 | 3.21 | | 4.93 | 1.23 |

* Railway express rates are for first class and include insurance up to $50, as well as local pickup and delivery service. For more than 100 lb., the charge is prorated on the 100-lb. figure.

† Freight rates are listed for printed matter only and are subject to a 3 per cent Federal transportation tax. Rates include local pickup and delivery as well as full insurance. Note that, although the minimum rate is for 100 lb., it is possible to ship less than 100 lb. at that price.

‡ Weight of parcel post shipments limited to 20 to 40 lb. between major cities. For details, see Appendix 4, Postal Information.

show card   A hand-lettered poster. (See LETTERING; SIGNS; POSTERS.)

sidehead   See HEADINGS.

side sewing   See illustration under BINDING.

side wiring   See STITCHING and illustration under BINDING.

signature   See also illustration under BOOKBINDING.

A folded printed sheet of paper ready for sewing into a book or pamphlet. It usually consists of 16 pages, but may have 8, 12, 24, 32, 48, or 64 pages.

signs   See also POSTERS; LETTERING; TRANSPORTATION ADVERTISING; OUTDOOR ADVERTISING.

Sign painters, sign letterers, show-card writers, and neon-sign manufacturers specialize just as printers do. Therefore it is important to go to one who seems to handle a lot of the kind of work wanted. Results will be better and cheaper.

A good sign or show-card man can take a brush and produce finished-looking lettering almost as fast as the layman can write. To pay $2 for a sign that he turns out in 10 min. is to pay for his skill. A beginner may work ten times as long over the same sign and turn out an inferior product.

There is a startling gulf, however, between fast hand-lettering that just flows out of the brush or pen and the meticulously finished lettering that appears in advertisements and in gold leaf on store windows. The former may cost $1 a sign, and the latter may cost $1 per letter or more. Hand-lettering on a sign can be much less expensive than actually setting type, or it can be much more expensive. See books on lettering listed in Appendix 2, Bibliography.

A good sign man knows many tricks to gain effectiveness and save money. It is best to tell him what is to be achieved and get his suggestions, not hand him a complete set of specifications.

Some of the myriad kinds of signs are hand-lettering in oil or water color on poster board or wood, letters embossed from special type (see EMBOSOGRAF), enamel on metal, gold leaf, neon, and billboards.

When only 3 to 10 signs or posters are wanted, it may be cheapest to make each by hand separately. When larger quantities are needed, the silk-screen process is often used. (See POSTERS.)

silhouette   To silhouette a halftone cut means to remove nonessential background in order to produce an outline effect instead of a plain rectangular effect. Silhouette halftones cost extra. The halftone illustration of a mimeograph duplicator on page 180 has been silhouetted. (See also VIGNETTE.)

silk screen   The silk-screen printing process is one of the simplest and most versatile of the printing processes. It is almost always the best and cheapest way of making from 25 to 1,000 posters, car cards, or billboards, in fact any kind of material except that containing photographs or large blocks of very small type. It can handle photographs (crudely) and fairly small type, but it cannot underbid offset on this kind of work. (See charts "How to Choose the Right Printing Process" inside the covers of this book.) It is often used for printing on felt pennants, glass bottles, metal containers, decalcomanias, etc.

Silk-screen work may be identified by the fact that its colors are usually rich and nonglossy. Under a magnifying glass, one can usually see the pattern of the silk, especially in an area of solid color. The color goes on quite thick, sometimes thick enough to feel. The process lends itself especially well to the reproduction of bold designs with broad, solid areas of color, although very delicate effects may also be obtained by good workmen.

Sign painters were among the first to see the advantages of the silk-screen

or photographically copied from type proofs.

Paint goes through the stencil openings in the silk screen, and on the paper positioned on the lower part of the frame. Here the frame is opened to show the design printed on the paper. A new piece of paper will be put in its place for the next impression.

The upper, hinged, part of the silk-screen frame has a tightly stretched piece of silk tacked across the underside. The stencil design is on the silk, blocking out certain portions for printing.

Now the frame is closed and paint is applied evenly to the silk screen by a squeegee which is pushed by hand from side to side.

process and perfect it. It enabled them to offer their customers 25 to 100 posters or show cards for the price of 5 or 10 individually painted ones.

Most sign shops today have silk-screen equipment (see SIGNS), and most commercial silk-screen operators are staffed to do attractive sign lettering. The lettering on silk-screen work is usually done by hand, although sometimes traced from enlarged type proofs

The essential equipment for doing silk-screen work consists of the following:

A wooden frame, like a window-screen frame

Silk bolting cloth, similar to that used for sifting flour, stretched tightly across the frame

Ink of semiliquid or paste consistency

A squeegee, like a windshield wiper or window-cleaning blade, for scraping ink from one end of the silk frame to the other

In the very simplest application of the process (rare in actual commercial use) a paper stencil (see STENCIL) is cut and laid on a table. (The table top should be protected by several layers of newspaper.) The silk screen is placed over it. Ink is poured onto the silk and spread around so that it goes through the silk and causes the paper stencil to stick to the silk. (Simple stencils will stay in place against the silk through the action of the ink alone, although for safety a few dabs of glue may be used.) The ink also goes through the open spaces in the paper stencil and makes an impression on the upper sheet of newspaper.

With the squeegee, the ink is now pushed to one end of the silk frame, and the frame is lifted. The upper layer of newspaper is removed, and replaced with a sheet of white paper or poster board. The frame is lowered, the ink is squeegeed to the other end of the frame, the frame is raised, and the first poster has received its first impression. After all have received this first impression, or color, another stencil and another run must be made for every other color.

This is the simplest silk-screen method. Another method is to stop up the openings in the silk by brushing glue into it wherever ink is not to penetrate. Still another begins by painting those areas which are to print with a benzene-soluble "tusche" liquid. After this, glue is spread thinly over the whole area with a strip of cardboard, allowed to harden, and then brushed with benzene. The glue that went on over the tusche floats off along with it, leaving the silk porous wherever tusche was applied.

The method most used commercially is the knife-cut film method. This is like the paper-stencil method, except that the film stencil can be chemically adhered to the silk and is supported by a paper backing until firmly adhered. After adhesion, the paper backing is removed. Film stencils can also be prepared photographically when the design is intricate and it would be time-consuming to cut it out with a knife. In fact, halftones have been successfully handled by the silk-screen method.

An excellent description of the whole process is contained in the illustrated book "Silk Screen Color Printing" by Harry Sternberg (McGraw-Hill, 1942. $5). The illustrations in the book are models of clarity and beauty.

Preparing one simple silk screen of medium size may cost $10 to $25 or more, depending on the amount of work involved. Running off impressions from this screen may cost about 3 to 5 cents each, including the paint. On long runs, posters are sometimes run "two-up," so that the running cost is halved, although the cost of preparing the screen is doubled.

Thus, a simple 14 by 22 poster or 11 by 28 car card in three flat colors may cost $30 or so for preparing the screens, and 9 cents per copy to run, plus the cost of the paper or poster board.

If paper is charged at 2 cents and poster board at perhaps $4\frac{1}{2}$ cents per poster, then quotations on the above three-color job might run as follows:

| | | |
|---|---|---|
| 100 copies, on paper | $ 41.00–$ | 92.50 |
| on board | 43.50– | 95.00 |
| 1,000 copies, on paper | 140.00– | 245.00 |
| on board | 165.00– | 270.00 |

If the silk-screen printer has been responsible for creating the design, he may, of course, charge for his services as an artist, as well as for the reproduction work.

Art work that is to be reproduced in silk screen should be done by an artist familiar with the process. For best results it should be done in a limited number of colors of tempera (show-card color), and these colors should be used flat and not mixed. For example, if an artist mixes seven basic colors and sticks to these, then the art work can be reproduced in seven impressions in silk screen and will closely duplicate the original. One of the assets of silk screen is its ability to make knife-cut film stencils from unfinished art work.

A process similar to silk screen but used more abroad than in the United States is the "roller process." This makes use of a fine net of tulle (with no more than 20 threads to the inch) and a paper stencil. The paper stencil is adhered to the tulle both by the ink and by dabs of glue. Then printer's ink is applied with a roller, through the tulle and the paper stencil. The process is much more economical of ink than the silk-screen process, and the screens are cheaper, though they do not last so long. It is mainly used for making rather large posters to be seen from a distance and which can, therefore, be a little rough.

**Singer sewing** See STITCHING and illustration under BINDING.

**Singletone paper** See SHADING TINTS.

**size, sizing** To "size" paper means to treat it chemically in order to modify its surface qualities. Writing paper is sized so that it will take writing ink satisfactorily. Offset paper is sized so that it will not take up too much water from the moist offset cylinder. Gelatin and resin are used as sizings. Such terms as "tub-sized" and "surface-sized" refer to different methods of the process.

**skid** See also PAPER SIZES AND WEIGHTS.
The cheapest way to accept paper delivery (other than in rolls) is on skids, i.e., simply piled on movable wooden platforms. A skid of paper is usually about 3,000 lb., but the amount varies with sheet size and bulk.

**slidefilm** See FILMSTRIPS.

**slip sheeting** When wet ink on a newly printed page is likely to smear or blot the back of the next sheet, an extra sheet of absorbent paper is slipped between as a kind of blotter to absorb the ink. This slip sheeting assures a clean job of mimeographing where it is necessary to print on non-absorbent paper or to use both sides of the paper.

**slitting** Sometimes a book is printed on a 38 by 50 sheet of paper, whereas it is to be folded as two separate 25 by 38 pieces. The larger sheet can be

divided by slitting on the press, thus making a later cutting operation unnecessary.

**slug** A piece of metal used for spacing between lines of type, usually 6 pt. thick, but sometimes 12 pt. thick. A piece of metal 1, 2, or 3 pt. thick is called a "lead." (See LEADING.)
Slug also means a line of type cast in one solid piece on LINOTYPE, INTERTYPE, or LUDLOW machines. (See illustration under LINOTYPE.)

**slug-casting machine** A machine that casts a line of type as one solid piece of metal. There are four in common use: the Linotype, the Intertype, and (for the larger sizes) the APL (All-Purpose Linotype), and the Ludlow. (See especially LINOTYPE and LUDLOW for further information.)

**small caps** THESE THREE WORDS are set in small caps, with the initial letter in caps. Most fonts of text type include small caps (but not italic small caps) in sizes up to 14 pt. Display variety can be added to otherwise straight type by using either

EVEN SMALL CAPS

or

CAPS AND SMALL CAPS

Since it is a little more trouble for a Linotype operator to use small caps, composition in which they are used extensively will cost extra. Words doubly underlined in manuscript will be set by the printer in small caps. Words with three underlines will be set in regular caps. (See proofreader's marks under PROOFREADING.)

**smashing** A binder's term. Paper that has been folded must also be smashed, i.e., stacked and put under pressure to get the air out of the folds, before it

can be trimmed. (See illustration under
BOOKBINDING.)

**Smyth sewing**  See STITCHING and illustration under BINDING.

**soda pulp**  The soda-pulp method is often used to make paper from deciduous trees like poplars. Soda-pulp paper is very white and soft, with high bulk and opacity but low strength. Soda pulp is often used to give a soft finish to a paper of sulphite pulp base.

**solid matter**  Solid matter may mean extensive areas of small type unbroken by headings or illustrations. It may also mean type that has been "set solid," *i.e.*, not been leaded (spaced between the lines). (See LEADING for examples of both solid and leaded type.)

**sound transcription**  See RECORDINGS.

**spacing**  For spacing between lines of type, see LEADING. For spacing between letters, see LETTER SPACING. Both are illustrated under TYPE.

**spatter**  A drawing technique in which ink or paint is spattered onto the paper, often by running a straightedge along the bristles of a toothbrush that has been dipped in ink or paint. The result is a dotted effect similar to stippling. (See STIPPLE.) Areas that are not to receive the spatter are first masked out.

**special delivery**  See Appendix 4, Postal Information.

**special handling**  See "Special Delivery and Special Handling" in Appendix 4, Postal Information.

**Speedaumat**  See ADDRESSOGRAPH.

**Speedball pen**  A special lettering pen used for show-card writing and lettering.

Speedball pens and pen lettering. (*Drawing, courtesy of Hunt Pen Co.*)

**Speeding delivery**  See "Special Delivery and Special Handling" in Appendix 4, Postal Information.

**spine**  The back of a book, *i.e.*, the part visible as it stands in a bookcase.

**spiral binding**  See MECHANICAL BINDINGS.

**spirit duplicator**  See also HECTOGRAPH; DUPLICATING METHODS.

A spirit duplicator, sometimes called a "fluid duplicator," a "liquid duplicator," or a "liquid hectograph," is an office duplicating machine that can produce up to 400 copies of typed, written, or drawn material at very low cost. In quantities greater than 400, the copies grow faint and progressively harder to read. To get more, it is necessary to prepare a new master.

A rotary spirit duplicator.

Up to five colors can be reproduced simultaneously from the same master: purple, red, blue, green, and black. A purple ink gives the maximum number of copies. The best results are attained when special spirit-duplicator paper is used.

The process works as follows: Special aniline-dye carbon paper is placed face up beneath a sheet of coated paper in a typewriter. As the message is typed or drawn with a hard pencil or a ball-point pen, a reversed copy is produced on the back of the sheet. A measurable amount of the dye on the carbon paper is thus transferred to the master. Copies are now printed directly from this master. The paper to be printed picks up a thin layer of the dye because, just before contacting the reverse carbon, it is moistened very slightly with a special solvent having an alcohol base. The moistening is so slight as not to be detectable in the finished copies.

On runs below 50 copies, work similar to that produced on the spirit duplicator can be done on a cheaper machine, the hectograph. (See HECTO-GRAPH.) Runs of over 400 copies perhaps can be more advantageously handled by the mimeograph or Multilith process. (See chart on inside of front cover.)

The greatest use of the spirit-duplicator process is in duplicating business forms. The largest manufacturer of both spirit and gelatin duplicators, Ditto, Inc., Harrison at Oakley Blvd., Chicago 12, states:

Ditto systems are based on the original writing of the transaction to reproduce all subsequent records. In order-billing procedures copies required for shipping and billing including bills of lading, tags, labels, and unit media for sales analysis and inventory control can be reproduced from a single writing. For parts and assembly orders, the Ditto master is used over and over to reproduce copies required on repeat orders without rewriting.

Spirit duplicators are marketed under the trade names Ditto, Standard Fluid Process, Wolber, and Rexograph.

A low-cost, portable spirit duplicator weighing 12 lb. and costing about $32.50 is available from the Master

Addresser Co., Minneapolis 16, Minn. The price includes carrying case and enough supplies to prepare and run six master letters. It will print a sheet 8½ by 11 inches, or smaller, and will make up to 200 letters or cards from one typing. The same firm offers a "Lab-L-Master" at $14.95 for running extra copies of labels and tags from a single original typing.

The Azograph, manufactured by the A. B. Dick Company, 5700 Touhy Ave., Chicago 31, employs the spirit-duplicator principle, but with the difference that the masters are yellow rather than the usual purple and thus are less likely to stain fingers and clothes. A dark image nevertheless results due to a chemical reaction between the carbon image and the moistening agent on the paper at the moment of impression.

**split fountain**   Two or more different colors of ink can be run on the same printing press at the same time by means of split fountain.

The trough of ink that feeds the ink rollers of a printing press is called the "ink fountain." This fountain can be split into two or more compartments by means of dividers, and a different color of ink poured into each compartment.

To prevent the different colors from running together on the ink rollers, the surface of the rollers themselves is cut away for an inch or so opposite the dividers. (For a novelty effect, blending of the inks on the rollers is occasionally permitted.)

Of course, any given section of the ink rollers will roll over only certain parts of the type form. This sets some limits on which pages of a form can be run in which colors.

The split-fountain technique is often used in magazine work. A form is run in black, and then with only one additional run through the press, one row of pages can receive red as the second color, another row can receive green as a second color, a third row can receive some blue, etc.

Since rollers are expensive, it does not pay a printer to cut them unless the run will be very long, or unless the same rollers will be re-used a number of times.

**split run**   A method of testing the comparative effectiveness of different mail-order or advertising appeals. Some publications are printed "two-up," i.e., two plates are made from each page or ad, and two copies are printed with each revolution of the press. In such a case, an advertiser can by special arrangement use two slightly differing ads, and test offer A against offer B, knowing that in all other respects the conditions under which subscribers receive the two ads will be statistically identical. Every other copy will contain ad A, alternate copies ad B. Often the term "split run" is also applied to similar testing procedures in the field of direct mail advertising.

**spray**   Krylon is one widely sold brand of spray that is offered in several formulations of special interest to the graphic arts field. It comes in pressurized cans and the clear variety is ready to use at a moment's notice as a fixative for drawings, cold type composition, etc. It gives good protection even when used so sparingly as to be almost invisible, but repeated coatings produce a glossy finish. Krylon can also be obtained in white, black, and colors. Krylon spray valves are guaranteed against clogging as are some, but not all, of the other brands of spray.

**spread**   See CENTER SPREAD; DUMMY.

**square serif**   A family of type styles sometimes called Egyptian. (See Appendix 1, Type Faces.)

**squeegee**   A rubber blade similar to the kind used by window washers.

Squeegees are used in silk-screen printing to push the ink through the mesh onto the paper. (See illustration under SILK SCREEN.)

**Standard Rate and Data Service**  See ADVERTISING.

**stapling**  See also STITCHING.

Pamphlets and magazines are usually fastened or "stitched" by stapling. Small ones are saddle-wired with staples. Thicker ones are side-wired with staples. (See illustration under BINDING.)

**station posters**  See TRANSPORTATION ADVERTISING.

**steel engraving**  See ENGRAVING.

**Stenafax**  An office machine designed for the automatic preparation of mimeograph stencils or offset duplicator masters. In operation the original to be copied (which may include typing, ruling, charts, graphs, etc., but not photographs) is placed on one drum of the Stenafax, scanned by an electric eye, and reproduced by electronic facsimile means on the other drum. Areas up to 8 by 14 in. can be copied. The process takes 6 minutes. The materials cost for either a stencil or "Planofax" offset master is about 20 cents, the cost for a single copy on paper, about 5 cents. The machine is quoted at $1,600 including a year's maintenance, and is manufactured by the Times Facsimile Corp., 540 W. 58 St., New York 19, N.Y.

**stenalith**  An orange-colored stencil similar to a mimeograph stencil, and prepared in the same way. Its use, however, is as a negative for printing down on an offset plate.

**stencil**  The stencil method of printing is one of the five basic methods (see PRINTING). Both the mimeograph and the silk-screen processes work on the stencil principle. (See MIMEOGRAPH; SILK SCREEN.)

An example of stencil printing. Ink or paint goes through the open part of the stencil to print on the paper underneath.

A simple stencil looks like the accompanying figure. The letters are simply holes cut in a piece of paper or metal. Ink can be daubed or sprayed through the openings onto any surface, such as a packing case. It is possible to buy an assortment of separate stencil letters and assemble them into any word.

Notice that there are gaps in stencil letters, where it is necessary to support the centers of such letters as "O" and "A" and give extra support to tongues of paper that might otherwise bend during use.

This problem of supporting the inside of an "O" and closed parts of other letters has had to be solved in all stencil processes. In the mimeograph process, a porous lattice of paper fibers supports the inside of an "O." In the silk-screen process, a piece of fine bolting silk gives strength to the open spaces between areas of Stenfilm or glue. In a special "roller process" more widely used abroad than in the United States, paper stencils are supported by a fine net of tulle (with no more than 20 threads per inch) and printing ink is rolled right through the tulle with rubber rollers.

Sears, Roebuck sells a 78-piece stencil set with 1-in. letters, stencil brush, and cake of black stencil ink for about $5.

The Stenso Lettering Co., Industrial Bldg., Baltimore 2, Md., offers a variety of stencil lettering guides from 15 cents up, some of which are sold in stationery, department, and five-and-ten-cent stores. (See also LETTERING.)

Stencil machines, both hand-operated and electric, cut shipping stencils in oiled stencil board or cardboard. Stencils of this type are now used extensively in American industry for marking shipments of all kinds and sizes. This method of marking is approved and recommended by the Association of American Railroads and the American Trucking Association.

Detailed information on stencil-cutting machines of this type, stencil inks, oiled board, fountain stencil brushes—all supplies used for stenciling of shipments—can be obtained by writing to Marsh Stencil Machine Company, Belleville, Ill.

**stereotype, stereo**  See also CUTS; ELECTRO; DUPLICATE PLATES; MAT SERVICES.

Stereotyping is one of the oldest and cheapest methods of making a duplicate metal printing plate from type and/or cuts. A paper matrix or "mat" of special composition is forced down over the type and cuts and made to take an impression from these. The mat then serves as a mold, and melted metal is poured into it. The result is a new metal printing surface duplicating the old surface. This stereo can be used for printing alongside type by mounting it on wood.

The biggest users of stereos today are newspapers. They use the stereo process in making curved plates to fit their rotary presses. (For illustration see NEWSPAPERS.)

Stereos are inexpensive: mounted (blocked) stereos of less than 10 sq. in. cost about $1.25 each; mounted stereos of 50 sq. in. cost about $3.75.

Stereo mats, being made of a paper composition, are light in weight and easy to mail. Printers who do any news-paper work are usually equipped to convert stereo mats into metal stereos.

Stereos have the disadvantages, however, of permitting some loss of detail, of being too crude for fine halftone work (65 screen is the practical limit), and of showing wear even before type itself begins to wear. They may also stretch or shrink somewhat, both when the mat is made and when the metal is cast.

For longer runs and critical work electrotypes, rubber plates, or plastic plates are usually ordered. (See ELECTRO; RUBBER PLATES; PLASTIC PLATES.)

Mats are frequently distributed to newspapers by national advertisers, cartoon syndicates, and feature syndicates. The local editor is more willing to include a plug for some worthy cause if he is presented with a mat of a cartoon or feature, ready for stereotyping and immediate printing. His advertising worries are simplified when he receives an ad in mat form, ready for the works.

Mats may be obtained in minimum quantity at rates of about 18 cents each for 5 sq. in. or less, larger sizes down to about 1 cent per sq. in. Most stereo firms offer both a minimum-priced mat, and one or more of higher cost and quality. (See the possibility of ordering mats through one of the MAT SERVICES.)

**stet**  A proofreader's marginal mark meaning "retain crossed-out material." (See proofreader's marks under PROOFREADING.)

**stick**  The receptacle that a hand-type compositor holds in his left hand to receive the type as he sets it. A stick will hold 10 or 15 lines of 10-pt. type. Hence, when a newspaper reporter is told to write a "stick" of copy, he knows that he is to write only a couple of paragraphs, or about two column inches. (See illustration under TYPE.)

**stickers**  See LABELS.

**stipple**   A stippled area in a drawing means an area composed of many fine dots. Stipple board is a kind of illustration board with a pattern of raised dots on its surface. A pencil or crayon drawn across stipple board leaves a dotted or stippled line, not a solid line. (See DRAWING TECHNIQUES.)

**stipple board**   See SHADING TINTS; DRAWING TECHNIQUES.

**stitching**   See also BINDING and the accompanying illustrations.

Most small pamphlets and magazines are saddle-wire stitched. Two wire staples are generally used and driven from the outside fold through to the center spread. One staple is usually enough for booklets less than 4 in. high. Saddle wiring is the cheapest method of stitching.

Thicker pamphlets and magazines (96 to 160 pages or more, depending on the thickness of the paper) may have to be side-wire-stitched if they are too thick for saddle wiring. The wire staples are driven from the front cover through to the back cover, about ⅛ in. from the spine. This makes a very strong binding, but the pages will not open flat. This is a little more expensive than saddle stitching.

Side thread stitching, known as Singer sewing, is used a good deal for textbooks because of its durability.

Smyth sewing is a method of sewing a thick book so that it will open flat. Most books are sewed in this way. The first 16-page unit of the book is fed into the machine and saddle-thread-stitched. The second 16-page unit is laid alongside the first, saddle-thread-stitched, and also linked to the stitching in the first signature. The third is sewed to the second, and so on.

**stock cuts**   See also MAT SERVICES.

There are a number of firms that specialize in supplying stock cuts for use by job printers and editors of house organs, school publications, etc. They procure humorous and decorative drawings of a sort likely to be adaptable to many uses, and sell these in proof form (for offset), mat form, or in the form of metal cuts. The purchaser usually pays less than he would have to pay to have a similar cut made up specially for his own use, and thus gets art work virtually free.

Suppliers of stock cuts include Hux Cuts, Inc., 80 W. 40 St., New York 18, Cobb Shinn, 721 Union St., Indianapolis 25, Ind., and Mail-A-Cut Service, P. O. 2038, Tyler, Tex.

"Clip books" containing assortments of stock illustrations are available in art supply stores, and permission to reproduce goes with the purchase of these books.

The A. B. Dick Company offers a monthly assortment of seasonal stock drawings in the form of stencils for use on the mimeograph. (See MIMEOGRAPH.)

**stock photos**   See PHOTO AGENCIES.

**stone proof**   A proof of a type form taken after it is locked up ready to go on the press. It shows everything that a press proof can show, except that it gives no indication as to the quality of the press make-ready and inking.

The stone proof takes its name from the fact that the pages are assembled on a large, flat table called a "stone" and are there locked up in a chase ready for press. Nowadays the "stone" may be of metal.

**streamers**   See POSTERS.

**Streamlined Copy Fitting Method**   A system for character counting and copy fitting which provides counts on 1,450 faces from 4 pt. to 24 pt., together with tables, scales, and instructions for speeding measurements and calculations. It is manufactured by Arthur B. Lee, 551 Fifth Ave., New York 17, and offered at $5.95 postpaid.

**strip, strip-in, stripping** When two or more photographic negatives are used together to make one printing plate, the process of combining them is known as "stripping." The term is used not only in photoengraving but also in offset and in every other process where photography is used.

If, for example, an offset printer is asked to reproduce a form letter, he will photograph it and use the result-

The illustration for this form letter was too big for the allotted space, so it was photographed separately and the resulting, reduced-size negative was then "stripped in" with scotch tape alongside the negative of the letter. The shaded area is opaque paper. The whole assembly is called a "flat." Offset plates are prepared by exposure to light through such a flat.

ing negative to prepare his printing plate. If he is also given a separate illustration and told to reduce it and drop it into place in a space left for it in the form letter, he must make a second negative of this illustration and then "strip" it alongside the first negative in the proper place before making his plate. He will make an extra charge of $1 or so for this strip-in.

In the stripping process, the various film negative elements are assembled on a large piece of orange-colored opaque paper called a "flat." A flat must be the same size as the plate that will be exposed through it. The negatives are then stuck to the flat with tiny strips of scotch tape in the exact positions assigned to them on the layout. The flat is cut away behind the essential parts of each negative so that light can come through.

**stuffer** See CIRCULAR.

**style sheet** See also COPY PREPARATION; PROOFREADING.

To prevent inconsistencies every copy writer and proofreader in an office needs a handy guide to the preferred spelling, capitalization, punctuation, etc., agreed upon by the staff. Such an editorial style sheet need list only those examples that are peculiar to that particular office. It need not duplicate the rules for correct spelling and usage in such a guide as the University of Chicago "Manual of Style" (listed in Appendix 2, Bibliography) or the "Government Printing Office Style Book" (which may be purchased from the Superintendent of Documents).

For example, one editor insists upon streamlined spelling such as "thru" not "through," "tho" not "though." A list of his more common simplifications heads his style sheet.

Another insists upon a comma before the conjunction in such a series as "Bodoni, Caslon, and Garamond" although style books usually leave a choice.

Most offices have some rules of distinctive capitalization or hyphenation usually relating to their own trade name or product. The Government Printing Office, for example, recommends capitalizing such nouns as Government and State.

No hard and fast rules can be given as to the contents of such a style sheet since it is necessarily a distinctive development in each office. Frequent additions and corrections should keep it up to date. Constant use of a good editorial style sheet should help at every stage of copy writing, copy editing, copy preparation, and proofreading.

A typographic style sheet for a periodical is equally valuable for those marking copy for the printer, preparing the layout, or pasting up the dummy. It should enumerate the chosen type faces and type sizes and usages for heads, subheads, titles, etc. (For details see PERIODICALS.)

**stylus** See MIMEOGRAPH.

**subhead** See HEADINGS.

**subscript** See INFERIOR CHARACTERS.

**substance** See BASIC WEIGHT.

**sulphate paper** Paper made from wood by the sulphate process is strong but cannot be bleached so white as soda or sulphite paper. Kraft paper, used for wrapping and for paper bags, is an unbleached sulphate paper. (See CHEMICAL PULP.)

**sulphite paper** See CHEMICAL PULP.

**supercalendered** See CALENDERED.

**superior numbers** When the mathematician writes the term $x^3$ or the writer indicates a numbered footnote, he is using a superior number. (See proofreader's marks under PROOFREADING for the correct way to tell a printer to use a superior number.)

**surface-sized** See SIZE, SIZING.

**surprinting** Type surprinted on 85-screen tint blocks in both light and heavy values is shown in the accompany-

ing illustration. Type can be printed on a photograph in much the same way. Note the loss of legibility where tone values of type and background are too similar. Note that legibility also suffers when type that is too small or too delicate is surprinted on tint blocks of too coarse a screen.

**swash letters** Letters with unusual flourishes used for ornamental purposes in headings, initial letters, or wherever the designer thinks they would look well. Swash caps are available for use instead of regular caps in most fonts of italic type. Typical swash characters with their standard counterparts are

$$\mathcal{J} \quad \mathcal{K} \quad \mathcal{N} \quad \mathcal{T} \quad \mathcal{Y}$$
$$J \quad K \quad N \quad T \quad Y$$

**sweating** "Sweating" a cut onto its block means soldering it on, using either a metal block, or metal plugs within a wooden block. This is done whenever it is impractical to leave shoulders through which nails can be driven. Sweating is unnecessary when cuts are mounted by means of adhesive.

# T | t

**tags**  Tags can be made by printing on an appropriate grade of Bristol (see CARDBOARD) and then die-cutting to the desired shape. (See DIE CUTTING.)

However, it is generally much cheaper to buy tags, whether plain or printed, from a company specializing in this work. One such company is the Standard Tag Co., 65 Duane St., New York 7, which can supply either stock tags or printed-to-order tags in almost any size, shape, or color, on any grade or weight of stock.

Other companies offering similar service include Acme-Monroe Tag Co., 701 S. LaSalle St., Chicago; and J. L. May Co., 111 W. 19 St., New York City.

**tape**  Imprinted typing tape for advertising purposes is obtainable from Neuer & Hoffman, Inc., 132 Green St., New York City.

Imprinted gummed-paper sealing tape is obtainable from Kraftape Printers, Inc., 148 W. 23 St., New York 11.

Imprinted scotch tape may be obtained from Transparent Products Co., Inc., 324 E. 24 St., New York 10.

Every editorial room and art department should be familiar with the many special varieties of scotch tape beyond the omnipresent scotch *cellophane* tape. There is a scotch *mending* tape that does not yellow, shrink, or dry out. There is a double-sided tape, in several degrees of stickiness. There is masking tape of the crinkly, stretchable kind. There is white tape, black tape, and colored tape. All are obtainable from art supply stores such as A. I. Friedman, 35 W. 45 St., New York 36, which will send a catalogue on request.

**tape recording**  See RECORDINGS.

**television**  Since 1949 the big development in the communications field has been television. For advertising, publicity, and promotion, television has opened new channels and established new patterns. It cannot be ignored in any campaign and will command a large part of the advertising budget in many situations. Certainly every campaigner or publicity director—from the advertising manager of the largest corporation to the publicity chairman of the local community chest—should explore the possibility of using television time to get his message across. He will need to have information about television and to compare this with information about advertising and publicity through other media. (See CAMPAIGN PLANNING; ADVERTISING; RADIO; PUBLICITY RELEASE; DIRECT MAIL; etc.) Certain facts are basic:

1. Television time is of two kinds: (*a*) Sustaining or free time and (*b*) commercial or paid-for time. Sustaining time is available for noncommercial, general-information programs in the public interest and for general entertainment programs of all kinds. Paid-for time may be obtained at rates that are based on the number of TV homes within range of the station.

2. The length of a television spot announcement may vary from a 10- or 20-sec. announcement to a 1-min. announcement. The actual program varies from 5 to 15 or even 90 minutes.

3. The use of television time may range from the simple word-of-mouth announcement to the elaborate variety show complete with stage sets, costumes, players, and full orchestra.

4. Television costs are of two kinds: (*a*) For station time on the air and (*b*) for the program itself. The average half-hour evening network program costs about $54,000 for the time and $34,000 for the program.

By 1955 over 36 million families had television sets. In these homes it is estimated that the TV set is turned on for an average of about 5.2 hours per day. Surveys indicate that the typical television home is one with a young housewife and a big family.

This is a mass audience which is highly desirable for some information and advertising campaigns. The decision to use television will depend upon the kind of message that is to be put across and whether it is desirable to pay the price to cover such a tremendous audience. If the message is one that affects all ages and all kinds of people, the seemingly high cost of television may be cheap for the results obtained. But with certain kinds of technical information a more carefully selected audience may be much more desirable.

The individual or the organization using television to present its message can select its audience in certain limited ways: (1) By choosing the time of day or night when the audience he wants to reach is likely to be viewing the TV screen; (2) by choosing the type of program that will attract the audience to be reached; (3) by pin-pointing the programs to certain areas or localities.

The nighttime television audience is estimated to be two and a half times the daytime audience. In some cases, the big night TV audience may reach a level seven to ten times larger than the morning audience. As might be expected, daytime rates are lower than nighttime, being from 50 to 60 per cent of the nighttime rates on most stations.

Throughout the day the make-up of the television audience varies as shown on the accompanying table:

| Time | Audience |
| --- | --- |
| Opening of the channel to 9 a.m. | Family audience coming in for brief periods |
| 9 a.m. to 3 p.m. | Housewives and preschool children |
| 3 p.m. to 7 p.m. | Largely children |
| 7 p.m. to close of the channel | Family audience including children over 12 |

Also seasonal variations cause some changes in the audience as in the summer, for example, when the size of the child audience declines. Sunday afternoon is a time when there are usually many public service programs, and Saturday morning is largely taken up with children's programs.

Thus you can select your television audience to some extent by selecting the time for a program or spot announcement.

Whether you hold that audience—or attract a particular segment of the potential audience—will depend in part on the nature of the program. For example, sports programs will usually attract an adult male audience, news programs will attract adult viewers, and a puppet show or animal performance is more likely to appeal to children.

Basically there are three ways to buy television time: (1) On a network basis, which means buying network time plus a program created by the network, by an outside program packager, or by the advertiser; (2) using national spots, which means buying local station time and a local program as a vehicle for a national advertiser to place his advertising in that particular area; and (3) buying time on local stations and providing programs or spot announcements on film or with live talent.

*Television time rates* are based on the number of television homes within the area reached by a particular station. This figure is the maximum potential for that station; it does not guarantee that the entire potential will view every program any more than the gross circulation of a magazine guarantees that every subscriber will read every advertisement within a magazine.

Various rating services estimate the number of sets which were actually tuned in to certain programs. (For a list of these rating services, see ADVERTISING.)

Although the exact time delimitations vary from one station to another, television time is generally classified as follows:

Class A time:
  Monday through Saturday, 6 P.M. to 11 P.M.
  Sunday, 5 P.M. to 11 P.M.
Class B time:
  Monday through Friday, 5 P.M. to 6 P.M.
  Saturday, 2 P.M. to 6 P.M.
  Sunday, 1 P.M. to 5 P.M.
Class C time:
  All other times

Station time rates vary for these three classes of time roughly as follows: Class B time rates are 75 per cent of Class A rates; Class C time rates are 50 per cent of Class A time rates.

Typical station time rates are given in the accompanying chart. The current rates for each television station in the country will be found in *Spot Television Rates and Data,* published by Standard Rate and Data Service, Inc.

**Typical Television Time Rates**

**(Class A time, 6 p.m. to 11 p.m., Mon. through Sat.)**

|  | Network (46 stations) | Large station | Small station |
|---|---|---|---|
| 60 minutes | $54,500 | $5,500 | $400 |
| 30 minutes | 32,700 | 3,300 | 240 |
| 15 minutes | 21,800 | 2,200 | 160 |
| 1 minute | ....... | 1,500 | 70 |

Perhaps the simplest way for an advertiser to get his products or his project on the TV screen is to buy time as a participant in an existing program. He may pay for a one-minute announcement, for example, and the star who MC's the program tells about the advertiser's product, holds it up to view, and may even give his own personal endorsement. Usually the cost is no more than the cost of station time though sometimes it may be time plus 10 per cent. Seldom does a participating program involve program costs for the advertiser.

*Program costs* are a tremendous factor in television. Writers, artists, actors, musicians, stage hands, and lighting men must be paid; scenery must be designed and built; properties must be procured; and rehearsal time in the studio must be purchased. Probably because of these high costs, a great many programs are created by the networks and sold as a package to the advertiser.

The advertiser, then, must devise a way to make his commercial spot announcement as palatable as the actual program. Again costs can run high if the commercial is to hold its own even for 10 or 20 seconds and commercials are usually filmed to permit spreading the cost over many showings.

The production of film commercials is costly and difficult. The cost will depend upon the number of actors, the nature of the sets, the production techniques, the degree of animation, etc. Live-action minute films can be made for as little as $750, but generally the cost is in the thousands. The cost of a 1-min. animated commercial will range from $1,500 to $10,000 with $5,000 being a fair average; 20-sec. commercials of the same type are generally about 40 per cent cheaper.

Many local stations have solved part of their local program problems by buying syndicated movies, both old and new, to which commercials can be attached. Frequently a local sponsor can tag his message onto such a film program with very good results and at comparatively low cost.

Building a local program is a sizable undertaking for the trained professional. Yet there are small cities in which very effective programs have been developed by people with no previous TV experience. In one city of 100,000 the director of the local children's nature museum started a 15-min. weekly television program with little more than the free time given by the local station and her own enthusiasm and innately good audience sense. The program has continued for several years and is credited with building tremendous community interest in the museum and with arousing the schools to a broader and more significant program of nature study.

This is one example of a number that could be cited where local TV programs have been developed effectively, despite lack of TV-programming experience, by community leaders who represent organizations and institutions concerned with the public welfare. The success of such programs will depend, of course, on the talent and ingenuity of the volunteer community leader, the cooperation and guidance which can be given by station personnel, the availability of free time, and the response of viewers.

Like a radio station, a television station receives its license with the understanding that it will be operated in the public interest. This means that station managers will make free time available for certain public-interest and general-information programs. On all vital public issues equal time must be allotted to both sides of a question. A person or organization is entitled to free time on the air if its opponents have had free time, or to the purchase of time if its opponents have had paid-for time.

For further information about television possibilities in your community, consult your local television station managers. For further reading about television as a communication medium, consult books listed in Appendix 2, Bibliography.

**Tenaplate**  A patented molding material used in making electros. (See ELECTRO; ELECTROTYPE.)

**text paper**  See PAPER; PAPER SIZES AND WEIGHTS: BOOK PAPER.

**Thermo-Fax**  An office machine for making dry copies of letters, invoices, price lists, etc., up to 8½ by 14, in less than 15 sec., and at a materials cost of about 5 cents a copy. The unit copies directly from any original, regardless of the color or weight of the paper on which the original is printed, and regardless of whether the original has anything on the back. Copies can be made on buff, pink, green, or yellow. They are rather flimsy but can be mounted on special backing paper. They are permanent unless exposed to heat in which case they turn black. The Thermo-Fax is priced from about $350 and is made by the Minnesota Mining and Manufacturing Co., St. Paul, Minn.

**thermography** Raised printing resembling the genuine engraving used on business cards, wedding announcements, etc.; also called "plateless engraving."

In thermography, a calling card is printed from ordinary type in the ordinary way, but while the ink is still wet, a special powder is sprinkled on and made to adhere to the wet ink. The card is then heated, and the result is raised lettering.

The letters on a thermographed busi-ness card are usually shinier than the letters on an engraved card, and not quite so clean cut. However, a dull surface is also possible in this process.

Typical retail prices for thermographed work are as follows: Business cards, up to $2\frac{5}{16}$ by $3\frac{15}{16}$, including the card stock and six lines of composition, approximately $4 per hundred; $6.50 for five hundred; changes in addresses or salesman's name, $1 per line.

Announcement cards, up to 4 by 5, including stock and up to 50 words of reading matter, approximately $11 per hundred; $25 per five hundred; $40 per thousand.

One firm specializing in thermography is the Everlast Process Printing Co., 27 W. 24 St., New York 10.

The Thermo-Fax machine.

**third-class mail**  See Appendix 4, Postal Information.

**three-color printing**  See PROCESS COLOR.

**thumb index**  Thumb-indexing, step-indexing, and tabbing are operations usually handled directly or on subcontract by the binder doing the rest of the work. Three firms that specialize in indexing are: G. J. Aigner Co., 426 S. Clinton St., Chicago 7; Robert Burlen & Son, 301 Congress St., Boston; and C. E. Finck Indexing Corp., 157 Hudson St., New York.

In thumb-indexing, markers are first placed in the books to locate the places to cut, then the thumb grooves are clipped out, and finally, half-round labels are pasted into place. Cost is proportional to the number of cuts.

In a typical step-indexing operation, all but the top inch of the right margin of the first section is cut away for ¼ inch, all but the top two inches of the second section, all but the top three inches of the third section, etc. The index headings can be printed along with the rest of the text, or may be added by means of a pasted label. Sometimes (and especially in mechanical bindings) the stepped index pages are made separately on heavier paper and inserted.

Tabbing means to paste tabs to the edges of pages without cutting or shaping the pages.

Edge-indexing is a method of indexing that requires no additional steps beyond normal printing and binding. (See EDGE INDEX.)

**tickets**  The complicated problems of numbering and dating theater tickets, and of running part of them on stock of one color and part on another, make ticket printing something that the specialist can do far cheaper than the job printer.

Unlike the product of the ordinary printing press, which reproduces any given number of exact copies of the original, a ticket press is designed to accomplish exactly the opposite, depending upon the specific use. This type of press makes each copy in a run of 1 or 10 million different from the first to the last by the inclusion of consecutive numbers. For other uses, the numbering may be repeated in duplicate, in series of 5's, etc.

Admission tickets for the motion-picture industry are printed in rolls of 2,000 or fan-folded for issuance through ticket registers, with a different color for each admission price. Reserved-seat tickets for stage shows and sporting events must show section, row, and seat numbers in accordance with individual house seating arrangement.

Admission tickets of every description must be especially printed to show the name and location of the establishment, established price, Federal tax, and total. Because of Federal tax regulations, tickets not so printed and with a face value of more than 50 cents are invalid.

Imprinted tickets (size 1 by 2 in.) can be had for as little as $15 for the first 10,000, and 22 cents per 1,000 for additional thousands of the same kind or color ordered at the same time.

Among the prominent ticket printers of the country, specializing in cash-control systems through numbering are the Globe Ticket Company, 112 N. 12 St., Philadelphia 7, with branches in New York, Boston, Atlanta, Dallas, Los Angeles, and Tacoma, Wash.; and Weldon, Williams & Lick, Fort Smith, Ark.

**time requirements**  See DELIVERY; SCHEDULING.

**tint**  See SHADING TINTS. For its relation to color, see COLOR.

**tint blocks**  Cuts used to print panels of plain color; or the printed panels themselves. Such panels are often used as a background for type or cuts. Small paragraphs of featured material are emphasized by printing them on a tint block.

Tint blocks are made like cuts, except that, for solid tints, no etching is required. Simple, solid shapes can be sawed, routed, or chiseled out of zinc, copper, rubber, or linoleum. If, however, the tint block is to have an overall screen, it must be prepared like a halftone, or like a Ben Day cut. (See SHADING TINTS.) A gray tint can be put behind black type or line drawings so as to print along with it, by any of the shading-tint techniques.

It is often more effective to add a spot of color to a page by using a tint block, than by running a line of display type in color. Type often looks weaker instead of stronger when run in color.

When a job contains process color work and is thus running in black, yellow, blue, and red, the editor may have an opportunity to use one or more of these colors "flat" on pages of the same forms. (See PROCESS COLOR.) None of the process colors looks well when used for printing display type. However, a tint block can be used to put a panel of solid yellow behind some item to be emphasized, and the result will be effective. Panels of blue look best if screened, using perhaps a 30 per cent tint instead of the solid color. The red used in process color work is a sort of magenta and does not usually look well either solid or reduced to a tint. It does, however, look well when black is added to it as, for example, when a rather dark line or scratchboard drawing is printed over a panel of solid red, or when a light tint of yellow is combined with it, to change it toward the vermilion.

**tip-ins** See also INSERTS.

Halftone illustrations on coated paper or other inserts are often tipped in or inserted at the proper place in books printed on rough paper. The leaf to be tipped in is first given a narrow coating of paste along its inner edge.

A tip-in is not so strong as a wrap. (See WRAP and the illustration under BINDING.)

**tone** See COLOR.

**Tone-Line Process** The Kodak Tone-Line Process is a method of converting a continuous-tone image to a line drawing by photographic operations. The result is similar to a pen-and-ink drawing and can sometimes be used without additional art work. In other cases, a Tone-Line rendering used as a base for further art work may save much time. It should be said that not all subjects give good results by this method.

In essence, the Kodak Tone-Line Process involves making a film positive from the original film negative, binding them back to back in perfect register, and making a print from the combination. The trick lies in slowly revolving the printing frame during the exposure under light coming from about a 45-degree angle. A little light leaks around the boundaries of images and creates a line image. Detailed instructions may be obtained on request to the Eastman Kodak Company, Rochester, N.Y.

**tr.** Abbreviation for transpose. (See proofreader's marks under PROOFREADING.)

**trade-marks** See also COPYRIGHT.

Any word, name, symbol, or device, or any combination thereof, adopted and used by a manufacturer or merchant to identify his goods and distinguish them from goods manufactured or sold by others.

Titles of periodical publications and titles of newspaper or magazine columns can be registered under the Federal trade-mark law.

The right to the exclusive use of a

particular trade-mark grows out of its use, not its mere adoption or registration. Common law recognizes the right to adopt and use a trade-mark for the purpose of distinguishing the goods or property made or sold by the person whose mark it is, to the exclusion of the use of that symbol by all other persons on the same type of goods.

Federal registration of a trade-mark is a way of proving when use of that mark began, and also of ascertaining whether the proposed trade-mark is thought to be defensible in the Federal courts. A trade-mark must have been used before it can be registered. Federal registration of trade-marks is handled by the Commissioner of Patents, Washington, D.C., who will supply a pamphlet on the subject free on request. Registration lasts 20 years and is renewable. The fee for registration of a trade-mark is $25.

State registration is helpful only where state laws provide more stringent local protection, where they deny common-law protection in the absence of local registration, or where the goods are sold in intrastate commerce.

A trade-mark that has been registered in the U.S. Patent Office should be used in conjunction with the phrase "Reg. U.S. Pat. Off." (By a recent change in the law, this phrase may be abbreviated to Ⓡ.)

**Trans-Adhesive Impressions** Name used by Monsen Typographers, 22 E. Illinois St., Chicago 11, for their proofs of type or art work made on self-adhering transparent acetate. Such proofs are much used in map work, and for making comprehensive visuals of all kinds such as labels, packages and layouts.

**transcriptions** See RECORDINGS.

**transfer printing** See DECALCOMANIAS.

**transfer process** See PHOTOCOPYING.

**transparencies** Pictures on transparent film that must be viewed by looking through them toward a light. It is relatively easy to produce color photographs of high quality by the Kodachrome, Anscocolor, and Ektachrome processes, but the result is a transparency. Color prints on paper can be made from transparencies. (See COLOR PHOTOGRAPHY.) Printing plates can also be made direct from transparencies.

**transportation advertising** See also POSTERS; OUTDOOR ADVERTISING.

The term "transportation advertising" is used to refer to car cards which are placed in the interior of street cars, busses, subways, and suburban trains; traveling displays which are placed on the outside of similar cars and busses; and station posters found in train and bus stations. All three constitute a flexible means of putting a message before commuters and shoppers in specified areas.

*Car cards* for local use are frequently printed by the silk-screen process in small quantities. National advertisers, needing larger quantities, tend to use the offset process. (See SILK SCREEN and OFFSET.)

In cities where much advertising is done by car cards, there are usually several firms which specialize in their production by the silk-screen process and which are in a position to give designing and lettering service as well as printing service to their customers.

The most popular size for car cards is 11 by 28 in. Other standard sizes include 11 by 14, 11 by 21, 11 by 42, 11 by 56, and 11 by 84 in. Car-card stock comes in 22½ by 42, or 23 by 43. At least ¾ in. must be allowed on either side for steel springs that hold the cards in place.

Transit systems that display car cards can provide the name of the agency through which such space can be purchased. Information about national coverage may be obtained from the National Association of Transportation Advertising, Inc., 30 Rockefeller Plaza, New York.

Most transit companies will design and produce car cards for advertisers, or supply stock designs ready for imprint.

Car-card advertising space is sold on the basis of a "full run," a "half run," or a "quarter run." A "full run" includes one card in every vehicle. Space rates are quoted on a monthly basis. Minimum rates are offered for 12 consecutive months. Shorter periods are slightly higher.

*Traveling displays* are placed on the outside of street cars and busses and are available in every major city with the exception of New York. Major standardization of size has been achieved in the following dimensions: 21 by 27, 21 by 36, and 21 by 44 in., the sizes most frequently found on the sides of vehicles. The most popular front and rear sizes are 11 by 42, and 7½ by 60, respectively.

Most traveling displays are produced by silk screen on waterproof stock.

*Station posters* are often used in the subway and train stations in New York, Chicago, Boston, and Philadelphia. Standard sizes are: "one sheet," 46 by 30 in. wide; "two sheet," 46 by 60 in. wide; and "three sheet," 84 by 42 in. wide. Offset is the most popular reproduction process for such posters.

**traveling displays**  See TRANSPORTATION ADVERTISING.

**trim**  An untrimmed book or pamphlet cannot be read until the pages have been cut open. Trimming opens the folds. Usually about ⅛ in. is taken off during this operation. A pamphlet that is 6¼ by 9½ before trim becomes 6⅛ by 9¼ after trim.

If any illustrations bleed (see BLEED), it is desirable to allow for a trim of ⅛

to ¼ in. (See illustrations under BINDING and BOOKBINDING.)

**trimetal plates**  See BIMETAL PLATES.

**trucking**  See also SHIPPING INFORMATION.

For hauls under 1,000 miles and weights of at least 300 lb., shipping by truck (motor express) may prove faster and easier than railway express or freight.

Trucking rates are slightly higher than freight rates but less expensive than express. As with freight, the minimum charge by truck is for 100 lb. Free insurance is included with the regular rate.

Shipping by truck means door-to-door delivery between any points that a truck can reach; freight and express may go only where there is a railroad station.

Most trucking lines operate within a certain limited area, as between New York, Pittsburgh, and Richmond, Va. However, a company may contract for shipments beyond its limits by subcontracting to another line. For companies in a certain area see Express and Transfer in the Classified Telephone Directory.

Invaluable help in locating motor-freight rates and routings can be found through the use of *Leonard's Guide and Service* and the five motor-freight directories (New York, Philadelphia, Chicago, Boston, and New England) published by the same firm and described in detail under SHIPPING INFORMATION.

**type**  See also Appendix 1, Type Faces; TYPE MEASUREMENTS; LINOTYPE; MONOTYPE; LUDLOW.

Gutenberg did not invent printing. For centuries the Chinese had been printing from wood blocks—one block carved for each page. Gutenberg's contribution was the invention of printing *from movable type.* He invented type-setting. His methods are still used, almost unchanged. Setting type is the first step in every printing job unless the work is to be hand-lettered or type-written. Type is set or "composed" by men called "compositors" who work in "composing rooms." The customer gets a bill for "type composition."

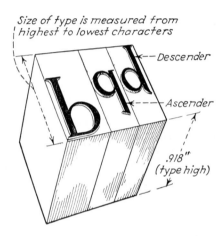

*Size of type is measured from highest to lowest characters*

Type was formerly set by hand, a letter at a time, in even the smallest sizes. It is still set by hand in much display and headline work and on very small jobs. Most type is now set by machine.

Handwork is still the basis of good typography, since the spacing of headlines and captions and the making of corrections still call for a lot of handwork.

Until recently almost all type composition started with metal type even if this metal type would be used only to make one inked proof to be photographed on film for use in offset, etc. Now there are several ways of going directly to film, including use of the Fotosetter, Photon, Monophoto, Linofilm, Coxhead-Liner, Hadego, etc. (See also COLD TYPE.) However, the traditional "hot metal" techniques, still most used, are worth learning first.

Note how 8-pt. type with short descenders may look as big as 10-pt. type with long descenders.

Everyone who orders type composition, or works on proofs, should have a mental picture of how the metal type is set and spaced. Otherwise, it is easy to ask for changes that are unnecessarily expensive.

Hand-set type is called "foundry type." Printers buy it from type foundries by the pound in standard assortments, and keep it in "type cases," which provide a compartment for every letter or character. (Printers who have Monotype equipment can cast their own foundry type, as needed.)

There are two big problems about foundry type: (1) it wears during printing and (2) it must be distributed after use, *i.e.,* put back in the case for re-use, unless the printer is willing and able to buy more and melt down any that is worn. It is difficult to get good work from type that is partly new and partly worn. Furthermore, distributing the type in the case after use is a time-consuming operation.

Therefore, the history of typesetting has been a continuous attempt to find economical ways to print every job from new type and to avoid the expense of distributing type after use. There are now many such ways.

1. The cost of new foundry type is higher than the cost of distributing type back in the case. Under certain circumstances, however, printers may absorb this extra expense and "throw in" foundry type after a single use.

Setting type by hand in a "stick." The size being set is 60-pt. Lydian Bold.

Specimens of hand type, showing how body must be large enough to accommodate both ascenders and descenders and how letters may be mortised for better fit.

After being set, type is stored in galleys like this one. The printer puts a number on each galley proof to tell him in which galley tray that type is to be found.

## Basic Methods of Lettering and Type Composition

| Direct hand preparation of printing surface | ART WORK for photographic transfer to printing surface | TYPEWRITER, VARITYPER | Hand-set TYPE | LUDLOW, APL | LINOTYPE, INTERTYPE | MONOTYPE |
|---|---|---|---|---|---|---|
| WOOD CUT | LETTERING by pen, brush, airbrush, or crayon | Ordinary TYPE-WRITING for offset and other reproduction | Also called foundry type | Instead of setting the type itself, molds or matrices are set. Then a solid line of lead type is cast from the line of matrices. Most used for display sizes | Keyboard action assembles matrices ready for casting solid lead lines of type. This is the most widely used method of setting type for newspapers, magazines, books, and job work | Keyboard action to control a machine that casts each letter singly. Does same work as Linotype and Intertype but offers greater flexibility on some kinds of work |
| LINOLEUM BLOCK | PHOTO LETTERING | Use of carbon-paper ribbon | Some hard-to-replace kinds of display type may be used only to make proofs or DUPLICATE PLATES, to prevent wear of the type itself | | | |
| Copper and steel ENGRAVING | | Typing on MIMEO-GRAPH stencils, SPIRIT DUPLICAT-ING masters, MUL-TILITH masters, EL-LIOTT ADDRESS-ING stencils | | | | |
| Grease pencil on lithograph plate | GRAPHOTYPE preparation of Addressograph and Dupligraph plates | | | | | |
| Stylus or lettering guide on MIMEO-GRAPH stencil or SPIRIT DUPLICAT-ING master | | | | | | |
| Brush or knife on SILK SCREEN | | | | | | |
| RETOUCHING on photo negative | | | | | | |

*Note: Further information may be found by looking up the words set in CAPS.*

When they prefer not to, or when they cannot do so, as with the rarer display faces, they may refuse to print from foundry type and may limit its use to the making of stereotypes or electrotypes or the pulling of proofs for reproduction. (See STEREOTYPES; ELECTRO.)

2. Text, especially headlines, can be set, using matrices (molds) instead of type. A completed line of matrices is then put into a casting machine, melted lead is forced against the matrices, and the result is a line of brand new type in the form of a solid lead slug. (See LUDLOW.)

Characters are sometimes mortised for better fit in headlines.

3. The smaller sizes of type, up to 14 pt., or even larger, can be handled as above. However, the same work on the Linotype or Intertype is much faster. (See LINOTYPE; INTERTYPE.) These machines also assemble matrices and force melted lead against them to produce lines of new type in the form of solid lead slugs. However, they do it automatically by keyboard action, and the matrices are automatically put back in their proper places, after use. All composing rooms of any size either have one or more of these machines, or else have Monotype equipment as described below.

4. The Monotype (see MONOTYPE) also casts lines of new type, but it casts them letter by letter instead of a full line at a time. It can also cast up type for hand composition or corrections. The Monotype is a little more flexible than the Linotype. On simple matter, it may be a little more expensive; on complicated matter, tabular matter, etc., it may be noticeably cheaper.

Many printers do not attempt to do their own type composition. They send their work out to "trade" composition houses or "advertising typographers" who do nothing but typesetting. These houses serve many printers and advertisers, and offer a greater variety of type faces than the average printer could possibly afford to buy for himself.

Big advertisers usually have their ads set by composition houses, and supply reproduction proofs, stereos, or electros to the magazines or newspapers. (See REPRODUCTION PROOFS; STEREOTYPES; ELECTRO.)

In selecting type faces, it is best to ask the printer what faces he has available and choose from among these, if possible. Delays may otherwise result if he must send out for type or wait until his composing room has finished using a particular type face on some other customer's job. On the other hand, printers who say they do not have the type face requested mean that they do not personally own it. Often they can send out and get it, if urged, and if the customer is willing to O.K. the expense or delay involved.

A page of good composition should show: (1) no worn letters, (2) no broken letters, (3) optically pleasing spacing between all elements, (4) correct grouping of elements—no widows (see WIDOW) and no subheads separated from the matter to which they refer, (5) even "color" and word spacing.

For further information on the subject of typography, type selection, and layout, consult the books listed in Appendix 2.

Inking type on a proof press, in order to pull a galley proof.

The same photo as at left, after retouching to sharpen the details.

Pulling a galley proof. The impression roller has just pressed the paper against the inked type.

A form of type and cuts locked up in a "chase" ready for printing, showing use of quoins (wedges) and furniture.

# CAPS, lower case *Italic,* p.d.q.

*Spacing type*

These lines of 24-point Caslon have been set with type-high spaces and leads to show how spacing is done. One lead (2 points thick) was inserted between each two lines.

The paragraphs are indented one em. Between words is the normal "3-em space" (3 to the em). Additional spaces were used as necessary to make the lines come out even.

Some 1½-em and 2-em "quads" were used at the ends of paragraphs. Here is some l e t t e r - s p a c i n g.

type faces For detailed information about the selection and use of type faces and for specimens of text type and display type, consult Appendix 1, Type Faces.

type-high The height of type is 0.918 in. Cuts, stereotypes, and electrotypes to be printed alongside actual type must be ordered blocked on wood or metal so that they are type-high.

Electros and stereos are often left unblocked when no type is to be used with them. In this case, their metal backing is made to a thickness suitable for clamping to a "patent base." Cuts that are to be used only for the making of duplicate plates are left unblocked.

type measurements See also PICA; POINT.

Printers measure type by "points." One point is 0.01384 in., and 72 points are almost exactly 1 in. Actually, 12 ×

72 points fall 4 points short of equaling 12 in.

Points are used in measuring type sizes and leads. These lines are set in 9-pt. type. The "pica," equal to 12 points, is used in measuring the length of type lines, the width of margins, the depth of columns, etc. These lines are 13 picas wide. (See illustrations.)

An em is another kind of measurement, being the square of the height of the body of any type size. Thus, a 1-em dash (—) in 9-pt. type is 9 pt. long. In 12-pt. type it would be 12 pt. long. These paragraphs are indented 1 em. An en is half an em.

typewriter The typewriter is more than a device for overcoming illegible handwriting. It is not only the universal method of writing business letters and other communications but also the preferred method of "type composition" for material to be produced on

## TYPE MEASUREMENTS

One inch = six picas = 72 points.

☐ 8 pt em        12 pt em ☐        24 pt em ☐

One em can be any size. One em is a space as wide as it is high. Thus one em in 12-pt. type is 12 pt. high and 12 pt. wide.

| Hair | 5-em | 4-em | 3-em | en | em | 2-em | 3-em |

Spaces for 12 pt        Quads for 12 pt

Spacing between words and letters is done with "spaces" and "quads."

the spirit duplicator, mimeograph, or Multilith. In the offset field, it is a stiff competitor of Linotype and Monotype.

A typewritten communication that has been well designed can be just as legible and effective as one set in type, and much less expensive.

For these reasons, the capabilities and special attributes of the typewriter as a composing machine deserve study by everyone whose work involves the use of the printed or duplicated word. (See COLD TYPE.) For a discussion of how a typewriter is helpful in making word counts and character counts, see COPY FITTING.

The ordinary typewriter writes six single-spaced lines to the inch, three double-spaced lines. If it has pica type, it writes 10 characters or spaces to the inch. If it has elite type, it writes 12 characters or spaces to the inch. Typewriter type looks different from book type because every letter, whether an "i" or a capital "W," must be of the same width, namely 1/10 or 1/12 in. In book type, each letter gets as much or as little space as it needs.

The ordinary typewriter prints through an inked ribbon. There are black ribbons and colored ribbons, heavily inked ribbons and lightly inked ones, cotton ribbons and silk ones, and special ribbons for hectograph, Multilith, decalcomania, and other work.

Ribbons tend to thicken the letters. Cleaner, crisper impressions for photographic reproduction are possible through the use of a carbon-paper ribbon. Machines not equipped to use a carbon ribbon can produce the same kind of work if the typing is done without a ribbon (*i.e.*, with the ribbon control lever in the non-print position) directly on the back of a piece of carbon paper. This cuts the carbon paper to pieces but produces a clean impression on the paper beneath. This procedure is used frequently in preparing copy for offset. (See OFFSET.)

Typewritten lines are ordinarily left unjustified; *i.e.*, they vary in length, producing a ragged right-hand margin. They are not justified to make them all of the same length, as in a book. They can, however, be justified either on an ordinary machine in a somewhat crude fashion or semimechanically by using a special margin justifier attachment. Both methods require a second typing.

Suppose it is decided to produce a news bulletin having two typewritten columns, each 36 characters wide. To justify the lines by hand, the copy is typed once so that no line exceeds 36 characters; many lines will be shorter. Then it is retyped, and in a line that is, say, 33 characters long, two spaces instead of one are skipped after each of the first three words, thus filling the line.

With a special margin justifier, the second typing is easier and quicker since each line may be condensed or extended automatically as much as four characters to make it equal to its neighbors. The operator simply notes the

| 1-pt. lead |
| 2-pt. lead |
| 3-pt. lead |
| 6-pt. slug |
| 12-pt. slug |

Spacing between lines is done with "leads" and "slugs." A lead is understood to be a 2-pt. lead unless stated to be 1-pt. or 3-pt. Leads and slugs do not print; they merely space. Rules print.

margin variation of each line on the first typing. On the second typing he sets the justifier for the variation of each line as he comes to it, and the machine does the rest.

An Edison margin justifier or "Marginator" may be installed on any standard typewriter for about $100. It does not in any way interfere with the normal operation of a typewriter.

The ordinary typewriter offers more variety than is generally made use of. Headings or words to be emphasized can be put in caps, or in underlined caps, or in underlined lower case. Headings can be centered, cut in, or put flush left. Text can be single-spaced, double-spaced, triple-spaced, indented, boxed, underlined, etc. Long paragraphs can be broken up into short ones. Certain kinds of information can, to good effect, be taken out of sentence form and put into tabular form.

Short paragraphs (no more than 5 lines). extra space between paragraphs, generous margins, and frequent subheads all help a message to look readable and to get read.

There are some specialized typewriters on the market for specialized jobs. (See VARITYPER; IBM EXECUTIVE TYPEWRITER; ELECTRIC TYPEWRITER; AUTOMATIC ELECTRIC TYPEWRITER.)

Some of these have built-in justifying devices, notably the Varityper, and the IBM Executive (proportional spacing) Typewriter.

Of these, the Varityper mechanism (offered on only the more expensive machines) is the most automatic. The operator types a line, strikes a tab key, the carriage moves into position for typing a second column, and then the operator simply re-types the line. This time it's automatically justified.

The IBM method (applicable also on nonautomatic Varitypers) works as follows. The operator types a line and then hits the space bar to fill out the line with blank spaces. She counts the units of space thus required, and notes the total in the margin.

When a rough draft has been completed, it is marked to show where to put the extra space during the retyping. The spacing can be very even, since the unit of space on the IBM is only half the width of an "i."

The Justowriter uses two IBM machines—the first punches a tape, the second runs from the tape and justifies the lines automatically—price about $4,750 per pair.

**Typograph**  See LUDLOW.

**typography**  See DESIGN; LAYOUT; Appendix 1, Type Faces.

**Typro**  A photo-lettering machine for use in office or art department which permits rapid, low-cost composition of display headlines. The operator winds the master film reels in the font magazine to the desired font, then turns the selector handle until the desired letter appears in the viewing window. Each selected letter is automatically printed down on a strip of photographic paper. There is provision for selective letter-spacing, centering, multiline composition, surprinting, mixing of fonts, and use of shading tints.

Fonts are available in many type styles and in sizes from 6 pt. to 144 pt. and cost about $20 each. From 10 to 15 fonts can be housed in a single font magazine, and the change from one magazine to another is quick and easy. Development of the exposed strips is automatic and immediate, and takes place in the machine. The Typro is made by the Halber Corp., 4151 Montrose Ave., Chicago 41, Ill., and costs, complete with basic equipment, about $650, fonts extra. Similar machines are the Coxhead-Liner and Filmotype, described under those headings.

# U | u

**u. & l.c.** Abbreviation for upper and lower case. (See proofreader's marks under PROOFREADING.)

**undelivered mail** See Appendix 4, Postal Information.

**union label** The printing industry is largely unionized. Particularly is this true of the larger and older plants doing quality work. Printed matter produced under union conditions may, at the option of the buyer, carry the union label.

The union label is always used on political campaign literature as a matter of practical politics. Many other printing buyers require that it appear on their literature in recognition of the fact that about one-quarter of the income receivers of the country are union members, and that they and their families and other supporters of the union movement are likely to be favorably influenced by seeing the union label.

The label, which reads

ALLIED PRINTING

TRADES UNION LABEL COUNCIL NO. 000

Name of City

signifies that the printed matter on which it appears has been produced in unionized plants by A.F. of L. union compositors, pressmen, photoengravers, stereotypers, electrotypers, and binders. The number identifies the actual firm that did the printing. In cities where there is no Allied Printing Trades Council, the labels of the separate unions of compositors, pressmen, engravers, electrotypers, stereotypers, and binders may be used.

The Amalgamated Lithographers of America have their own label which reads as shown below:

Photoengravers have a union label of their own, which they will engrave in the corner of any cut on request. Because union printers are not allowed to use nonunion cuts, the regular union label of the Allied Printing Trades

Council implies the use of cuts made by members of the International Photo Engravers Union, with or without the I.P.E.U. label on the face of the cut.

## PHOTO-ENGRAVERS' LABEL

**upper case** The printer's term for capital letters. Hand type always used to be kept in twin drawers or "cases," the upper one containing the capital letters and the lower one, the small letters. "U. & l.c." means set in upper and lower case. Another way of saying the same thing is "c. & l.c.," meaning caps and lower case. (See illustration under CASE.)

# V | v

**vandyke**  See also BLUEPRINTS.

Simply a brown blueprint. Offset printers sometimes make a vandyke print from their negatives, to enable the customer to catch any mistakes (*e.g.,* misplaced captions) before the printing plates are made. Vandykes are used primarily as master prints from which to make more blueprints.

**Varityper**  See also TYPEWRITER.

The following entry was composed on the Varityper and then made into a zinc line cut which could be printed alongside the regular type.

The *Vari-Typer* is a specialized typewriter which offers a variety of type styles. The operator can change easily and quickly from *italic styles,* EXTRA SMALL EXTRA LARGE, **EXTRA BOLD**, etc. The *Vari-Typer* is really an office composing machine. It is used effectively to cut mimeograph stencils, and to prepare paper and metal masters and plates for hectograph, spirit duplicator, and office litho duplication. Copy for photo-off-

set reproduction can be prepared on it. It uses a special carbon-paper ribbon giving cleaner, sharper letters than are obtainable with a fabric ribbon.

The standard *Vari-Typer* offers faces that are very similar to book types, but it cannot duplicate them exactly, since the machine can give the '*W*' no more room than the '*i.*' These paragraphs were done on the *Vari-Typer*. The new Model D.S.J. *Vari-Typer* can give wide letters three times as much space as narrow letters.

*The following paragraphs are set on the DSJ.*

Varityping is much used in offset work where economy is of first importance. It is much cheaper for an offset printer to have a manuscript Varityped than to have it set up by Linotype or Monotype and then to have proofs pulled from the lead type.

Varityper work can be "justified" so as to have an even right-hand margin. This requires two typings:

329

the first to find out how much too long or too short each line is, and the second to shorten or lengthen the lines accordingly. This paragraph has been left unjustified.

The Varityper is manufactured by the Ralph C. Coxhead Corporation, 720 Frelinghuysen Ave., Newark 5, New Jersey. Models range in price from about $480 to $750, with extra fonts costing $27.50. The Model DSJ costs from $1795 to $2320.

**varnishing** Any printed job will have more eye appeal if it is spirit-varnished, or laminated with plastic sheeting. Book jackets are often given a glossy finish in one of these ways.

Quick-drying varnish (or lacquer) can be flowed on over the whole surface of a printed job; or it can be applied like ink to any given area.

For varnishing an average book jacket, one printer charges $8 for the first thousand and $5 for each additional thousand. Another charges about $62 per thousand for a 72 by 68 sheet. The thicker the paper or cardboard, the higher the cost.

Even when varnish is flowed on, parallel strips can be left unvarnished if they run from edge to edge. This is often done on can labels and box wraps to leave unvarnished the areas that will later take glue.

Plastic sheeting can be made to adhere to paper through a laminating process costing three or four times as much as varnish but giving a still more luxurious and durable finish.

As contrasted to the varnishing (or lacquering) which is done on special sheet-coating machines, any letterpress printer can do varnishing work, with varnish in place of ink on a regular press and with rubber plates to apply it. This is called "spot varnishing."

The following companies handle a good deal of varnishing and laminat-

ing: John W. Crawford Co., 160 Varick St., New York 13; Greggory, Inc., 2929 S. Wabash Ave., Chicago 16; and Arvey Corp., 3462 N. Kimball Ave., Chicago, Ill.

**vellum** See PARCHMENT.

**Velox** The trade name of a sensitized photographic printing paper, but the word has come to be used to describe a special process used for reducing the cost of halftone engravings. The process is much used in newspaper advertising work.

In an ordinary square halftone, there are very faint dots even in the "white" areas. If an engraver is asked to make a "highlight" halftone, he paints out these faint dots before etching, and they appear pure white. This operation does not always improve ordinary photographs, but it can greatly improve the quality of reproduction of pencil and crayon drawings, wash drawings, etc. However, a highlight halftone costs three times as much as an ordinary halftone, and a combination (line and halftone) highlight halftone costs still more.

By the Velox process, these costs can be greatly reduced. The original art work is converted into a duplicate photographic print which is screened, and highlighted. The print can be retouched as desired. Near blacks can be painted solid black. Ruling and other line work can be added. Type can be surprinted on the print or type proofs on acetate can later be laid over the print.

The finished Velox print can then be made into a halftone engraving at regular Ben Day line-cut rates. Very often the cost of a cut made in this way (including the cost of the Velox print) is less than half what the cost would be if the whole job had been done by a photoengraver.

For best results, the screen of the drawings when printed should be no finer than 85 because it is difficult for the camera to "hold" the dots of a finer screen. It is necessary, therefore, to tell the firm that makes the Veloxes, the size in which they will be reproduced and the desired screen.

**Verifax**   See PHOTOCOPYING.

**verso**   A right-hand page in a book is called a "recto," and the back of it, *i.e.,* a left-hand page, is a "verso."

**vignette**   To vignette a halftone illustration means to make it fade softly into the whiteness of the paper with no sharp edge. Vignetting used to be done much more than it is today, especially with portraits. Vignetting costs extra. It tends to be a little more successful in offset, photogelatin, or gravure than in letterpress. Vignetted letterpress halftones often show a definite edge when printed, no matter how hard the engraver and the pressman try to avoid this.

**vinylite**   A plastic that is coming into increasing use as a substitute for wax in the electrotype process (see ELECTROTYPE), as an unbreakable substitute for shellac in phonograph records and as the essential ingredient of plastic printing plates.

# W | w

**wash drawing**  See also DRAWING TECHNIQUES.

A wash drawing is made with a brush and water color. If it is a black-and-white wash drawing, it is made with black water color, diluted to obtain the various grays. Since a wash drawing contains grays that are neither white nor black, it must be reproduced as a halftone; it cannot be reproduced as a line drawing. (See HALFTONE; LINE DRAWING.)

**watermark**  Paper that reveals lettering or a design when held up to the light is said to have been watermarked. Watermarking is not necessarily an indication of high quality.

**waterproof paper**  See WET-STRENGTH PAPER.

**wax engraving**  A process for preparing letterpress printing plates. The process is like electrotyping except that the wax mold is prepared by hand instead of, or in addition to, being molded from type and cuts. (See ELECTRO.) The process lends itself especially

to the production of finely detailed maps, ruled forms, instrument dials, etc.

A copper plate is given a thin coating of black wax. The wax engraver, who must be something of a draftsman, then rules lines with instruments that remove the wax and reveal the bare copper, adds other details in the same way, and puts in the lettering by pressing printing type into and through the wax to the copper base.

The wax engraver works with the aid of a precision engraving machine that helps him place his lines and lettering with micrometric exactness. He can produce finished work from a rough sketch, or, if he has a more exact sketch to go by, he can begin by having this sketch photographically transferred to the surface of the wax.

When the wax plate is finished, it is handled exactly like an electrotype mold: copper is deposited on it electrolytically; this copper shell is then peeled off the wax, backed up with lead, and made ready for printing.

The wax-engraving technique is also used to "retouch" wax molds taken from type and cuts. By retouching "in

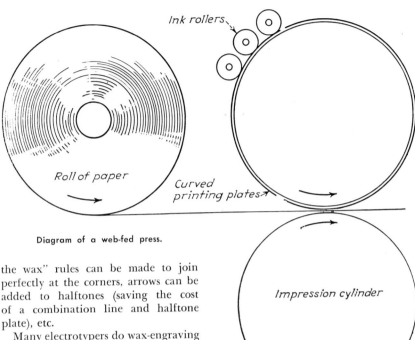

Ink rollers

Roll of paper

Curved printing plates

Impression cylinder

Diagram of a web-fed press.

the wax" rules can be made to join perfectly at the corners, arrows can be added to halftones (saving the cost of a combination line and halftone plate), etc.

Many electrotypers do wax-engraving work. There are also firms which specialize in the process and which may be found under Wax Engraving in the Classified Directories.

**web, web-fed press** Paper pulp is converted into a web of paper as it moves through a papermaking machine. Sometimes this web of paper is cut into sheets; sometimes it is not cut but put on rolls. Printing presses designed to accept paper from a roll instead of in separate sheets are known as "web-fed" presses. Newspapers are printed on web-fed rotary presses. (See ROTARY PRESS.)

**Weber Addressing Machine** A low-cost addressing machine operating on the spirit duplicator principle and very similar to the Master Addresser, (see MASTER ADDRESSER). Advantages claimed for the Weber machine include automatic ejection of addressed pieces, face up. For information write the

Weber Addressing Machine Co., Mt. Prospect, Ill.

**wet-strength paper** Paper is obtainable that does not lose its strength when wet. Such paper is known as "wet-strength" paper. It is indistinguishable from ordinary paper when dry.

Wet-strength paper is not waterproof. Water will pass through it but will not weaken it. In fact wet-strength filter papers have come into wide use in tea bags, coffee filters, etc.

Waterproof paper which will not permit water to penetrate it is also obtainable for special uses.

**w.f.** Abbreviation for wrong font. (See proofreader's marks under PROOFREADING; FONT.)

**whiteprint** See also BLUEPRINT.
The whiteprint or *diazo* process employed in Ozalid and Bruning equipment is an improved blueprint process. As in blueprinting, it makes same-size copies of translucent originals. Unlike blueprinting, it makes a positive from a positive, makes copies that do not stretch or shrink in the developing since they are dry-developed, and can make copies in black, blue, or red at will.

The cost per letter-size copy is as little as 5 cents commercially, 2 cents where a company operates its own equipment.

Simply by changing from one kind of sensitized material to another, prints can be made on white paper, transparent paper, clear film, frosted film, tracing cloth, opaque cloth or film, both sides of the same paper, etc. The process gives excellent reproduction of photographs in sepia, black, or two-tone sepia-blue, although to duplicate a photograph it is necessary first to make a positive print on film instead of on the usual paper.

Whiteprint equipment is being widely installed by blueprint services, and by firms that have a lot of copying work. The smallest Ozalid machine costs about $400 and can make copies up to 9 in. wide and any length at speeds up to 10 ft. a minute.

The whiteprint process is based on the use of light-sensitive dyes that are destroyed when exposed to strong light, *unless first made permanent by exposure to ammonia fumes.* When the sensitized paper is exposed to strong light through a master tracing, the dye is destroyed except where protected by the opaque lines of the original. The image is then made permanent by passing through a machine that exposes it to ammonia fumes.

For a comparison of whiteprint and other printing processes, see the charts inside the covers of this book.

Further information about the white-print process may be obtained from the Ozalid Division of General Aniline and Film Corp., Johnson City, N.Y., or from the Charles Bruning Co., 100 Read St., New York City. For a method of making small offset plates by the whiteprint process, see OZALITH.

**widow** When a column or page begins with the short last line of a paragraph carried over from the previous column or page, this short line is called a "widow." The meticulous make-up man, proofreader, or editor will always cut, expand, or adjust the text to avoid widows. In books, they can often be eliminated by making a pair of facing pages one line longer or shorter than the rest of the pages in the book.

**window displays** See DISPLAYS.

**window envelope** An envelope with a transparent panel in it through which the name and address typed on the enclosure can be read. It is usually cheaper to buy window envelopes than to pay for having a complete name and address typed on both the letter and the envelope. People have come to associate window envelopes with bills, and this militates against their widespread use in direct mail work. Envelopes can be ordered with the window in any desired position. (See also ENVELOPES.)

**Wing Mailer** See DICK STRIP.

**wire recording** See RECORDINGS.

**wire stitching** See STITCHING and illustration under BINDING.

**woodcut** See BLOCK PRINTING; WOOD ENGRAVINGS.

**wood engravings** Until the invention of the halftone, the wood engraving was the principal method of making illustrations for letterpress printing. Wood engravings were (and are) entirely engraved by hand into the surface of a type-high wooden block and printed, of course, the actual size in which they were engraved.

Wood engravers became highly skilled in rendering objects requiring fine shading and detail, and developed a style (see sample) that has never been surpassed for the reproduction of textures and details on almost any printing surface.

This process has therefore survived in competition with the halftone. More recently it has been imitated with scratchboard drawings, by which artists

The above illustration was printed from an electro made from a wood engraving.

attempt to duplicate the effective shadings and feeling of the genuine woodcut.

The Sander Engraving Co., Inc., of 542 S. Dearborn St., Chicago 5, is one of the leading firms of wood engravers, and calls attention to the following advantages of the process: (1) The work can be done directly from merchandise or unretouched photos. (2) For a single charge the customer gets both art work

and original printing plate. The art work is created directly on the printing plate, so that the purchaser has both a cut from which etch proofs and electrotypes can be made, and a number of etch proofs, each of which is, in a sense, original art work. (3) While wood engravings are made to the actual reproduction size, the etch proofs can be enlarged and reduced to meet many size requirements. (4) The single woodcut, in addition to showing textures and detail with a clarity not possible any other way, will print perfectly on any kind of paper, and by any printing process. (Woodcut etch proofs are excellent art work for offset printing.) (5) Because woodcut proofs are "line" art work, they frequently eliminate the costs of combination plates when used in newspaper or magazine ads. (6) They do away with problems of suiting screen to medium.

**wood pulp**  Most paper is made from wood pulp, either groundwood pulp or the more expensive but better chemical pulp. (See GROUNDWOOD PULP; CHEMICAL PULP.)

**work and turn**  By means of the work-and-turn technique, a printer can print 1,000 copies of a small pamphlet *on both sides* with only 1,000 impressions. He cuts his paper to double the size required for each pamphlet and runs the job as shown in the illustration. The phrase "work and tumble" is used when the pile is turned from front to back instead of from left to right. A job too big to run work and turn is run "sheetwise" in the ordinary way. (See illustration on page 336.)

**work-up**  Occasionally a space, quad, or lead that is not supposed to print works up to the height of the type, is inked, and prints. Work-ups are caused when parts of the form are not perfectly square. It is the pressman's job to catch and correct them when they occur.

**wove paper**  See LAID PAPER.

**wrap**  See also INSERTS.

A wrap in a book or magazine is an insert that has not been pasted in (tipped in) but has been wrapped around one of the signatures, so that it is stitched into the binding as securely as any other page.

In books printed on antique paper, illustrations on coated paper are often inserted as wraps or tip-ins. (See TIP-INS.) Wraps are stronger, but it is not so easy to get them opposite the desired page of text. (For an illustration, see INSERTS.)

**wrapping and packing**  See also SHIPPING INFORMATION.

Sooner or later everyone who works with words or who must meet deadlines and take responsibility for the movement of printed materials will need to know something about wrapping, packing, and shipping. In some organiza-

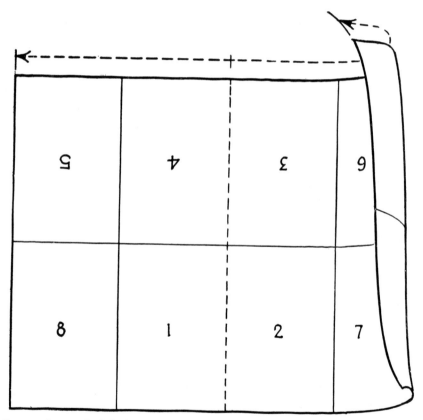

How an 8-page, 6 x 9 leaflet is printed "work and turn." When the pile is turned over as indicated, page 5 will print on the back of page 6, page 8 on the back of page 7, etc. After being printed on both sides, the sheet is cut along the dotted line, and each half folds to make one complete leaflet.

tions it is safe to leave such matters to the shipping room. In others it is not quite so safe to rely on the shipping-room people, especially if the problem at hand is out of their usual line. In any case, the man who makes plans and places orders involving wrapping and shipping owes it to his shipping-room people to consult them in advance, give them notice of his requirements, and see to it that they have on hand the necessary wrapping materials.

Besides, rare is the executive who does not occasionally have to put some rush proofs, art work, or samples into the mail after office closing.

When printing and mailing activities are not the main functions of a firm, it may be necessary for a department either to set up its own wrapping table, or to procure, place in the regular shipping room, and earmark for its own use the special materials that it will need.

For example, stiff cardboard, often in large sizes, is essential for protecting art work in transit. Cut sizes of cardboard and corrugated board are useful for protecting the contents of envelopes. Mailing tubes are indispensable for protecting posters and other flexible materials that must not be creased. Special rubber stamps or stickers may help packages get the best attention at the receiving end.

Careful packing must precede wrapping and shipping. The following reminders may prevent damage to materials:

1. Use adequate cardboard backing for photographs, art work, and copy to be reproduced photographically. Tape the art work to the cardboard backing to prevent its being damaged by slipping back and forth or extending beyond the cardboard.

2. Use ample packing within a box so that printed materials will not be damaged by slipping into the odd crannies. Wadded newspaper makes good packing material.

3. Small pieces, such as cards or pamphlets, will be less easily damaged from shuffling around if they are banded or packaged by the printer in lots of, say, 100. Having them in packages may facilitate distribution also.

Shipping containers will vary according to the product being shipped and whether or not the shipments are standardized. When many similar items are to be shipped, ready-to-use boxes will save time that would otherwise be wasted in cutting board to wrap each separately. Both folded and set-up boxes are available in different sizes and strengths.

If originally packed by the printer in corrugated boxes holding about 35 lb., material is ready for bulk mailing, can be moved easily by a shipping clerk, and is within the 40-lb. parcel-post weight limit. (For further information on size and weight limitations, see Appendix 4, Postal Information. See CONTAINER PRINTING for suggestions on printing boxes, tubes, etc.)

Outside wrapping may be unnecessary if the material is in a strong, well-marked package. In many cases, however, the outside wrapping is really the container and as such must be strong and durable. It should be legibly addressed and marked as to contents. (See Appendix 4 for postal requirements on sealing, labeling, and marking for postal inspection.)

Case packing is a science in itself. Let no man assume he can do it until he has taken some lessons from experienced hands. Two or three hundred pounds of printed materials in an up-ended packing case often crush the wadded newspapers that were supposed to wedge them snug, and then slide around and do themselves endless damage. The case packer must assume that any and every element in a case may have to bear the entire weight of all the other items.

The shipping and wrapping room of a firm or department should be located where it it convenient for the delivery of new stock and the shipment of outgoing materials. It should be large enough not only to permit efficient handling of big, rush jobs, but also to allow for storage of materials.

A large table, with space above or below for a roll of wrapping paper and corrugated paper, is a necessity. The following materials will help solve the average wrapping problems:

Gummed tape and dispenser.

Twine.

Scissors.

Mat knife for cutting string, cardboard, and corrugated paper.

Gummed labels, *e.g.,* "CONTENTS: BOOKS: May be opened for postal inspection if necessary."

Scales (the dial-reading kind is a great timesaver over the beam type). It is helpful to have a small scale for letters, and a larger one for packages.

Grease stick or felt-tipped pen, for addressing cartons and marking weight or postage required.

Rubber stamps, *e.g.,* "FIRST CLASS," "SPECIAL DELIVERY," "AIRMAIL."

Roll of brown kraft wrapping paper, with cutting blade.

Roll of single-faced corrugated paper. (The standard width is 36 in. but suppliers will slit this, on request, into 10-, 12-, and 14-in. rolls.)

Yardstick and 100-in. tape measure, for checking size limits for parcel post and air express.

Kraft envelopes.

Newspapers for wadding.

Mailing tubes.

Cardboard and double-corrugated backing sheets.

Boxes, set up or knocked down.

U.S. mail bag for bulk shipments. (See Appendix 4.)

Stamps, precanceled stamps, stamped envelopes, or postage meter.

NOTE: Shipping rooms can be a fire hazard unless neatness and care prevail.

Shipping information should be readily available in the simplest and handiest form. One small office found that it was helpful to post such information on a special bulletin board where every part-time helper could get the facts easily.

Since wrapping and packing are influenced by the method of shipping, every shipping clerk (whether a full-time expert, a well-meaning volunteer, or the boss racing for a printer's midnight deadline) should know (1) how best to ship the material and (2) how to wrap it for such shipping.

Helps in answering these questions may be given through posting the following:

1. Location of the nearest post office, hours for postal service, time of outgoing airmail, etc.

2. Sample rate chart showing comparative costs of shipping by parcel post, express, and freight. (See SHIPPING INFORMATION.)

3. Postage rates, and weight limits for first-, second-, and third-class mail. (See Appendix 4.)

4. Fourth-class postal rate chart and local post-office zone key for use with a "Postal Manual." (See Appendix 4.)

5. Zone map showing an approximation of the fourth-class zones. (See Appendix 4.)

6. Local air express rate chart available from the Railway Express Agency.

7. Office rules for wrapping, mailing, packaging, and recording of routine shipments.

Wrapping and shipping are not all. The shipping clerk must have or be a bookkeeper to keep the records of packages sent or received, whether insured, registered, COD, special delivery, special handling, returned for insufficient postage, air or railway express, freight, etc. If the shipment is lost or damaged, these receipts and records must be immediately available.

**Wrico Lettering Guides** See LEROY.

**wrong font** The s*e*cond word in this sentence contains a letter that is of the wrong font of type. (See proofreader's marks under PROOFREADING; FONT.)

# X | x

**xerography, Xerox** Xerography is a recent and basic process with applications in both printing and photography. Its commercial applications are being developed by the Haloid Corp., Rochester, N.Y., under the name Xerox. Xerox equipment is in wide use for the making of master plates for small offset duplicators such as Multiliths, considerably shortening the time otherwise required for preparing plates by conventional photographic methods. The quality, though below the best photographic standards, is entirely acceptable for many applications. The minimum basic equipment sells for about $4,000, or rents for about $900 a year. Equipment that can enlarge or reduce costs more, as does an accessory to permit working from originals containing screened subjects. The equipment is not adapted to *introducing* a screen into unscreened originals.

A halftone effect can be obtained in a Xerox camera by placing a paper printed screen on the copyboard, and exposing the Xerox plate to this immediately before exposure to the subject. This will create a screen dot pattern on the plate surface, which is then exposed to the subject which will

340

further modify the charge on the plate in proportion to the shades of the original.

Up to eight prints can be made from a single exposure on the Model D Xerox Processor. This is done by the use of a negative charge in addition to the conventional positive charge found on earlier models of the Processor. After the plate image has been developed, a sheet of paper is placed in contact, and a positive charge applied. Before the paper is peeled from the plate a negative charge is applied, which has the effect of repelling most of the powder image back onto the plate surface. Thus, there is sufficient powder left for up to eight copies to be transferred by the same method from one plate image. This improvement in the process has been made possible by the addition of the negative charging feature, and by improvements in the developing powders and toners.

A Xerox image can be transferred onto a Trans-Positive Sheet, which is a translucent material that can then be used for making diazo (whiteprint) copies, or for burning in a positive acting offset metal plate. In the latter case this completely eliminates the complications of darkroom and skilled labor in the preparation of a conventional negative.

The first cost of installing xerography is greater than such processes as Thermo-Fax and Verifax, but a Xerox installation is more versatile. It can make single copies on plain paper, offset masters, spirit masters and transparencies for positive metal plates, diazo machines, transparent overlays, visual aid projection slides, etc.

How xerography works, 1. Surface of specially controlled plate is being electrically charged as it passes under wires. 2. Coating of plate is shown charged with positive electricity. 3. Copy (**E**) is projected through lens in camera. Plus marks show projected image with positive charges. Positive charges disappear in areas exposed to light as shown by white spaces. 4. A negatively charged powder adheres to positively charged image. 5. After powder treatment (Fig. 4) a sheet of paper is placed over plate and receives positive charge. 6. Positively charged paper attracts powder from plate, forming direct positive image. 7. Print is heated for a few seconds to fuse powder and form permanent print.

**Z** | **z**

**zinc engraving**  See LINE CUT.

**Zip-a-Tone**  See SHADING TINTS.

# Appendix 1

# Type Faces

Type faces come in hundreds of designs and sizes and weights, but it is possible to classify them roughly as follows:

| | | |
|---|---|---|
| Text faces | *vs.* | **display faces** |
| Roman | *vs.* | *italic* |
| Lightface | *vs.* | **boldface** |
| Old style | *vs.* | modern |
| Serif | *vs.* | sans serif |
| Serif | *vs.* | square serif |

Text types, like the one used for the text of this book (9-pt. Baskerville), commonly come in the following sizes (see POINT):

6-pt. Caslon

8-pt. Baskerville

10-pt. Baskerville

12-pt. Baskerville

14-pt. Baskerville

Often they are available in 7-, 9-, and 11-pt. sizes. Text type can be set by hand but is usually set on the Linotype, Intertype, or Monotype. (See LINOTYPE; INTERTYPE; MONOTYPE.)

Display sizes include 18, 24, 30, 36, 48, 60, 72 pt., and sometimes 96 or even 144 pt. Rarer sizes are 16, 21, 42, 54, 84, and 120 pt.

Further information about display faces, along with 106 specimens of display type, is given under the heading "Display Faces" beginning on page 362 of this appendix.

A standard font of text type includes caps, small caps, lower case, figures, punctuation, and special signs. Usually it includes also italic or boldface. (A Linotype operator working with a font of matrices containing both roman and italic letters can mix roman and italic with virtually no loss of speed. But if the matrices contain roman and italic, they cannot contain boldface, and the setting of boldface may put the operator to extra trouble and so slow him down. The setting of small caps also slows down a Linotype operator and thus provides an incentive to the man who will pay the bills not to use small caps any more than necessary.)

Considerable variety can be obtained even within one size and style of type, as shown in the following lines. Often, requirements of display and emphasis can be met without going to another type font, especially if the variations shown here are emphasized further by spacing, indenting, centering, etc.

CAPITAL LETTERS

L E T T E R S P A C E D   C A P S

Caps and Small Caps
EVEN SMALL CAPS
Caps and Lower Case
*ITALIC CAPS*
*L E T T E R S P A C E D   I T A L I C*
*C A P S*
*Italic Caps and Lower Case*

On the following pages some of the most used type styles are illustrated. Note that the same, or similar, styles are sometimes put out under different names by different companies, and types of the same name may differ slightly in weight or compactness between one company and another, and even within one company, e.g., Linotype Garamond and Garamond No. 3. The best-known type founders are Linotype, Intertype, Monotype, Ludlow, and (for hand-set type) American Type Founders and Bauer Type Foundry.

An important thing about text type is its weight on the page, or "color." Boldfaces, without leading, look very dark on the page. Lightfaces, with leading, have a light color. Boldfaces, generously leaded, have about the same weight on the page as lightfaces without leading, but they have a different texture. Old-style type faces differ in texture from modern faces and from sans-serif faces.

Good design requires that each block of type should have appropriate weight or texture. A block of type constitutes an area of gray. Whether it will be a dark gray or a light gray and whether it will be of unobtrusive texture or of distinctive texture are determined by the choice of type face and amount of leading. Type prints heavier on soft paper than on glossy paper.

Long lines need more leading than short lines and require larger type to be read easily. The most readable lines of type are those whose length is between 1½ and 2½ times the length of the alphabet in the type face chosen, *i.e.*, between 39 and 65 characters in length.

Copy fitting (see COPY FITTING) is the technique of making the words fit into the space available. Sometimes the copy is written or rewritten "to space." Sometimes the type size is chosen to accommodate the copy. Either way it is necessary to know how many words of copy will go into a given space in a given size and kind of type. Information for calculating this is given with each type specimen. This is an alphabet of 10-pt. Granjon:

abcdefghijklmnopqrstuvwxyz

This is an alphabet of 10-pt. Bookman:

abcdefghijklmnopqrstuvwxyz

It is clear that, although they are the same size, 10-pt. Bookman is less compact than 10-pt. Granjon. In fact, a given area of Granjon will accommodate 13 per cent more copy than the same area of Bookman.

Thus, the alphabet length of a given size and style of type is an important piece of information. It is generally given in points. (It is not difficult to measure the point length of an alphabet with an ordinary ruler, if it is remembered that there are 72 points to the inch, 9 points to the ⅛ inch. Alphabet length means lower-case alphabet length unless otherwise stated.)

More useful, however, than alphabet length, is characters per pica (c.p.p.). This is easily figured from the alphabet length (in points). The formula [1] is as follows:

$$\frac{341}{\text{Alphabet length}} = \text{characters per pica}$$

[1] This is sometimes given as 26 (number of letters in the alphabet) ÷ alphabet length in picas, or $26 \times 12$ divided by alphabet length in points. However, it will be found that about 28.4 characters fit into one alphabet length in practice since thin letters are used more often than the thicker ones. The formula, therefore, becomes $28.4 \times 12 \div$ alphabet length in points.

For example, 10-pt. Linotype Baskerville has an alphabet length of 129 points. $341 \div 129 = 2.64$ c.p.p.

The characters per pica are given after each sample of type in the following pages. For example, the notation "C.p.p.: 10 pt., 2.94" as applied to Granjon means that the 10-pt. size of Granjon averages 2.94 lower-case letters and spaces per pica. For character counts of other point sizes see the tables on pages 354 and 355.

From this it is easy to calculate that a line of 10-pt. Granjon 20 picas long will hold about 59 characters. A table for simplifying such calculations is given on page 356.

Note, however, that lines set entirely in capital letters are likely to run half again as long as lines set in small letters, or accommodate one-third fewer letters for the same length.

The ideal type specimen book would show complete alphabets of every style of type in every size, with character counts for each size. This book is not big enough to attempt that, but it does offer complete alphabets of nearly every popular style in the 24-pt. size on pages 365 to 396 with character counts for the 24-pt. size. These 24-pt. character counts can be converted into character counts for any other size by consulting the tables on pages 362 and 363. The conversion may not be exact, but it will almost always come close enough for practical purposes.

Note that much information about type is contained within the actual specimens of text types shown in the appendix—this seemed a more profitable use of space than the more conventional repetition of the same paragraph over and over again for each type specimen.

If you work much with type you will treasure any type books you can get hold of, and this is often difficult—few printers have adequate ones. If yours is a big account, your compositor will supply you with one at his own expense, but if not you may want to buy one. For $35 you can get one of the best from Howard O. Bullard, Inc., 150 Varick Street, New York 13. (Sample type faces on pages 346 to 396.)

**8-pt. Baskerville (Lino), set solid. C.p.p.: 3.22**

The following pages constitute a "type book" showing the most frequently used type faces, in both text and display sizes. No printer or composition house will have all the types shown in the full range of sizes. Most will have other types not shown here. *e.g.*, the Cheltenham series, which is no longer in favor with most designers and is not shown here. If possible, type users should obtain a type book from the printer who will be doing most of their composition, showing what types he has. Unfortunately, most printers have no type book, have no copies of it left, or have an inadequate one that does not have large enough samples to help much in the selection of text types. *To make the type showings in the following pages most helpful, marginal notes can be inserted stating which local printers have which styles and sizes.* 1234567890 ABCDEFGHIJKLMNOPQRSTUVWXYZ abcdefghijklmnopqrstuvwxyz

**10-pt. Baskerville (Lino), set solid. C.p.p.: 2.64**

A personal loose-leaf scrapbook of type specimens can also be exceedingly helpful. It can be made up of clippings from the printer's publications, labeled for type style, size, and leading. Such a scrapbook is particularly helpful when a periodical is being edited since it can contain samples of the different styles of text, headlines, captions, etc., each marked with name, size, and characters per column. *The abbreviation, C.p.p. stands for "characters per pica." For a full explanation of its use, turn to the entries on* TYPE *and* COPY FITTING. 1234567890 ABCDEFGHIJKLMNOPQRSTUVWXYZ abcdefghijklmnopqrstuvwxyz

**12-pt. Baskerville (Lino), set solid. C.p.p.: 2.30**

The name of the manufacturer is given beside each specimen. This is an important piece of information for two reasons. First, Linotype Garamond No. 1 is not quite the same face as Intertype Garamond or Monotype Garamont. Second, Linotype, Intertype, Monotype, and Ludlow type faces are cast fresh for each use. ATF (American Type Founders), Continental, Bauer, etc., type faces may or may not be available for actual printing. (See TYPE.) *Sometimes, to prevent wear, printers will use them only to pull proofs, or to make duplicate plates.* 1234567890 ABCDEFGHIJKLMNOPQRSTUVWXYZ abcdefghijklmnopqrstuvwxyz

**14-pt. Baskerville (Lino), set solid. C.p.p.: 2.01**

Baskerville is one of the best loved of the so-called "body," or text, types. The specimens on this page are faithful reproductions of the types designed and used by John Baskerville about 1760. *Cuttings of this face have been made also for the Intertype and the Monotype and are virtually identical.* 1234567890 ABCDEFGHIJKLMNOPQRSTUVWXYZ abcdefghijklmnopqrstuvwxyz

**10/11 Times Roman (Lino). C.p.p.: 2.75**

These lines have been set in 10 pt., leaded 1 pt. The leading could have been inserted by hand between lines of 10 pt., but as a matter of convenience the 10-pt. type was cast on an 11-pt. slug, or body. (For an explanation of how this is done, see LINOTYPE.) It is therefore correct to say that these lines have been set in 10 on 11. In specifying the type, this would be written "10/11." More leading can easily be added, but removal of the 1-pt. space between lines would necessitate resetting on a 10-pt. slug. *The Monotype, which casts type characters singly instead of in one solid line of type, can also cast 10-pt. type on an 11-pt. or larger body.*

**10/12 Times Roman (Lino). C.p.p.: 2.75**

These lines have been set in 10 pt. on a 12-pt. body, *i.e.,* leaded 2 points. Long lines like these really need leading if they are to be legible. Short lines can more readily do without it. Sometimes small type, well leaded, is more readable than a larger type set solid. Leading can completely change the appearance of a block of copy. Heavy type appears lighter when widely leaded. Some type, especially the sans serifs, can stand extra-generous leading, at least in the larger sizes, but it is unusual to lead 8- and 10-pt. lightface types more than 2 or 3 points. *Printing a type on soft (antique) paper makes it look heavier than the same type on a coated or hard-surfaced paper.*

**10/13 Times Roman (Lino). C.p.p.: 2.75**

These lines have been set in 10 pt. on a 13-pt. body, *i.e.,* leaded 3 points. Wider leading demands wider margins. Otherwise the type will not appear as a well-defined block. Mixed leading is considered bad practice. When a story falls short of filling the space intended for it, printers sometimes add enough extra leading to fill the space. When a story runs long, they may take out some leading. The result is to produce a spotty-looking page, with some parts of the text lighter in tone value than others. *The correct remedy is to cut or add copy so as to fill the space while maintaining uniform leading.*

**12/14 Times Roman (Lino). C.p.p.: 2.32**

These lines have been set in 12 pt. on a 14-pt. body, *i.e.,* leaded 2 points. 12 pt. is the largest type size in common use for large amounts of text matter, although most type faces also come in 14 pt. In selecting a type size it is well to remember that most people read 7- or 8-pt. type every day without complaint of eyestrain. Newspapers are commonly printed in 7-pt. type, leaded 1 pt.; the publishers, however, use a narrow column.

**10/10 Granjon (Lino). C.p.p.: 2.94**

Eight popular text types are shown on this page and the one following. All are set in 10 pt., unleaded. All are available in 6-, 8-, 10-, 12-, and 14-pt. sizes, and usually in 9 and 11 pt. as well. Granjon is a particularly compact, space-saving type. In fact, 10-pt. Granjon is slightly more compact than 9-pt. Bookman. Since Granjon is small for its point size, it is more often used without leading than are less compact faces like Bookman. *Some printers have Granjon with bold instead of, or in addition to, Granjon with italic.* This is a sample of **Granjon Bold.**
ABCDEFGHIJKLMNOPQRSTUVWXYZ 1234567890
abcdefghijklmnopqrstuvwxyz C.p.p.: 8 pt., 3.48; 12 pt., 2.49

**10/10 Garamond (Intertype). C.p.p.: 2.92**

The most popular type faces are offered by all the type companies. This is true of Caslon, Garamond, Bodoni, and Bookman. Sometimes the different cuttings are almost identical; sometimes they vary noticeably. On one of the following pages the different cuttings of Garamond are compared. Linotype Garamond No. 3, Intertype Garamond, and Monotype Garamont are all similar in weight. Linotype Garamond No. 1 is a little heavier. All the Garamonds have their bold counterparts. *All, including the bolds, have particularly attractive italics.* This is a sample of **Intertype Garamond Bold.**
ABCDEFGHIJKLMNOPQRSTUVWXYZ 1234567890
abcdefghijklmnopqrstuvwxyz C.p.p.: 8 pt., 3.35; 12 pt., 2.58

**10/10 Caslon No. 137 (Mono). C.p.p.: 2.66**

Some types are available with either long descenders or short descenders. When 10-pt. type is cast on a 10-pt. body there is room for only short descenders. When the body size is 2 points larger than the type size, it is possible and desirable to ask that matrices with long descenders be used. Type with long descenders is somewhat more attractive and readable than type with short descenders. Occasionally long descenders are standard, with short descenders available only on special order. *This explains the otherwise curious notation in some type books to the effect that a so-called 10-pt. face must be cast on an 11-pt. body.*
ABCDEFGHIJKLMNOPQRSTUVWXYZ 1234567890
abcdefghijklmnopqrstuvwxyz C.p.p.: 8 pt., 3.32; 12 pt., 2.21

**10/10 Bookman (Mono). C.p.p.: 2.58**

Bookman, called Bookface in its Intertype cutting, is a big type face for its size. 10-pt. Bookman usually looks as big as 11 pt. in any other type style. This impression of size is obtained by using short descenders and ascenders, thus permitting the central part of the lower-case letters to be somewhat larger than usual. The letters are also a bit heavier than most other faces. Bookman is a versatile face. It will print well on either rough or smooth paper. *It is well adapted for offset or gravure reproduction, having no thin hairlines or delicate serifs to get lost in reproduction.*
ABCDEFGHIJKLMNOPQRSTUVWXYZ 1234567890
abcdefghijklmnopqrstuvwxyz C.p.p.: 8 pt., 3.10; 12 pt., 2.19

**10/10 Cloister (Lino). C.p.p.: 3.10**

Cloister, or Cloister Old Style as it is sometimes called, is widely available on the Intertype and the Monotype as well as on the Linotype. There is also a Cloister Bold, and a Cloister Wide. It should not be confused with Cloister Black, which is an Old English style. Cloister is derived from a type cut in 1470 in Venice by Nicholas Jenson. It definitely belongs with the old-style faces like Centaur, Bookman, and Old Style, and not with the modern faces like Bodoni, or the transitional faces like Scotch, Baskerville, and Caledonia. *Note that small caps are available with almost all text types through 14 pt., but not in larger sizes.*
ABCDEFGHIJKLMNOPQRSTUVWXYZ  1234567890
abcdefghijklmnopqrstuvwxyz  C.p.p.: 8 pt., 3.56; 12 pt., 2.75

**10/10 Scotch (Lino). C.p.p.: 2.73**

Cuttings of Scotch, or Scotch Roman as it may be called, are made by Intertype and Monotype also. Like Baskerville, Scotch is a compromise between the old-style letters of Caslon and the modern letters of Bodoni. Note that figures are classed as old-style and modern just as letters are. The figures shown above under Granjon are old-style figures and have ascenders and descenders. The figures shown below under Bodoni are modern or lining figures because they align at top and bottom like capital letters. Modern figures are preferred for tabular work, and many type faces are cut with both. The Scotch figures, if compared closely with modern and old-style figures, betray their transitional character.
ABCDEFGHIJKLMNOPQRSTUVWXYZ  1234567890
abcdefghijklmnopqrstuvwxyz  C.p.p.: 8 pt., 3.10; 12 pt., 2.19

**10/10 Bodoni Book (Lino). C.p.p.: 2.79**

Giambattista Bodoni first designed the types that bear his name about one hundred and fifty years ago. He broke away entirely from the old-style types like Garamond and Caslon. These had always imitated the mannerisms of pen lettering to greater or lesser degree. Bodoni designed his letters along formal, geometric lines, with clean hairline serifs, and exaggerated "thicks" and "thins." Where the old-style types were designed to print on rough, antique papers, Bodoni's types looked their best on smooth-surfaced or coated papers that would not thicken his delicate hairlines. *This face, Bodoni Book, is particularly suitable for bookwork.*
ABCDEFGHIJKLMNOPQRSTUVWXYZ  1234567890
abcdefghijklmnopqrstuvwxyz  C.p.p.: 8 pt., 3.31; 12 pt., 2.50

**10/10 Bodoni (Lino). C.p.p.: 2.58**

The Bodoni series includes Bodoni Book, Bodoni, Bodoni Bold, and Ultra Bodoni, each with its own italic. These faces and related modern type styles are compared on a later page. Bodoni is itself heavy enough to compare with most boldfaces. It looks best when generously leaded. Bodoni shows to best advantage in 12 pt., 14 pt., and larger display sizes. Although typographers often combine two quite different type families, they do not often mix old-style and modern types. *They are more likely to stick to one or the other, or to contrast either with a sans serif.*
ABCDEFGHIJKLMNOPQRSTUVWXYZ  1234567890
abcdefghijklmnopqrstuvwxyz  C.p.p.: 8 pt., 3.13; 12 pt., 2.35

**10/10 Excelsior (Lino). C.p.p.: 2.4**

In these pages reference has frequently been made to "text type" or "body type" meaning a type suitable for use in a book and in small sizes as opposed to display sizes. However, the word "text" sometimes is used to designate the heavy, broad-pen style of type known as Old English, Black Text, Wedding Text, or Text.
ABCDEFGHIJKLMNOPQRSTU
VWXYZ 1234567890
abcdefghijklmnopqrstuvwxyz

**10/10 Benedictine Book (Lino). C.p.p.: 2.53**

The Benedictine type family is less popular than it once was, but a good many printers have it. It comes in three weights: Benedictine Book, Benedictine, and Benedictine Bold. It somewhat resembles Goudy Oldstyle. *The most used types today are Caslon, Bodoni, Garamond, Baskerville, Futura, and the square-serif series.*
ABCDEFGHIJKLMNO
PQRSTUVWXYZ 1234567890
abcdefghijklmnopqrstuvwxyz

**10/10 Century Expanded (Lino). C.p.p.: 2.40**

One of the many points on which printing terminology is confusing is in the use of the word "gothic." The term is sometimes used synonymously with Old English, Wedding Text, etc., to designate the broad-pen, blackletter style used in manuscripts beginning about the twelfth century. It is also used to refer to the modern sans-serif type styles, as for example, Franklin Gothic. *Century Expanded is available on Lino, Intertype and Mono, with italic or with bold.*
ABCDEFGHIJKLMNO
PQRSTUVWXYZ 1234567890
abcdefghijklmnopqrstuvwxyz

**10/11 Janson (Lino). C.p.p.: 2.60**

This face is also offered by Monotype. The 8-, 10-, and 12-pt. sizes must be cast on 9-, 11-, and 13-pt. slugs, respectively. Since the point size of a type face is generally understood to be the smallest body slug on which it can be cast, *it is not quite clear why these were not called 9-, 11-, and 13-pt. sizes.*
ABCDEFGHIJKLMNOPQRSTU
VWXYZ 1234567890
abcdefghijklmnopqrstuvwxyz

**10/11 Caledonia (Lino). C.p.p.: 2.62**

This is a recent type designed by W. A. Dwiggins. It is reminiscent both of Scotch Roman and of Bulmer; it is a little more modern in its design than Baskerville. It has become very popular. *The designer took particular care to give the italic the same weight and color as the roman.* **There is also a Caledonia Bold.**
ABCDEFGHIJKLMNOPQRSTU
VWXYZ 1234567890
abcdefghijklmnopqrstuvwxyz

**10/10 Linotype No. 21. C.p.p.: 2.62**

"This is a printing office—crossroads of civilization, refuge of all the arts against the ravages of time, armory of fearless truth against whispering rumor, incessant trumpet of trade. From this place words may fly abroad, not to perish on waves of sound, not to vary with the writer's hand, but fixed in time, having been verified by proof. *Friend, you stand on sacred ground. This is a printing office."*—Beatrice L. Warde.
ABCDEFGHIJKLMNOPQRSTU
VWXYZ 1234567890
abcdefghijklmnopqrstuvwxyz

## 10/11 Fairfield (Lino). C.p.p.: 2.79

Fairfield is another modern type face and was designed by Rudolph Ruzicka. Type designing is a subtle art. The artist must of necessity adapt rather than innovate. Type must never call attention to itself, but rather to its message. Its forms must, therefore, be the old familiar ones.
ABCDEFGHIJKLMNOPQRSTU
VWXYZ    1234567890
abcdefghijklmnopqrstuvwxyz

## 10/11 Electra (Lino). C.p.p.: 2.75

Electra is a modern type face designed by W. A. Dwiggins, who also designed Caledonia and Metro. It has both an "oblique" and a "cursive." Its oblique is often called an "oblique roman," or an "inclined roman." *This sentence is set in Electra Oblique. This sentence is set in Electra Cursive.*
ABCDEFGHIJKLMNOPQRSTU
VWXYZ    1234567890
abcdefghijklmnopqrstuvwxyz
NOTE: Electra must be leaded at least 1 pt.

## 10/10 Garamont (Mono). C.p.p.: 2.71

The type first cut by Claude Garamond about 1530–1540 has been recut for machine composition by all three manufacturers. The specimens in this column show how even the subtlest differences can affect the weight and color of a type. Garamond type tends to identify itself by the very small loop on the lower-case "e." *Note that the Monotype cutting (redrawn by Goudy) is spelled with a final "t."*
ABCDEFGHIJKLMNOPQRSTUVW
XYZ    1234567890
abcdefghijklmnopqrstuvwxyz

## 10/10 Garamond (Lino). C.p.p.: 2.82

The type first cut by Claude Garamond about 1530–1540 has been recut for machine composition by all three manufacturers. The specimens in this column show how even the subtlest differences can affect the weight and color of a type. Garamond type tends to identify itself by the very small loop on the lower-case "e." *All the Garamonds shown here are available in bold and bold italic as well as in italic.*
ABCDEFGHIJKLMNOPQRSTUV
WXYZ    1234567890
abcdefghijklmnopqrstuvwxyz

## 10/10 Garamond No. 3 (Lino). C.p.p.: 2.90

The type first cut by Claude Garamond about 1530-1540 has been recut for machine composition by all three manufacturers. The specimens in this column show how even the subtlest differences can affect the weight and color of a type. Garamond type tends to identify itself by the very small loop on the lower-case "e." *All the Garamonds shown here are available in bold and bold italic as well as in italic.*
ABCDEFGHIJKLMNOPQRSTUVW
XYZ    1234567890
abcdefghijklmnopqrstuvwxyz

## 10/10 Garamond (Intertype). C.p.p.: 2.92

The type first cut by Claude Garamond about 1530–1540 has been recut for machine composition by all three manufacturers. The specimens in this column show how even the subtlest differences can affect the weight and color of a type. Garamond type tends to identify itself by the very small loop on the lower-case "e." *All the Garamonds shown here are available in bold and bold italic as well as in italic.*
ABCDEFGHIJKLMNOPQRSTUVW
XYZ    1234567890
abcdefghijklmnopqrstuvwxyz

**10/10 Futura Light (Intertype) C.p.p.: 3.05**

Everyone who deals with the printed word should sooner or later read "Layout in Advertising" by W. A. Dwiggins, described in the Bibliography. The book was written in 1928, and in it Mr. Dwiggins calls attention to the need for a well-designed sans-serif type. *The Futura designs, imported from Germany during the thirties, met this need.*
ABCDEFGHIJKLMNOPQRSTUVWXYZ
1234567890
abcdefghijklmnopqrstuvwxyz

**10/10 Futura Medium (Intertype) C.p.p.: 2.87**

Sans-serif types have been in use for more than a hundred years, but the earlier ones lacked grace. Only in recent years have sans-serif types matured into a beauty of their own, thanks to the men who designed the Vogue series, Franklin Gothic, Alternate Gothic, Kabel, Gill Sans Serif, Metro, Erbar, Futura, etc. *The Futura series has perhaps been the most widely copied of all.*
ABCDEFGHIJKLMNOPQRSTUVWXYZ
1234567890
abcdefghijklmnopqrstuvwxyz

**10/10 Futura Demibold (Intertype) C.p.p.: 2.59**

**The Futura types are now distributed by all the leading type manufacturers, but may be called Spartan, Tempo, or Twentieth Century as well as Futura. Furthermore, the weight that one manufacturer calls "bold" may be called "black," "heavy," or "extrabold" by the other manufacturers.** *This rather confusing nomenclature may be clarified by comparing samples on page 358.*
**ABCDEFGHIJKLMNOPQRSTUVWX YZ 1234567890**
**abcdefghijklmnopqrstuvwxyz**

**10/10 Futura Bold (Intertype). C.p.p.: 2.40**

**Sans-serif types are used more for display headings and in advertising brochures than for the main text of books or magazines. Many people feel that large masses of sans-serif type are somewhat less readable than the same wordage set in roman type. This may be merely a question of familiarity, just as Bismarck is said to have proved to his own satisfaction that the German Fraktur type is much more readable than roman type.**
**ABCDEFGHIJKLMNOPQRSTUVW XYZ 1234567890**
**abcdefghijklmnopqrstuvwxyz**

**10/10 Memphis Light (Lino). C.p.p.: 2.56**

Memphis belongs to a family of type styles called "Egyptian" or "square serif." Substantially identical type faces put out by other type manufacturers include Karnak, Stymie, Beton, and Cairo. These are compared on a subsequent page. The serifs on these types are of the same thickness as the rest of the letters.
ABCDEFGHIJKLMNOPQRSTUV WXYZ 1234567890
abcdefghijklmnopqrstuvwxyz

**10/10 Memphis Medium (Lino). C.p.p.: 2.56**

Square-serif types have become popular because they can be contrasted effectively with either roman or sans-serif styles. They are much used in display work, less used for text matter. The design is rather static and lacks the movement and grace that is obtainable in roman or sans-serif faces.
ABCDEFGHIJKLMNO PQRSTUVWXYZ 1234567890
abcdefghijklmnopqrstuvwxyz

**10/10 Memphis Bold (Lino). C.p.p.: 2.56**

The profusion of different type faces is bound to be confusing to anyone entering the field for the first time. One of the best ways to bring some order out of the confusion is to study lettering. Type characteristics are determined by the pen or brush or chisel that originally formed the letters. For a few good books about lettering see the Bibliography.
ABCDEFGHIJKLMNOPQRSTUV
WXYZ   1234567890
abcdefghijklmnopqrstuvwxyz

**10/10 Memphis Extrabold (Lino). C.p.p.: 2.06**

The heaviest cuttings of the square-serif family, like this one, provide the typographer with some of his heaviest ammunition. They pack a terrific wallop, whether for display use, or for small chunks of text. They have a texture all their own.
ABCDEFGHIJKLMNOP
QRSTUVWXYZ 1234567890
abcdefghijklmnop
qrstuvwxyz

**10/10 Caslon Bold No. 3 (Lino). C.p.p.: 2.45**

The most used text faces come in bold as well as light, each with its matching italic. It would be very uncommon to find a book set in boldface throughout, but many books use a lightface for the text, and the matching boldface for subheads, marginal heads, etc. *The same is true in catalogue work.*
ABCDEFGHIJKLMNO
PQRSTUVWXYZ   1234567890
abcdefghijklmnopqrstuvwxyz

**10/10 Garamond Bold (Intertype)
C.p.p.: 2.73**

A printer who has Garamond Bold may have it on the same matrices as Garamond Light, or he may have it on matrices of its own, along with Garamond Bold Italic. It will be extra trouble for him to mix bold and light on the same line *unless he has both on the same matrices.*
ABCDEFGHIJKLMNOPQRSTUV
WXYZ   1234567890
abcdefghijklmnopqrstuvwxyz

**10/10 Bodoni Bold (Mono). C.p.p.: 2.41**

Regardless of what other type faces they may have or lack, most good printers have the complete Bodoni series. Advertising layout tends to use the Bodoni oftener than any other type family. *A showing of the complete Bodoni family and related styles is given on page 357.*
ABCDEFGHIJKLMNOPQRSTU
VWXYZ   1234567890
abcdefghijklmnopqrstuvwxyz

**10/10 Poster Bodoni (Lino). C.p.p.: 1.99**

This heaviest version of Bodoni is variously called ultra, poster, modern or black, depending on which type manufacturer makes it. It compresses large attention value into small space. It looks well in caps, lower case, or italic. It is at its best when generously leaded, on smooth paper.
ABCDEFGHIJKLMNO
PQRSTUVWXYZ
1234567890
abcdefghijklmno
pqrstuvwxyz

CHARACTERS PER PICA

| Type face | Size of type face | | | | | | | |
|---|---|---|---|---|---|---|---|---|
| | 6 pt. | 7 pt. | 8 pt. | 9 pt. | 10 pt. | 11 pt. | 12 pt. | 14 pt. |
| Antique No. 1 w. ital. (Inter, Lino)...... | 3.52 | 3.2 | 2.8 | | 2.42 | | 2.08 | 1.8 |
| Baskerville w. ital. & s.c. (Inter)......... | 3.92 | | 3.2 | 3.05 | 2.78 | 2.63 | 2.33 | 2.03 |
| Baskerville w. ital. & s.c. (Lino)......... | 3.8 | 3.6 | 3.22 | 2.95 | 2.64 | 2.46 | 2.30 | 2.01 |
| Baskerville No. 353 (Mono)............. | 4.08 | 3.66 | 3.25 | 3.06 | 2.76 | 2.5 | 2.3 | 2.11 |
| Baskerville Bold w. ital. (Lino).......... | | 3.57 | 3.2 | 2.89 | 2.61 | 2.42 | 2.28 | 1.98 |
| Baskerville Bold No. 453 (Mono) *...... | | | 2.97 | 2.79 | 2.52 | 2.29 | 2.1 | |
| Benedictine......................... | 4.08 | 3.56 | 3.12 | 2.82 | 2.52 | 2.31 | 2.12 | 1.85 |
| Benedictine Bold..................... | | | 2.94 | | 2.33 | | 1.93 | 1.66 |
| Benedictine Book.................... | 4.08 | 3.56 | 3.13 | 2.82 | 2.53 | 2.31 | 2.12 | 1.85 |
| Beton Medium w. Bold (Inter).......... | | | 3.48 | 2.97 | 2.65 | 2.35 | 2.12 | 1.91 |
| Bodoni w. ital. & s.c. (Inter, Lino)....... | 4.19 | 3.55 | 3.13 | | 2.59 | | 2.35 | 2.1 |
| Bodoni No. 175 (Mono)................ | 3.83 | 3.33 | 3.15 | 2.96 | 2.66 | 2.41 | 2.23 | 1.89 |
| Bodoni Ital. No. 175 (Mono)............ | 4.25 | 3.63 | 3.44 | 3.22 | 2.91 | 2.64 | 2.43 | 2.07 |
| Bodoni No. 375 (Mono)................ | 3.95 | 3.55 | 3.15 | 2.96 | 2.66 | 2.42 | 2.23 | 2.11 |
| Bodoni No. 375 Ital. (Mono)............ | 3.95 | 3.88 | 3.15 | 3.22 | 2.71 | 2.64 | 2.33 | 2.14 |
| Bodoni Bold w. ital. & s.c. (Inter, Lino).. | 3.75 | | 2.87 | | 2.44 | | 2.17 | 1.95 |
| Bodoni Bold No. 275 (Mono) *.......... | 3.43 | 2.97 | 2.82 | 2.65 | 2.41 | 2.23 | 2.00 | 1.96 |
| Bodoni Book w. ital. & s.c. (Inter, Lino)... | 4.21 | 3.71 | 3.32 | 2.99 | 2.78 | | 2.5 | 2.25 |
| Bodoni Book No. 875 (Mono) *......... | 4.3 | 3.78 | 3.33 | 3.15 | 2.85 | 2.7 | 2.58 | |
| Bookface w. ital. & s.c. (Inter).......... | 3.67 | 3.41 | 3.10 | 2.89 | 2.59 | 2.36 | 2.21 | 1.80 |
| Bookman w. ital. & s.c. (Lino).......... | 3.67 | 3.38 | 3.10 | 2.87 | 2.58 | 2.37 | 2.19 | 1.84 |
| Bookman Old Style No. 98 (Mono) *..... | 3.68 | 3.33 | 3.15 | 2.98 | 2.61 | 2.44 | 2.23 | 1.87 |
| Cairo (Inter)........................ | 3.57 | | 3.03 | | 2.55 | | 2.09 | 1.78 |
| Caledonia w. ital. & s.c. (Lino).......... | | | 3.13 | 2.87 | 2.62 | 2.44 | 2.26 | 2.01 |
| Caslon w. ital & s.c. (Inter, Lino)........ | 3.88 | 3.63 | 3.17 | 2.99 | 2.82 | 2.42 | 2.18 | 1.89 |
| Caslon No. 3 w. ital. & s.c. (Inter, Lino)... | 3.84 | 3.45 | 3.16 | 2.75 | 2.46 | | 2.06 | 1.77 |
| Caslon No. 137 w. ital. & s.c. (Lino)..... | | 3.8 | 3.32 | 2.95 | 2.65 | 2.42 | 2.18 | |
| Caslon Old Face w. ital. & s.c. (Lino).... | 4.44 | | 3.67 | 3.22 | 3.08 | 2.80 | 2.42 | 2.15 |
| Caslon Old Style No. 137 (Mono) *...... | 4.11 | | 3.32 | 3.04 | 2.66 | 2.41 | 2.21 | |
| Caslon Bold No. 79 (Mono) *.......... | 3.43 | 3.00 | 2.82 | 2.68 | 2.35 | 2.19 | 2.00 | 1.59 |
| Caslon, New, No. 537 (Mono) *......... | 3.78 | | 3.15 | 2.69 | 2.36 | | 2.11 | 1.75 |
| Century Expanded w. ital. & s.c. (Inter, Lino)............................ | 3.6 | 3.2 | 2.87 | 2.67 | 2.41 | 2.30 | 2.11 | 1.77 |
| Century Expanded No. 20 (Mono) *..... | 3.83 | 3.35 | 3.07 | 2.76 | 2.56 | 2.44 | 2.23 | 1.79 |
| Cheltenham w. ital. & s.c. (Inter)........ | | | 3.6 | 3.2 | 2.97 | 2.71 | 2.54 | 2.15 |
| Cheltenham Old Style No. 64 (Mono) *... | 4.43 | | 3.67 | | 2.97 | | 2.55 | 2.24 |
| Cheltonian w. ital. & s.c. (Inter)........ | | 3.88 | 3.56 | | 2.97 | | 2.54 | 2.15 |
| Cloister w. ital. & s.c. (Lino)............ | 4.27 | | 3.56 | | 3.10 | 2.95 | 2.75 | 2.45 |
| Cloister Bold w. ital. (Lino)............. | 3.8 | | 3.13 | | 2.71 | | 2.49 | 2.18 |
| Cloister Old Style w. ital. & s.c. (Inter)... | 4.33 | | 3.71 | | 3.16 | | 2.84 | 2.56 |
| Deepdene No. 315 (Mono) *............ | 4.39 | | 3.62 | | 3.08 | | 2.56 | 2.31 |
| Deepdene Bold No. 317 (Mono) *....... | 4.02 | | 3.32 | | 2.83 | | 2.35 | 1.99 |
| Egmont Light w. ital. & s.c. (Inter)...... | | | 3.63 | | 2.94 | | 2.59 | 2.25 |
| Electra w. ital. & s.c. (Lino)............ | | 3.67 | 3.28 | 2.92 | 2.73 | 2.54 | 2.40 | 2.14 |
| Fairfield w. ital. & s.c. (Lino)........... | | | 3.21 | 2.99 | 2.79 | 2.61 | 2.45 | |
| Futura Bold w. oblique (Inter).......... | 3.64 | | 3.1 | | 2.4 | | 1.98 | 1.74 |
| Futura Book w. oblique (Inter)......... | 4.39 | | 3.88 | | 3.05 | | 2.6 | 2.22 |
| Futura Medium w. oblique (Inter)....... | 4.21 | | 3.56 | | 2.87 | | 2.42 | 2.10 |

* Also comes in italic, which sets a bit narrower than the roman.

CHARACTERS PER PICA (*continued*)

| Type face | \
Size of type face 6 pt. | 7 pt. | 8 pt. | 9 pt. | 10 pt. | 11 pt. | 12 pt. | 14 pt. |
|---|---|---|---|---|---|---|---|---|
| Garamond w. ital. & s.c. (Inter) | 3.93 | 3.64 | 3.35 | 3.05 | 2.92 | 2.73 | 2.58 | 2.3 |
| Garamond w. ital. & s.c. (Lino) | 4.27 | | 3.52 | 3.13 | 2.82 | 2.54 | 2.29 | 2.05 |
| Garamond Bold w. ital. (Inter) | 3.75 | 3.45 | 3.20 | 2.87 | 2.73 | 2.50 | 2.41 | 2.15 |
| Garamond Bold w. ital. (Lino) | 3.84 | | 3.16 | | 2.54 | | 2.02 | 1.83 |
| Garamond No. 3 w. ital. & s.c. (Lino) | 3.93 | 3.6 | 3.02 | 3.08 | 2.90 | 2.73 | 2.30 | 2.28 |
| Garamond Bold No. 3 w. ital. & s.c. (Lino) | 3.65 | 3.28 | 3.02 | 2.78 | 2.63 | 2.44 | 2.31 | 2.04 |
| Garamont No. 248 (Mono) | 4.69 | | 3.41 | 3.00 | 2.71 | 2.44 | 2.23 | 2.01 |
| Garamont Bold No. 548 (Mono) * | 3.68 | 3.29 | 3.01 | 2.75 | 2.61 | 2.47 | 2.31 | 2.08 |
| Goudy Oldstyle w. ital. & s.c. (Inter) | 4.02 | | 3.35 | | 2.73 | | 2.39 | 1.99 |
| Goudy Old Style No. 394 (Mono) * | 3.99 | | 3.25 | | 2.68 | | 2.34 | 1.95 |
| Granjon w. ital. & s.c. (Lino) | 4.24 | | 3.48 | 3.16 | 2.94 | 2.71 | 2.49 | 2.24 |
| Ionic No. 5 w. ital. & s.c. (Lino) | 3.27 | 2.99 | 2.68 | 2.49 | 2.34 | | 2.09 | |
| Janson (Lino) | | | 3.07 | 2.81 | 2.60 | 2.46 | 2.30 | 2.08 |
| Kenntonian w. ital. & s.c. (Inter) | 4.19 | | 3.25 | | 2.84 | | 2.44 | 2.14 |
| Memphis Light w. bold (Lino) | 3.52 | | 3.28 | 2.85 | 2.56 | | 2.06 | 1.75 |
| Memphis Medium w. ital. & s.c. (Lino) | 3.52 | | 3.28 | 2.82 | 2.56 | | 2.04 | 1.73 |
| Metrolite No. 2 w. Metroblack No. 2 (Lino) | 3.63 | | 3.16 | | 2.50 | | 2.09 | 1.8 |
| Metromedium No. 2 w. Metrothin No. 2 (Lino) | 3.97 | | 3.52 | | 2.80 | | 2.34 | 2.02 |
| No. 21 (Lino) | 3.80 | 3.22 | 3.10 | 2.96 | 2.62 | 2.41 | 2.20 | |
| Old Style No. 1 w. ital. & s.c. (Lino) | 3.75 | 3.38 | 3.13 | 2.89 | 2.69 | 2.52 | 2.28 | 1.92 |
| Opticon w. boldface No. 2 (Lino) | 3.13 | 2.87 | 2.63 | 2.56 | 2.37 | 2.24 | 2.14 | |
| Original Old Caslon No. 337 (Mono) * | | 3.68 | 3.34 | 2.98 | 2.67 | 2.44 | 2.23 | 2.14 |
| Sans Serif Light No. 329 (Mono) * | 4.27 | | 3.39 | | 2.89 | | 2.52 | 2.55 |
| Sans Serif Medium No. 331 (Mono) | 4.23 | | 3.35 | | 2.85 | | 2.49 | 2.29 |
| Scotch w. ital. & s.c. (Lino) | 3.52 | | 3.10 | | 2.73 | 2.56 | 2.20 | 1.84 |
| Spartan Light w. Medium (Lino) | | | 3.67 | | 2.92 | | 2.47 | 2.16 |
| Spartan Heavy w. ital. (Lino) | | | 3.48 | | 2.61 | | 2.26 | 2.02 |
| Stymie Light No. 190 * (Mono) | 3.92 | | 3.23 | | 2.61 | | 2.18 | 1.82 |
| Stymie Bold No. 189 * (Mono) | 3.43 | | 2.82 | | 2.29 | | 2.02 | 1.57 |
| Stymie Medium No. 290 * (Mono) | 3.92 | | 3.23 | | 2.61 | | 2.20 | 1.73 |
| Times Roman w. ital & s.c. (Lino) | 3.79 | 3.44 | 3.14 | 2.91 | 2.75 | 2.56 | 2.32 | 2.13 |
| Twentieth Century Light No. 606 * (Mono) | 4.68 | | 3.81 | | 3.08 | | 2.61 | 2.26 |
| Twentieth Century Medium No. 605 * (Mono) | 4.68 | | 3.66 | | 2.94 | | 2.44 | 2.09 |
| Twentieth Century Bold No. 604 * (Mono) | 4.00 | | 3.48 | | 2.61 | | 2.26 | 2.01 |
| Vogue w. Vogue Bold (Inter) | 3.97 | | 3.52 | | 2.92 | | 2.44 | 2.12 |

*Also comes in italic, which sets a bit narrower than the roman.

TABLE FOR CONVERTING CHARACTERS PER PICA INTO CHARACTERS PER LINE

| C.p.p. | Alphabet length, points | 10 | 12 | 14 | 16 | 18 | 20 | 22 | 24 | 26 | 28 | 30 |
|---|---|---|---|---|---|---|---|---|---|---|---|---|
| | | Length of line, picas — Characters per line | | | | | | | | | | |
| 0.55 | 620 | 5 | 6 | 7 | 8 | 9 | 11 | 12 | 13 | 14 | 15 | 16 |
| 0.60 | 579 | 6 | 7 | 8 | 9 | 10 | 12 | 13 | 14 | 15 | 16 | 18 |
| 0.65 | 525 | 6 | 7 | 9 | 10 | 11 | 13 | 14 | 15 | 16 | 18 | 19 |
| 0.70 | 488 | 7 | 8 | 9 | 11 | 12 | 14 | 15 | 16 | 18 | 19 | 21 |
| 0.75 | 455 | 7 | 9 | 10 | 12 | 13 | 15 | 16 | 17 | 19 | 21 | 22 |
| 0.80 | 427 | 8 | 9 | 11 | 12 | 14 | 16 | 17 | 19 | 20 | 22 | 24 |
| 0.85 | 402 | 8 | 10 | 11 | 13 | 15 | 17 | 18 | 20 | 22 | 23 | 25 |
| 0.90 | 379 | 9 | 10 | 12 | 14 | 16 | 18 | 19 | 21 | 23 | 25 | 27 |
| 0.95 | 360 | 9 | 11 | 13 | 15 | 17 | 19 | 20 | 22 | 24 | 26 | 28 |
| 1.00 | 341 | 10 | 12 | 14 | 16 | 18 | 20 | 22 | 24 | 26 | 28 | 30 |
| 1.05 | 325 | 10 | 12 | 14 | 16 | 18 | 21 | 23 | 25 | 27 | 29 | 31 |
| 1.10 | 310 | 11 | 13 | 15 | 17 | 19 | 22 | 24 | 26 | 28 | 30 | 33 |
| 1.15 | 296 | 11 | 13 | 16 | 18 | 20 | 23 | 25 | 27 | 29 | 32 | 34 |
| 1.20 | 284 | 12 | 14 | 16 | 19 | 21 | 24 | 26 | 28 | 31 | 33 | 36 |
| 1.25 | 273 | 12 | 15 | 17 | 20 | 22 | 25 | 27 | 30 | 32 | 35 | 37 |
| 1.30 | 262 | 13 | 15 | 18 | 20 | 23 | 26 | 28 | 31 | 33 | 36 | 39 |
| 1.35 | 253 | 13 | 16 | 18 | 21 | 24 | 27 | 29 | 32 | 35 | 37 | 40 |
| 1.40 | 244 | 14 | 16 | 19 | 22 | 25 | 28 | 30 | 33 | 36 | 39 | 42 |
| 1.45 | 235 | 14 | 17 | 20 | 23 | 26 | 29 | 31 | 34 | 37 | 40 | 43 |
| 1.50 | 227 | 15 | 18 | 21 | 24 | 27 | 30 | 33 | 36 | 39 | 42 | 45 |
| 1.60 | 213 | 16 | 19 | 22 | 25 | 28 | 32 | 35 | 38 | 41 | 44 | 48 |
| 1.70 | 200 | 17 | 20 | 24 | 27 | 30 | 34 | 37 | 40 | 44 | 47 | 51 |
| 1.80 | 189 | 18 | 21 | 25 | 28 | 32 | 36 | 39 | 43 | 46 | 50 | 54 |
| 1.90 | 179 | 19 | 22 | 26 | 30 | 34 | 38 | 41 | 45 | 49 | 53 | 57 |
| 2.00 | 170 | 20 | 24 | 28 | 32 | 36 | 40 | 44 | 48 | 52 | 56 | 60 |
| 2.10 | 162 | 21 | 25 | 29 | 33 | 37 | 42 | 46 | 50 | 54 | 58 | 63 |
| 2.20 | 155 | 22 | 26 | 30 | 35 | 39 | 44 | 48 | 52 | 57 | 61 | 66 |
| 2.30 | 148 | 23 | 27 | 32 | 36 | 41 | 46 | 50 | 55 | 60 | 64 | 69 |
| 2.40 | 142 | 24 | 28 | 33 | 38 | 43 | 48 | 52 | 57 | 62 | 67 | 72 |
| 2.50 | 136 | 25 | 30 | 35 | 40 | 45 | 50 | 55 | 60 | 65 | 70 | 75 |
| 2.60 | 131 | 26 | 31 | 36 | 41 | 46 | 52 | 57 | 62 | 67 | 72 | 78 |
| 2.70 | 126 | 27 | 32 | 37 | 43 | 48 | 54 | 59 | 64 | 70 | 75 | 81 |
| 2.80 | 121 | 28 | 33 | 39 | 44 | 50 | 56 | 61 | 67 | 73 | 78 | 84 |
| 2.90 | 118 | 29 | 34 | 40 | 46 | 52 | 58 | 63 | 69 | 75 | 81 | 87 |
| 3.00 | 114 | 30 | 36 | 42 | 48 | 54 | 60 | 66 | 72 | 78 | 84 | 90 |
| 3.10 | 110 | 31 | 37 | 43 | 49 | 55 | 62 | 68 | 74 | 80 | 86 | 93 |
| 3.20 | 106 | 32 | 38 | 45 | 51 | 57 | 64 | 70 | 76 | 83 | 89 | 96 |
| 3.30 | 103 | 33 | 39 | 46 | 52 | 59 | 66 | 72 | 79 | 86 | 92 | 99 |
| 3.40 | 100 | 34 | 40 | 47 | 54 | 61 | 68 | 74 | 81 | 88 | 95 | 102 |
| 3.50 | 98 | 35 | 42 | 49 | 56 | 63 | 70 | 77 | 84 | 90 | 98 | 105 |
| 3.60 | 95 | 36 | 43 | 50 | 57 | 64 | 72 | 79 | 86 | 93 | 100 | 108 |
| 3.70 | 92 | 37 | 44 | 52 | 59 | 66 | 74 | 81 | 89 | 96 | 104 | 111 |
| 3.80 | 90 | 38 | 45 | 53 | 60 | 68 | 76 | 83 | 91 | 99 | 106 | 114 |
| 3.90 | 88 | 39 | 46 | 54 | 62 | 70 | 78 | 85 | 93 | 102 | 109 | 117 |
| 4.00 | 85 | 40 | 48 | 56 | 64 | 72 | 80 | 88 | 96 | 104 | 112 | 120 |

THE BODONI FAMILY         (Shown in 12 pt. where possible)

| Approxi-mate c.p.p. 12 pt. | Approxi-mate c.p.p. 24 pt. | TYPE FACE |
|---|---|---|
| 2.50 | 1.43 | Bodoni Book, *Bodoni Book Italic* (ATF, Inter-type, Lino, Mono) |
| 2.35 | 1.28 | Bodoni, *Bodoni Italic* |
| 2.17 | 1.21 | **Bodoni Bold, *Bodoni Bold Italic*** |
| 1.56 | 0.83 | **Bodoni Ultra, *Bodoni Ultra Italic* (ATF, Mono)** |
| 1.86 | 0.89 | **Bodoni Black (Ludlow)** *Bodoni Black Italic* **(Ludlow)** |
| 1.55 | 0.88 | **Bodoni Modern, *Bodoni Modern Italic* (Inter)** |
| 1.73 | 0.83 | **Bodoni Poster** *Bodoni Poster Italic* **(Lino)** |
|  | 1.51 | **Bodoni Bold Condensed (Lino, Mono, Intertype) 14 pt.** |
|  | 1.72 | **Bodoni Campanile,** *Bodoni Campanile Italic (Ludlow)* |
| 2.14 | 1.23 | **Bodoni Ultra Extra Condensed (14 pt.)** |
| 2.32 | 1.25 | Bodoni Open (ATF) |
|  | 1.78 | **Onyx (ATF, Mono) 18 pt.** |
|  | 1.73 | **Bodoni Poster Compressed (APL) (24 pt.)** |
| 1.20 | 0.62 | **Nubian (ATF)** |

NOTE: Where no figures appear, the type does not come in that size or else counts were unobtainable.

## THE FUTURA FAMILY (Shown in 12 pt. where possible)

| Approximate c.p.p. 12 pt. | Approximate c.p.p. 24 pt. | Intertype and Bauer call it *Futura;* Linotype and ATF call it *Spartan;* Ludlow calls it *Tempo;* Monotype calls it *Twentieth Century.* Remember that what one firm calls "bold" others call "black," "heavy," or "extrabold" |
|:---:|:---:|:---|
| 2.60 | | Futura Light, *Futura Oblique Light* (Inter) |
| 2.47 | 1.29 | Spartan Light (Lino) |
| 2.74 | 1.29 | Tempo Light, *Tempo Light Italic* (Ludlow) |
| 2.61 | | Twentieth Century Light, and *Italic* (Mono) |
| 2.60 | | Futura Book, *Futura Book Oblique* |
| 2.42 | 1.31 | Futura Medium, *Futura Oblique Medium* |
| 2.47 | 1.38 | Spartan Medium, *Spartan Medium Italic* |
| 2.70 | 1.29 | Tempo Medium *Tempo Medium Italic* |
| 2.44 | 1.32 | Twentieth Century Medium, and *Italic* |
| 2.30 | 1.23 | **Futura Demibold, *Futura Demibold Oblique*** |
| 2.26 | 1.24 | **Spartan Heavy, *Spartan Heavy Italic*** |
| 2.30 | 1.07 | **Tempo Bold and *Bold Italic*** |
| 2.26 | 1.24 | **Twentieth Century Bold and *Bold Italic*** |
| 1.98 | 1.07 | **Futura Bold, *Futura Bold Oblique*** |
| 1.98 | 1.07 | **Spartan Black, *Spartan Black Italic*** |
| 2.00 | 0.99 | **Tempo Heavy and *Heavy Italic*** |
| 2.01 | 0.99 | **Twentieth Century Extrabold, and *Extrabold Italic*** |

NOTE: Where no figures appear, the type does not come in that size or else counts were unobtainable.

THE FUTURA FAMILY (*Cont.*) (Shown in 12 pt. where possible)

| Approxi-mate c.p.p.12pt. | Approxi-mate c.p.p.12pt. | Intertype and Bauer call it *Futura;* Linotype and ATF call it *Spartan;* Ludlow calls it *Tempo;* Monotype calls it *Twentieth Century.* Remember that what one firm calls "bold" others call "black," "heavy," or "extrabold" |
|---|---|---|
| 2.78 | | **Futura Bold Condensed** |
| 2.60 | 1.54 | **Spartan Black Condensed, and *Condensed Italic*** |
| 2.80 | 1.48 | **Tempo Heavy Condensed** |
| | 1.47 | **Twentieth Century Extrabold Condensed and *Italic*** |
| 3.11 | | Futura Medium Condensed |
| 2.97 | 1.48 | Tempo Bold Condensed |
| 2.66 | 1.34 | Twentieth Century Medium Condensed |
| | | **Futura Black** |
| 1.67 | 0.97 | **Twentieth Century Ultrabold** |
| 2.00 | 1.18 | **Twentieth Century Ultrabold Condensed (14 pt.)** |
| | | **Futura Display (14 pt.)** |
| | 0.91 | **Tempo Black (18 pt.)** |
| | | FUTURA INLINE (18 PT.) |
| | | TEMPO HEAVY INLINE (18 PT.) |

NOTE: Where no figures appear, the type does not come in that size or else counts were unobtainable.

## SOME OTHER SANS-SERIF FACES (Shown in 12 pt. if possible)

| Approximate c.p.p. 12 pt. | Approximate c.p.p. 24 pt. | TYPE FACE |
|---|---|---|
| 2.44 | 1.26 | Vogue, *Vogue Oblique* (Intertype) |
| 2.52 | 1.57 | Sans Serif Light and *Light Italic* (Mono) |
| 2.35 | 1.25 | Metrothin (Lino) |
| 2.49 | 1.61 | Sans Serif Medium |
| 2.09 | 1.13 | Metrolite, *Metrolite Italic* |
| 2.37 | 1.23 | **Vogue Bold, *Vogue Bold Oblique*** |
| 2.49 | 1.52 | **Sans Serif Bold, *Sans Serif Bold Italic*** |
| 2.35 | 1.25 | **Metromedium, *Metromedium Italic*** |
| 2.03 | 1.11 | **Vogue Extra Bold, *Extra Bold Oblique*** |
| 2.07 | 1.23 | **Sans Serif Extrabold, *Extrabold Italic*** |
| 2.07 | 1.16 | **Metroblack, *Metroblack Italic*** |
| 1.86 | 0.97 | **Franklin Gothic** |
|  |  | **Franklin Gothic Wide** |
|  | 2.05 | Sans Serif Light Condensed |
| 2.99 | 1.75 | Vogue Bold Condensed |
|  | 1.73 | Sans Serif Medium Condensed (14 pt.) |
| 3.28 | 1.80 | Erbar Light Condensed (Lino) |
| 2.99 | 1.60 | **Vogue Extra Bold Condensed** |
|  | 1.45 | **Sans Serif Extra Bold Condensed** |
| 2.21 | 1.20 | **Franklin Gothic Condensed (ATF)** |
| 1.75 | 1.54 | **Franklin Gothic Extra Cond. (ATF and Ludlow)** |
| 2.96 | 1.55 | **Alternate Gothic No. 2 (Intertype and ATF)** |
| 3.31 | 1.79 | **Alternate Gothic No. 1 (Intertype and ATF)** |
| 3.28 | 1.69 | **Erbar Bold Condensed (Linotype)** |

NOTE: Where no figures appear, the type does not come in that size or else counts were unobtainable.

# The Egyptian (Square Serif) Family (12 pt. where possible)

| Approximate c.p.p. 12 pt. | Approximate c.p.p. 24 pt. | Ludlow calls it *Karnak;* Linotype calls it *Memphis;* Monotype and ATF call it *Stymie;* Intertype calls it *Beton* or *Cairo* |
|---|---|---|
| 2.12 | 1.04 | Karnak Light (Ludlow) |
| 2.06 | 1.10 | Memphis Light, *Light Italic* (Lino) |
| 2.18 | 1.14 | Stymie Light, *Light Italic* (Mono, ATF) |
| 2.06 | 1.09 | Cairo, *Cairo Italic* (Inter) |
| 2.07 | 0.98 | Karnak Intermediate, *Intermediate Italic* |
| 2.04 | 1.06 | Memphis Medium, *Medium Italic* |
| 2.20 | 1.08 | Stymie Medium, *Medium Italic* |
| 2.12 | 1.20 | Beton Medium *with Italic* |
| 2.07 | 1.11 | Cairo Medium *with Italic* |
| 2.00 | 0.98 | **Karnak Medium** |
| 2.04 | 1.07 | **Memphis Bold, *Memphis Bold Italic*** |
| 2.02 | 1.03 | **Stymie Bold, *Stymie Bold Italic*** |
| 2.12 | 1.14 | **Beton Bold** |
| 2.05 | 1.10 | **Cairo Bold, *Cairo Bold Italic*** |
| 1.80 | 0.94 | **Karnak Black, *Karnak Black Italic*** |
| 1.70 | 0.93 | **Memphis Extra Bold, *Italic*** |
| 1.86 | 0.91 | **Stymie Extra Bold, *Italic*** |
| 1.73 | 0.93 | **Stymie Black *and Italic*** |
| 1.67 | 1.03 | **Beton Extra Bold,** |
| | | **Beton Extra Bold Oblique** |
| 2.52 | 1.45 | Memphis Medium Condensed |
| 2.66 | 1.46 | **Memphis Bold Condensed** |
| 2.46 | 1.40 | **Cairo Bold Condensed** |
| | 1.35 | **Karnak Black Condensed (14 pt.)** |
| 2.52 | 1.44 | **Memphis Extra Bold Condensed (14)** |
| 1.69 | 1.03 | Beton Wide |
| | 1.99 | Karnak Obelisk (14 pt.) |

NOTE: Where no figures appear, the type does not come in that size or else counts were unobtainable.

### DISPLAY FACES

106 of the most popular display types are shown on pages 365 to 396. Complete upper- and lower-case alphabets are given for each, in the 24-pt. size. This is by no means a complete listing of existing display types; however, an attempt has been made to show at least one example of each of the most used basic type styles. No one printer will have all the faces shown, and only large advertising typographers will come anywhere near having them all.

The range of sizes given is that available from the manufacturer. Printers often buy only one or a few of the sizes available in any given face.

After each listing is given the characters per pica of the 24-pt. size shown, for both small letters and capital letters. From this information it is possible to calculate approximately how much space any given headline will occupy in any desired style and size of type.

TABLE FOR ESTIMATING THE LENGTH OF A HEADLINE WHEN THE NUMBER OF CHARACTERS IN THE HEADLINE IS KNOWN

| Characters per pica in 24-pt. size as given on pp. 319 to 350 | Number of letters and spaces | | | | | | | | | | |
|---|---|---|---|---|---|---|---|---|---|---|---|
| | 8 | 12 | 16 | 20 | 24 | 28 | 32 | 36 | 40 | 44 | 48 |
| | Length (in picas) of a headline (in 24-pt. type) | | | | | | | | | | |
| 0.55 | 15 | 21 | 29 | 36 | 43 | 51 | 58 | 65 | 72 | 80 | 87 |
| 0.60 | 14 | 20 | 26 | 33 | 40 | 46 | 53 | 60 | 66 | 73 | 80 |
| 0.65 | 13 | 18 | 24 | 30 | 37 | 43 | 49 | 55 | 61 | 68 | 74 |
| 0.70 | 12 | 17 | 22 | 28 | 34 | 40 | 46 | 51 | 57 | 63 | 68 |
| 0.75 | 11 | 16 | 21 | 26 | 32 | 37 | 43 | 48 | 53 | 58 | 64 |
| 0.80 | 10 | 15 | 20 | 25 | 30 | 35 | 40 | 45 | 50 | 55 | 60 |
| 0.85 | 10 | 14 | 18 | 23 | 28 | 33 | 38 | 42 | 47 | 51 | 56 |
| 0.90 | 9 | 13 | 17 | 22 | 26 | 31 | 36 | 40 | 44 | 48 | 53 |
| 0.95 | 9 | 12 | 16 | 21 | 25 | 29 | 34 | 37 | 42 | 46 | 50 |
| 1.00 | 8 | 11 | 16 | 20 | 24 | 28 | 32 | 36 | 40 | 44 | 48 |
| 1.05 | 8 | 11 | 15 | 19 | 22 | 26 | 30 | 34 | 38 | 42 | 45 |
| 1.10 | 8 | 10 | 14 | 18 | 21 | 25 | 29 | 32 | 36 | 40 | 43 |
| 1.15 | 7 | 10 | 13 | 17 | 20 | 24 | 27 | 31 | 34 | 38 | 41 |
| 1.20 | 7 | 10 | 13 | 16 | 20 | 23 | 26 | 29 | 33 | 36 | 40 |
| 1.25 | 7 | 9 | 12 | 16 | 19 | 22 | 25 | 28 | 31 | 35 | 38 |
| 1.30 | 7 | 9 | 12 | 15 | 18 | 21 | 24 | 27 | 30 | 33 | 36 |
| 1.35 | 6 | 8 | 11 | 14 | 17 | 20 | 23 | 26 | 29 | 32 | 35 |
| 1.40 | 6 | 8 | 11 | 14 | 17 | 20 | 22 | 25 | 28 | 31 | 34 |
| 1.45 | 6 | 8 | 11 | 13 | 16 | 19 | 22 | 24 | 27 | 30 | 33 |
| 1.50 | 6 | 8 | 10 | 13 | 15 | 18 | 21 | 24 | 26 | 29 | 32 |
| 1.55 | 6 | 7 | 10 | 12 | 15 | 18 | 20 | 23 | 25 | 28 | 31 |
| 1.60 | 5 | 7 | 10 | 12 | 15 | 17 | 20 | 22 | 24 | 27 | 30 |
| 1.65 | 5 | 7 | 9 | 12 | 14 | 16 | 19 | 21 | 24 | 26 | 29 |
| 1.70 | 5 | 7 | 9 | 11 | 14 | 16 | 18 | 21 | 23 | 25 | 28 |
| 1.75 | 5 | 6 | 9 | 11 | 13 | 15 | 18 | 20 | 22 | 25 | 27 |
| 1.80 | 5 | 6 | 8 | 11 | 13 | 15 | 17 | 20 | 22 | 24 | 26 |
| 1.85 | 5 | 6 | 8 | 10 | 12 | 15 | 17 | 19 | 21 | 23 | 25 |
| 1.90 | 5 | 6 | 8 | 10 | 12 | 14 | 16 | 18 | 21 | 23 | 25 |
| 2.00 | 4 | 6 | 8 | 10 | 12 | 14 | 16 | 18 | 20 | 22 | 24 |

NOTE: Be sure to take the caps p.p. count if the headline is to be set in all caps. Take the lower-case c.p.p. count if the headline is to be in lower case. Count incidental caps as two lower-case characters.

TABLE FOR ESTIMATING THE LENGTH OF A HEADLINE (OTHER THAN 24-PT.)
WHEN THE LENGTH OF A 24-PT. HEADLINE IS KNOWN

| Length of 24-pt. headline in picas | Approximate length of same headline in type face of other sizes | | | | | | |
|---|---|---|---|---|---|---|---|
| | 18 pt. | 30 pt. | 36 pt. | 48 pt. | 60 pt. | 72 pt. | 96 pt. |
| 4 | 3 | 5 | 6 | 8 | 10 | 12 | 16 |
| 6 | 4.5 | 8 | 9 | 12 | 15 | 18 | 24 |
| 8 | 6 | 10 | 12 | 16 | 20 | 24 | 32 |
| 10 | 7.5 | 13 | 15 | 20 | 25 | 30 | 40 |
| 12 | 9 | 15 | 18 | 24 | 30 | 36 | 48 |
| 14 | 10.5 | 18 | 21 | 28 | 35 | 42 | 56 |
| 16 | 12 | 20 | 24 | 32 | 40 | 48 | 64 |
| 18 | 13.5 | 23 | 27 | 36 | 45 | 54 | 72 |
| 20 | 15 | 25 | 30 | 40 | 50 | 60 | 80 |
| 22 | 16.5 | 28 | 33 | 44 | 55 | 66 | 88 |
| 24 | 18 | 30 | 36 | 48 | 60 | 72 | 96 |
| 26 | 19.5 | 33 | 39 | 52 | 65 | 78 | 104 |
| 28 | 21 | 35 | 42 | 56 | 70 | 84 | 112 |
| 30 | 22.5 | 38 | 45 | 60 | 75 | 90 | 120 |
| 35 | 27 | 44 | 53 | 70 | 88 | 105 | 140 |
| 40 | 30 | 50 | 60 | 80 | 100 | 120 | 160 |
| 45 | 34 | 56 | 68 | 90 | 113 | 135 | 180 |
| 50 | 38 | 63 | 75 | 100 | 125 | 150 | 200 |
| 55 | 41 | 69 | 83 | 110 | 138 | 165 | 220 |
| 60 | 45 | 75 | 90 | 120 | 150 | 180 | 240 |
| 65 | 49 | 81 | 98 | 130 | 163 | 195 | 260 |
| 70 | 52 | 88 | 105 | 140 | 175 | 210 | 280 |
| 75 | 56 | 94 | 113 | 150 | 188 | 225 | 300 |
| 80 | 60 | 100 | 120 | 160 | 200 | 240 | 320 |
| 85 | 64 | 106 | 128 | 170 | 213 | 255 | 340 |
| 90 | 68 | 112 | 135 | 180 | 225 | 270 | 360 |

*Example.* The headline "PRINT-ING HANDBOOK" is to be set in Memphis Medium caps, to fill a line 28 picas long. The headline consists of 16 letters and 1 space, or 17 characters in all. Under Memphis Medium (see p. 389) is found the information that there are about 0.81 caps per pica in 24 pt. 17 times 0.81 gives 13.7. The headline will therefore occupy about 13.7 picas if set in 24 pt. If set twice as big, in 48 pt., it should occupy about 27.4 picas. If set 2½ times as big, in 60 pt., it should occupy 34.4 picas. 48 pt. is, therefore, the indicated size.

This system does not claim perfect accuracy, but it is usually accurate enough. When working with headlines that are to be set in caps and lower case, one usually counts caps as equal to two small letters. When headlines are short, it may be wise to count "i" and "l" as ½ character, "m" and "w" as 1½ characters, etc.

The accompanying tables make it easy to translate characters per pica into length of headline; and length of a 24-pt. headline into the length of the same heading in another size. First, find the characters per pica in the 24-pt. size of the desired type face (see pages 365 to 396), and find the length of the headline if it was set in 24-pt. type. Then, with the second table, find the approximate length of the same headline in this type in a different size.

The count for characters per pica (c.p.p.) is given only for the version shown. There are likely to be slight differences in character counts as between Monotype Bodoni and Linotype Bodoni, etc. However, these differences are not usually great enough to jeopardize the utility of a calculation; noticeable differences are commented upon below; see Caslon, for example, pages 371 and 372.

Information is given with each type specimen as to whether it is available on the Linotype, Intertype, Monotype, Ludlow, or, as foundry type, from American Type Founders (ATF), Bauer, Continental, etc.

Linotype, Intertype, and Ludlow faces are cast fresh for each use. A printer may or may not be able to cast up more Monotype characters as he needs them, depending on whether he has purchased the matrices or just the cast type.

The machine faces are usually favored if the type itself is to be printed from. This is because printers are understandably reluctant to let their foundry type undergo the wear of actual printing unless they can get more of it, promptly and at a reasonable price. Foundry type is often reserved for the making of reproduction proofs (as for offset) or for making electros.

# Alternate Gothic No. 2 (Mono.)
# ABCDEFGHIJKLMNOPQRSTUVWXYZ&
# abcdefghijklmnopqrstuvwxyz 1234567890

Mono: c.p.p. (24 pt.) 1.55; caps p.p., 1.31. 6-36 pt. ATF: 6-72 pt. No italic. Alternate Gothic No. 1 is slightly narrower; No. 3 somewhat wider.

# BALLOON BOLD (ATF)
# ABCDEFGHIJKLMNOPQRSTUVWXYZ&
# 1234567890

ATF: caps only. Caps p.p. (24 pt.) 1.24. Available in 10-96 pt. in Light and Extra-bold as well as in the Bold shown here.

# Barnum, P. T. (ATF)
# ABCDEFGHIJKLMNOPQRSTUVW
# XYZ& abcdefghijklmnopqrstuvwxyz
# 1234567890

ATF: c.p.p. (24 pt.) 1.35; caps p.p. 0.91. 6-36 pt.

# Baskerville (Mono No. 353)
# ABCDEFGHIJKLMNOPQRST
# UVWXYZ& 1234567890
# abcdefghijklmnopqrstuvwxyz

Mono:c.p.p. (24 pt.) 1.29; caps p.p., 0.86. 6-36 pt. ATF: 6-72 pt. Lino and Intertype: 6-14 pt.

NOTE: c.p.p. means lower-case characters per pica. Caps p.p. means caps per pica. Character counts may differ somewhat between one typefounder and another for similar faces and between italic and roman.

# Baskerville Italic (Mono No. 353)
## ABCDEFGHIJKLMNOPQRST UVWXYZ& 1234567890
### abcdefghijklmnopqrstuvwxyz

Mono: c.p.p. (24 pt.) 1.48; caps p.p. 0.91. 6-36 pt. ATF: 6-18 pt. Lino and Intertype: 6-14 pt.

# Baskerville Bold (Mono. No. 453)
## ABCDEFGHIJKLMNOPQRSTU VWXYZ& 1234567890
### abcdefghijklmnopqrstuvwxyx

Mono: c.p.p. (24 pt.) 1.18; caps p.p., 0.82. 8-72 pt. No italic. Linotype has a Baskerville Bold Italic in 7-14 pt.

# Bernhard Modern Bold (ATF)
## ABCDEFGHIJKLMNOPQR STUVWXYZ& 1234567890
### abcdefghijklmnopqrstuvwxyz

ATF: c.p.p. (24 pt.) 1.21; caps p.p., 0.80. Available also in a matching italic, and in a lighter Bernhard Modern Roman.

# Beton Series (Inter)

See MEMPHIS and also page 361.

---

NOTE: c.p.p. means lower-case characters per pica. Caps p.p. means caps per pica. Character counts may differ somewhat between one typefounder and another for similar faces and between italic and roman.

# Bodoni (Mono)
## ABCDEFGHIJKLMNOPQRS TUVWXYZ& 1234567890
### abcdefghijklmnopqrstuvwxyz

Mono: c.p.p. (24 pt.) 1.26; caps p.p. 0.90. 5-36 pt. Every manufacturer offers the Bodoni series in a wide range of sizes. See page 357.

# *Bodoni Italic (Mono)*
## *ABCDEFGHIJKLMNOPQRS TUVWXYZ& 1234567890*
### *abcdefghijklmnopqrstuvwxyz*

Mono: c.p.p. (24 pt.) 1.28; caps p.p. 0.89. 6-72 pt.

# Bodoni Bold (Mono)
## ABCDEFGHIJKLMNOPQRS TUVWXYZ& 1234567890
### abcdefghijklmnopqrstuvwxyz

Mono: c.p.p. (24 pt.) 1.15; caps p.p. 0.87. 6-72 pt.

# *Bodoni Bold Italic (Mono)*
## *ABCDEFGHIJKLMNOPQR STUVWXYZ& 1234567890*
### *abcdefghijklmnopqrstuvwxyz*

Mono: c.p.p. (24 pt.) 1.17; caps p.p. 0.85. 6-72 pt.

NOTE: c.p.p. means lower-case characters per pica. Caps p.p. means caps per pica. Character counts may differ somewhat between one typefounder and another for similar faces and between italic and roman.

# Bodoni, Ultra (ATF)
# ABCDEFGHIJKLMNO
# PQRSTUVWXYZ&
# abcdefghijklmnopqrst
# uvwxyz 1234567890

ATF: c.p.p. (24 pt.) 0.82; caps p.p. 0.63. 6-120 pt. Ludlow offers a similar face called Bodoni Black (6-72 pt.); Intertype, Bodoni Modern (8-36 pt.); Linotype, Poster Bodoni (8-144 pt.)

# *Bodoni Italic, Ultra (ATF)*
# *ABCDEFGHIJKLMNO*
# *PQRSTUVWXYZ&*
# *abcdefghijklmnopqrst*
# *uvwxyz 1234567890*

ATF: c.p.p. (24 pt.) 0.84; caps p.p. 0.62. 6-72 pt. Ludlow offers a similar face called Bodoni Black Italic with swash characters (12-48 pt.); Intertype, Bodoni Modern Italic (8-24 pt.) Linotype, Poster Bodoni Italic (8-60 pt.)

# Bookman (Ludlow)
# ABCDEFGHIJKLMNOP
# QRSTUVWXYZ& abcdefg
# hijklmnopqrstuvwxyz 12345

Ludlow: c.p.p. (24 pt.) 0.99; caps p.p. 0.66. 12-48 pt. ATF: Bookman Oldstyle comes in 6-36 pt. Linotype has it in 6-14 pt. Monotype has it in 6-36 pt. and also has New Bookman in 14-72. Intertype calls it Bookface and offers sizes 6-30 pt.

NOTE: c.p.p. means lower-case characters per pica. Caps p.p. means caps per pica. Character counts may differ somewhat between one typefounder and another for similar faces and between italic and roman.

# *BOOKMAN ITALIC (ATF)*

## *ABCDEFGHIJKLMNOPQRSTUV XYZ& 1234567890*

*abcdefghijklmnopqrstuvwxyz*

Same range of sizes as above, except ATF and Intertype have the italic only to 24 pt. (18 pt. shown here.)

# BOUL MICH (ATF)

## ABCDEFGHIJKLMN OPQRSTUVWXYZ& 1234567890

ATF: caps only. Caps p.p. (24 pt.) 0.55. 12-72 pt.

# BROADWAY (ATF)

## ABCDEFGHIJKLM NOPQRSTUVWXY Z& 1234567890

ATF: caps only. Caps p.p. (24 pt.) 0.52. 6-72 pt. Monotype has it in 12-36 pt.

# Bulmer (ATF)

## ABCDEFGHIJKLMNOPQRST UVWXYZ& 1234567890

abcdefghijklmnopqrstuvwxyz

ATF: c.p.p. (24 pt.) 1.36; caps p.p. 0.91. 6-48 pt.

NOTE: c.p.p. means lower-case characters per pica. Caps p.p. means caps per pica. Character counts may differ somewhat between one typefounder and another for similar faces and between italic and roman.

# Bulmer Italic (ATF)
ABCDEFGHIJKLMNOPQRSTUVW
XYZ&  abcdefghijklmnopqrstuvwxyz
1234567890

ATF: c.p.p. (24 pt.) 1.47; caps p.p. 0.94. 6-48 pt.

## Cairo Series (Inter)

This comes in the same general range of sizes and weights as Memphis. See also page 361.

# Cameo (Ludlow)
ABCDEFGHIJKLMNOPQ
RSTUVWXYZ& abcdefghi
jklmnopqrstuvwxyz 123456

Ludlow: c.p.p. (24 pt.) 0.97; caps p.p. 0.69. 12-72 pt. Similar type styles include Narciss, Goudy Open, Goudy Handtooled, Cloister Bold Tooled, and Caslon Openface.

# Cameo Italic (Ludlow)
ABCDEFGHIJKLMNOP
QRSTUVWXYZ&abcdefg
hijklmnopqrstuvwxyz123

Ludlow: c.p.p. (24 pt.) 0.93; caps p.p. 0.65. 12-48 pt.

NOTE: c.p.p. means lower-case characters per pica. Caps p.p. means caps per pica. Character counts may differ somewhat between one typefounder and another for similar faces and between italic and roman.

# Caslon (Lino)

ABCDEFGHIJKLMNOPQRS
TUVWXYZ& 1234567890
abcdefghijklmnopqrstuvwxyz

Lino: c.p.p. (24 pt.) 1.28; caps p.p. 0.78. 7-36 pt. Every type manufacturer puts out one or more versions of Caslon in a wide range of sizes. ATF Caslon Oldstyle No. 471 is considered by many to be one of the most beautiful cuttings of this type.

# Caslon Italic (Lino)

ABCDEFGHIJKLMNOPQRSTU
VWXYZ& 1234567890
abcdefghijklmnopqrstuvwxyz

Lino: c.p.p. (24 pt.) 1.42; caps p.p. 0.84. 7-30 pt.

# Caslon Bold (Lino)

ABCDEFGHIJKLMNOPQ
RSTUVWXYZ& abcdefghij
klmnopqrstuvwxyz 12345678

Lino: c.p.p. (24 pt.) 1.02; caps p.p. 0.71. 5-72 pt. Caslon Bold is also called Caslon No. 3. Every type manufacturer puts out a version of Caslon Bold in a wide range of sizes.

NOTE: c.p.p. means lower-case characters per pica. Caps p.p. means caps per pica. Character counts may differ somewhat between one typefounder and another for similar faces and between italic and roman.

# *Caslon Bold Italic (Lino)*
# *ABCDEFGHIJKLMNOP*
# *QRSTUVWXYZ& abcdef*
# *ghijklmnopqrstuvwxyz 123*

Lino: c.p.p. (24 pt.) 0.97; caps p.p. 0.64. 5-72 pt.

# Century Expanded (Mono)
# ABCDEFGHIJKLMNOPQRS
# TUVWXYZ& 1234567890
# abcdefghijklmnopqrstuvwxyz

Mono: c.p.p. (24 pt.) 1.09; caps p.p. 0.78. 6-72 pt. Lino: 4-24 pt. Intertype: 4-36 pt.; Ludlow: 12-42 pt.

# *Century Expanded Italic (Mono)*
# *ABCDEFGHIJKLMNOPQR*
# *STUVWXYZ& 1234567890*
# *abcdefghijklmnopqrstuvwxyz*

Mono: c.p.p. (24 pt.) 1.12; caps p.p. 0.74. 6-36 pt. Intertype: 4-14 pt. Lino: 4-24 pt.

# **Century Bold (Mono)**
# **ABCDEFGHIJKLMNOPQRS**
# **TUVWXYZ& 1234567890**
# **abcdefghijklmnopqrstuvwxyz**

Mono: c.p.p. (24 pt.) 1.11; caps p.p. 0.78. 5½-72 pt. Lino: 6-72 pt. Intertype: 6-36 pt. Ludlow: 12-48 pt. ATF: 6-120 pt.

NOTE: c.p.p. means lower-case characters per pica. Caps p.p. means caps per pica. Character counts may differ somewhat between one typefounder and another for similar faces and between italic and roman.

# Century Bold Italic (Mono)
# ABCDEFGHIJKLMNOPQRS TUVWXYZ& 1234567890
## abcdefghijklmnopqrstuvwxyz

Mono: c.p.p. (24 pt.) 1.06; caps p.p. 0.76. 6-72 pt. Lino: 8-48 pt. Intertype: 6-36 pt. Ludlow: 12-72 pt. ATF: 6-72 pt.

# Cheltenham Bold
# ABCDEFGHIJKLMNOPQRST UVWXYZ& 1234567890
## abcdefghijklmnopqrstuvwxyz

This series, which scored a huge success in the early part of the century, is widely available in Condensed, Wide, Old Style, etc., as well as in Bold. There are cuttings by all the typefounders. However, it is not so much used as formerly, and space will not be taken to give a full showing of it here. C.p.p. (24 pt.) 1.14; caps p.p. 0.79.

# Civilite (ATf)
# ABCDEFGHIJKLMNOP QRSTUVWXYZ&
## abcdefghijklmnopqrstuvwxyz 1234567890

ATF: c.p.p. (24 pt.) 2.05; caps not used separately. 10-48 pt.

NOTE: c.p.p. means lower-case characters per pica. Caps p.p. means caps per pica. Character counts may differ somewhat between one typefounder and another for similar faces and between italic and roman.

# COPPERPLATE GOTHIC LIGHT EXTENDED (ATF)
# ABCDEFGHIJKLM NOPQRSTUVWXYZ & 1234567890

ATF: caps p.p. (24 pt.*) 0.54. 6-24 pt.

# COPPERPLATE GOTHIC HEAVY (ATF)
# ABCDEFGHIJKLMNOP QRSTUVWXYZ& 1234 567890

ATF: caps p.p. (24 pt.*) 0.67. 6-24 pt.

# COPPERPLATE GOTHIC BOLD (ATF)
# ABCDEFGHIJKLMNOP QRSTUVWXYZ& 1234 567890

ATF: caps p.p. (24 pt.*) 0.64. 6-24 pt.

* The size shown, having no descenders, can be and is cast on an 18-pt. body, and is therefore sometimes called 18 pt., even though it compares in size with any 24 pt. This possibility for misunderstanding must be watched whenever specifying a face that has no lower case.

# Cochin, Nicolas (Mono)
## ABCDEFGHIJKLMNOPQ RSTUVWXYZ& 1234567890
abcdefghijklmnopqrstuvwxyz

Mono: c.p.p. (24 pt.) 1.40; caps p.p. 0.70. 14-36 pt. ATF: 6-72 pt.

# *Cochin, Nicolas, Italic (Mono)*
## *ABCDEFGHIJKLMNOPQ RSTUVWXYZ& 1234567890*
*abcdefghijklmnopqrstuvwxyz*

Mono: c.p.p. (24 pt.) 1.51; caps p.p. 0.70. 14-36 pt. ATF: 6-48 pt.

# *Commercial Script (ATF)*
## *A B C D E F G H I J K L M N O P Q R S T U V W X Y Z &*
*abcdefghijklmnopqrstuvwxyz 12345*

ATF: c.p.p. (24 pt.) 1.28. Caps not used separately. 12-60 pt.
There are too many scripts in too many weights to permit showing even a representative collection of them here.

NOTE: c.p.p. means lower-case characters per pica. Caps p.p. means caps per pica. Character counts may differ somewhat between one typefounder and another for similar faces and between italic and roman.

# Cooper Black (Mono)
# ABCDEFGHIJKLMNOP
# QRSTUVWXYZ&
# abcdefghijklmnopqrstu
# vwxyz 1234567890

Mono: c.p.p. (24 pt.) 0.83; caps p.p. 0.66. 6-72 pt. ATF: 6-120 pt.
Similar faces are Ludlow Black (8-48 pt.) and Linotype Pabst Extra Bold. These latter two faces have a matching italic.

*Coronet Light (Ludlow)*
*ABCDEFGHIJKLMNOPQ*
*RSTUVWXYZ& abcdefghijklmnopqrstuvwxyz*
*1234567890*

Ludlow: c.p.p. (24 pt.) 2.12; caps not used separately. 14-72 pt.

*Coronet Bold (Ludlow)*
*ABCDEFGHIJKLMNOPQ*
*RSTUVWXYZ& 1234567890*
*abcdefghijklmnopqrstuvwxyz*

Ludlow: c.p.p. (24 pt.) 1.85; caps not used separately. 14-72 pt.

NOTE: c.p.p. means lower-case characters per pica. Caps p.p. means caps per pica. Character counts may differ somewhat between one typefounder and another for similar faces and between italic and roman

# Corvinus Medium (Bauer)
## ABCDEFGHIJKLMNOPQRSTUVW
## XYZ& abcdefghijklmnopqrstuvwxyz
## 1234567890

Bauer: c.p.p. (24 pt.) 1.31; caps p.p. 0.98. 8-60 pt. Corvinus is also available in a
Light (8-48 pt.) and a Bold (8-48 pt.)

# Corvinus Medium Italic (Bauer)
## ABCDEFGHIJKLMNOPQRSTUVW
## XYZ& abcdefghijklmnopqrstuvwxyz
## 1234567890

Bauer: c.p.p. (24 pt.) 1.32; caps p.p. 1.04. Same range of sizes as above. The light
has an italic, but the bold has no italic.

# Deepdene (Mono)
## ABCDEFGHIJKLMNOPQRSTUV
## WXYZ& 1234567890
## abcdefghijklmnopqrstuvwxyz

Mono: c.p.p. (24 pt.) 1.36; caps p.p. 0.89. 6-72 pt.

# Deepdene Italic (Mono)
## ABCDEFGHIJKLMNOPQRSTUV
## WXYZ& abcdefghijklmnopqrstuvwxyz
## 1234567890

Mono: c.p.p. (24 pt.) 1.69; caps p.p. 0.96. 6-72 pt.

NOTE: c.p.p. means lower-case characters per pica. Caps p.p. means caps per pica. Character counts may
differ somewhat between one typefounder and another for similar faces and between italic and roman.

# Deepdene Bold (Mono)
## ABCDEFGHIJKLMNOPQRST UVWXYZ& 1234567890
abcdefghijklmnopqrstuvwxyz

Mono: c.p.p. (24 pt.) 1.18; caps p.p. 0.81. 6-72 pt.

# Deepdene Bold Italic (Mono)
## ABCDEFGHIJKLMNOPQRSTUV WXYZ& 1234567890
abcdefghijklmnopqrstuvwxyz

Mono: c.p.p. (24 pt.) 1.38; caps p.p. 0.88. 6-72 pt.

# DELPHIAN OPEN (Ludlow)
## ABCDEFGHIJKLMNOPQR STUVWXYZ& 1234567890

Ludlow: caps only. Caps p.p. 0.70. 24-60 pt.

# Dom Casual (ATF)
## ABCDEFGHIJKLMNOPQRSTUVWXYZ& abcde fghijklmnopqrstuvwxyz 1234567890

ATF: c.p.p. (24 pt.) 1.85; caps p.p. 1.28. 18-72 pt.

NOTE: c.p.p. means lower-case characters per pica. Caps p.p. means caps per pica. Character counts may differ somewhat between one typefounder and another for similar faces and between italic and roman.

# Eden Bold (Ludlow)
# ABCDEFGHIJKLMNOPQ
# RSTUVWXYZ&   1234567890
## abcdefghijklmnopqrstuvwxyz

Ludlow: c.p.p. (24 pt.) 1.30; caps p.p. 0.96. 10-72 pt.

# Egmont Light (Inter)
# ABCDEFGHIJKLMNOPQRST
# UVWXYZ 1234567890
## abcdefghijklmnopqrstuvwxyz

Intertype: c.p.p. (24 pt.) 1.31; caps p.p. 0.79. 8-30 pt.

# *Egmont Light Italic (Inter)*
# *ABCDEFGHIJKLMNOPQRST*
# *UVWXYZ 1234567890*
## *abcdefghijklmnopqrstuvwxyz*

Intertype: c.p.p. (24 pt.) 1.35; caps p.p. 0.83. 8-30 pt.

# Egmont Bold (Inter)
# ABCDEFGHIJKLMNOPQRS
# TUVWXYZ 1234567890
## abcdefghijklmnopqrstuvwxyz

Intertype: c.p.p. (24 pt.) 1.21; caps p.p. 0.77. 8-24 pt. Continental: 8-60 pt.

NOTE: c.p.p. means lower-case characters per pica. Caps p.p. means caps per pica. Character counts may differ somewhat between one typefounder and another for similar faces and between italic and roman.

# Egmont Bold Italic (Inter)
## ABCDEFGHIJKLMNOPQRS TUVWXYZ 1234567890
### abcdefghijklmnopqrstuvwxyz

Intertype: c.p.p. (24 pt.) 1.21; caps p.p. 0.77. 8-24 pt.

# Franklin Gothic (Ludlow)
## ABCDEFGHIJKLMNOPQRS TUVWXYZ& abcdefghijklm nopqrstuvwxyz 12345678

Ludlow: c.p.p. (24 pt.) 0.98; caps p.p. 0.75. 6-72 pt. ATF: 4-96 pt. Intertype: 18-24 pt. Lino: 18-144 pt. Mono: 4-72 pt.

# Franklin Gothic Wide (ATF)
## ABCDEFGHIJKLMNO PQRSTUVWXYZ& abc defghijklmnopqrstuvw xyz 1234567890

ATF: c.p.p. (24 pt.) 0.83; caps p.p. 0.62. 14-72 pt.

NOTE: c.p.p. means lower-case characters per pica. Caps p.p. means caps per pica. Character counts may differ somewhat between one typefounder and another for similar faces and between italic and roman.

# Futura Light (Bauer)
# ABCDEFGHIJKLMNOPQRSTUVW
# XYZ& abcdefghijklmnopqrstuvwxyz
# 1234567890

Bauer: c.p.p. (24 pt.) 1.37; caps p.p. 1.04. 6-84 pt. Intertype: 6-14 pt. Virtually identical faces are Linotype Spartan Light, 8-14 pt.; Ludlow Tempo Light, 6-72 pt.; and Monotype Twentieth Century Light, 6-72 pt.

# *Futura Light Oblique (Bauer)*
# *ABCDEFGHIJKLMNOPQRSTUVWXYZ*
# *abcdefghijklmnopqrstuvwxyz& 123456*

Bauer: c.p.p. (24 pt.) 1.45; caps p.p. 1.05. 8-48 pt. Intertype: 6-14 pt. Virtually identical faces are Ludlow Tempo Light Italic, 10-72 pt.; and Monotype Twentieth Century Light Italic, 6-72 pt.

# Futura Book (Bauer)
# ABCDEFGHIJKLMNOPQRSTUVWXYZ&
# abcdefghijklmnopqrstuvwxyz 1234567

Bauer: c.p.p. (24 pt.) 1.40; caps p.p. 1.09. 8-48 pt. Intertype: 6-14 pt. Intertype has a Futura Book Oblique in 6-14 pt.

NOTE: c.p.p. means lower-case characters per pica. Caps p.p. means caps per pica. Character counts may differ somewhat between one typefounder and another for similar faces and between italic and roman.

# Futura Medium (Bauer)
## ABCDEFGHIJKLMNOPQRSTUVW
## XYZ& abcdefghijklmnopqrstuvwxyz
## 1234567890

Bauer: c.p.p. (24 pt.) 1.31; caps p.p. 1.02, 6-84 pt. Intertype: 6-18 pt. Virtually identical faces are Linotype Spartan Medium, 6-24 pt.; ATF Spartan Medium, 8-120 pt.; Ludlow Tempo Medium, 6-72 pt.; and Monotype Twentieth Century Medium, 6-72 pt.

# *Futura Medium Oblique (Bauer)*
## *ABCDEFGHIJKLMNOPQRSTUVW*
## *XYZ& abcdefghijklmnopqrstuvwxyz*
## *1234567890*

Bauer: c.p.p. 1.32; caps p.p. 1.01. 8-48 pt. Intertype: 6-14 pt. Virtually identical faces are Linotype Spartan Medium Italic, 6-24 pt.; ATF Spartan Medium Italic, 8-72 pt.; Ludlow Tempo Medium Italic, 8-48 pt.; and Monotype Twentieth Century Medium Italic, 6-72 pt.

# Futura Demibold (Inter)
## ABCDEFGHIJKLMNOPQRSTUVW
## XYZ& 1234567890
## abcdefghijklmnopqrstuvwxyz

Intertype: c.p.p. (24 pt.) 1.23; caps p.p. 0.96. Bauer: 8-24 pt. Virtually identical faces are Linotype Spartan Heavy, 6-24 pt.; ATF Spartan Heavy, 6-36 pt.; Ludlow Tempo Bold, 6-72 pt.; and Monotype Twentieth Century Bold, 6-72 pt.

NOTE: c.p.p. means lower-case characters per pica. Caps p.p. means caps per pica. Character counts may differ somewhat between one typefounder and another for similar faces and between italic and roman.

# *Futura Demibold Oblique* (Inter)
# *ABCDEFGHIJKLMNOPQRSTUVW*
# *XYZ& 1234567890*
# *abcdefghijklmnopqrstuvwxyz*

Intertype: c.p.p. (24 pt.) 1.24; caps p.p. 0.96. 6-30 pt. Virtually identical faces are Linotype Spartan Heavy Italic, 6-24 pt.; ATF Spartan Heavy Italic, 6-36 pt.; Ludlow Tempo Bold Italic, 12-48 pt.; and Monotype Twentieth Century Bold Italic, 6-72 pt.

# **Futura Bold** (Bauer)
# **ABCDEFGHIJKLMNOPQRST**
# **UVWXYZ& abcdefghijklmno**
# **pqrstuvwxyz 1234567890**

Bauer: c.p.p. (24 pt.) 1.03; caps p.p. 0.87. 8-84 pt. Intertype: 6-18 pt. Virtually identical faces are Linotype Spartan Black, 6-24 pt.; ATF Spartan Black, 6-36 pt.; Ludlow Tempo Heavy, 6-72 pt.; Monotype Twentieth Century Extrabold, 6-72 pt.

# ***Futura Bold Italic***
# ***ABCDEFGHIJKLMNOPQRSTUV***
# ***WXYZ& 1234567890***
# ***abcdefghijklmnopqrstuvwxyz***

The above specimen lines of Futura Bold Italic are actually set in Mono Twentieth Century Extrabold Italic, since Bauer has no such italic, and Intertype has it only from 6-18 pt. This was done to keep all specimens of the Futura family together and similar. C.p.p. (24 pt.) 1.07; caps p.p. 0.88. Virtually identical faces are Linotype Spartan Black Italic, 6-24 pt.; ATF Spartan Black Italic, 6-36 pt.; Ludlow Tempo Heavy Italic, 12-72 pt.; and Monotype Twentieth Century Extrabold Italic, 6-72 pt.

NOTE: c.p.p. means lower-case characters per pica. Caps p.p. means caps per pica. Character counts may differ somewhat between one typefounder and another for similar faces and between italic and roman.

# Futura Medium Condensed (Bauer)
## ABCDEFGHIJKLMNOPQRSTUVWXYZ&
## abcdefghijklmnopqrstuvwxyz 1234567890

Bauer: c.p.p. (24 pt.) 1.85; caps p.p. 1.58. 8-84 pt. Intertype: 8-14 pt. Virtually identical faces are Ludlow Tempo Medium Condensed, 30-72 pt.; and Monotype Twentieth Century Medium Condensed, 14-72 pt.

# Futura Bold Condensed (Bauer)
## ABCDEFGHIJKLMNOPQRSTUVWXYZ&
## abcdefghijklmnopqrstuvwxyz 1234567890

Bauer: c.p.p. (24 pt.) 1.60; caps p.p. 1.26. 8-84 pt. Intertype: 6-14 pt. Virtually identical faces are Linotype Spartan Black Condensed, 14-24 pt.; ATF Spartan Black Condensed, 10-36 pt.; Ludlow Tempo Heavy Condensed, 10-72 pt.; and Monotype Twentieth Century Extrabold Condensed, 14-84 pt.

# Garamond (Inter)
## ABCDEFGHIJKLMNOPQRSTUV WXYZ& 1234567890
## abcdefghijklmnopqrstuvwxyz

Inter: c.p.p. (24 pt.) 1.36; caps p.p. 0.89. 6-36 pt. ATF: 6-72 pt. Lino: (Garamond No. 3), 6-42 pt. Mono: (Garamont), 6-72 pt. The above cuttings of Garamond are quite similar in weight and character count. Linotype Garamond (6-36 pt.) (not Garamond No. 3) is a little heavier, with (in 24 pt.) 1.22 c.p.p. Ludlow Garamond (8-72 pt.) is a little more compact, with (in 24 pt.) 1.44 c.p.p.

NOTE: c.p.p. means lower-case characters per pica. Caps p.p. means caps per pica. Character counts may differ somewhat between one typefounder and another for similar faces and between italic and roman.

# *Garamond Italic (Inter)*
## *ABCDEFGHIJKLMNOPQRSTUVW*
## *XYZ& abcdefghijklmnopqrstuvwxyz*
## *1234567890*

Inter: c.p.p. (24 pt.) 1.56; caps p.p. 0.94. 6-48 pt. ATF: 6-48 pt. Mono: (Garamont) 6-72 pt.
Also (but see note above) Lino (Garamond) : 6-30 pt. Ludlow: 8-72 pt.

# Garamond Bold (Inter)
## ABCDEFGHIJKLMNOPQRST
## UVWXYZ& 1234567890
## abcdefghijklmnopqrstuvwxyz

Inter: c.p.p. (24 pt.) 1.22; caps p.p. 0.84. 6-36 pt. ATF: 6-120 pt. Mono: 6-72 pt. Lino: (Garamond No. 3) , 6-144 pt.
Linotype Garamond Bold (6-36 pt.) is a little heavier and broader than the rest; Ludlow Garamond Bold (8-72 pt.) is a little more compact.

# *Garamond Bold Italic (Inter)*
## *ABCDEFGHIJKLMNOPQRSTU*
## *VWXYZ& 1234567890*
## *abcdefghijklmnopqrstuvwxyz*

Inter: c.p.p. (24 pt.) 1.36; caps p.p. 0.87. 6-30 pt. ATF: 6-72 pt. Mono: 6-72 pt. Lino: (Garamond No. 3) , 6-72 pt.
Lino Garamond Bold (see above) , 6-30 pt. Ludlow Garamond Bold (see above) , 8-72 pt.

# Girder Series
See MEMPHIS and also page 361.

NOTE: c.p.p. means lower-case characters per pica. Caps p.p. means caps per pica. Character counts may differ somewhat between one typefounder and another for similar faces and between italic and roman.

# HEADLINE GOTHIC (ATF)
# ABCDEFGHIJKLMNOPQRSTUVW
# XYZ& 1234567890

ATF: caps only, caps p.p. (24 pt.) 0.83. 24-120 pt. (Note: This face, having no descenders, sets larger on the body than normal.)

## News Gothic (ATF)
## ABCDEFGHIJKLMNOPQRSTUVW
## XYZ& 1234567890
abcdefghijklmnopqrstuvwxyz

ATF: c.p.p. (24 pt.) 1.20; caps p.p. 0.94. 6-72 pt.

## News Gothic Condensed (ATF)
## ABCDEFGHIJKLMNOPQRSTUVWXYZ& abc
defghijklmnopqrstuvwxyz 1234567890 ·

ATF: c.p.p. (24 pt.) 1.55; caps p.p. 1.25. 12-48 pt.

## News Gothic Extra Condensed (ATF)
## ABCDEFGHIJKLMNOPQRSTUVWXYZ& 1234567890
abcdefghijklmnopqrstuvwxyz

ATF: c.p.p. (24 pt.) 2.40; caps p.p. 1.99. 6-72 pt.

---

NOTE: **c.p.p.** means lower-case characters per pica. Caps p.p. means caps per pica. Character counts may differ somewhat between one typefounder and another for similar faces and between italic and roman.

# Hauser Script ( Ludlow )
## ABCDEFGHIJKLMNOPQRSTUVW
## XYZ& 1234567890
abcdefghijklmnopqrstuvwxyz

Ludlow: c.p.p. (24 pt.) 1.57. Caps not used separately. 24-72 pt.

# Kabel Series

See SANS SERIF and also page 360. Mono Sans Serif series is substantially identical with the Kabel Light, Kabel Bold, and Kabel Black faces imported by Continental and European.

# Karnak Series (Ludlow)

See MEMPHIS and also page 361.

# Kaufmann Bold (ATF)
## ABCDEFGHIJKLMNOPQRSTU
## VWXYZ& 1234567890
abcdefghijklmnopqrstuvwxyz

ATF: c.p.p. (24 pt.) 1.37. Caps not used by themselves. 10-96 pt. There is also a Kaufmann Script which is lighter. Similar faces include Gillies Gothic Light and Bold, and Signal Light, Medium and Black.

# Lydian (ATF)
## ABCDEFGHIJKLMNOPQRSTUV
## WXYZ& 1234567890
abcdefghijklmnopqrstuvwxyz

ATF: c.p.p. (24 pt.) 1.22; caps p.p. 0.92. 10-96 pt.

NOTE: c.p.p. means lower-case characters per pica. Caps p.p. means caps per pica. Character counts may differ somewhat between one typefounder and another for similar faces and between italic and roman.

# Lydian Italic (ATF)
## ABCDEFGHIJKLMNOPQRSTUVWX YZ& abcdefghijklmnopqrstuvwxyz 1234567890

ATF: c.p.p. (24 pt.) 1.35; caps p.p. 0.98.

# Lydian Cursive ( A V F )
## ABCDEFGHIJKLMNOPQRST UVWXYZ& 1234567890 abcdefghijklmnopqrstuvwxyz

ATF: c.p.p. (24 pt.) 1.47; Caps not used by themselves. 18-72 pt.

# Lydian Bold (ATF)
## ABCDEFGHIJKLMNOPQRSTUV WXYZ& 1234567890 abcdefghijklmnopqrstuvwxyz

ATF: c.p.p. (24 pt.) 1.19; caps p.p. 0.91. 10-96 pt.

# Lydian Bold Italic (ATF)
## ABCDEFGHIJKLMNOPQRSTUV WXYZ& 1234567890 abcdefghijklmnopqrstuvwxyz

ATF: c.p.p. (24 pt.) 1.25; caps p.p. 0.94. 10-96 pt.

NOTE: c.p.p. means lower-case characters per pica. Caps p.p. means caps per pica. Character counts may differ somewhat between one typefounder and another for similar faces and between italic and roman.

# Memphis Light (Lino)
## ABCDEFGHIJKLMNOPQRS TUVWXYZ& 1234567890
### abcdefghijklmnopqrstuvwxyz

Lino: c.p.p. (24 pt.) 1.10; caps p.p. 0.82. 6-24 pt. See page 361 for a list of virtually identical faces by other typefounders.

# Memphis Medium (Lino)
## ABCDEFGHIJKLMNOPQRS TUVWXYZ& 1234567890
### abcdefghijklmnopqrstuvwxyz

Lino: c.p.p. (24 pt.) 1.06; caps p.p. 0.81. 6-144 pt. Virtually identical faces are Karnak Intermediate, Stymie Medium, Beton Medium. Cairo Medium is similar. See page 361.

# Memphis Medium Italic (Lino)
## ABCDEFGHIJKLMNOPQRS TUVWXYZ& 1234567890
### abcdefghijklmnopqrstuvwxyz

Lino: c.p.p. (24 pt.) 1.08; caps p.p. 0.80. 6-48 pt.

# Memphis Bold (Lino)
## ABCDEFGHIJKLMNOPQRS TUVWXYZ& 1234567890
### abcdefghijklmnopqrstuvwxyz

Lino: c.p.p. (24 pt.) 1.07; caps p.p. 0.81. 6-144 pt. Virtually identical faces are Karnak Medium, Stymie Bold, Beton Bold. Cairo Bold is similar. See page 361.

NOTE: c.p.p. means lower-case characters per pica. Caps p.p. means caps per pica. Character counts may differ somewhat between one typefounder and another for similar faces and between italic and roman.

# Memphis Bold Italic (Lino)
## ABCDEFGHIJKLMNOPQRS TUVWXYZ& 1234567890
### abcdefghijklmnopqrstuvwxyz

Lino: c.p.p. (24 pt.) 1.08; caps p.p. 0.80. 6-24 pt.

# Memphis Extra Bold (Lino)
## ABCDEFGHIJKLMNOPQ RSTUVWXYZ& abcdefg hijklmnopqrstuvwxyz 1234567890

Lino: c.p.p. (24 pt.) 0.93; caps p.p. 0.71. 8-144 pt. Virtually identical faces are Karnak Black, Stymie Extra Bold, Beton Extra Bold. Cairo Heavy and Stymie Black are similar. See page 361.

# Memphis Extra Bold Italic (Lino)
## ABCDEFGHIJKLMNOP QRSTUVWXYZ& abcde fghijklmnopqrstuvwxyz

Lino: c.p.p. (24 pt.) 0.87; caps p.p. 0.66. 8-24 pt.

# Metro Series (Lino)

This Linotype series includes Metrothin, Metrolite, Metromedium, and Metroblack. See page 360 for a comparison between it and other sans serif faces.

# NEULAND (CONTINENTAL)
## ABCDEFGHIJKLMNOPQRSTU VWXYZ& 1234567890

Continental: caps only. Caps p.p. 0.81. 14-72 pt. Europ Type: 14-72 pt.

---

NOTE: c.p.p. means lower-case characters per pica. Caps p.p. means caps per pica. Character counts may differ somewhat between one typefounder and another for similar faces and between italic and roman.

# NEULAND INLINE (CONTINENTAL)
# ABCDEFGHIJKLMNOPQRSTU
# VWXYZ& 1234567890

Continental: caps only. Caps p.p. 0.85. 14-72 pt. Europ Type: 14-72 pt.

# Old English (Ludlow)
# ABCDEFGHIJKLMNOPQRS
# TUVWXYZ& 1234567890
## abcdefghijklmnopqrstuvwxyz

Ludlow: c.p.p. (24 pt.) 1.25. Caps not used by themselves. 8-48 pt. Similar faces include Cloister Black (ATF and Mono), Engravers' Old English (Inter and Mono) and Caslon Text (Lino).

# Onyx (Mono)
# ABCDEFGHIJKLMNOPQRSTUVWXYZ&
## abcdefghijklmnopqrstuvwxyz 1234567890

Mono: c.p.p. (24 pt.) 1.74; caps p.p. 1.44. 24-72 pt. ATF: 18-120 pt.

# Pabst Extra Bold (Lino)

See COOPER BLACK

# Park Avenue ( ATF )
# ABCDEFGHIJKLMNO
# PQRSTUVWXYZ&
## abcdefghijklmnopqrstuvwxyz 1234567890

ATF: c.p.p. (24 pt.) 1.64. Caps not used by themselves. 12-72 pt. Inter: 12-18 pt. Similar faces are ATF Piranesi Italic and Raleigh Cursive, and Ludlow Mayfair Cursive.

NOTE: c.p.p. means lower-case characters per pica. Caps p.p. means caps per pica. Character counts may differ somewhat between one typefounder and another for similar faces and between italic and roman.

# Post Roman Light (Amst.)

## ABCDEFGHIJKLMNOPQRST UVWXYZ& 1234567890

abcdefghijklmnopqrstuvwxyz

Amst.: c.p.p. (24 pt.) 1.08; caps p.p. 0.82. 6-48 pt.

# Post Roman Medium (Amst.)

## ABCDEFGHIJKLMNOPQR STUVWXYZ& 1234567890

abcdefghijklmnopqrstuvwxyz

Amst.: c.p.p. (24 pt.) 1.15; caps p.p. 0.70. 6-48 pt.

# Post Roman Bold (Amst.)

## ABCDEFGHIJKLMNOPQRS TUVWXYZ& 1234567890

abcdefghijklmnopqrstuvwxyz

Amst.: c.p.p. (24 pt.) 1.08; caps p.p. 0.75. 6-72 pt.

# Radiant Heavy (Ludlow)

## ABCDEFGHIJKLMNOPQRS TUVWXYZ& abcdefghijklm nopqrstuvwxyz 123456789

Ludlow: c.p.p. (24 pt.) 1.00; caps p.p. 0.79. 10-72 pt. There is also a Radiant Bold Condensed (12-72 pt.) and a Radiant Bold Extra Condensed (14-72 pt.) .

NOTE: c.p.p. means lower-case characters per pica. Caps p.p. means caps per pica. Character counts may differ somewhat between one typefounder and another for similar faces and between italic and roman.

# Sans Serif Bold (Mono)
# ABCDEFGHIJKLMNOPQRSTUV
# WXYZ& abcdefghijklmnopqrstuvwxyz
# 1234567890

The Monotype Sans Serif series includes Light, Medium, Bold, Extrabold (each with matching italic) and Light Condensed, Medium Condensed and Extrabold Condensed. This series is substantially identical with the imported Kabel series and is often used interchangeably with Vogue, Futura, Metro, etc. See page 360 for a comparison with similar faces. C.p.p. (Bold 24 pt.) 1.50; caps p.p. 0.94.

# Studio (Amst.)
# ABCDEFGHIJKLMNOPQRST
# UVWXYZ& abcdefghijklmno
# pqrstuvwxyz 1234567890

Amst.: c.p.p. (24 pt.) 0.99; caps p.p. 0.83. 8-72 pt.

# Spartan Series (Lino)

See FUTURA and also pages 358-359.

# STENCIL (ATF)
# ABCDEFGHIJKLMNO
# PQRSTUVWXYZ&
# 1234567890

ATF: caps only. Caps p.p. (24 pt.) 0.62. 18-60 pt. Ludlow: 36-pt. caps only.

# Stymie Series (Mono)

See MEMPHIS and also page 361.

NOTE: c.p.p. means lower-case characters per pica. Caps p.p. means caps per pica. Character counts may differ somewhat between one typefounder and another for similar faces and between italic and roman.

# Tempo Series (Ludlow)
See FUTURA and also pages 358-359.

*Trafton Script (Bauer)*

*ABCDEFGHIJKLMNOPQ*
*RSTUVWXYZ&*

*abcdefghijklmnopqrstuvwxyz 1234567890*

Bauer: c.p.p. (24 pt.) 1.96. Caps not used by themselves. 14-84 pt.

# UMBRA (LUDLOW)
# ABCDEFGHIJKLMNOPQ
# RSTUVWXYZ&
# 1234567890
Ludlow: caps only. Caps p.p. (24 pt.) 0.69. 24-72 pt.

# Venus Extra Bold
# Extended (Bauer)

**ABCDEFGHIJKLMNOPQR**
**STUVWXYZ&1234567890**
**abcdefghijklmnopqrstuv**
**wxyz**
Bauer: c.p.p. (18 pt.) 0.75; caps p.p. 0.52. 8-84 pt.

NOTE: c.p.p. means lower-case characters per pica. Caps p.p. means caps per pica. Character counts may differ somewhat between one typefounder and another for similar faces and between italic and roman.

# Vogue Series (Inter)

See page 360 for a comparison of the various weights of Vogue with similar faces.

## Vogue (Inter)
## ABCDEFGHIJKLMNOPQRSTUV
## WXYZ 1234567890
## abcdefghijklmnopqrstuvwxyz

Intertype: c.p.p. (24 pt.) 1.28; caps p.p. 0.90. 6-60 pt.

## *Vogue Oblique (Inter)*
## *ABCDEFGHIJKLMNOPQRSTUV*
## *WXYZ 1234567890*
## *abcdefghijklmnopqrstuvwxyz*

Intertype: c.p.p. (18 pt.) 1.28; caps p.p. 0.90. 6-18 pt.

## Vogue Bold (Inter)
## ABCDEFGHIJKLMNOPQRSTUV
## WXYZ 1234567890
## abcdefghijklmnopqrstuvwxyz

Intertype: c.p.p. (24 pt.) 1.24; caps p.p. 0.88. 6-60 pt.

NOTE: c.p.p. means lower-case characters per pica. Caps p.p. means caps per pica. Character counts may differ somewhat between one typefounder and another for similar faces and between italic and roman.

*Vogue Bold Oblique (Inter)*
*ABCDEFGHIJKLMNOPQRSTUV*
*WXYZ 1234567890*
*abcdefghijklmnopqrstuvwxyz*

Intertype: c.p.p. (24 pt.) 1.24; caps p.p. 0.88. 6-24 pt.

**Vogue Extra Bold (Inter)**
**ABCDEFGHIJKLMNOPQRST**
**UVWXYZ 1234567890**
**abcdefghijklmnopqrstuvwxyz**

Intertype: c.p.p. (24 pt.) 1.11; caps p.p. 0.83.

𝔚𝔢𝔡𝔡𝔦𝔫𝔤 𝔗𝔢𝔵𝔱 (𝔐𝔬𝔫𝔬)
𝔄𝔅ℭ𝔇𝔈𝔉𝔊ℌℑ𝔍𝔎𝔏𝔐𝔑𝔒𝔓𝔔ℜ𝔖𝔗𝔘𝔙𝔚
𝔛𝔜𝔝& abcdefghijklmnopqrstuvwxyz
1234567890

Mono: c.p.p. (24 pt.) 1.78. Caps not used by themselves. 8-36 pt. ATF: 6-48 pt. There are two sizes each of 18 and 24 pt.

Weiss Roman (Bauer)
ABCDEFGHIJKLMNOPQRSTUVW
XYZ& 123456789o
abcdefghijklmnopqrstuvwxyz

Bauer: c.p.p. (24 pt.) 1.56; caps p.p. 0.95. 16-60 pt. (also Intertype)

NOTE: c.p.p. means lower-case characters per pica. Caps p.p. means caps per pica. Character counts may differ somewhat between one typefounder and another for similar faces and between italic and roman.

# Appendix 2

# Bibliography

There are some basic books and working tools that every user of print will want to keep at hand. These include the following:

Dictionary. Popular desk dictionaries include the Merriam-Webster "Collegiate Dictionary," the "American College Dictionary," and the "World Dictionary." Probably the most widely used unabridged dictionary is "Webster's New International Dictionary."

Classified Telephone Directories for New York and Chicago. These are invaluable for locating firms offering specialized services.

Type books of printers who are being dealt with.

Paper sample books from paper merchants.

Ink sample books from ink manufacturers.

Most of those who have to plan, produce, and use the printed word will also want to be familiar with as many as possible of the other books listed below, consulting some of them at the public library and buying those which are needed for repeated reference. The list is a selected one, including only those books that the authors of the present volume have found to be readable, authoritative, and helpful in their everyday work of planning, editing, and buying printing of all varieties.

The books are grouped as follows:

General Reference
Advertising
　(See also Layout)
Art Work
Book Publishing
Color
Copyright
Copy Writing
Direct Mail
Displays
Editing and Proofreading
Layout and Design
Lettering
Magazine Publishing
Newspaper Publishing
Packaging
Paper
Photography
Printing Processes
Publicity and Public Relations
Radio and Television
Shipping
Typography
Visual Aids

Note that many of the books listed under General Reference and Printing

Processes have chapters on art, layout, paper, photography, etc. There is considerable overlapping among the groups. Because much valuable material is issued by the trade magazines, they are listed along with the books.

### GENERAL REFERENCE

ADVERTISING AND PUBLISHING PRODUCTION YEAR BOOK, The Reference Manual of the Graphic Arts. New York: Colton Press Inc., 468 Fourth Ave. 9th Ed., 1950. $15.

Every professional production man will want to have this book on his desk. It presents both elementary and technical information on every aspect of printing, both the basic processes and the latest developments. Its many advertisements serve also as samples of various printing processes.

There is a type face directory showing 1,200 one-line specimens, and there is also a directory showing which printers have which machine faces in the major cities of the United States.

THE PENROSE ANNUAL, edited by R. B. Fishenden. New York: Hastings House, Publishers, Inc., 41 E. 50 St. About $8.50.

This British annual contains excellent summaries of the new developments in the graphic arts, and includes also essays on design, and many specimens of printing. Though British, its coverage of progress in the United States is excellent.

REFRESHER COURSE IN ADVERTISING, SELLING AND MERCHANDISING, by Printers' Ink editors and contributors. Pleasantville, N.Y.: Printers' Ink Books, 1947. 265 pp. $4.

Reprint of Printers' Ink articles giving pointers on ways to better sales through advertising, sales techniques, and merchandising.

CUTTING ADVERTISING AND PRINTING COSTS, by Printers' Ink editors and contributors. Pleasantville, N.Y.: Printers' Ink Books, 1948. 391 pp. $5.

Over 500 ways to reduce advertising production costs are given here as practical helps in planning ads; buying paper; ordering printing, art, cuts; sampling, etc.

THE TECHNIQUE OF ADVERTISING PRODUCTION, by Thomas B. Stanley. New York: Prentice-Hall, Inc., 70 Fifth Ave., 1954. 214 pp. $9.

Good chapters on visualizing the appeal, focusing attention by layout, illustrating ads, understanding color, using photoengraving, gravure, and lithography, learning to recognize type, putting type to work, getting acquainted with paper, and planning printed matter.

HOW TO PLAN AND BUY PRINTING, by R. Randolph Karch. New York: Prentice-Hall, Inc., 70 Fifth Ave., 1950. 192 pp. $6.35.

A guide to copy preparation, buying art and cuts, recognizing and selecting type faces, and planning booklets and mailing pieces.

RETAIL ADVERTISING FOR THE SMALL STORE, by Philip W. Burton. New York: Prentice-Hall, Inc., 70 Fifth Ave., 1951. 480 pp. $6.70.

This book offers a wealth of information on how to handle an effective, economical advertising program. Specific instructions are given on copy, layout, preparation of material for the printer, and use of direct mail.

SALES PROMOTION HANDBOOK, by J. C. Aspley. Chicago: Dartnell Corp., Ravenswood and Leland Ave., 1954. 1,104 pp. $12.50.

Although this bumper reference book is designed primarily for sales managers of large firms seeking detailed help on promotion techniques, it contains valuable pointers and extensive reference material for advertising men, promotion directors, buyers of printing, and those who are responsible for direct mail letters, mailing lists, distribution, styling, and proofreading. The book includes extensive tables listing parcel-post rates, air and railway express rates, circulation and rates of principal magazines and newspapers, advertising rates of principal radio and television stations, principal business directories, business paper editors, etc.

SALES PROMOTION IDEA BOOK, by *Printers' Ink* editors and contributors. Pleasantville, N.Y.: Printers' Ink Books, 1950. 384 pp. $5.

648 capsule ideas furnish data and suggestions to promote sales and stimulate business.

SALES EXECUTIVE'S HANDBOOK, edited by Harry Simmons. New York: Prentice-Hall, Inc., 70 Fifth Ave., 1950. 790 pp. $10.

Part IV, entitled "Using Modern Marketing Tools," will be particularly helpful to those who plan sales-promotion, advertising, public-relations, direct mail, and mail-order campaigns.

THE LITERARY MARKET PLACE. New York: R. R. Bowker Co., 62 W. 45 St. About 200 pp. Published annually. $5.

A directory of firms, organizations, and individuals actively engaged in the production, marketing, or use of literary material. The key personnel in each organization are named. The listings cover book publishers (with notes on specialties of each), major magazines, book clubs, feature syndicates, newspapers, radio and TV stations and programs, motion-picture studios, literary agents, book reviewers, columnists and commentators, lecturers and lecture agents, literary awards and prizes, clipping bureaus, book wholesalers, photographers, free-lance designers, artists, indexers, editors, etc.

DICTIONARY OF PRINTING TERMS, by Roy Trewin Porte, Salt Lake City, Utah: Porte Publishing Co. 1941. 169 pp. $1.75.

Definitions of approximately 4,600 terms related to printing, advertising, paper, and publishing.

PRINTING MAGAZINE YEAR BOOK. New York: Walden, Sons & Mott, Inc., 93 Worth St. About 200 pp. $1. Published annually for subscribers to *Printing* only.

A comprehensive buyers' guide to printing services and materials with reference information on postal rates and regulations, copyright and patent laws, trade associations, and supplementary lists of new equipment and supplies as well as new books, movies, and slide films on the graphic arts.

BOOKS FOR THE ADVERTISING MAN: A CLASSIFIED BIBLIOGRAPHY ON ADVERTISING, MARKETING, AND RELATED SUBJECTS, edited by Alfred T. Falk. New York: Bureau of Research and Education, Advertising Federation of America, 330 W. 42 St., 1954. $1.

1,300 books classified by subject, but not evaluated. Price of each book included.

*Advertising Requirements: The Workbook of Production, Promotion and Merchandising.* Published monthly at 200 E. Illinois St., Chicago 11, Ill. $3 per year.

A down-to-earth magazine, filled with material that the advertising or promotion man can apply directly to his work, including art and photography, labeling and packaging, shows and exhibits, window and store displays, radio and TV production, layout and typography, paper, printing, and platemaking.

## ADVERTISING
(See also LAYOUT)

PRINCIPLES OF ADVERTISING, by Philip W. Burton. New York: Prentice-Hall, Inc., 70 Fifth Ave., 1955. 608 pp. $8.65. Illus.

An entirely new review of the whole field of advertising, with chapters on the structure of advertising, how advertising is regulated, market research, where to advertise, layout, copy, budgeting, etc.

ENCYCLOPEDIA OF ADVERTISING, by Irvin Graham. New York: Fairchild Publications, Inc., 7 E. 12 St., 1952. 622 pp. $6.50.

A reference book organized in very much the same way as the "Printing and Promotion Handbook" except that it provides rather fuller coverage of advertising and somewhat less coverage of such topics as direct mail, duplicating, type, and paper.

ADVERTISING CAMPAIGNS, by Irvin Graham. New York: Harper and Brothers, 49 E. 33 St., 1951. $5.

A splendid discussion of factors to consider in planning an advertising campaign, how to select and use various magazines, business papers, newspapers, radio, TV, direct mail, premiums, contests, outdoor advertising, transportation advertising, etc., with case histories to illustrate.

ADVERTISING IDEA BOOK, by Printers' Ink editors and contributors. Pleasantville, N.Y.: Printers' Ink Books, 1951. 348 pp. $5.

Some 634 tested ideas in capsule form are given here in dictionary style for quick reference.

ADVERTISING COPYWRITING, by Philip Ward Burton and others. New York:

Prentice-Hall, Inc., 70 Fifth Ave., 1949. 521 pp. $7.65.

A practical handbook of suggestions for those who plan and write advertising copy of all kinds including retail selling, fashions, mail order, business papers, outdoor displays, radio, and television.

HOW TO WRITE ADVERTISING THAT SELLS, by Clyde Bedell. New York: McGraw-Hill Book Co., Inc., 330 W. 42 St., 1952. 523 pp. $6.50.

This is a real how-to-do-it book which provides a systematic and methodical approach to creative advertising. It discusses in detail the problems of the advertising copy writer, the tools with which he works, the elements of selling strategy, and the methods of applying them to produce effective ads.

WHICH AD PULLED BEST?, by Carroll J. Swan. New York: Funk and Wagnalls Co., 153 E. 24 St., 1951. 163 pp. $7.50.

139 tests of such elements as headline, copy, illustrations, layout.

SMALL-SPACE ADVERTISING, by Printers' Ink editors and contributors. New York: Funk and Wagnalls Co., 153 E. 24 St., in association with Printers' Ink Publishing Co., Inc., 1948. 237 pp. $4.

Pertinent suggestions on the use and design of the small-space ad.

ESSENTIALS OF OUTDOOR ADVERTISING. New York: Association of National Advertisers, Inc., 285 Madison Ave., 1952. 128 pp. $2.

A manual of the basic practices and procedures in outdoor advertising.

ADVERTISING PRODUCTION, by Ben Dalgin. New York: McGraw-Hill Book Co., Inc., 330 W. 42 St., 1946. 243 pp. $6.

A manual on the mechanics of newspaper printing offering a clear, well-illustrated explanation of the letterpress and gravure processes. It will be invaluable to those who must prepare advertisements for newspaper reproduction.

So You're Going to Choose an Advertising Agency, by James Thomas Chirurg. Pleasantville, N.Y.: Printers' Ink Books, 1950. 107 pp. $3.

This book includes definite yardsticks for judging agency operation in general and for evaluating work within specific departments.

Advertising Agency Practice, by Irvin Graham. New York: Harper & Brothers, 49 E. 33 St., 1952. $4.

Designed primarily for agency owners and staff to explain agency procedure, this handbook will prove helpful to all who work with agencies or are considering the possibility of an agency tie-in.

Advertising Agency Operations and Management, by Roger Barton. New York: McGraw-Hill Book Co., Inc., 330 W. 42 St., 1955. 348 pp. $6.

An authoritative guide to effective methods of operating an advertising agency, this book will also be of interest to those who work with agencies as clients, consultants, free-lance artists, etc. Noteworthy case material reveals how particular accounts have been handled for various objectives.

Standard Advertising Register. New York: National Register Publishing Co., 130 W. 42 St. Approximately 875 pp.

Lent to subscribers for $90 per year. Weekly revisions and special bulletins are included in this fee. A concise record of 14,000 advertisers with facts about the product, advertising appropriation, advertising media, ad execu-tives, and ad agency of each. Information is listed (1) geographically, (2) alphabetically, and (3) by trade names. For agencies, publishers, commercial artists, printers, radio-TV stations, etc.

McKittrick's Directory of Advertisers. New York: McKittrick's Directory of Advertisers, Inc., 108 Fulton St. About 1,200 pp. Published yearly in two editions: classified and geographical. Each $90 a year including weekly and monthly service.

The Classified Edition lists 20,000 national advertisers by commodity or service along with the officers, advertising manager, and advertising agency of each, as well as the advertising appropriation when known. The Geographical Edition gives the same information grouped by state and by city or town within each state. Directory subscribers receive "McKittrick's Agency List" as part of their regular service.

McKittrick's Agency List. New York: McKittrick's Directory of Advertisers, Inc., 108 Fulton St. Issued three times a year. About 1,200 pp. $15 per issue or $35 per year.

This directory lists some 3,000 advertising agencies, their officers, account executives, and accounts. The complete list of accounts is about 60,000 advertisers, many local. The "Agency List" is given to subscribers to "McKittrick's Directory of Advertisers."

Tide: The Newsmagazine of Advertising, Marketing and Public Relations. Published weekly, 232 Madison Ave., New York 16. $6.50 per year.

News of the advertising media and how various advertisers are using them.

Printers' Ink: The Weekly Magazine of Advertising Management and Sales. Printers' Ink Publishing Co., Inc., 205 E. 42 St., New York 17. $5 per year.

Latest news in the advertising field: new techniques, trends in business, pointers on preparation of copy and art work, developments in radio advertising, and the weekly advertising index.

*Advertising Age: The National Newspaper of Marketing.* Published weekly at 200 E. Illinois St., Chicago 11. $3.

News of the advertising market, leading advertisers, market surveys, trends, etc.

*Advertising and Selling.* Published monthly by Robbins Publishing Co., 48 W. 38 St., New York 16. $4.

Illustrated articles, feature departments, and news reports present the latest news and ideas in the advertising field, covering copy and layout, likes and dislikes of certain reader audiences, and helps for the advertising agency.

BOOKS FOR THE ADVERTISING MAN: A CLASSIFIED BIBLIOGRAPHY ON ADVERTISING, MARKETING, AND RELATED SUBJECTS. New York: Bureau of Research and Education, Advertising Federation of America, 330 W. 42 St., 1953. $1.

1,300 books classified by subjects, but not evaluated. Price of each book included.

## ART WORK

COMMERCIAL ART TECHNIQUES, by S. Ralph Maurello. New York: Tudor Publishing Co., 221 Fourth Ave., 1952. 126 pp. $3.

A practical handbook telling how to develop art techniques for 18 different media. Specific materials and equipment are discussed and evaluated for the commercial artist.

COMMERCIAL ART AS A BUSINESS, by Fred Rodewald. New York: The Viking Press, Inc., 18 E. 48 St., 1954. 129 pp. $2.95.

Although written for the commercial artist to assist him in the business of selling, making contracts, etc., this book will also be helpful to editors and art directors who plan and purchase commercial art.

CAREERS IN COMMERCIAL ART, by J. I. Biegeleisen. New York: E. P. Dutton & Co., Inc., 300 Fourth Ave., 1952. 255 pp. $4.

Chapters on sign painting, show-card writing, lettering, typography, trademarks, book jackets, illustrating, posters, fashion work, textiles, cartooning, animated cartoons, industrial designing, packaging, window display, stage designing, government jobs, and how an ad agency works. Vocational guidance is the purpose of this book, but art buyers will find invaluable its hints on the prices charged for various kinds of art work.

NEW TECHNIQUES IN PRACTICAL ART REPRODUCTION, by J. Bourges Mayfield. New York: Bourges, Inc., 80 Fifth Ave., 1951. 140 pp. $7.50.

Profusely illustrated explanation of the practical use of the Bourges Process materials in commercial art for presentations, layouts, color separations, background modifications, etc. Thoroughly practical and interesting.

HOW TO PREPARE ART AND COPY FOR OFFSET LITHOGRAPHY, by W. J. Stevens and J. McKinven. Maywood, N.J.: Dorval Publishing Co., 170 Parkway, 1948. 107 pp. $5.25.

This book contains very practical suggestions on art and copy treatment in offset lithography. 125 illustrations.

SCIENTIFIC ILLUSTRATION, by John Livesy Ridgway. Stanford University, Calif.: Stanford University Press, 1938. 173 pp. Out of print.

Although the illustrations under discussion are technical ones, this book goes so thoroughly into the objectives and techniques of illustration that it will interest any artist, draftsman, author, or editor. It contains a useful section on how and where to get base maps and the permission to use them.

## BOOK PUBLISHING

A PRIMER IN BOOK PRODUCTION, by Frank B. Myrick. New York: Bookbinding and Book Production Magazine, 50 Union Sq., 1945. 95 pp. $1.50. Out of print.

This concise book is the best source of information on book manufacturing. It is readable, practical, and thorough. It covers estimating and preparing copy, selecting and ordering paper, setting type, handling proofs, reproducing illustrations, and planning binding and jacket. It then goes into the technical details of ordering offset and gravure plates and duplicate printing plates. There are chapters on presswork, imposition, folding, gathering, sewing and trimming, casemaking, cover finishing, and casing-in.

THE BOOK, THE STORY OF PRINTING AND BOOKMAKING, by Douglas C. McMurtrie. New York: Oxford University Press, 114 Fifth Ave., 1943. 676 pp. $10.

The history and development of a book from the origin of the alphabet and paper to current practices in typography, design, binding, and illustration.

THE BOOKMAN'S GLOSSARY: A COMPENDIUM OF INFORMATION RELATING TO THE PRODUCTION AND DISTRIBUTION OF BOOKS. New York: R. R. Bowker Co., 62 W. 45 St., 1951. 198 pp. $2.50.

Definitions of about 1,200 printers' and editors' terms.

*Publishers' Weekly.* Published by R. R. Bowker Co., 62 W. 45 St., New York. $9 a year.

The trade journal of the book-publishing and book-selling industries.

*Bookbinding and Book Production Magazine.* Published monthly, 50 Union Sq., New York 3. $3 per year.

Journal of the book-manufacturing (as distinct from book-publishing) industry.

## COLOR

BASIC COLOR, by Egbert Jacobson. Chicago: Paul Theobald, 5 N. Wabash Ave., Chicago 2, 1949. 207 pp. $14.75. 460 illus.

Through text, color charts, color illustrations, and diagrams, this book gives a very practical and understandable interpretation of the Ostwald color system.

## COPYRIGHT

A MANUAL OF COPYRIGHT PRACTICE FOR WRITERS, PUBLISHERS, AND AGENTS, by Margaret Nicholson. New York: Oxford University Press, 114 Fifth Ave., 1956. $6.50.

For the layman seeking information in a specific situation involving copyright. Simple, readable, and authoritative. Some 49 of the major problems that arise are dealt with in detail.

## COPY WRITING

THE ART OF READABLE WRITING, by Rudolf Flesch. New York: Harper &

Brothers, 49 E. 33 St., 1949. 237 pp. $3.

Copy writers and copy editors will get concrete help from this book. It shows how short sentences, simple words, and personal references make nonfiction more readable. It explains how to sample, test, and measure the readability of copy and then classify it scientifically according to the grade level of the readers. The author's common-sense approach and keen humor help make this book a perfect illustration of the lessons that it teaches.

THE COMPLETE REPORTER, by Stanley P. Johnson and Julian Harriss. New York: The Macmillan Co., 60 Fifth Ave., 1942. 424 pp. $4.75

General textbook in news writing and editing with exercises and problems. Detailed "how-to-do" on writing the news lead and news story, simple items such as personals, complex stories about business and politics, special stories or features.

## DIRECT MAIL

SUCCESSFUL DIRECT-MAIL ADVERTISING AND SELLING, by Robert Stone. New York: Prentice-Hall, Inc., 70 Fifth Ave., 1955. 320 pp. $5.75.

A discussion of the factors that make direct mail an effective method of selling, along with specific suggestions for writing selling letters, developing and using mailing lists, profiting from direct mail tests, and applying direct mail mathematics.

HOW TO SELL THROUGH MAIL ORDER, by Irvin Graham. New York: McGraw-Hill Book Co., Inc., 330 W. 42 St., 1949. 443 pp. $4.

This practical guide to mail-order advertising through mass media and direct mail to special lists gives particularly good suggestions on precampaign planning and postcampaign analysis.

HOW TO RAISE FUNDS BY MAIL, by Margaret M. Fellows and Stella Koenig. New York: McGraw-Hill Book Co., Inc., 330 W. 42 St. 1950. 338 pp. $6.

Specific, practical directions for writing good fund-raising letters along with methods of reproducing letters, sources for building mailing lists, rules for testing letters, and suggestions for packaging the message and enclosures.

HELP YOURSELF TO BETTER MAIL ORDER, by Robert A. Baker. Pleasantville, N.Y.: Printers' Ink Books, 1953. 384 pp. $5.50.

Detailed information about mail-order advertising for the beginner or seasoned campaigner.

*The Reporter of Direct Mail Advertising.* Published by Henry Hoke, 53 Hilton Ave., Garden City, N.Y. $6 per year.

The trade paper of the direct mail advertising industry. Published monthly.

THE ROBERT COLLIER LETTER BOOK, by Robert Collier. New York: Prentice-Hall, Inc., 70 Fifth Ave., 1950. 350 pp. $5.65.

This book is one of the classics of the profession and should be read and re-read by everyone who has to move people to action by mail. It includes literally hundreds of letters and sales approaches of proved effectiveness in getting attention, arousing interest, convincing, and getting action.

GUIDE TO AMERICAN DIRECTORIES FOR COMPILING MAILING LISTS. New York: B. Klein and Co., 27 E. 22 St., 1956. 110 pp. $10.

This directory contains complete information on all available directories, yearbooks, annuals, etc., that can be used for market research or sales-promotion work. It is valuable in finding sources for compiling up-to-date mailing lists in all fields.

## DISPLAYS

DESIGN FOR POINT OF SALE, by Ladislav Sutnar. New York: Farrar, Straus and Cudahy, Inc., 101 Fifth Ave., 1952. 128 pp. $8.50. 334 illus.

An evaluation of the aspects of point-of-sale design and helps in planning for better visual interest.

HANDBOOK OF WINDOW DISPLAY, by Nestor Castro. New York: Architectural Book Publishing Co., Inc., 112 W. 46 St., 1954. 194 pp. $8.50.

With many illustrations to amplify the text, the author gives practical and detailed instructions on how to make the best use of window space.

MODERN SIGN PAINTING, by Edward J. Duvall. Wilmette, Ill.: Frederick J. Drake Co., 1952. 160 pp. $4.

How-to-do-it book for the commercial sign painter with directions for such varied techniques as sprayed signs, gold leaf, neon repaints, cut-in signs, silk-screen signs, etc.

POINT-OF-PURCHASE CARDBOARD DISPLAYS, by Victor Strauss. New York: Presentation Press, Box 3, Planetarium Station. 1954. $15.

A heavily illustrated encyclopedia of display that will interest even those who need only one display of a kind, although it is aimed at sales managers, artists, and printers who have to produce several hundred at a clip. It covers silk screen, collotype, die cutting, scoring, easeling, and laminating plus such action devices as the hot-air motor, flasher, reversing turntable, and pendulum motor.

WINDOW AND INTERIOR DISPLAY, by Robert Kretschmer. Scranton, Pa.: Laurel Press, 1952. 156 pp. $4.75.

A good introduction to the work of the display man with chapters on the tricks of the trade, the machines and materials, lighting and layout, signs and show cards, use of color, etc.

## EDITING AND PROOFREADING

EDITOR AT WORK, by Julie Eidesheim. New York: Rinehart and Co., Inc., 232 Madison Ave., 1939. 231 pp. $2.50.

This is one of the best and most readable books on what an editor's work consists of and how to do it. Long experience as an editor (defined as "one who prepares the work of others for publication") qualifies Miss Eidesheim to give concrete advice on the technique of editing, the tools of the editor, how to do library research, sentence construction, punctuation, spelling and capitalization, the mechanics of composition, and style.

MANUAL OF STYLE. Chicago: University of Chicago Press, 11th Rev. Ed., 1949. 394 pp. $4.

This authoritative guide for authors and editors gives rules for capitalization, punctuation, word division, footnotes, etc., as well as directions for the preparation of manuscripts and copy estimating. The emphasis is on book publishing. Specimens of type used at the University of Chicago Press are included.

PROOFREADING AND COPY-PREPARATION: A TEXTBOOK FOR THE GRAPHIC ARTS INDUSTRY, by Joseph Lasky. New York: Mentor Press, 131 W. 23 St., 1954. 656 pp. $7.50.

Excellent reference book for the proofreader and copy preparer, with problems illustrated by actual examples. Gives authoritative principles for compounding English words, division of words into syllables, capitalization, punctuation, and abbreviations, as well as extensive reference lists of compound words, words divided into syllables, abbreviations, homonyms, etc.

WORDS INTO TYPE, by Marjorie E. Skillin and Robert M. Gay. New York: Appleton-Century-Crofts, Inc., 35 W. 32 St., 1948. 585 pp. $5.

A guide to modern form, style, and usage for writers, reporters, editors, proofreaders, advertising men—all who use the written or printed word. It includes detailed information on manuscript preparation, copy editing, typography and illustration, proofreading, make-up, and printing style.

## LAYOUT AND DESIGN

ADVERTISING AND EDITORAL LAYOUT, by Matlack Price. New York: McGraw-Hill Book Co., Inc., 330 W. 42 St., 1949. 359 pp. $7. 160 pp. of illus., 16 in color.

This book covers both theory and practice of designing layout for the advertising and editorial pages of magazines and newspapers. The interrelation of pictures, lettering, and typography are described with a helpful analysis of the role of color in layout.

ADVERTISING LAYOUT AND TYPOGRAPHY by Eugene de Lopatecki. New York: The Ronald Press Co., 15 E. 26 St., 1952. $4.

For those who purchase printing and those who make the actual layouts, this book offers helpful pointers on the principles of design, use of the thumbnail sketch, type selection, and visualization.

DESIGN FOR PRINT, by John Brinkley. Peoria, Ill.: Charles A. Bennett Co., 1949. 168 pp. $4.25.

This handbook for student designers of printed matter gives a good explanation of type. the basic processes of

graphic reproduction, and the designer's over-all job.

LAYOUT: THE PRACTICAL APPLICATION OF THE PRINCIPLES OF DESIGN TO ADVERTISING AND PRINTING, by Charles J. Felten. New York: Appleton-Century-Crofts, Inc., 35 W. 32 St., 1954. 170 pp. $6.

Valuable pointers are given on the mechanics of layout with patterns and procedures that apply to the small printer's rough as well as to the art director's visual. Fully illustrated with numerous sketches and how-to-do-it illustrations.

PRACTICAL HANDBOOK ON HEADLINE DESIGN, by Kenneth B. Butler. Mendota, Ill.: Butler Typo-Design Research Center, 1954. 96 pp. $3.75.

Hundreds of headlines and page layouts are shown to illustrate suggestions for headline type selection, headline length and shape, style and spacing, etc., in magazine layout.

PRACTICAL HANDBOOK ON EFFECTIVE ILLUSTRATION, by Kenneth B. Butler. Mendota, Ill.: Butler Typo-Design Research Center, 1952. 82 pp. $3.75.

This book is jam-packed with suggestions—tricky and otherwise—for using illustrations by cropping, mortising, twisting, outlining, montaging, and using with type.

101 USABLE PUBLICATION LAYOUTS, by Kenneth B. Butler, George C. Likeness, and Stanley A. Kordek. Mendota, Ill.: Butler Typo-Design Research Center, 1954. 111 pp. $3.75.

Each page presents a one-page layout with analysis of the layout and an explanation of the techniques involved. Layouts range from those with no illustrations to those having as many as eight on a single page.

HOUSE MAGAZINE LAYOUT, by K. C. Pratt. Hamilton, Ohio: The Champion Paper and Fibre Company, 1952. 42 pp. Free.

A good introduction to the problems of format, design, and typography in the house magazine. Particularly good suggestions are given for varying the layout on facing pages with 40 possibilities analyzed and compared.

### LETTERING

THE ABC OF LETTERING, by J. I. Biegeleisen. New York: Harper & Brothers, 49 E. 33 St., 1940. 221 pp. $6.

An excellent manual for artists, showcard writers, poster artists, display letterers, or students, with notes on equipment, exercises, and 105 pages of alphabet styles.

THE ELEMENTS OF LETTERING, by John Howard Benson and Arthur Graham Carey. New York: McGraw-Hill Book Co., Inc., 330 W. 42 St., 1950. 135 pp. $5.25.

Theoretical, practical, and historical elements in the art of lettering are given here, primarily for the artist and letterer who will create, but also of interest to those who will plan, design, and finally evaluate lettering as a part of design.

LETTERING ART IN MODERN USE, by Raymond A. Ballinger. New York: Reinhold Publishing Corp., 430 Park Ave., 1952. 246 pp. $12.

A lavishly illustrated art book showing the history of lettering and modern use of lettering in art, advertising, packaging, and labeling.

LETTERS AND LETTERING, by Paul Carlyle and Guy Oring. New York: McGraw-Hill Book Co., Inc., 330 W. 42 St., 1943. 159 pp. $6.

Loose-leaf notebook of samples of hand-lettering with good suggestions on spacing and inking for the lettering

student and the layout man who must buy lettering.

SPEEDBALL TEXTBOOK, by Ross F. George. Camden, N.J.: Hunt Pen Co., 1952. 96 pp. $.50.

Over 100 styles of lettering are given with illustrations showing exactly how to use pen or brush to form every letter. This is perhaps the most practical, explicit, and thorough brief book on the subject. Suggestions on poster design are included.

### MAGAZINE PUBLISHING

BUSINESS PAPER PUBLISHING PRACTICES, edited by Julien Elfenbein. New York: Harper & Brothers, 49 E. 33 St., 1952. 422 pp. $6.

Handbook of recommended practices in all phases of business-paper publishing—administrative, editorial, layout and production, circulation, advertising, and sales promotion.

HOUSE MAGAZINE COPY WRITING AND PREPARATION FOR THE PRINTER, by K. C. Pratt. Hamilton, Ohio: Champion Paper and Fibre Co., 1946. 43 pp. Free.

Recommendations for solving the editorial problems peculiar to the company editor: gathering news, training volunteer reporters, editing for a company audience. Problems of layout and type specification are omitted.

MAGAZINE PUBLISHING, by Lenox R. Lohr. Baltimore: The Williams & Wilkins Co., 1932. 328 pp. Out of print.

From the working notes that one editor compiled for his successor. Elementary facts about the organization and management of a magazine, how to secure and edit articles and write editorials, the mechanics of reproducing illustrations, steps in production, advertising, etc. This editor's view of the problems of buying printing contains many tips of value to other editors of business papers. Although obtainable only at libraries or in the second-hand book market, this book is well worth whatever effort may be involved in seeing a copy. It is one of the best for the beginner.

## NEWSPAPER PUBLISHING

NEWSPAPER EDITING, MAKE-UP, AND HEADLINES, by Norman J. Radder and John E. Stempel. New York: McGraw-Hill Book Co., Inc., 330 W. 42 St., 1942. 394 pp. $5.50.

An excellent and complete handbook for both beginners and old hands.

*Editor and Publisher.* Published weekly at Times Tower, 42 St. and Broadway, New York 36. $5 per year.

The trade paper of the newspaper world with news of editorial and advertising affairs and ventures.

## PACKAGING

MODERN PACKAGING ENCYCLOPEDIA IS-SUE. Sold as a part of the magazine *Modern Packaging.* Published by Packaging Catalog Corp., 575 Madison Ave., New York. 775 pp. Magazine subscription, $6.

The Encyclopedia Issue of the magazine is a basic reference work, textbook, and buyer's directory of the packaging industry, with well-indexed material on package planning and design. It tells how and where to buy plain or printed cans, tubes, cartons, boxes, glass containers, aerosols, and plastics. It covers package printing methods, displays, adhesives, waterproofing, wet-strength papers, etc. It contains a great many advertisements by package manufacturers and printers and by materials suppliers, with samples of papers, films, foils, flock printing, etc. The emphasis is on

packaging for sales, but shipping and industrial packaging are also covered.

## PAPER

THE PAPER YEARBOOK. Duluth, Minn.: Davidson Publishing Company, 405 E. Superior St. Published annually, Feb. 1. About 570 pages. $10.

This encyclopedia of the paper industry describes, explains the special properties and uses of, and gives the sources of supply for more than 1,500 different kinds of papers and paper products. It is well illustrated and indexed.

## PHOTOGRAPHY

PICTURE EDITING, by Stanley E. Kalish and Clinton C. Edom. New York: Rinehart and Co., Inc., 232 Madison Ave., 1951. $6.

How to develop a feeling for pictures, how to create good picture ideas and work with photographers, and how to cope with the specific problems of scaling, cropping, determining print quality, retouching, caption writing, making layouts, and using color.

## PRINTING PROCESSES

MODERN ILLUSTRATION PROCESSES, by Charles W. Gamble, London: Sir Isaac Pitman & Sons, Ltd., 3d Ed., 409 pp. $7.50.

A thorough and fairly technical explanation of the gravure, offset, and relief processes of line, halftone, and color reproduction.

ILLUSTRATION AND REPRODUCTION, by John R. Biggs. New York: Farrar, Straus and Cudahy, Inc., 101 Fifth Ave., 1952. 240 pp. $8.50.

How to prepare art work for reproduction by any of the three basic processes with more than 140 reproductions to illustrate the directions and compare the various printing methods, materials, and techniques. A 55-page supplement contains examples of printing by letterpress, lithography, photogravure, collotype, and silk screen.

SILK SCREEN COLOR PRINTING, by Harry Sternberg. New York: McGraw-Hill Book Co., Inc., 330 W. 42 St., 1942. 79 pp. Illus. $5.

For clarity of text and illustrations it would be hard to beat this book, which tells how to make a silk-screen print, with utmost simplicity and complete, explicit detail. Written for artists but valuable also to buyers.

SCREEN PROCESS METHODS OF REPRODUCTION, by Bert Zahn. Wilmette, Ill.: Frederick J. Drake and Co., 1950. 252 pp. $4. 179 illus.

Detailed description of methods, materials, and equipment now in use in reproduction by the screen process, including such widely varied techniques as silk-screen stenciling, paint press method, flocking, photographic methods, zinc plate emulsion method, and automatic screen process.

OFFSET DUPLICATOR TECHNIQUES, by Richard Caruzzi, revised by Fred W. Hoch and Carl B. Harris. New York: Fred W. Hoch Associates, Inc., 461 Eighth Ave., 1951. 95 pp. $5.

Written for the layman in simple, non-technical language, this concise reference guide covers various angles of the small offset press process including platemaking, typesetting, and preparation of material.

## PUBLICITY AND PUBLIC RELATIONS

PUBLICITY FOR PRESTIGE AND PROFIT, by Howard Stephenson and Wesley Fiske Pratzner. New York: McGraw-Hill Book Co., Inc., 330 W. 42 St., 1953. 304 pp. $4.50.

A working manual of all phases of public relations, emphasizing the publicity point of view and describing techniques of building prestige through publicity. Helpful suggestions are given on the preparation of a press release. how to organize a community-relations program, how to produce good photographs, how to prepare for the various publicity media, etc.

EFFECTIVE PUBLIC RELATIONS, by Scott M. Cutlip and Allen H. Center. New York: Prentice-Hall, Inc., 70 Fifth Ave., 1952. 464 pp. $7.65.

A basic public-relations guide and reference book for business firms, professional organizations, welfare agencies, and school systems.

PUBLIC RELATIONS AT WORK, by Herbert M. Baus, New York: Harper & Brothers, 49 E. 33 St., 1948. 256 pp. $3.50.

Public relations defined and analyzed, with meaty chapters on all the basic techniques for working with employees, stockholders, customers, communities, trade outlets, political parties, etc.

PUBLIC RELATIONS HANDBOOK, edited by Philip Lesly. New York: Prentice-Hall, Inc., 70 Fifth Ave., 1950. 902 pp. $8.

An exhaustive discussion of every aspect of public relations by 36 experts in the field.

PUBLIC RELATIONS IDEA BOOK, by *Printers' Ink* editors and contributors. Pleasantville, N.Y.: Printers' Ink Books, 1953. 349 pp. $5.

Tested ideas are given for informing employees, customers, stockholders, community groups, and the general public, with special helps on making the most of special occasions, press notices, and annual reports.

## RADIO AND TELEVISION

SUCCESSFUL RADIO AND TELEVISION AD-VERTISING, by Eugene F. Seehafer and J. W. Laemmar. New York: Mc-Graw-Hill Book Co., Inc., 330 W. 42 St., 1951. 558 pp. $7.

A practical guide for those exploring the field of radio and television advertising.

HANDBOOK OF BROADCASTING, THE FUN-DAMENTALS OF AM, FM, FAX, AND TV, by Waldo Abbot. New York: McGraw-Hill Book Co., Inc., 330 W. 42 St., 1950. 492 pp. $5.50.

This guide gives nontechnical explanations of FM, AM, TV, FAX, recording, etc., discussing not only the "before the microphone or camera" aspects, but also the business and production techniques used most effectively in actual practice for each. Covers every aspect of broadcasting in all media.

RADIO AND TELEVISION COMMUNICA-TION, by Charles F. Lindsley. New York: McGraw-Hill Book Co., Inc., 330 W. 42 St., 1952. 492 pp. $5.50.

A thorough treatment of the historical, social, cultural, business, and technical aspects of radio and television, designed primarily as a classroom textbook, but of equal interest to the general reader.

SELLING AND PROMOTING RADIO AND TELEVISION, by Jacob A. Evans. New York: Printers' Ink Publishing Co., 205 E. 42 St., 1954. 348 pp. $5.95.

Nowhere are the requirements and opportunities of radio and TV more clearly set forth for both those inside and those outside the stations and networks.

RADIO ADVERTISING FOR RETAILERS, by C. H. Sandage. Cambridge, Mass.: Harvard University Press, 1945. 279 pp. $4.

An excellent reference book on radio advertising for the local and regional retailer based on a nation-wide survey of retail advertisers and radio stations. Both old and new advertisers will get invaluable help from the findings on radio-audience listening habits, experience in selling specific merchandise, radio program building, spot announcements vs. programs, bringing the community into program participation, and evaluating radio advertising.

## SHIPPING

POSTAL MANUAL, Superintendent of Documents, Government Printing Office, Washington 25, D.C. 65¢.

The authoritative source of postal information in brief form and simple language for the lay reader. It includes information about both domestic and foreign mail service.

LEONARD'S GUIDE AND SERVICE. Leased, not sold, by G. R. Leonard and Co., 79 Madison Ave., New York 16, and 123 N. Wacker Dr., Chicago 6. $15 a year for New York, Philadelphia, and Chicago, $20 a year elsewhere.

A loose-leaf, indexed book kept up-to-date by mail service, which gives complete shipping information including rates and regulations for parcel post, railway express, rail freight, airmail and air parcel post. A subscriber receives a "Guide" made up for his city listing rates and routings that apply from that point of origin to the various cities and towns throughout the United States.

The same firm publishes five motor freight directories (New York, Philadelphia, Chicago, New England, and Boston)—the first three available at $5 each, the other two at $2.50 each.

BULLINGER'S POSTAL AND SHIPPERS GUIDE for the United States, Canada, and Newfoundland. New York: Bullinger's Guides, Inc., 303 Lafayette St. Published annually. About 1,200 pp. $12.

Lists every post office, railroad station, landing (175,000 names), or nearest communicating point, with county, and whether or not there is a telegraph office. Contains a digest of postal rate information but nothing on express or freight rates.

### TYPOGRAPHY

An Approach to Type, by John R. Biggs. New York: Farrar, Straus and Cudahy, Inc., 101 Fifth Ave., 1952. 152 pp. $4.75.

A concise, workable introduction to the study of type faces with specimen book showing complete fonts of the best-known type faces.

Design with Type, by Carl Dair. New York: Farrar, Straus and Cudahy, Inc., 101 Fifth Ave., 1952. 144 pp. $4.50.

A practical and at the same time stimulating analysis of the principles underlying good typographic design with some 90 working layouts employing only type elements and requiring no art work.

How to Recognize Type Faces, by R. Randolph Karch. Bloomington, Ill.: McKnight and McKnight Publishing Co., 1952. 265 pp. $6.

A practical reference book which is intended to assist the reader in identifying close to 1,500 type faces which are grouped in this book by certain distinguishing features.

Introduction to Typography, by Oliver Simon. Cambridge, Mass.: Harvard University Press, 1949. 137 pp. $3.

A concise and informative handbook dealing with the fine points of typography in book production. Many examples of type are given with an explanation of their particular uses in bookwork.

Type for Books and Advertising, by Eugene M. Ettenburg. New York: D. Van Nostrand Co., Inc., 250 Fourth Ave., 1947. 160 pp. $8.50.

A generously illustrated presentation of the basic mechanical details of typesetting, with good chapters on design and layout. The book devotes about 20 pages to a review of the work of 20 leading typographers, with specimens and quotations from each. Another 10 pages give brief biographies of 22 twentieth-century type designers. There is an interesting chapter on period typography.

### VISUAL AIDS

The Preparation and Use of Visual Aids, by Kenneth B. Haas and Harry Q. Packer. New York: Prentice-Hall, Inc., 70 Fifth Ave., 1946. 224 pp. Out of print.

This book covers motion pictures, sound and silent filmstrips, slides, the use of the opaque projector, the preparation of maps, charts, graphs, diagrams, posters, photographs, etc. Much of its information is hard to find elsewhere. It contains valuable lists of sources of visual materials.

# Appendix 3

# Graphic Arts Films

A number of motion pictures and filmstrips have been produced by educational and manufacturing concerns explaining the techniques of the graphic arts. These films are frequently quite helpful in explaining visually the various printing and duplicating processes.

The films listed and described below vary somewhat in their maturity level and quality of production so that users should try to preview a particular film, before using it, in order to determine its appeal and suitability for a particular audience.

Specific instructions are given for borrowing, renting, and purchasing each film, but it is possible, in many cases, to obtain the film also from a local or state film library. Film users can obtain a list of these local sources in "A Directory of 2660 16mm Film Libraries," available for 50 cents from the Superintendent of Documents, U.S. Government Printing Office, Washington 25, D.C.

The following list is selective and film users should also consult "Educational Film Guide" and its supplements, a catalogue of 11,000 films published by the H. W. Wilson Co., 950 University Place, New York. This is a standard reference book, available in most public and university libraries.

## BOOK PUBLISHING

BOUND TO LAST. 18 min, sd, b&w. 1935. Free loan from William J. Ganz, 40 E. 49 St., New York 17, N.Y.

The steps in printing and bookbinding made clear and vivid by showing each step done first by hand and then by machine. Although the manufacture of binder's board is stressed, that does not overshadow such steps as typesetting, page make-up, lock-up, folding, gathering, stitching, smashing, trimming, lining, casemaking, and casing-in.

IN BLACK AND WHITE. 20 min, sd, b&w. 1952. Purchase ($55) or rent ($2.50)

412

from British Information Services, 30 Rockefeller Plaza, New York 20.

An explanation of and a tribute to the traditions of British printing. Dramatized sequences portray the discoveries through the ages that have led to improvements in printing processes. Surveys the status (1952) and future of the British publishing industry.

MAKING BOOKS. 11 min, sd, b&w. 1947. Purchase ($50) or rent ($2.50) from Encyclopaedia Britannica Films, Wilmette, Ill.

Such important steps in bookmaking are shown as Linotype composition, make-up, lock-up, electrotyping, cutting the plates apart, make-ready, inking, printing both sides of the paper in 'one operation, folding, gathering, sewing, trimming, casing-in, and stamping.

### ELECTROTYPES, STEREOTYPES, AND MATS

THE ELECTROTYPE. 28 min, sd, color. 1954. Free loan from the Electrotypers and Stereotypers Association of New York, 110 E. 42 St., or from other electrotyping firms which have purchased copies.

Begins with a quick review of the history of the printed word and then shows in some detail how both flat and curved electrotypes and stereotypes are made. The information is non-technical in the sense that it is intended for the man who buys printing plates rather than the technician who makes them.

### ETCHING AND CUTTING BLOCKS

JOAN MIRÓ MAKES A COLORED PRINT. 20 min, sd, color. 1951. Rent ($25) from Thomas Bouchard Productions, 80 W. 40 St., New York 18.

Demonstration by Joan Miró, Catalonian artist, of the complete process from the first work on a copper plate to the finished etching print.

HOW TO MAKE AN ETCHING. 20 min, sd, b&w. 1951. Purchase ($90) from Almanac Films, 516 Fifth Ave., New York 18.

Detailed demonstration of etching—the original drawing, its transfer to a metal plate, mixing of the acid, heating, inking, and wiping. Also shows the aquatint process and the final printing of the plate.

A NEW WAY OF GRAVURE. 12 min, sd, b&w. 1951. Purchase ($40) or rent ($4) from Film Images, Inc., 18 E. 60 St., New York 22.

Describes the artist's technique (Stanley William Hayter) for engraving on copper from his first rough sketches on paper to pulling the final print, one of his series of "Angels Wrestling."

BLOCK CUTTING AND PRINTING. 13 min, sd, color. 1952. Purchase ($115), Stout Institute, Menomonie, Wis.

Shows how to cut and print a two-color design, including details of transferring the design, cutting, proofing, correcting, registering for color, and printing the blocks by three different methods.

### INK

RAINBOWS TO ORDER. 21 min, sd, color. 1949. Free loan from International Chemical Corp., Printing Ink Division, 67 W. 44 St., New York 36.

Explains and illustrates the processes used in manufacturing printing inks, and the characteristics of different kinds of inks.

### LETTERPRESS PRINTING

ANOTHER MAN'S BUSINESS. 25 min, sd, color. 1949. Free loan from Syndicated Films, 1022 Forbes St., Pittsburgh 19.

Sponsored by the Miller Printing Machinery Co., shows the production of a new printing press—engineering, pilot model, manufacture, tools, gauges, tests, and final assembly. Also shows operation of a Miller two-color press.

PRINTING. 11 min, sd, b&w. 1947. Purchase ($55) from Vocational Guidance Films, 215 E. 3 St., Des Moines 9, Iowa.

Although made to tell high-school students about job opportunities in printing, this film is of interest to buyers of printing because it gives a quick showing of all the simpler operations and equipment in letterpress printing. The scenes show hand composition, machine composition, proofreading, make-up, lock-up, make-ready, and presswork (on platen, flat-bed, rotary, hand-fed, and machine-fed presses). It carries no reference to offset, gravure, engraving, photography, or electrotyping, and only passing reference to bindery work.

PRINTING THRU THE AGES. 13 min, sd, b&w. 1950. Purchase ($62.50) or rent ($3) from Encyclopaedia Britannica Films, Wilmette, Ill. Also available in 40-min. version, STORY OF PRINTING, purchase ($165) or rent ($8.50).

Traces the story of printing from ancient times to the present day. Includes sequences illustrating Gutenberg's contributions, shows evolution of modern type faces and improvements in paper, suggests the impact of the Industrial Revolution, and concludes with scenes of modern book and newspaper presses in operation.

**OFFSET LITHOGRAPHY**

A BETTER RUN FOR YOUR MONEY. 21 min, sd, color. 1948. Free loan from

Harris-Seybold Co., 4510 E. 71 St., Cleveland 10, Ohio.

Describes the advantages of offset lithography which are most important to the buyers of printed materials. The three major sequences are: the importance of printed salesmanship; what makes printed salesmanship effective; and why lithography gives you a better run for your money.

HOW TO MAKE A GOOD IMPRESSION. 25 min, sd, color. 1947. Free loan from Harris-Seybold Co., 4510 E. 71 St., Cleveland 10, Ohio.

One of the best graphic arts films ever made, giving an excellent explanation of offset lithography, with emphasis on its advantages over gravure and letterpress printing. The camera follows a pamphlet from the first rough layout to the finished product. The intervening steps include detailed explanations of making a halftone, color separations, stripping-in, platemaking, multicolor runs, deep-etch, and the use of four-color presses.

THE MAKING OF A 24-SHEET POSTER. 30 min, si, b&w with color sequences. 1937 revised as of 1954. Purchase ($55) or free loan from McCandlish Lithograph Corp., Roberts Ave. and Stokley St., Philadelphia 29.

An excellent picture for those who may become buyers of 24-sheet posters and for those interested in the lithographic process as such. A poster (billboard) is traced from the first discussion with the artist to the final trimming, wrapping, and shipping. Two processes are shown: hand preparation of plates by the crayon process and the process-color technique.

THE MODERN LITHOGRAPHER. 11 min, sd, b&w. 1940. Purchase ($50) from Encyclopaedia Britannica Films, Inc., 1150 Wilmette Ave., Wilmette, Ill., or rent ($2) from Association Films,

347 Madison Ave., New York 17, N.Y.

A beautiful explanation of the offset principle. This film is so crammed with information and moves so fast that no layman can absorb more than a fraction of its message at the first showing. It should be shown once with sound, and again without sound at silent speed with a narrator explaining things that may have puzzled the audience. Hand lithographing from stone, simple offset work from metal plates, and the steps in making a four-color fine arts reproduction are shown.

## PAPER

GIFT OF TS'AI LUN—PAPER. 33 min, sd, color. 1946. Free loan from Hammermill Paper Co., 122 E. 42 St., New York 17, N.Y.

Shows all the stages of paper manufacture from logging to the final sheets or rolls, with a thorough explanation of the technical and economic problems.

GREAT WHITE TRACKWAY. 28 min, sd, color. 1954. Free loan with exception of transportation charges from the Hammermill Paper Co., 122 E. 42 St., New York 17, N.Y.

Shows the importance of paper and printing to American business and shows also the pulp and papermaking process as employed at Hammermill.

THE MIRACLE OF PAPER. 28 min, sd, color. 1954. Free loan from P. H. Glatfelter Co., Spring Grove, Pa.

As good as a conducted tour of the Glatfelter paper mill.

NEWSPRINT. 23 min, sd, color. 1950. Free loan from Canadian National Film Board, 1270 Avenue of the Americas, New York 20, or 400 W. Madison Ave., Chicago 6.

Follows the whole cycle of newsprint production, from the time of the first timber cruise, until the final roll of newsprint tumbles down the sloping railway to the ships waiting to carry it to overseas markets. The main locale of the forest scenery is the north shore of the St. Lawrence River in the province of Quebec, in an area about 400 miles downriver from Montreal.

TREES TO TRIBUNES. 26 min, sd, b&w. 1948. Free loan from Chicago Tribune, 33 W. Madison Ave., Chicago 11.

The first 15 min. of this film deals with papermaking. The last 11 min. reviews rapidly such publication activities as news gathering, feature writing, use of pictures and cartoons, making engravings, setting type, proofreading, make-up, matrix making, casting stereotypes, and press lock-up.

## PHOTOENGRAVING

ART AND TECHNIQUE OF PHOTO-ENGRAVING. 27 min, sd, color. 1954. Free loan from Horan Engraving Co., 44 W. 28 St., New York 1.

Takes you through all the steps of photoengraving, including reproduction. Touches upon color reproduction and also on Ben Day.

PICTURE'S THE THING. 18 min, sd, color. 1952. Free loan from Collins, Miller, & Hutchings, Inc., 207 N. Michigan Ave., Chicago.

Illustrates the various processes in the making of an engraving at the plant of Collins, Miller, & Hutchings, Inc. Includes preparation of photographic plates, stripping the film on glass, application of staging ink, multicolored proof press and proof inspection.

## SILK-SCREEN PRINTING

HASTY SIGN MAKING. 21 min, sd, b&w. 1953. Purchase ($32.54) from United World Films, 1445 Park Ave., New York 29.

Demonstrates procedures to be followed, using an army kit of materials, in making signs by the silk-screen process.

MAKING A SERIGRAPH. 30 min, si, color. 1948. Purchase ($180) or rent ($60) from Harmon Foundation, 140 Nassau St., New York 38.

Shows the technique of the artist in producing original art work in five colors by silk-screen methods. Also shows an exhibition of prints by the National Serigraph Society.

SILK SCREEN PRINTING. 18 min, sd, b&w. 1945. Rent ($5) from New York University Film Library, Washington Square, New York 3.

The profilm method of silk-screen printing is shown in detail for the silk-screen artist rather than for the buyer of printing. By this method a film stencil is cut and adhered to the silk screen.

SILK SCREEN TEXTILE PRINTING. 11 min, sd, color. 1952. Purchase ($100) or rent ($4.50) from Bailey Films, 6509 De Longpre Ave., Hollywood 28.

Selects a dress-material design and translates it into a silk-screen stencil and textile print. Shows use of swivel stencil knife, lacquer film, lithographer's crayon, liquid tusche, registration board. Explains basic silk-screen process. Suggests use of this method of printing for Christmas cards, place mats, and other gifts, as well as for dress and drapery textiles.

MEET PHOTOSCREEN PRINTING. 15 min, sd, color. 1955. Free loan from Camera Club and School Service, Eastman Kodak Co., Rochester 4, N.Y.

A demonstration of the Kodak Ektagraph process for making silk screens by photographic methods. Stresses the versatility of the silk-screen process for displays, sales promotion, and in fact for printing almost any image on any object. An 8-page pamphlet with the same title is also available, free, for distribution to audiences.

## TYPE

FIVE CENTURIES OF TYPE FOUNDING. 35mm, b&w, filmstrip, 71 frames, plus 16-in. disk, $33\frac{1}{3}$ r.p.m., 30 min. 1949. Free loan from American Type Founders Sales Corp., 200 Elmora Ave., Elizabeth, N.J.

Type design is illustrated here, not type casting or type use. The film traces the development of certain type faces with illustrations of some of today's type faces as derived from the early sources.

TYPE AND ITS ORIGIN. 35mm, color, filmstrip, 96 frames, plus disk, 78 or $33\frac{1}{3}$ r.p.m., 16 min. 1951. Rent from Monsen, Inc., 22 E. Illinois St., Chicago 11.

Describes examples of the important steps in the development of the printed word—from the first crude markings on cave walls through the most modern typography.

TYPE SPEAKS. 25 min, sd, color. 1948. Free loan from American Type Founders Sales Corp., 200 Elmora Ave., Elizabeth, N.J.

Reviews the history of foundry type and then explains how it is made and used today. A type designer is shown at work on his original drawings which are copied before pattern drawings are made. Then pattern plates are cut, and matrices made in different sizes.

## TYPING AND OFFICE DUPLICATING

TEN COPIES, PLEASE. 21 min, sd, color. 1952. Free loan from Movies U.S.A., 729 Seventh Ave., New York 19.

Presents several important historical events which illustrate the difficulty of writing and making multiple copies before the advent of the typewriter. Concludes with a demonstration of the advantages of the Underwood "All-Electric" typewriter.

HOW TO OPERATE A MIMEOGRAPH DUPLICATOR. 20 min, sd, b&w. 1945. Rental ($3.50) from Business Education Films, 630 Ninth Ave., New York 36.

A good explanation of the preparation of a stencil, the cleaning of type, the correction of errors on the stencil, the use of Mimeograph Model 91, the Mimeoscope, and stylus, running post cards, etc.

# Appendix 4

# Postal Information

Certain facts about postal regulations are well worth memorizing, as a handy guide to efficient distribution.

The first-class postage rate is 3 cents per oz.; postal cards 2 cents. (For details see FIRST-CLASS MAIL below.)

Second-class privileges apply only to periodicals, but rates are much lower than on any other class. (For details see SECOND-CLASS MAIL below.)

Third-class postage applies to circulars and other miscellaneous printed matter, also to merchandise weighing up to and including 8 oz. The regular rate is 2 cents for the first 2 oz. and 1 cent for each additional oz.; bulk mailings made under post-office permit cost only 14 cents per lb. with a minimum of 1½ cents per piece. (For details see THIRD-CLASS MAIL below.)

Fourth-class postage is parcel post, with rates depending both on the weight and the zone to which it is to be delivered. Rates range from 18 cents for local delivery of a 1-lb. package to $12.78 for 8-zone delivery of a 70-lb. package.

Note that the weight limit on most shipments is 20 or 40 lb.—not 70 lb. as formerly, and as now allowed only in certain circumstances. (For details see FOURTH-CLASS MAIL below.)

418

*Major exceptions.* Third-class rate for books, pamphlets, and catalogues of 24 pages or more is 2 cents for 2 oz. and 1½ cents for each additional 2 oz. (It often pays to design a pamphlet to have 24 small pages instead of 12 or 16 bigger ones, just to save on postage.)

Third-class mail can be weighed instead of counted under the rates for "bulk mailing." Thus 200 pieces, weighing 2 oz. each would cost 2 cents per piece or 1¾ cents each if weighed in bulk. (See THIRD-CLASS MAIL below.)

Books not containing advertising matter may be mailed to any part of the United States for 8 cents for the first pound or fraction, 4 cents for each additional pound up to and including 70 lb. (See BOOK POSTAGE RATES below.)

The post office goes much further than simply fixing rates for certain classes of mail and then getting that mail to its destination. In addition, the following services are offered:

*COD* service is ideal where the shipper does not wish to extend credit or the customer does not wish to pay in advance. (See COD below.)

*Insurance.* Insurance up to $200 may be taken out on third- and fourth-class mail within the United States and its possessions. (See REGISTERED MAIL, page

'31, for comparison of Insured and Registered mail.)

*Registered mail.* This service provides special handling for valuable articles and indemnity up to $1,000. (See REGISTERED MAIL, page 435.)

*Certified mail.* For a 20-cent fee over and above the regular postage, the post office will now guarantee *personal* delivery of a letter to the addressee or his representative, or return to sender. This is somewhat the same service offered under "registered mail," but without the indemnity and at a lower rate. (See CERTIFIED MAIL below.)

*Postal cards.* Both single and double postal cards, separate or in sheets of 20 or 40 for printing, may be secured for the price of the postage, 2 cents per card. (See POST CARDS below.)

*Envelopes.* Envelopes with postage stamp embossed on the paper of the envelope itself may be purchased through the post office. For small extra charge the post office will print them with return name and address. 1,000 No. 5 envelopes ($3\frac{1}{2}$ by $6\frac{5}{16}$) unprinted cost (1955) $5.06, printed $7.06, in addition to postage. (See ENVELOPES below.)

*Business reply cards, envelopes, and labels.* Forms guaranteeing that the addressee will pay postage may be printed by special post-office permit. (See BUSINESS REPLY CARDS below.)

*Mailing-list corrections.* These can be assembled readily by the careful use of printed instructions to the postmaster asking for notice of change of address or guaranteeing postage for forwarding or return of third-class mail. (See MAILING-LIST CORRECTIONS below.)

*Payment of postage.* To avoid the labor of affixing stamps and, in the case of third-class bulk mailing, to take advantage of the cheaper postage rate, permission may be obtained to use precanceled stamps, the printed "indicia" in place of the stamp, or the imprint of a postage meter machine. (Third-class bulk-rate economies are offered

only on condition that the mail is handled in such a way as to save the post office the labor of canceling and sorting.)

*Precanceled postage.* This is used chiefly on third- and fourth-class matter. (See PRECANCELED POSTAGE below.) Permission must be obtained from the postmaster; no fee is required.

*Printed postage impressions.* Such a permit for permit-imprint, nonstamped mail may be obtained from the postmaster. The fee is $10, no part of which may be applied as postage. (See PRINTED POSTAGE IMPRESSIONS below.)

*Postage meter machines.* These may be used for all classes of mail. (See POSTAGE METER MACHINES below.)

*Transit time.* No guarantee can be given as to the exact time required for collection, transportation, and delivery of mail. City post offices frequently issue a local schedule of transit time to certain points for first-class mail. Usually this does not include time allowance for mailbox pickup, post-office sorting, or delivery at point of destination.

Additional time for these may be estimated to some extent as follows:

1. Approximately 1 to 2 hr. elapse between the time when mail is received in a post office and the time when it is put on the train.

2. Collections are made from train mailboxes located in railroad stations about 15 min. before train departure time.

3. From 1 to 3 hr. are required for sorting at the station or post office of destination, depending on quantity of mail on hand before delivery begins. This is shortened in the case of special delivery mail. The time of delivery of regular mail depends upon the established delivery schedules.

4. The earlier mail is dispatched in the afternoon the more likely it is to make overnight trains and be delivered in the morning.

5. First-class mail and that marked

for special handling usually requires about half the transit time required for regular second-, third-, and fourth-class mail.

Almost any business office or its mailing room will profit by posting the table of transit time of the local post office; or by assembling this information and posting it for easy reference if a printed table is not available.

(For shipping by air and railway express see EXPRESS, also FREIGHT and TRUCKING in the main text of this book.)

*Unmailable matter.* The following articles are among those listed as unmailable: poisons, explosives, matches (except safety matches packed as prescribed by postal regulations), intoxicating liquors, obscene and indecent matter, matter involving lottery or fraud, with certain exceptions firearms capable of being concealed on the person, libelous matter on the outside of the mail. In addition, stringent regulations govern the mailing and packaging of meat and meat-food products, plant and plant products, dentures and prosthetic devices, live animals, fowls, insects, and reptiles.

The "Postal Manual," Chapters I and II, is the authoritative source of postal information. Copies may be obtained from the Superintendent of Documents, Government Printing Office, Washington 25, D.C., 65 cents.

**airmail** Airmail, carried by air and the fastest connecting surface carriers, is given the most expeditious handling in dispatch and delivery. Airmail is not given special delivery to the addressee unless a special delivery fee is paid in addition to the airmail postage.

It is limited to 70 lb. in weight and 100 in. in combined length and girth, and may be left sealed or unsealed without affecting the rate.

Airmail outside of continental United States and possessions may be sent for rates that vary from 10 cents per ½ oz. to Latin American republics to 15 cents per ½ oz. to England and 25 cents per ½ oz. to China.

Registered, insured, and COD mail may be sent by air on payment of the proper fees. (See REGISTERED MAIL, INSURED MAIL, COD.)

Material of unlimited weight may be sent by air express. Rates depend upon the nature, weight, and volume of the

AIRMAIL RATES

DOMESTIC RATES (WITHIN CONTINENTAL UNITED STATES AND TO AND FROM ITS POSSESSIONS)

| Weight | | Rate |
|---|---|---|
| 8 oz. or less | Air postal or post cards<br>Business reply cards<br>Letters and packages<br>Airmail in business reply envelopes | 4¢ each<br>5¢ collected when delivered<br>6¢ an ounce<br>6¢ an ounce plus 1¢ per piece, collected when delivered |

| | Zones 1, 2, 3 | Zone 4 | Zone 5 | Zone 6 | Zone 7 | Zone 8 |
|---|---|---|---|---|---|---|
| Over 8 oz. to 1 lb............ | $0.60 | $0.65 | $0.70 | $0.75 | $0.75 | $0.80 |
| Each additional pound........ | .48 | .50 | .56 | .64 | .72 | .80 |

material being shipped. (See RAILWAY EXPRESS in the main text of this book.)

**air parcel post** A term sometimes applied to airmail weighing 8 oz. or over. (See AIRMAIL.)

**book postage rates** See also THIRD-CLASS MAIL; FOURTH-CLASS MAIL; also chart below.

Books of 24 pages or more, free of advertising (except the publisher's own on the jacket), may be mailed at special "book rates" which do not change with the zone of destination. Ineligible for these rates, however, are books which are primarily priced catalogs. These go at third-class rates up to 8 ounces, but at parcel-post zoned rates over 8 ounces.

**business reply cards and envelopes** A business reply card, envelope, or label requires no postage from the sender since the addressee (who originally sent it out) agrees to pay return postage. This is not to be confused with the stamped post card or envelope which may also be sent out for reply.

The advantage of a business reply card, envelope, or label over one that is prepaid is that the addressee pays postage only on those cards which he receives instead of paying postage on all that he sends out, many of which may never be returned. However, the rate is 2 cents higher for each piece received than on regular mail. That is, the business-reply-card postage rate is 4 cents collected on delivery, and a business reply envelope or package is 2 cents in addition to regular postage.

Application for permission to send out business reply cards, envelopes, and labels must be made to the postmaster at the office where they are to be returned, by filing post-office Form 3614.

BOOK RATES

| Description of book | Weight limit | Class | Rate | |
|---|---|---|---|---|
| | | | Single | Bulk |
| Books and catalogues having 24 pages or more at least 22 of which are printed | 8 oz. | Third | 2¢ first 2 oz., 1½¢ each additional 2 oz. or fraction of 2 oz. To authorized nonprofit organizations 1½¢ for each 2 oz. or fraction | 10¢ per lb. or fraction; 1½¢ minimum charge per piece, except 1¢ for authorized nonprofit organizations |
| Books of 24 pages or more, made up wholly of reading matter | 9 oz. to 70 lb. | Fourth | First pound, 8¢ Each additional pound, 4¢ Same rate to all zones | |
| Library books consisting wholly of reading matter when sent by public libraries and similar organizations | 9 oz. to 70 lb. | Fourth | First pound, 4¢ Each additional pound, 1¢ Same rate to all zones | |
| Catalogues and similar advertising matter | 9 oz. to 10 lb. | Fourth | Zone rates apply beginning at 12¢ per lb. for local | |

No fee is required to accompany this application.

The permit number, address, and other stipulated information must be imprinted on the address side of a card, envelope, or label in one of the forms supplied by the post office when the permit is issued. No illustrations, trade-marks, or advertising may be printed on the address side. No stipulation is made regarding the reverse side.

Business reply cards, like post cards, may be no smaller than 2¾ by 4 in. and no larger than 3⁹⁄₁₆ by 5⁹⁄₁₆ in. (If larger, they are charged at the rate applicable to business reply envelopes.)

*Double reply cards.* When the reply half of a double reply card is imprinted as a business reply card, the address side carrying the permit number, etc., must be folded inside when the double card is originally mailed.

**certified mail** See also REGISTERED MAIL below.

In the past, registered mail has ac-complished two functions: (1) Certification that the piece of registered mail is delivered to the addressee in person and (2) indemnity against loss or damage. Certified mail, a new type of service inaugurated in 1955, accomplishes the first of these two functions at a lower rate than registered mail.

Certified mail is used to make sure that a piece of first-class mail is delivered in person to the addressee or his representative. If certified mail is lost in transit, no insurance or indemnity may be collected.

The fee in addition to postage is 20 cents; for return receipts showing to whom and when delivered, 10 cents, or showing to whom, when, and address where delivered, 35 cents. The fee and postage may be paid by ordinary postage stamps, meter stamps, or by permit imprints.

You may mail certified mail at the post office or in a street letter box provided you follow specific directions as to the use of certified mail coupons and blank return receipt forms if those

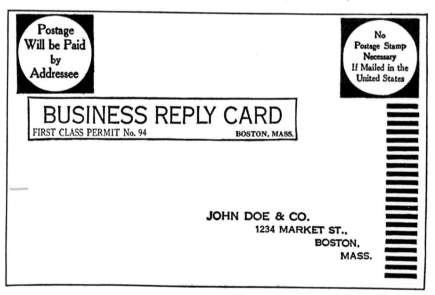

This is one of three forms prescribed by the Post Office for a business reply card. For an envelope or label, the word "envelope" or "label" is substituted for the word "card."

are needed. For details see the "Postal Manual" or consult your local post office.

The sender of a certified letter retains a receipt. If he does not request a return receipt at time of mailing, he may later request one from the addressee's post office by accompanying his request with his receipt and a 10-cent fee.

**COD** Through its COD (collect-on-delivery) service, the post office helps solve the problem created when a shipper does not wish to extend credit or the customer does not wish to pay in advance. For a fee the post office delivers a package and collects the money, which is returned to the shipper by postal money order. The addressee may not examine the COD parcel until charges have been paid and a receipt given. A COD shipment must be a bona fide order for the contents or be in conformity with an agreement between the sender and the addressee.

Fees for collection include automatic insurance against loss, rifling, or dam-

age in an amount equivalent to the actual value or the cost of repairs, or against nonreceipt of COD collections. The maximum amount collectible on a single parcel is $200 unless the parcel is sent by registered mail. (See below.)

If a COD shipment is sent by registered mail, it is assured the extra care in handling that is given all registered mail. Since fourth-class mail may be registered only if first-class postage is paid, it would be superfluous to add a special-handling stamp.

Shipments valued at more than $200 must be registered. No more than $200 can be collected from the addressee, but indemnity in case of loss greater than this can be secured through registration.

*COD tags.* These must be attached to parcels sent COD. Each tag must be filled in by the sender to show the complete name and address of the sender and of the addressee, the amount of charges to be collected upon delivery and remitted to the sender by money order, and the money-order fee charged the addressee for the amount involved.

FEES (IN ADDITION TO POSTAGE)

| Indemnity (and COD collection to $200) | COD Fees | |
|---|---|---|
| | Registered | Unregistered |
| $5.00 and under | $0.80 | $0.30 |
| $5.01 to $10 | 0.80 | 0.40 |
| $10.01 to $25 | 1.10 | 0.60 |
| $25.01 to $50 | 1.10 | 0.70 |
| $50.01 to $100 | 1.20 | 0.80 |
| $100.01 to $150 | 1.40 | 0.90 |
| $150.01 to $200 | 1.40 | 1.00 |
| $200.01 to $300 | 1.50 | |
| $300.01 to $400 | 1.60 | Indemnity for unregistered COD mail is limited to $200; for |
| $400.01 to $500 | 1.70 | registered COD mail $1,000, the same as for all registered mail. |
| $500.01 to $600 | 1.80 | Collection for COD mail, unregistered or registered, is limited |
| $600.01 to $700 | 1.90 | to $200. |
| $700.01 to $800 | 2.00 | |
| $800.01 to $1,000 | 2.10 | |

Consult the local postmaster for information about the four styles of COD tags that are used for the service.

Advance notice of the shipment of a COD parcel is recommended so that the addressee may know its contents and may be ready with the exact change when it is delivered. Such notices cut down the instances where addressees refuse delivery and the sender must pay return postage.

For further details, consult the local postmaster or the "Postal Manual."

**envelopes** The U.S. Post Office sells envelopes at very low rates and will imprint them with return name and address. For example, in 1955 the Post Office was supplying a 4⅛-by-9½ commercial envelope made from 24# white sulphite bond at $6.54 per 1,000 plus postage. For $2 additional per 1,000 the customer's name and return ad-

dress could be imprinted in a standard form in the corner. Imprinted regular envelopes (meaning envelopes which have no window, are not for airmail, and are not precanceled) were available in three sizes in lots of 500 and 1,000.

Unprinted regular envelopes were available in any quantity with 2- or 3-cent stamp imprinted.

Unprinted window envelopes and precanceled envelopes were available only in box lots.

**first-class mail** First-class mail includes:

1. *Written and typewritten matter* such as letters (including carbons), post cards (both government and private mailing cards), business reply cards, letters in business reply envelopes, and manuscript or typewritten copy for the printer unless accompanied by proofs

RATES FOR FIRST-CLASS MAIL (DOMESTIC)

| Kind of mail | Rate |
|---|---|
| All first-class mail except postal and post cards (United States and possessions) | 3 cents per oz. |
| Single post cards (United States and possessions) | 2 cents each |
| Double post cards (reply portion does not have to bear postage when originally mailed) | 4 cents (2 cents each portion) |
| Business reply cards (good only in United States and possessions except Canal Zone) | 3 cents each, collected when delivered |
| Mail enclosed in business reply envelopes (good only in United States and possessions except Canal Zone) | 3 cents per oz. plus 1 cent per piece, collected when delivered |
| Airmail (United States and all possessions) | 6 cents per oz. (8 oz. or less) over 8 oz., use air parcel post |

RATES FOR FIRST-CLASS MAIL (INTERNATIONAL)

| Kind of mail | Rate |
|---|---|
| Letters to Canada and Mexico | 3 cents per oz. |
| Letters to all other countries | 8 cents for the first oz., 4 cents for each additional oz. |

LIMITATIONS ON FIRST-CLASS MATTER

In United States and possessions.. Maximum weight limit is the same as for fourth-class mail (see fourth-class mail). No size limit.

To Canada.................... Maximum length, 24 in. Maximum length, breadth, and thickness combined, 36 in. Weight limit, 60 lb.

To all countries except Canada.... Maximum length, 24 in. Maximum length, breadth, and thickness combined, 36 in. Weight limit, 4 lb., 6 oz.

thereof. (For rates on copy accompanied by proofs, see THIRD-CLASS MAIL below.)

2. *Matter partly in writing* like printed cards or letters with added handwritten notes. printed forms filled out by hand, drawings and art work that are hand-lettered.

3. *Sealed matter* of any class except sealed third- or fourth-class matter bearing printed notice "May be opened for postal inspection if necessary." Miscellaneous printed matter under 8 oz. may not be sealed unless paid at first-class rates.

*Registered mail.* For special registry rates, surcharges, indemnity limit, and return receipt, see REGISTERED MAIL below.

*Certified mail.* A service for first-class mail to certify personal delivery to the addressee without providing insurance or indemnity in case of loss. For rates see CERTIFIED MAIL above.

*Return to sender.* When marked with name and address of sender, undeliverable first-class mail except post cards is returned to sender without additional postage, provided the original postage was paid in full. If through error it is only partly prepaid, it is returned for deficient postage. For information about return of post cards, see POST CARDS.

*Forwarding.* Unopened first-class mail is forwarded without additional charge, provided postage was fully prepaid at the first-class rate.

*Speeding delivery.* First-class mail moves faster than any other class except airmail since it is handled first and on the fastest trains. The same speed may be purchased for third- and fourth-class

mail in either of two ways: (1) By "special handling" which guarantees that fourth-class matter will be handled and transported as first class but will be delivered on scheduled parcel post trips, and (2) by paying for "special delivery" which guarantees the parcel's being expedited with first-class mail as well as being delivered by special messenger at the point of destination between 7 A.M. and 7 P.M. In larger cities special delivery matter is delivered from 7 A.M. to 11 P.M. (See SPECIAL DELIVERY and SPECIAL HANDLING below.)

**forwarding and return of undeliverable mail** Mail will be forwarded to another post office under certain conditions and at certain fees given below:

First-class mail: Forwarded; no charge.

Second-class mail: Forwarded when forwarding postage is guaranteed by sender or addressee.

Third-class mail: Forwarded only if it is of obvious value or when forwarding postage is guaranteed by the sender or addressee.

Fourth-class mail: Forwarded to addressee from whom additional postage is collected.

Airmail weighing 8 oz. or less: Forwarded without additional charge. Air transportation is used when available to the new address.

Airmail weighing over 8 oz.: Forwarded by air at the applicable air zone rates to be collected on delivery unless the article bears sender's instructions to forward by surface mail. Forwarding postage is collected from addressee on delivery.

Registered, insured COD mail: Forwarded without payment of additional *fees,* but the ordinary forwarding *postage* charges, if any, must be paid.

Mail that cannot be delivered because of incomplete or incorrect address, or which is unclaimed or refused by the addressee, is handled in various ways:

First-class mail except post cards: Returned to sender without additional charge.

Second-class mail: Returned to sender if it bears a pledge to pay return postage except where the sender is a publisher or news agent, in which case special rules apply. (See the "Postal Manual.")

Third-class mail: Returned to sender if it is of obvious value or bears the sender's pledge to pay return postage.

Fourth-class mail: Returned to sender and return postage collected.

Airmail weighing 8 oz. or less: Returned by surface transportation at no additional charge.

Airmail weighing over 8 oz.: Returned by surface transportation unless it bears the sender's instructions to be returned by airmail. Return charges are collected on delivery to sender.

**fourth-class mail**  See also BOOK POSTAGE RATES, COD, REGISTERED MAIL in this appendix.

Fourth-class mail, commonly called "parcel post," is used for matter that is not first-, second-, or third-class, that weighs over 8 oz., but does not exceed the limitations shown in the accompanying table.

| | Size limit (combined length and girth) | Weight limit |
|---|---|---|
| Between first-class (large) post offices: In local zone and Zones 1 and 2.... | 72 in. | 40 lb. |
| In Zones 3 through 8 | 72 in. | 20 lb. |
| Mailed at or to any second-, third-, or fourth-class post office............ | 100 in. | 70 lb. |
| Books mailed to any zone............ | 100 in. | 70 lb. |

For further details, consult the "Postal Manual."

Larger or heavier packages may be shipped by express, freight, or truck. (See EXPRESS, RAIL FREIGHT, TRUCKING, and for comparative rates, SHIPPING INFORMATION in the main text of this book.)

Length

Girth

The way to measure combined length and girth is shown above. This package measures 25 in. in combined length and girth, being 9 in. long and 16 in. around.

FOURTH-CLASS, OR PARCEL-POST, ZONE RATES

| Pounds | Local | 1 and 2 zones | 3 zone | 4 zone | 5 zone | 6 zone | 7 zone | 8 zone |
|---|---|---|---|---|---|---|---|---|
| 1..... | $0.18 | $0.23 | $0.23 | $0.24 | $0.26 | $0.28 | $0.30 | $0.32 |
| 2..... | .20 | .27 | .29 | .31 | .36 | .40 | .46 | .51 |
| 3..... | .21 | .31 | .34 | .38 | .45 | .52 | .61 | .69 |
| 4..... | .23 | .35 | .39 | .45 | .54 | .64 | .76 | .87 |
| 5..... | .24 | .39 | .44 | .52 | .63 | .76 | .91 | 1.05 |
| 6..... | .26 | .43 | .49 | .59 | .73 | .88 | 1.06 | 1.23 |
| 7..... | .27 | .47 | .54 | .66 | .82 | 1.00 | 1.22 | 1.41 |
| 8..... | .29 | .51 | .60 | .73 | .91 | 1.12 | 1.37 | 1.59 |
| 9..... | .30 | .55 | .65 | .80 | 1.00 | 1.24 | 1.52 | 1.77 |
| 10..... | .32 | .59 | .70 | .87 | 1.10 | 1.36 | 1.67 | 1.95 |
| 11..... | .33 | .63 | .75 | .93 | 1.19 | 1.48 | 1.82 | 2.13 |
| 12..... | .34 | .67 | .80 | 1.00 | 1.28 | 1.60 | 1.98 | 2.31 |
| 13..... | .36 | .71 | .85 | 1.07 | 1.37 | 1.72 | 2.13 | 2.49 |
| 14..... | .37 | .75 | .90 | 1.14 | 1.47 | 1.84 | 2.28 | 2.67 |
| 15..... | .39 | .79 | .96 | 1.21 | 1.56 | 1.96 | 2.43 | 2.85 |
| 16..... | .40 | .83 | 1.01 | 1.28 | 1.65 | 2.08 | 2.58 | 3.03 |
| 17..... | .42 | .87 | 1.06 | 1.35 | 1.74 | 2.20 | 2.74 | 3.21 |
| 18..... | .43 | .91 | 1.11 | 1.42 | 1.84 | 2.32 | 2.89 | 3.39 |
| 19..... | .45 | .95 | 1.16 | 1.49 | 1.93 | 2.44 | 3.04 | 3.57 |
| 20..... | .46 | .99 | 1.21 | 1.56 | 2.02 | 2.56 | 3.19 | 3.75 |
| 21..... | .47 | 1.02 | 1.26 | 1.62 | 2.11 | 2.67 | 3.34 | 3.93 |
| 22..... | .49 | 1.06 | 1.32 | 1.69 | 2.21 | 2.79 | 3.50 | 4.12 |
| 23..... | .50 | 1.10 | 1.37 | 1.76 | 2.30 | 2.91 | 3.65 | 4.30 |
| 24..... | .52 | 1.14 | 1.42 | 1.83 | 2.39 | 3.03 | 3.80 | 4.48 |
| 25..... | .53 | 1.18 | 1.47 | 1.90 | 2.48 | 3.15 | 3.95 | 4.66 |
| 26..... | .55 | 1.22 | 1.52 | 1.97 | 2.58 | 3.27 | 4.10 | 4.84 |
| 27..... | .56 | 1.26 | 1.57 | 2.04 | 2.67 | 3.39 | 4.26 | 5.02 |
| 28..... | .58 | 1.30 | 1.63 | 2.11 | 2.76 | 3.51 | 4.41 | 5.20 |
| 29..... | .59 | 1.34 | 1.68 | 2.18 | 2.85 | 3.63 | 4.56 | 5.38 |
| 30..... | .61 | 1.38 | 1.73 | 2.25 | 2.95 | 3.75 | 4.71 | 5.56 |
| 31..... | .62 | 1.42 | 1.78 | 2.31 | 3.04 | 3.87 | 4.86 | 5.74 |
| 32..... | .63 | 1.46 | 1.83 | 2.38 | 3.13 | 3.99 | 5.02 | 5.92 |
| 33..... | .65 | 1.50 | 1.88 | 2.45 | 3.22 | 4.11 | 5.17 | 6.10 |
| 34..... | .66 | 1.54 | 1.93 | 2.52 | 3.32 | 4.23 | 5.32 | 6.28 |
| 35..... | .68 | 1.58 | 1.99 | 2.59 | 3.41 | 4.35 | 5.47 | 6.46 |
| 36..... | .69 | 1.62 | 2.04 | 2.66 | 3.50 | 4.47 | 5.62 | 6.64 |
| 37..... | .71 | 1.66 | 2.09 | 2.73 | 3.59 | 4.59 | 5.78 | 6.82 |
| 38..... | .72 | 1.70 | 2.14 | 2.80 | 3.69 | 4.71 | 5.93 | 7.00 |
| 39..... | .74 | 1.74 | 2.19 | 2.87 | 3.78 | 4.83 | 6.08 | 7.18 |
| 40..... | .75 | 1.78 | 2.24 | 2.94 | 3.87 | 4.95 | 6.23 | 7.36 |

FOURTH-CLASS, OR PARCEL-POST, ZONE RATES (*Continued*)

| Pounds | Local | 1 and 2 zones | 3 zone | 4 zone | 5 zone | 6 zone | 7 zone | 8 zone |
|---|---|---|---|---|---|---|---|---|
| 41..... | .76 | 1.81 | 2.29 | 3.00 | 3.96 | 5.06 | 6.38 | 7.54 |
| 42..... | .78 | 1.85 | 2.35 | 3.07 | 4.06 | 5.18 | 6.54 | 7.73 |
| 43..... | .79 | 1.89 | 2.40 | 3.14 | 4.15 | 5.30 | 6.69 | 7.91 |
| 44..... | .81 | 1.93 | 2.45 | 3.21 | 4.24 | 5.42 | 6.84 | 8.09 |
| 45..... | .82 | 1.97 | 2.50 | 3.28 | 4.33 | 5.54 | 6.99 | 8.27 |
| 46..... | .84 | 2.01 | 2.55 | 3.35 | 4.43 | 5.66 | 7.14 | 8.45 |
| 47..... | .85 | 2.05 | 2.60 | 3.42 | 4.52 | 5.78 | 7.30 | 8.63 |
| 48..... | .87 | 2.09 | 2.66 | 3.49 | 4.61 | 5.90 | 7.45 | 8.81 |
| 49..... | .88 | 2.13 | 2.71 | 3.56 | 4.70 | 6.02 | 7.60 | 8.99 |
| 50..... | .90 | 2.17 | 2.76 | 3.63 | 4.80 | 6.14 | 7.75 | 9.17 |
| 51..... | .91 | 2.21 | 2.81 | 3.69 | 4.89 | 6.26 | 7.90 | 9.35 |
| 52..... | .92 | 2.25 | 2.86 | 3.76 | 4.98 | 6.38 | 8.06 | 9.53 |
| 53..... | .94 | 2.29 | 2.91 | 3.83 | 5.07 | 6.50 | 8.21 | 9.71 |
| 54..... | .95 | 2.33 | 2.96 | 3.90 | 5.17 | 6.62 | 8.36 | 9.89 |
| 55..... | .97 | 2.37 | 3.02 | 3.97 | 5.26 | 6.74 | 8.51 | 10 07 |
| 56..... | .98 | 2.41 | 3.07 | 4.04 | 5.35 | 6.86 | 8.66 | 10.25 |
| 57..... | 1.00 | 2.45 | 3.12 | 4.11 | 5.44 | 6.98 | 8.82 | 10.43 |
| 58..... | 1.01 | 2.49 | 3.17 | 4.18 | 5.54 | 7.10 | 8.97 | 10.61 |
| 59..... | 1.03 | 2.53 | 3.22 | 4.25 | 5.63 | 7.22 | 9.12 | 10.79 |
| 60..... | 1.04 | 2.57 | 3.27 | 4.32 | 5.72 | 7.34 | 9.27 | 10.97 |
| 61..... | 1.05 | 2.60 | 3.32 | 4.38 | 5.81 | 7.45 | 9 42 | 11 15 |
| 62..... | 1.07 | 2.64 | 3.38 | 4.45 | 5.91 | 7.57 | 9.58 | 11 34 |
| 63..... | 1.08 | 2.68 | 3.43 | 4.52 | 6.00 | 7.69 | 9.73 | 11 52 |
| 64..... | 1.10 | 2.72 | 3.48 | 4.59 | 6.09 | 7.81 | 9.88 | 11 70 |
| 65..... | 1.11 | 2.76 | 3.53 | 4.66 | 6.18 | 7.93 | 10.03 | 11 88 |
| 66..... | 1.13 | 2.80 | 3.58 | 4.73 | 6.28 | 8.05 | 10.18 | 12.06 |
| 67..... | 1.14 | 2.84 | 3.63 | 4.80 | 6.37 | 8.17 | 10.34 | 12.24 |
| 68..... | 1.16 | 2.88 | 3.69 | 4.87 | 6.46 | 8.29 | 10.49 | 12.42 |
| 69..... | 1.17 | 2.92 | 3.74 | 4.94 | 6.55 | 8.41 | 10.64 | 12.60 |
| 70..... | 1.19 | 2.96 | 3.79 | 5.01 | 6.65 | 8.53 | 10.79 | 12.78 |

If a fourth-class parcel is sealed, it must bear a printed label stating: "*May be opened for postal inspection.*" If books are being shipped at book rate, add "*Contents: Books.*"

*Postage rates on fourth-class matter.* Domestic rates are charged according to the distance, or zone, of the point of destination, and the weight. When the zone and the weight are known, the postage can be computed from the chart of fourth-class (parcel post) rates on pages 427 and 428.

To determine the zone of a post office, look it up in the "Directory of Post Offices" where a unit number is listed by each city or post office. Then on a local "zone key," which the local postmaster will supply on request, find the zone number that corresponds to the unit number.

For easy reference in a shipping

FOURTH-CLASS CATALOGUE RATES

| | Zone | | | | | | | |
|---|---|---|---|---|---|---|---|---|
| | Local | 1 and 2 | 3 | 4 | 5 | 6 | 7 | 8 |
| | Rate, cents | | | | | | | |
| First pound............ | 12 | 13 | 14 | 15 | 17 | 18 | 19 | 20 |
| Each additional pound... | 1½ | 3 | 4 | 5 | 6½ | 8 | 10 | 12 |

room, a large zone map of the United States can be made for the wall with the zones marked off in concentric circles around the local shipping point.

*Overseas rates.* For the exact rate to a particular country, consult the local postmaster.

*Catalogue rates* apply to individually addressed catalogues and similar printed advertising matter in bound form of 24 or more pages and weighing over 8 oz.

*Book rates* apply to books containing 24 or more pages with only incidental announcements of other books. They are classified as fourth class if weighing over 8 oz. (For special book rates, see BOOK POSTAGE RATES above.)

Speed in delivery of fourth-class mail can be requested by paying a special delivery or special-handling fee. Either of these assures the parcel's being handled on fast trains along with first-class mail. Special delivery also provides local delivery by special messenger. (For details, see SPECIAL DELIVERY below.)

**insured mail** See chart comparing registered, insured, and certified mail, p. 434.

**mailing-list corrections** See also MAILING LISTS in main text of this book.

Two valuable allies for keeping mailing lists up to date are the post office and the addressee.

*Help from the post office.* The post office provides various methods for getting correct information about changes of address on third-class mail. (See THIRD-CLASS MAIL and FORWARDING AND RETURN OF UNDELIVERABLE MAIL in this appendix.)

On envelopes being mailed third class most mailers print the phrase "Form 3547 Requested," together with their return address. Without such notice, undeliverable mail of no obvious value is destroyed. With it, any change of address or the fact that addressee has moved and left no address is reported back to the sender, either on the undelivered item itself, or (where delivery could be made to the new address) on special Form 3547 notification card, cost 5 cents. If the addressee's move was local, delivery is made to his new address without extra charge. If he moved to another post office, where forwarding postage will be required, a third-class item is forwarded only if he left such instructions. It is possible for a mailer to put also "Forwarding Postage Guaranteed" on his envelopes, meaning addressee will be required to pay forwarding postage, but it is really easier and just as quick to omit this, and remail direct to the new address if desired when an undelivered piece comes back with the information on the new address. The Form 3547 notice can also be used on fourth-class (parcel post) shipments.

*Help from the addressee.* The addressee may help keep a mailing list correct if he is asked to do so and if it is made easy for him. Naturally, he can help only if the mailing piece reaches him; so such corrections eliminate only minor errors.

By printing on the envelope a request for corrections in the name and address as shown, many firms have been able to correct errors in spelling and street number and get the names of new personnel. Enclosing a postage-paid envelope will increase the returns as well as the good will of the addressee. Two popular forms for requesting this information are shown.

**metered postage** A postage meter may be used for printing and recording postage. The postage imprint may be put directly on the letter or package or it may be put on paper tape and pasted to the article.

Metered postage must show the date of mailing on first-class mail, special delivery, or airmail, and on all mail sent registered, insured, or COD. The month and year must be shown, but the day may be omitted on labels and stickers on second-, third-, and fourth-class mail.

Metered mail must be mailed from the post office shown in the meter postmark, but you may deposit first-class metered mail in street or building letter boxes. All other metered mail must be deposited in the post office.

Unless packages are too irregular, all metered mail must be separated by class of mail, faced, and bundled.

Small mailings as well as large mailings can be expedited, with considerable saving in time and postage, through the use of a postage meter machine which is a sort of mechanical post office capable of printing postage of any denomination, for any class of mail, directly on the envelope (or on a gummed label to be affixed to a package).

There is a variety of hand and electric models capable of stamping, postmarking, and sealing from 2,000 to 15,000 pieces per hour.

Postage is paid in advance, as when buying ordinary postage, or making a deposit for "permit mail." The meter is checked at the post office and is set to print meter stamps up to the value paid in. Instead of buying and keeping track of loose stamps in various denominations and quantities, you simply have your meter set for the sum paid in,

Mailing list corrections may be obtained by using such forms as these on the envelope.

from which you "dial" and print any stamp value as and when needed. Postage can be added to the meter at any time before the prepaid value runs out.

*Advantages.* Nearly all postage meter machines provide the following features:

1. Meter stamps can be printed by a single machine in many denominations, from 1 cent up.

2. Mail can be sealed and postmarked when it is stamped, or sealing can be omitted.

3. Postage labels for fourth-class mail can be printed by using a separate attachment on some postage machines. Other machines only print labels instead of printing directly on envelopes.

4. Metered mail saves time at the post office, since it is already postmarked and needs no facing or canceling there.

5. The meter provides accurate postage records of the postage used and the amount of authorized postage on hand.

6. The meter can be locked against use by unauthorized persons.

7. "Postmarked ads" (see illustration) can be printed with the meter stamp at no extra cost except for the printing plates.

*Securing postage meter machines.* Postage meter equipment generally consists of two parts (except for a new small desk model available from one manufacturer, which is in a single unit). One part is an office mailing machine, and the other is its detachable postage meter, licensed for use by the Post Office Department. Since meters print U.S. postage and account for government revenue under official lock and seal, they cannot be sold outright, as the mailing machines are, but are leased from an authorized manufacturer who is held responsible for their location, operation, and servicing.

In recent years the Post Office Department has liberalized metered mail regulations with new conveniences for the small mailer. These include the elimination of the former daily statement of mailing, the ability to deposit first-class metered mail in any regular mailbox within your post office jurisdiction, and faster procedure for dispatching metered mail through the outgoing post office.

Postage meter machines are made by The National Cash Register Co., Dayton, Ohio; Pitney-Bowes, Inc., Walnut and Pacific Sts., Stamford, Conn.; International Postal Supply Co., 634 Prospect Pl., Brooklyn 16; Commercial Controls Corp., Lexington Ave., Rochester 2, N.Y.

**parcel post**   See FOURTH-CLASS MAIL above.

**postage meters**   See METERED POSTAGE above.

A postage meter for first-class mail shows the amount of postage, the date, place, and meter number. The Cancer Society notice at the left is a "postmark ad" which may be changed or omitted as desired. (*Imprint courtesy of Pitney-Bowes, Inc.*)

**post cards** Government post cards, or private mailing cards which conform to the same general specifications, are accorded the special privilege of being handled as first-class mail even though they mail for 2 cents instead of the 3 cents minimum charged on first-class envelopes or outsized private mailing cards. Of course, private mailing cards that contain no writing and can qualify as third-class matter can be mailed at third-class rates, which may be lower. (For example, a double-reply government post card costs 4 cents; a private double reply card of the same size, mailed third class, may require only 1½ cents outgoing postage, and provide for return either under stamp supplied by recipient, or under a business reply card permit.)

The fact that true post cards are first class of course insures that they will be forwarded where necessary. The 2-cent rate applies in the U.S. and its possessions and Mexico; the rate to other countries is 4 cents.

*Government postal cards.* For domestic use these cost 2 cents each for both card and imprinted stamp. Double (reply) postal cards are 4 cents each. Cards purchased from the post office may be imprinted with advertisements and illustrations on the back and left third of the face. For printing purposes both single and double cards may be obtained as shown in the accompanying table.

| Kind of card | No. of cards to a sheet | No. of cards to a case |
|---|---|---|
| 3¼ x 5½ single..... | 40 | 10,000 |
| 3¼ x 5½ double.... | 20 | 5,000 |
| 3 x 5 single..... | 20 | 5,000 |

*Private mailing cards.* These cannot be smaller than 2¾ by 4 in. nor larger than 3⁹⁄₁₆ by 5⁹⁄₁₆ in. They must be of cardboard similar to that of the government postal card and may carry advertising and illustrations on the back and left half of the face. The postage rate is 2 cents each.

*Double reply postal cards.* These must be folded with no enclosures and have no metal clasps. They may be obtained from the post office at 4 cents each with stamp imprinted on each card. Privately printed double cards within prescribed size must carry 2 cents postage, with reply half subject to the same when mailed. The stamp may be used to hold the card together only if precanceled stamps are used.

*Business reply cards.* These are the ones for which the sender guarantees return postage of 3 cents each by filing Form 3614 and securing permission from the postmaster of the office where the cards are to be returned. (See BUSINESS REPLY CARDS above.)

*Return to sender.* Undeliverable postal cards, single or double, will be returned to the sender, provided his name and address are given in the upper left corner of the address side along with the statement "Return Postage Guaranteed," pledging payment of return postage of 2 cents each.

**precanceled postage** Precanceling means the cancellation of postage stamps, stamped envelopes, or postal cards in advance of mailing. The use of precanceled postage reduces the time and costs of mail handling. Because precanceled mail is sorted and tied in packages by the mailer, it requires less processing time in the post office and is therefore dispatched more quickly.

Precanceled stamps may be used to pay postage on post cards (but on no other first-class mail, unless specifically authorized by the postmaster on Form 3620), and on second-, third-, and fourth-class mail.

Precanceled postage may be of two kinds: (1) Adhesive postage stamps which may be canceled only by the post office, and (2) postage which may be canceled by any individual or organization which has secured a post-office permit to precancel stamped envelopes or postal cards with its own precancellation mark. Your canceling mark must include the name of the post office and state, your permit number, and (for first-class mail only) the date of the mailing. (See illustration.)

Any number of pieces of precanceled mail may be mailed at the same time regardless of whether they are identical, except for pieces of third-class bulk mail which must be identical. (See THIRD-CLASS MAIL below.)

## BULK RATE

With precanceled stamps, third-class bulk mail must be marked with this inscription, with or without box rule, either printed or hand-stamped in the upper right corner.

**printed indicia**  See PRINTED POSTAGE IMPRESSIONS below.

**printed postage impressions**  Neither stamps nor the imprint of a postage meter is necessary when printed postage impressions, often called "printed indicia," are used. Application to use the printed postage impression must be made to the post office in advance, accompanied by an application fee of $10.

Postage must be paid at the time the mail is brought to the post office unless the sender has set up a credit account with the post office in advance by depositing a sum of money large enough to cover postage for the mailing. Many firms that frequently make third-class bulk mailings keep a working cash balance at the post office so that postage for any mailing may be taken care of without delay. (Deposits may also be used for all classes of mail sent under nonmetered permit.)

One of these three permit indicia must be *printed* on third-class bulk mail which is mailed, without stamps affixed, as nonmetered mail.

The printed postage impression must be made by printing press, mimeograph, Multigraph, or other device, not hand-stamped. It must conform with those illustrated.

All classes of mail may be sent with printed impressions provided each mailing consists of certain minimum quantities, as follows:

First-class mail: 300 pieces of identical weight

Second- and third-class mail: 300 pieces of identical matter, except with third-class bulk mail which must weigh at least 20 lb. or consist of 200 identical pieces

Fourth-class mail: 250 pieces of identical mail

For information about exceptions to these minimum quantities, consult your local postmaster.

[*Continued on page 435*]

COMPARISON OF REGISTERED, INSURED, AND CERTIFIED MAIL

| | Registered mail | Insured mail | Certified mail |
|---|---|---|---|
| What safety provisions are made? | Handled separately from other mail in locked bags with record of each person handling en route | Handled with other mail. Record made only on receipt and delivery, but no delivery record on minimum-fee parcels | Handled with regular first-class mail. Record made of delivery |
| To what classes of mail can it apply? | First, second, third, and fourth. Fourth class may be registered only if first-class postage is paid | Third and fourth | First |
| What is the maximum that will be paid in case of loss, damage, etc.? | $10,000 | $200 | Nothing |
| What are the requirements about sealing? | In most cases it must be sealed with no requirement that postal inspection be authorized | Cannot be sealed except when marked to authorize postal inspection | Must be sealed |
| What does it cost? | Usually requires first-class postage fee plus a registry fee as follows:<br><br>Indemnity    Fee<br>$ 0.01–$ 10..... $0.50<br>10.01– 100..... 0.75<br>100.01– 200..... 1.00<br>200.01– 400..... 1.25<br>Increasing gradually to<br>$9,000.01 to<br>$10,000........ $4.25 | Requires third- or fourth-class postage plus insurance fee as follows:<br><br>Insurance    Fee<br>Not over $10..... $0.10<br>$ 10.01– 50..... 0.20<br>50.01– 100..... 0.30<br>100.01– 200..... 0.40 | Requires 20¢ fee in addition to first-class postage |
| Is a receipt returned to the sender? | Yes, if requested | Yes, if requested | Yes, if requested |

*Mailing procedures.* Before mailing, all classes of mail carrying a printed postage impression must be faced, separated into classes, and sorted by cities and states. Such mail must be deposited at the post office that issued the permit or at a deposit point designated by the postmaster. Each mailing must be accompanied by a Mailing Statement, Form 3602.

**registered mail** You may obtain added protection for your valuable and important mail and evidence that it has been delivered by having it registered. Because registered mail is always carried in locked bags and a record is kept of every person who handles it, it is less likely to be lost or rifled. The registry fee (paid in addition to regular postage) provides indemnity against loss, damage, or rifling up to $10,000 of declared value. When the declared value exceeds this $10,000 maximum indemnity, an additional charge (surcharge) is made. (Insured parcels can be protected only to $200. Certified mail does not provide any indemnity or insurance if the mail is lost in transit.)

Registered mail is recommended for money and articles having a monetary value. Note that registered mail service is the only service that provides indemnity for first-class mail. (Only third- and fourth-class mail can be insured.) Certified mail, which is handled just as registered mail is handled, is recommended for those items which have no monetary value but which the sender wishes delivered to the addressee in person or for which he wishes a return receipt. (See CERTIFIED MAIL above.)

*Requirements for registry.* Nearly all registered mail must be sealed and requires first-class postage in addition to the registry fee and possible surcharge. The chief exception is third-class mail valued at $100 or less, which may be sealed subject to postal inspection and sent at third-class rates in addition to the registry fee. (See THIRD-CLASS MAIL below.)

*Return receipt cards.* A return receipt, showing to whom and when registered mail was delivered, will be mailed to sender for a fee of 10 cents if requested at the time of mailing; if requested after mailing, the fee is 25 cents. For a return receipt showing the address where registered mail was delivered, a fee of 35 cents is charged. Such a receipt must be requested at time of mailing.

**return of undeliverable mail** See FORWARDING AND RETURN OF UNDELIVERABLE MAIL above.

**second-class mail** Newspapers, magazines, and other periodicals may be sent for extremely low rates when mailed by the publisher or registered news agents under second-class mailing privileges. For example, under certain circumstances a four-page newsletter weighing ¼ oz. mails for a minimum rate of ⅛ cent per copy.

*Eligibility for second-class rates.* A newspaper or periodical must be printed (not duplicated in imitation of a typewriter) and published from a known office at stated intervals, numbered consecutively with date of issue, have a legitimate list of paying subscribers, and be issued for the dissemination of information of a public character or devoted to literature, the sciences, arts, or some special industry. It must not be designed primarily for advertising purposes, for free circulation, or for circulation at nominal rates. Application for second-class entry must be made through the postmaster on Form 3501 accompanied by payment of an application fee. Fees are graduated according to the circulation of the periodical.

*Rates of postage on second-class matter.* These vary according to the kind of publication (daily, weekly, or otherwise), whether or not delivery is to be made within the county of publication, and the ratio of reading to advertising matter contained therein.

Within the county of publication, postal rates range from "free" (when the publication is printed within the county and, there being no city or village letter-carrier service, the subscriber picks up his own mail), to 2 cents per copy for periodicals published less often than weekly and weighing over 2 oz.

Outside the county of publication, rates are changed as follows: (1) 1½ cents per lb. for publications issued by nonprofit religious, educational, scientific, philanthropic, agricultural, labor, or fraternal organizations; and (2) 1½ cents per lb. plus 30 per cent for publications other than nonprofit with less than 5 per cent advertising.

Where advertising covers more than 5 per cent of the area of the publication, zone rates per pound are charged for the advertising portions as shown in the accompanying table.

| Zone | Rate per lb., cents | |
|---|---|---|
| First and second... | 1½ | |
| Third............ | 2 | Plus 30 per cent Minimum ⅛ cent per copy |
| Fourth.......... | 3 | |
| Fifth............ | 4 | |
| Sixth........... | 5 | |
| Seventh......... | 6 | |
| Eighth.......... | 7 | |

For further details regarding envelopes, wrappers, payment of postage, sorting, and mailing, consult the local postmaster or see the "Postal Manual."

**special delivery and special handling**
For greater speed, the post office provides two special services: special delivery and special handling.

*Special delivery* may be provided for all classes of mail. A letter or package carrying a special delivery stamp is expedited with first-class mail, which is handled first and on the fastest trains. In addition, special delivery guarantees that a letter parcel will be delivered by special messenger at the point of destination between 7 A.M. and 7 P.M.; in larger cities between 7 A.M. and 11 P.M.

*Special handling* applies only to fourth-class mail. It guarantees that fourth-class matter will be handled and transported as speedily as first-class mail, but will be delivered on regular parcel-post trips, not by special messenger. Nothing is gained by putting a special handling stamp on an item also bearing a special delivery stamp, since the latter alone entitles the item to both kinds of service.

**special handling**  See SPECIAL DELIVERY AND SPECIAL HANDLING above.

**speeding delivery**  See SPECIAL DELIVERY AND SPECIAL HANDLING above.

**third-class mail**  See also FOURTH-CLASS MAIL above.

Third-class postage applies only to nonpersonal matter weighing up to and including 8 oz. that is either unsealed or subject to postal inspection if sealed.

This includes form letters, circulars, catalogues, books (see BOOK POSTAGE RATES), printed matter not in the nature of personal correspondence, proof sheets, corrected proof sheets, manuscript copy accompanied by corrected proof sheets thereof, drawings that have no handwriting or hand-lettering, photographs, and merchandise.

Third-class mail may be sealed provided the parcels carry printed (not typewritten) labels, stating: "*May be opened for postal inspection.*"

Miscellaneous printed matter prepaid at third-class rate may not be sealed under the above arrangement.